A PROJECT TO FIND
THE FUNDAMENTAL
THEORY OF PHYSICS

STEPHEN WOLFRAM

A PROJECT TO FIND
THE FUNDAMENTAL
THEORY OF PHYSICS

STEPHEN WOLFRAM

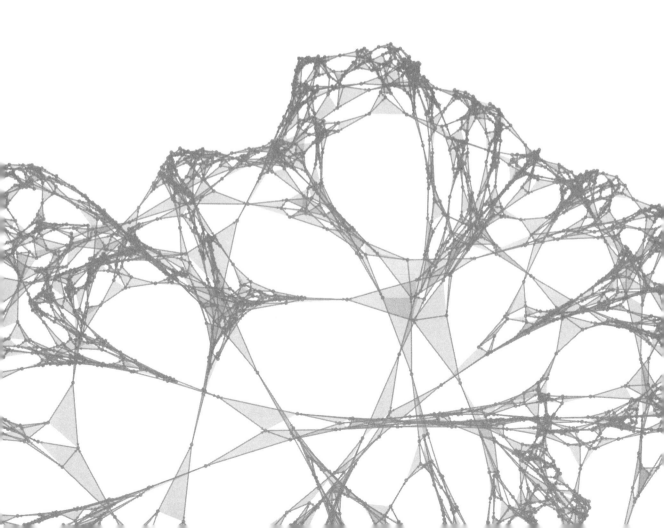

A Project to Find the Fundamental Theory of Physics

Copyright © 2020 Stephen Wolfram, LLC

Wolfram Media, Inc. | wolfram-media.com

ISBN 978-1-57955-035-6 (hardback)
ISBN 978-1-57955-031-8 (ebook)

Science / Physics

Cataloging-in-publication data available at wolfr.am/physics-cip

For permission to reproduce images, contact permissions@wolfram.com. Sources for photos and archival materials that are not from the author's collection, the results of author's research, or in the public domain: p. 513: *Australian Journal of Physics*; p. 517: *Reviews of Modern Physics*; p. 518: *Physical Review Letters*; p. 524: *The New York Times*; p. 527: TED, www.ted.com/talks/stephen_wolfram_computing_a_theory_of_all_knowledge

Typeset with Wolfram Notebooks: wolfram.com/notebook

Printed by Friesens, Manitoba, Canada. ∞ Acid-free paper. First edition. First printing.

Contents

Preface · vii

THE ANNOUNCEMENT

**Finally We May Have a Path to the Fundamental Theory of Physics...
and It's Beautiful** · 3

TECHNICAL INTRODUCTION

A Class of Models with the Potential to Represent Fundamental Physics

1 | Introduction · 73

2 | Basic Form of Models · 75

3 | Typical Behaviors · 91

4 | Limiting Behavior and Emergent Geometry · 147

5 | The Updating Process for String Substitution Systems · · · · · · · · · · · · · · 201

6 | The Updating Process in Our Models · 303

7 | Equivalence and Computation in Our Models · 377

8 | Potential Relation to Physics · 405

9 | Notes & Further References · 477

HISTORY

How We Got Here: The Backstory of the Wolfram Physics Project · · · · · · · · · · · · 503

BACKGROUND

***A New Kind of Science*: A 15-Year View** (2017) · 547

What Is Spacetime, Really? (2015) · 571

THE FOUNDATIONS

Fundamental Physics, Chapter 9 from *A New Kind of Science* (2002) · · · · · · · · · · · 591

The Problems of Physics 591 · The Notion of Reversibility 593 · Irreversibility and the
Second Law of Thermodynamics 599 · Conserved Quantities and Continuum Phenomena 616
Ultimate Models for the Universe 623 · The Nature of Space 630 · Space as a Network 633
The Relationship of Space and Time 639 · Time and Causal Networks 644 · The Sequencing of
Events in the Universe 655 · Uniqueness and Branching in Time 662 · Evolution of Networks 666
Space, Time and Relativity 674 · Elementary Particles 683 · The Phenomenon of Gravity 688
Quantum Phenomena 695 · Historical & Technical Notes 705

Index · 757

Preface

We're issuing this book to capture the state of our thinking as we launch the Wolfram Physics Project, and to serve as a resource for those who want to understand and potentially participate in the project.

The majority of the book consists of new material specifically created for the launch of the project. But we've also included earlier material that traces the evolution of my thinking, and provides additional background. In particular, it includes the key chapter about fundamental physics from my 2002 book, *A New Kind of Science*. And while we've now been able to take the ideas significantly further—and have made some technical modifications—almost everything that was in *A New Kind of Science* still stands, and now provides the foundation for our new project.

Beyond this book, we're making many other resources available on the website for the Wolfram Physics Project, wolframphysics.org, which we hope will see frequent updates and additions as the project progresses.

Join us in what we hope will be the final quest for the fundamental theory of physics!

Stephen Wolfram

April 17, 2020

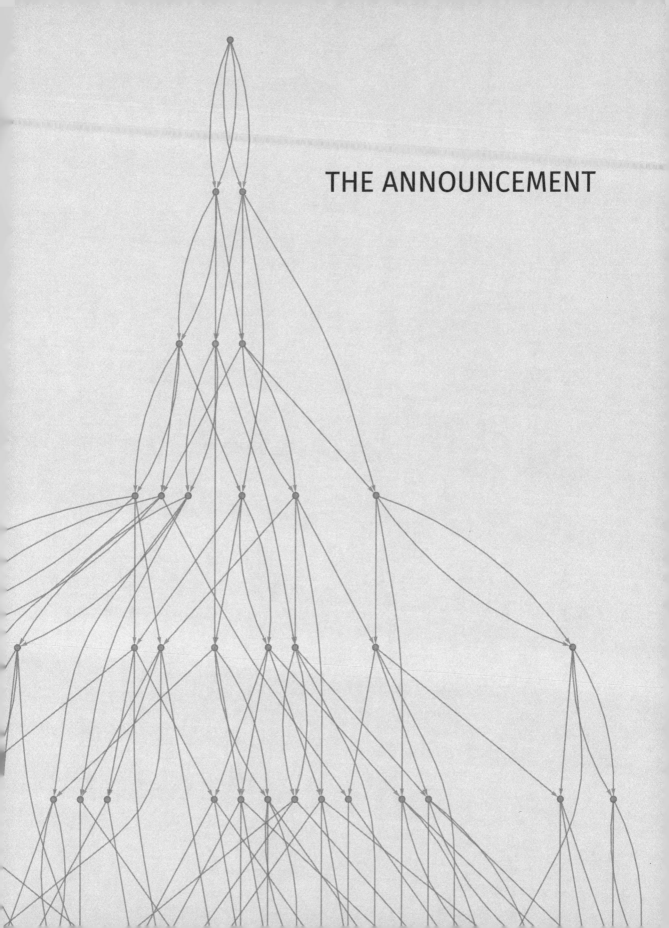

THE ANNOUNCEMENT

Finally We May Have a Path to the Fundamental Theory of Physics... and It's Beautiful

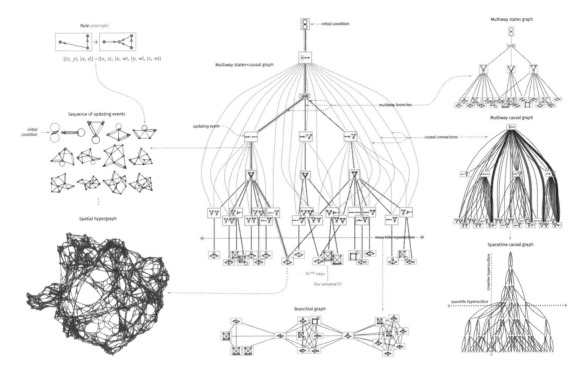

I Never Expected This

It's unexpected, surprising—and for me incredibly exciting. To be fair, at some level I've been working towards this for nearly 50 years. But it's just in the last few months that it's finally come together. And it's much more wonderful, and beautiful, than I'd ever imagined.

In many ways it's the ultimate question in natural science: How does our universe work? Is there a fundamental theory? An incredible amount has been figured out about physics over the past few hundred years. But even with everything that's been done—and it's very impressive—we still, after all this time, don't have a truly fundamental theory of physics.

Back when I used do theoretical physics for a living, I must admit I didn't think much about trying to find a fundamental theory; I was more concerned about what we could figure out based on the theories we had. And somehow I think I imagined that if there was a fundamental theory, it would inevitably be very complicated.

But in the early 1980s, when I started studying the computational universe of simple programs I made what was for me a very surprising and important discovery: that even when the underlying rules for a system are extremely simple, the behavior of the system as a whole can be essentially arbitrarily rich and complex.

And this got me thinking: Could the universe work this way? Could it in fact be that underneath all of this richness and complexity we see in physics there are just simple rules? I soon realized that if that was going to be the case, we'd in effect have to go underneath space and time and basically everything we know. Our rules would have to operate at some lower level, and all of physics would just have to emerge.

By the early 1990s I had a definite idea about how the rules might work, and by the end of the 1990s I had figured out quite a bit about their implications for space, time, gravity and other things in physics—and, basically as an example of what one might be able to do with science based on studying the computational universe, I devoted nearly 100 pages to this in my book *A New Kind of Science*.

I always wanted to mount a big project to take my ideas further. I tried to start around 2004. But pretty soon I got swept up in building Wolfram|Alpha, and the Wolfram Language and everything around it. From time to time I would see physicist friends of mine, and I'd talk about my physics project. There'd be polite interest, but basically the feeling was that finding a fundamental theory of physics was just too hard, and only kooks would attempt it.

It didn't help that there was something that bothered me about my ideas. The particular way I'd set up my rules seemed a little too inflexible, too contrived. In my life as a computational language designer I was constantly thinking about abstract systems of rules. And every so often I'd wonder if they might be relevant for physics. But I never got anywhere. Until, suddenly, in the fall of 2018, I had a little idea.

It was in some ways simple and obvious, if very abstract. But what was most important about it to me was that it was so elegant and minimal. Finally I had something that felt right to me as a serious possibility for how physics might work. But wonderful things were happening with the Wolfram Language, and I was busy thinking about all the implications of finally having a full-scale computational language.

But then, at our annual Summer School in 2019, there were two young physicists (Jonathan Gorard and Max Piskunov) who were like, "You just have to pursue this!" Physics had been my great passion when I was young, and in August 2019 I had a big birthday and realized that, yes, after all these years I really should see if I can make something work.

So—along with the two young physicists who'd encouraged me—I began in earnest in October 2019. It helped that—after a lifetime of developing them—we now had great computational tools. And it wasn't long before we started finding what I might call "very interesting things". We reproduced, more elegantly, what I had done in the 1990s. And from tiny, structureless rules out were coming space, time, relativity, gravity and hints of quantum mechanics.

We were doing zillions of computer experiments, building intuition. And gradually things were becoming clearer. We started understanding how quantum mechanics works. Then we realized what energy is. We found an outline derivation of my late friend and mentor Richard Feynman's path integral. We started seeing some deep structural connections between relativity and quantum mechanics. Everything just started falling into place. All those things I'd known about in physics for nearly 50 years—and finally we had a way to see not just what was true, but why.

I hadn't ever imagined anything like this would happen. I expected that we'd start exploring simple rules and gradually, if we were lucky, we'd get hints here or there about connections to physics. I thought maybe we'd be able to have a possible model for the first 10^{-100} seconds of the universe, but we'd spend years trying to see whether it might actually connect to the physics we see today.

In the end, if we're going to have a complete fundamental theory of physics, we're going to have to find the specific rule for our universe. And I don't know how hard that's going to be. I don't know if it's going to take a month, a year, a decade or a century. A few months ago I would also have said that I don't even know if we've got the right framework for finding it.

But I wouldn't say that anymore. Too much has worked. Too many things have fallen into place. We don't know if the precise details of how our rules are set up are correct, or how simple or not the final rules may be. But at this point I am certain that the basic framework we have is telling us fundamentally how physics works.

It's always a test for scientific models to compare how much you put in with how much you get out. And I've never seen anything that comes close. What we put in is about as tiny as it could be. But what we're getting out are huge chunks of the most sophisticated things that are known about physics. And what's most amazing to me is that at least so far we've not run across a single thing where we've had to say "oh, to explain that we have to add something to our model". Sometimes it's not easy to see how things work, but so far it's always just been a question of understanding what the model already says, not adding something new.

At the lowest level, the rules we've got are about as minimal as anything could be. (Amusingly, their basic structure can be expressed in a fraction of a line of symbolic Wolfram Language code.) And in their raw form, they don't really engage with all the rich ideas and structure that exist, for example, in mathematics. But as soon as we start looking at the consequences of the rules when they're applied zillions of times, it becomes clear that they're very elegantly connected to a lot of wonderful recent mathematics.

There's something similar with physics, too. The basic structure of our models seems alien and bizarrely different from almost everything that's been done in physics for at least the past century or so. But as we've gotten further in investigating our models something amazing has happened: we've found that not just one, but many of the popular theoretical frameworks that have been pursued in physics in the past few decades are actually directly relevant to our models.

I was worried this was going to be one of those "you've got to throw out the old" advances in science. It's not. Yes, the underlying structure of our models is different. Yes, the initial approach and methods are different. And, yes, a bunch of new ideas are needed. But to make everything work we're going to have to build on a lot of what my physicist friends have been working so hard on for the past few decades.

And then there'll be the physics experiments. If you'd asked me even a couple of months ago when we'd get anything experimentally testable from our models I would have said it was far away. And that it probably wouldn't happen until we'd pretty much found the final rule. But it looks like I was wrong. And in fact we've already got some good hints of bizarre new things that might be out there to look for.

OK, so what do we need to do now? I'm thrilled to say that I think we've found a path to the fundamental theory of physics. We've built a paradigm and a framework (and, yes, we've built lots of good, practical, computational tools too). But now we need to finish the job. We need to work through a lot of complicated computation, mathematics and physics. And see if we can finally deliver the answer to how our universe fundamentally works.

It's an exciting moment, and I want to share it. I'm looking forward to being deeply involved. But this isn't just a project for me or our small team. This is a project for the world. It's going to be a great achievement when it's done. And I'd like to see it shared as widely as possible. Yes, a lot of what has to be done requires top-of-the-line physics and math knowledge. But I want to expose everything as broadly as possible, so everyone can be involved in—and I hope inspired by—what I think is going to be a great and historic intellectual adventure.

Today we're officially launching our Physics Project. From here on, we'll be livestreaming what we're doing—sharing whatever we discover in real time with the world. (We'll also soon be releasing more than 400 hours of video that we've already accumulated.) I'm posting all my working materials going back to the 1990s, and we're releasing all our software tools. We'll be putting out bulletins about progress, and there'll be educational programs around the project.

Oh, yes, and we're putting up a Registry of Notable Universes. It's already populated with nearly a thousand rules. I don't think any of the ones in there yet are our own universe— though I'm not completely sure. But sometime—I hope soon—there might just be a rule entered in the Registry that has all the right properties, and that we'll slowly discover that, yes, this is it—our universe finally decoded.

How It Works

OK, so how does it all work? I've written a 448-page technical exposition (yes, I've been busy the past few months!). Another member of our team (Jonathan Gorard) has written two 60-page technical papers. And there's other material available at the project website. But here I'm going to give a fairly non-technical summary of some of the high points.

It all begins with something very simple and very structureless. We can think of it as a collection of abstract relations between abstract elements. Or we can think of it as a hypergraph—or, in simple cases, a graph.

We might have a collection of relations like

{{1, 2}, {2, 3}, {3, 4}, {2, 4}}

that can be represented by a graph like

All we're specifying here are the relations between elements (like {2,3}). The order in which we state the relations doesn't matter (although the order within each relation does matter). And when we draw the graph, all that matters is what's connected to what; the actual layout on the page is just a choice made for visual presentation. It also doesn't matter what the elements are called. Here I've used numbers, but all that matters is that the elements are distinct.

OK, so what do we do with these collections of relations, or graphs? We just apply a simple rule to them, over and over again. Here's an example of a possible rule:

$$\{\{x, y\}, \{x, z\}\} \rightarrow \{\{x, z\}, \{x, w\}, \{y, w\}, \{z, w\}\}$$

What this rule says is to pick up two relations—from anywhere in the collection—and see if the elements in them match the pattern $\{\{x,y\},\{x,z\}\}$ (or, in the Wolfram Language, {{x_,y_},{x_,z_}}), where the two x's can be anything, but both have to be the same, and the y and z can be anything. If there's a match, then replace these two relations with the four relations on the right. The w that appears there is a new element that's being created, and the only requirement is that it's distinct from all other elements.

We can represent the rule as a transformation of graphs:

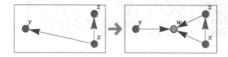

Now let's apply the rule once to

$$\{\{1, 2\}, \{2, 3\}, \{3, 4\}, \{2, 4\}\}$$

The {2,3} and {2,4} relations get matched, and the rule replaces them with four new relations, so the result is:

$$\{\{1, 2\}, \{3, 4\}, \{2, 4\}, \{2, 5\}, \{3, 5\}, \{4, 5\}\}$$

We can represent this result as a graph (which happens to be rendered flipped relative to the graph above):

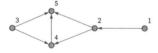

OK, so what happens if we just keep applying the rule over and over? Here's the result:

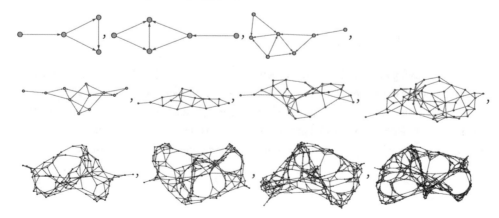

Let's do it a few more times, and make a bigger picture:

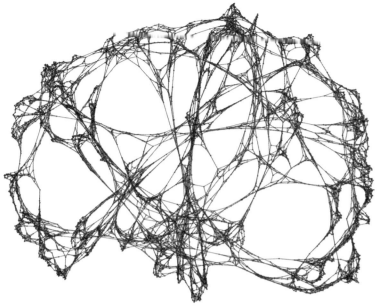

What happened here? We have such a simple rule. Yet applying this rule over and over again produces something that looks really complicated. It's not what our ordinary intuition tells us should happen. But actually—as I first discovered in the early 1980s—this kind of intrinsic, spontaneous generation of complexity turns out to be completely ubiquitous among simple rules and simple programs. And for example my book *A New Kind of Science* is about this whole phenomenon and why it's so important for science and beyond.

But here what's important about it is that it's what's going to make our universe, and everything in it. Let's review again what we've seen. We started off with a simple rule that just tells us how to transform collections of relations. But what we get out is this complicated-looking object that, among other things, seems to have some definite shape.

We didn't put in anything about this shape. We just gave a simple rule. And using that simple rule a graph was made. And when we visualize that graph, it comes out looking like it has a definite shape.

If we ignore all matter in the universe, our universe is basically a big chunk of space. But what *is* that space? We've had mathematical idealizations and abstractions of it for two thousand years. But what really is it? Is it made of something, and if so, what?

Well, I think it's very much like the picture above. A whole bunch of what are essentially abstract points, abstractly connected together. Except that in the picture there are 6704 of these points, whereas in our real universe there might be more like 10^{400} of them, or even many more.

All Possible Rules

We don't (yet) know an actual rule that represents our universe—and it's almost certainly not the one we just talked about. So let's discuss what possible rules there are, and what they typically do.

One feature of the rule we used above is that it's based on collections of "binary relations", containing pairs of elements (like {2,3}). But the same setup lets us also consider relations with more elements. For example, here's a collection of two ternary relations:

{{1, 2, 3}, {3, 4, 5}}

We can't use an ordinary graph to represent things like this, but we can use a hypergraph—a construct where we generalize edges in graphs that connect pairs of nodes to "hyperedges" that connect any number of nodes:

(Notice that we're dealing with directed hypergraphs, where the order in which nodes appear in a hyperedge matters. In the picture, the "membranes" are just indicating which nodes are connected to the same hyperedge.)

We can make rules for hypergraphs too:

$\{\{x, y, z\}\} \to \{\{w, w, y\}, \{w, x, z\}\}$

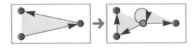

And now here's what happens if we run this rule starting from the simplest possible ternary hypergraph—the ternary self-loop {{0,0,0}}:

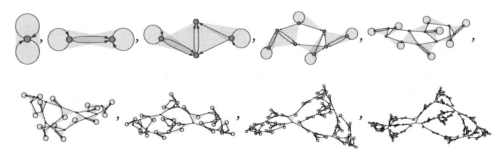

Alright, so what happens if we just start picking simple rules at random? Here are some of the things they do:

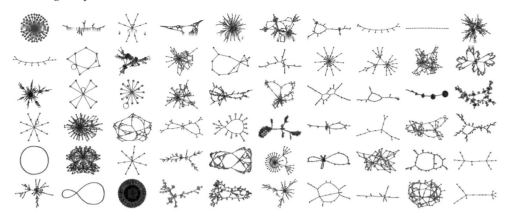

Somehow this looks very zoological (and, yes, these models are definitely relevant for things other than fundamental physics—though probably particularly molecular-scale construction). But basically what we see here is that there are various common forms of behavior, some simple, and some not.

Here are some samples of the kinds of things we see:

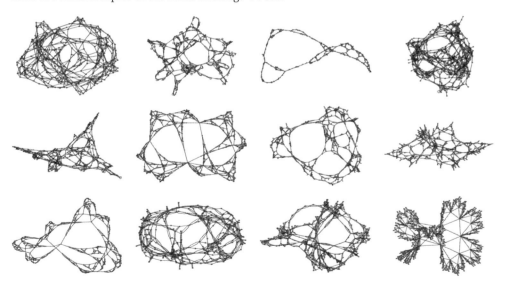

And the big question is: if we were to run rules like these long enough, would they end up making something that reproduces our physical universe? Or, put another way, out in this computational universe of simple rules, can we find our physical universe?

A big question, though, is: How would we know? What we're seeing here are the results of applying rules a few thousand times; in our actual universe they may have been applied 10^{500} times so far, or even more. And it's not easy to bridge that gap. And we have to work it from both sides. First, we have to use the best summary of the operation of our universe that what we've learned in physics over the past few centuries has given us. And second, we have to go as far as we can in figuring out what our rules actually do.

And here there's potentially a fundamental problem: the phenomenon of computational irreducibility. One of the great achievements of the mathematical sciences, starting about three centuries ago, has been delivering equations and formulas that basically tell you how a system will behave without you having to trace each step in what the system does. But many years ago I realized that in the computational universe of possible rules, this very often isn't possible. Instead, even if you know the exact rule that a system follows, you may still not be able to work out what the system will do except by essentially just tracing every step it takes.

One might imagine that—once we know the rule for some system—then with all our computers and brainpower we'd always be able to "jump ahead" and work out what the system would do. But actually there's something I call the Principle of Computational Equivalence, which says that almost any time the behavior of a system isn't obviously simple, it's computationally as sophisticated as anything. So we won't be able to "outcompute" it—and to work out what it does will take an irreducible amount of computational work.

Well, for our models of the universe this is potentially a big problem. Because we won't be able to get even close to running those models for as long as the universe does. And at the outset it's not clear that we'll be able to tell enough from what we can do to see if it matches up with physics.

But the big recent surprise for me is that we seem to be lucking out. We do know that whenever there's computational irreducibility in a system, there are also an infinite number of pockets of computational reducibility. But it's completely unclear whether in our case those pockets will line up with things we know from physics. And the surprise is that it seems a bunch of them do.

What Is Space?

Let's look at a particular, simple rule from our infinite collection:

$$\{\{x, y, y\}, \{z, x, u\}\} \to \{\{y, v, y\}, \{y, z, v\}, \{u, v, v\}\}$$

Here's what it does:

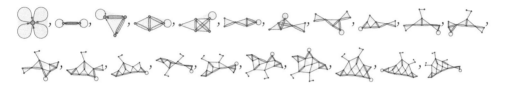

And after a while this is what happens:

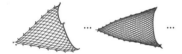

It's basically making us a very simple "piece of space". If we keep on going longer and longer it'll make a finer and finer mesh, to the point where what we have is almost indistinguishable from a piece of a continuous plane.

Here's a different rule:

$$\{\{x, x, y\}, \{z, u, x\}\} \to \{\{u, u, z\}, \{v, u, v\}, \{v, y, x\}\}$$

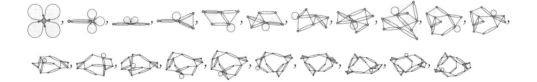

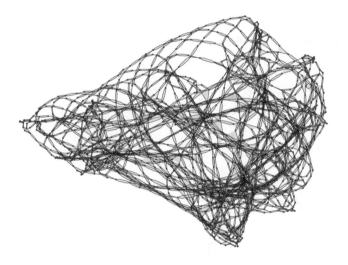

It looks it's "trying to make" something 3D. Here's another rule:

$$\{\{x, y, z\}, \{u, y, v\}\} \rightarrow \{\{w, z, x\}, \{z, w, u\}, \{x, y, w\}\}$$

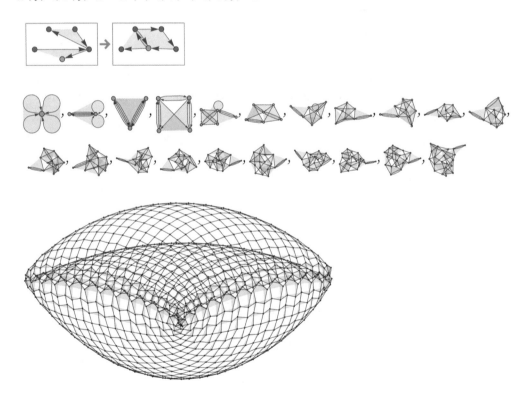

Isn't this strange? We have a rule that's just specifying how to rewrite pieces of an abstract hypergraph, with no notion of geometry, or anything about 3D space. And yet it produces a hypergraph that's naturally laid out as something that looks like a 3D surface.

Even though the only thing that's really here is connections between points, we can "guess" where a surface might be, then we can show the result in 3D:

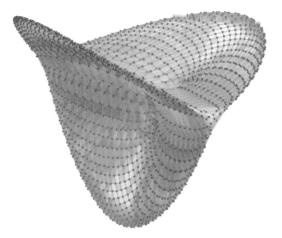

If we keep going, then like the example of the plane, the mesh will get finer and finer, until basically our rule has grown us—point by point, connection by connection—something that's like a continuous 3D surface of the kind you might study in a calculus class. Of course, in some sense, it's not "really" that surface: it's just a hypergraph that represents a bunch of abstract relations—but somehow the pattern of those relations gives it a structure that's a closer and closer approximation to the surface.

And this is basically how I think space in the universe works. Underneath, it's a bunch of discrete, abstract relations between abstract points. But at the scale we're experiencing it, the pattern of relations it has makes it seem like continuous space of the kind we're used to. It's a bit like what happens with, say, water. Underneath, it's a bunch of discrete molecules bouncing around. But to us it seems like a continuous fluid.

Needless to say, people have thought that space might ultimately be discrete ever since antiquity. But in modern physics there was never a way to make it work—and anyway it was much more convenient for it to be continuous, so one could use calculus. But now it's looking like the idea of space being discrete is actually crucial to getting a fundamental theory of physics.

The Dimensionality of Space

A very fundamental fact about space as we experience it is that it is three-dimensional. So can our rules reproduce that? Two of the rules we just saw produce what we can easily recognize as two-dimensional surfaces—in one case flat, in the other case arranged in a certain shape. Of course, these are very bland examples of (two-dimensional) space: they are effectively just simple grids. And while this is what makes them easy to recognize, it also means that they're not actually much like our universe, where there's in a sense much more going on.

So, OK, take a case like:

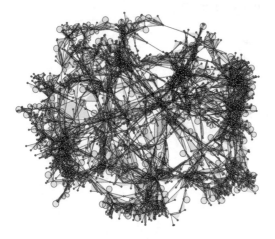

If we were to go on long enough, would this make something like space, and, if so, with how many dimensions? To know the answer, we have to have some robust way to measure dimension. But remember, the pictures we're drawing are just visualizations; the underlying structure is a bunch of discrete relations defining a hypergraph—with no information about coordinates, or geometry, or even topology. And, by the way, to emphasize that point, here is the same graph—with exactly the same connectivity structure—rendered four different ways:

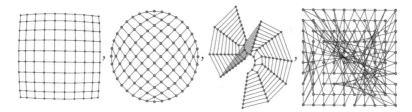

But getting back to the question of dimension, recall that the area of a circle is πr^2; the volume of a sphere is $\frac{4}{3}\pi r^3$. In general, the "volume" of the d-dimensional analog of a sphere is a constant multiplied by r^d. But now think about our hypergraph. Start at some point in the hypergraph. Then follow r hyperedges in all possible ways. You've effectively made the analog of a "spherical ball" in the hypergraph. Here are examples for graphs corresponding to 2D and 3D lattices:

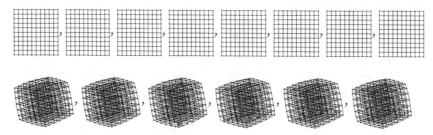

And if you now count the number of points reached by going "graph distance r" (i.e. by following r connections in the graph) you'll find in these two cases that they indeed grow like r^2 and r^3.

So this gives us a way to measure the effective dimension of our hypergraphs. Just start at a particular point and see how many points you reach by going r steps:

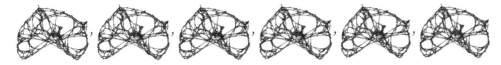

Now to work out effective dimension, we in principle just have to fit the results to r^d. It's a bit complicated, though, because we need to avoid small r (where every detail of the hypergraph is going to matter) and large r (where we're hitting the edge of the hypergraph)—and we also need to think about how our "space" is refining as the underlying system evolves. But in the end we can generate a series of fits for the effective dimension—and in this case these say that the effective dimension is about 2.7:

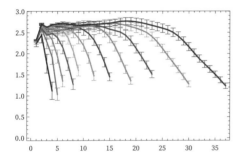

If we do the same thing for

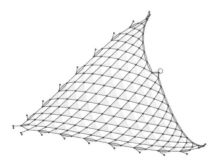

it's limiting to dimension 2, as it should:

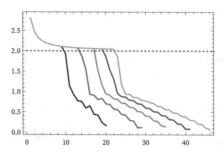

What does the fractional dimension mean? Well, consider fractals, which our rules can easily make:

$$\{\{x, y, z\}\} \rightarrow \{\{x, u, w\}, \{y, v, u\}, \{z, w, v\}\}$$

If we measure the dimension here we get 1.58—the usual fractal dimension $\log_2(3)$ for a Sierpiński structure:

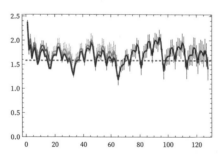

Our rule above doesn't create a structure that's as regular as this. In fact, even though the rule itself is completely deterministic, the structure it makes looks quite random. But what our measurements suggest is that when we keep running the rule it produces something that's like 2.7-dimensional space.

Of course, 2.7 is not 3, and presumably this particular rule isn't the one for our particular universe (though it's not clear what effective dimension it'd have if we ran it 10^{100} steps). But the process of measuring dimension shows an example of how we can start making "physics-connectable" statements about the behavior of our rules.

By the way, we've been talking about "making space" with our models. But actually, we're not just trying to make space; we're trying to make everything in the universe. In standard current physics, there's space—described mathematically as a manifold—and serving as a kind of backdrop, and then there's everything that's in space, all the matter and particles and planets and so on.

But in our models there's in a sense nothing but space—and in a sense everything in the universe must be "made of space". Or, put another way, it's the exact same hypergraph that's giving us the structure of space, and everything that exists in space.

So what this means is that, for example, a particle like an electron or a photon must correspond to some local feature of the hypergraph, a bit like in this toy example:

To give a sense of scale, though, I have an estimate that says that 10^{200} times more "activity" in the hypergraph that represents our universe is going into "maintaining the structure of space" than is going into maintaining all the matter we know exists in the universe.

Curvature in Space & Einstein's Equations

Here are a few structures that simple examples of our rules make:

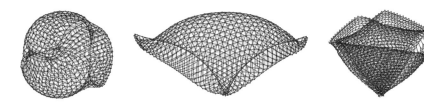

But while all of these look like surfaces, they're all obviously different. And one way to characterize them is by their local curvature. Well, it turns out that in our models, curvature is a concept closely related to dimension—and this fact will actually be critical in understanding, for example, how gravity arises.

But for now, let's talk about how one would measure curvature on a hypergraph. Normally the area of a circle is πr^2. But let's imagine that we've drawn a circle on the surface of a sphere, and now we're measuring the area on the sphere that's inside the circle:

This area is no longer πr^2. Instead it's $\pi r^2 (1 - \frac{r^2}{12\,a^2} + \frac{r^4}{360\,a^4} - ...)$, where a is the radius of the sphere. In other words, as the radius of the circle gets bigger, the effect of being on the sphere is ever more important. (On the surface of the Earth, imagine a circle drawn around the North Pole; once it gets to the equator, it can never get any bigger.)

If we generalize to d dimensions, it turns out the formula for the growth rate of the volume is $r^d (1 - \frac{r^2}{6\,(d+2)}\,R + ...)$, where R is a mathematical object known as the Ricci scalar curvature.

So what this all means is that if we look at the growth rates of spherical balls in our hypergraphs, we can expect two contributions: a leading one of order r^d that corresponds to effective dimension, and a "correction" of order r^2 that represents curvature.

Here's an example. Instead of giving a flat estimate of dimension (here equal to 2), we have something that dips down, reflecting the positive ("sphere-like") curvature of the surface:

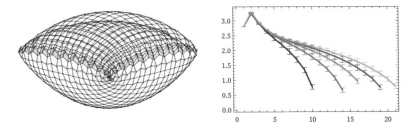

What is the significance of curvature? One thing is that it has implications for geodesics. A geodesic is the shortest distance between two points. In ordinary flat space, geodesics are just lines. But when there's curvature, the geodesics are curved:

In the case of positive curvature, bundles of geodesics converge; for negative curvature they diverge. But, OK, even though geodesics were originally defined for continuous space (actually, as the name suggests, for paths on the surface of the Earth), one can also have them in graphs (and hypergraphs). And it's the same story: the geodesic is the shortest path between two points in the graph (or hypergraph).

Here are geodesics on the "positive-curvature surface" created by one of our rules:

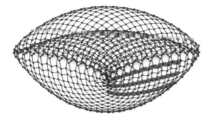

And here they are for a more complicated structure:

Why are geodesics important? One reason is that in Einstein's general relativity they're the paths that light (or objects in "free fall") follows in space. And in that theory gravity is associated with curvature in space. So when something is deflected going around the Sun, that happens because space around the Sun is curved, so the geodesic the object follows is also curved.

General relativity's description of curvature in space turns out to all be based on the Ricci scalar curvature R that we encountered above (as well as the slightly more sophisticated Ricci tensor). But so if we want to find out if our models are reproducing Einstein's equations for gravity, we basically have to find out if the Ricci curvatures that arise from our hypergraphs are the same as the theory implies.

There's quite a bit of mathematical sophistication involved (for example, we have to consider curvature in space+time, not just space), but the bottom line is that, yes, in various limits, and subject to various assumptions, our models do indeed reproduce Einstein's equations. (At first, we're just reproducing the vacuum Einstein equations, appropriate when there's no matter involved; when we discuss matter, we'll see that we actually get the full Einstein equations.)

It's a big deal to reproduce Einstein's equations. Normally in physics, Einstein's equations are what you start from (or sometimes they arise as a consistency condition for a theory): here they're what comes out as an emergent feature of the model.

It's worth saying a little about how the derivation works. It's actually somewhat analogous to the derivation of the equations of fluid flow from the limit of the underlying dynamics of lots of discrete molecules. But in this case, it's the structure of space rather than the velocity of a fluid that we're computing. It involves some of the same kinds of mathematical approximations and assumptions, though. One has to assume, for example, that there's enough effective randomness generated in the system that statistical averages work. There is also a whole host of subtle mathematical limits to take. Distances have to be large compared to individual hypergraph connections, but small compared to the whole size of the hypergraph, etc.

It's pretty common for physicists to "hack through" the mathematical niceties. That's actually happened for nearly a century in the case of deriving fluid equations from molecular dynamics. And we're definitely guilty of the same thing here. Which in a sense is another way of saying that there's lots of nice mathematics to do in actually making the derivation rigorous, and understanding exactly when it'll apply, and so on.

By the way, when it comes to mathematics, even the setup that we have is interesting. Calculus has been built to work in ordinary continuous spaces (manifolds that locally approximate Euclidean space). But what we have here is something different: in the limit of an infinitely large hypergraph, it's like a continuous space, but ordinary calculus doesn't work on it (not least because it isn't necessarily integer-dimensional). So to really talk about it well, we have to invent something that's kind of a generalization of calculus, that's for example capable of dealing with curvature in fractional-dimensional space. (Probably the closest current mathematics to this is what's been coming out of the very active field of geometric group theory.)

It's worth noting, by the way, that there's a lot of subtlety in the precise tradeoff between changing the dimension of space, and having curvature in it. And while we think our universe is three-dimensional, it's quite possible according to our models that there are at least local deviations—and most likely there were actually large deviations in the early universe.

Time

In our models, space is defined by the large-scale structure of the hypergraph that represents our collection of abstract relations. But what then is time?

For the past century or so, it's been pretty universally assumed in fundamental physics that time is in a sense "just like space"—and that one should for example lump space and time together and talk about the "spacetime continuum". And certainly the theory of relativity points in this direction. But if there's been one "wrong turn" in the history of physics in the past century, I think it's the assumption that space and time are the same kind of thing. And in our models they're not—even though, as we'll see, relativity comes out just fine.

So what then is time? In effect it's much as we experience it: the inexorable process of things happening and leading to other things. But in our models it's something much more precise: it's the progressive application of rules, that continually modify the abstract structure that defines the contents of the universe.

The version of time in our models is in a sense very computational. As time progresses we are in effect seeing the results of more and more steps in a computation. And indeed the phenomenon of computational irreducibility implies that there is something definite and irreducible "achieved" by this process. (And, for example, this irreducibility is what I believe is responsible for the "encrypting" of initial conditions that is associated with the law of entropy increase, and the thermodynamic arrow of time.) Needless to say, of course, our modern computational paradigm did not exist a century ago when "spacetime" was introduced, and perhaps if it had, the history of physics might have been very different.

But, OK, so in our models time is just the progressive application of rules. But there is a subtlety in exactly how this works that might at first seem like a detail, but that actually turns out to be huge, and in fact turns out to be the key to both relativity and quantum mechanics.

At the beginning of this piece, I talked about the rule

$$\{\{x, y\}, \{x, z\}\} \rightarrow \{\{x, z\}, \{x, w\}, \{y, w\}, \{z, w\}\}$$

and showed the "first few steps" in applying it

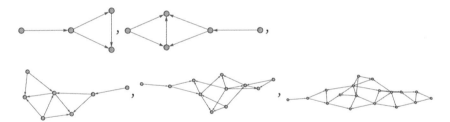

But how exactly did the rule get applied? What is "inside" these steps? The rule defines how to take two connections in the hypergraph (which in this case is actually just a graph) and transform them into four new connections, creating a new element in the process. So each "step" that we showed before actually consists of several individual "updating events" (where here newly added connections are highlighted, and ones that are about to be removed are dashed):

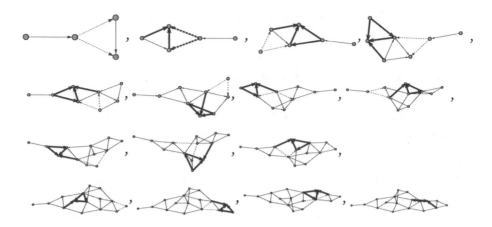

But now, here is the crucial point: this is not the only sequence of updating events consistent with the rule. The rule just says to find two adjacent connections, and if there are several possible choices, it says nothing about which one. And a crucial idea in our model is in a sense just to do all of them.

We can represent this with a graph that shows all possible paths:

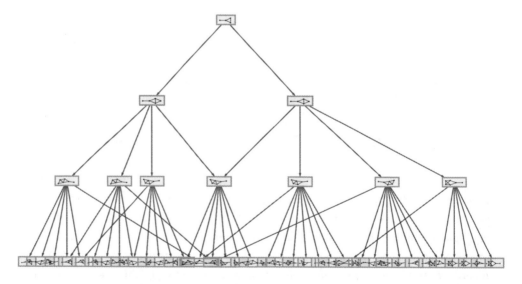

For the very first update, there are two possibilities. Then for each of the results of these, there are four additional possibilities. But at the next update, something important happens: two of the branches merge. In other words, even though we have done a different sequence of updates, the outcome is the same.

Things rapidly get complicated. Here is the graph after one more update, now no longer trying to show a progression down the page:

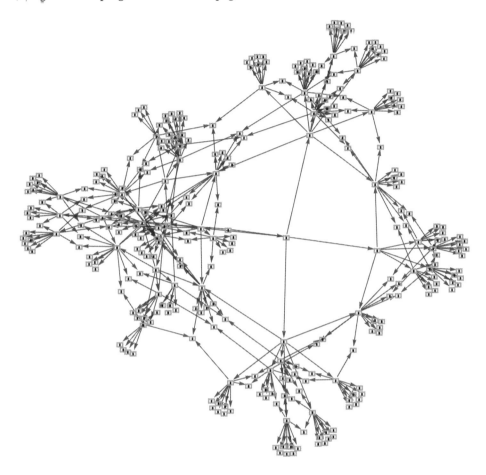

So how does this relate to time? What it says is that in the basic statement of the model there is not just one path of time; there are many paths, and many "histories". But the model—and the rule that is used—determines all of them. And we have seen a hint of something else: that even if we might think we are following an "independent" path of history, it may actually merge with another path.

It will take some more discussion to explain how this all works. But for now let me say that what will emerge is that time is about causal relationships between things, and that in fact, even when the paths of history that are followed are different, these causal relationships can end up being the same—and that in effect, to an observer embedded in the system, there is still just a single thread of time.

The Graph of Causal Relationships

In the end it's wonderfully elegant. But to get to the point where we can understand the elegant bigger picture we need to go through some detailed things. (It isn't terribly surprising that a fundamental theory of physics—inevitably built on very abstract ideas—is somewhat complicated to explain, but so it goes.)

To keep things tolerably simple, I'm not going to talk directly about rules that operate on hypergraphs. Instead I'm going to talk about rules that operate on strings of characters. (To clarify: these are not the strings of string theory—although in a bizarre twist of "pun-becomes-science" I suspect that the continuum limit of the operations I discuss on character strings is actually related to string theory in the modern physics sense.)

OK, so let's say we have the rule:

{A → BBB, BB → A}

This rule says that anywhere we see an A, we can replace it with BBB, and anywhere we see BB we can replace it with A. So now we can generate what we call the multiway system for this rule, and draw a "multiway graph" that shows everything that can happen:

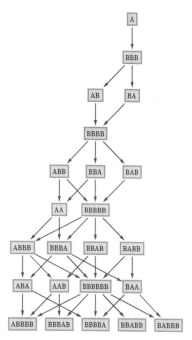

At the first step, the only possibility is to use A→BBB to replace the A with BBB. But then there are two possibilities: replace either the first BB or the second BB—and these choices give different results. On the next step, though, all that can be done is to replace the A—in both cases giving BBBB.

So in other words, even though we in a sense had two paths of history that diverged in the multiway system, it took only one step for them to converge again. And if you trace through the picture above you'll find out that's what always happens with this rule: every pair of branches that is produced always merges, in this case after just one more step.

This kind of balance between branching and merging is a phenomenon I call "causal invariance". And while it might seem like a detail here, it actually turns out that it's at the core of why relativity works, why there's a meaningful objective reality in quantum mechanics, and a host of other core features of fundamental physics.

But let's explain why I call the property causal invariance. The picture above just shows what "state" (i.e. what string) leads to what other one. But at the risk of making the picture more complicated (and note that this is incredibly simple compared to the full hypergraph case), we can annotate the multiway graph by including the updating events that lead to each transition between states:

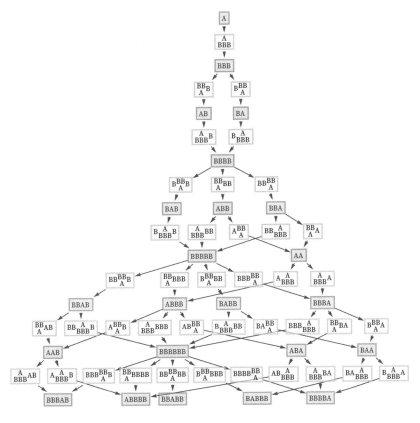

But now we can ask the question: what are the causal relationships between these events? In other words, what event needs to happen before some other event can happen? Or, said another way, what events must have happened in order to create the input that's needed for some other event?

Let us go even further, and annotate the graph above by showing all the causal dependencies between events:

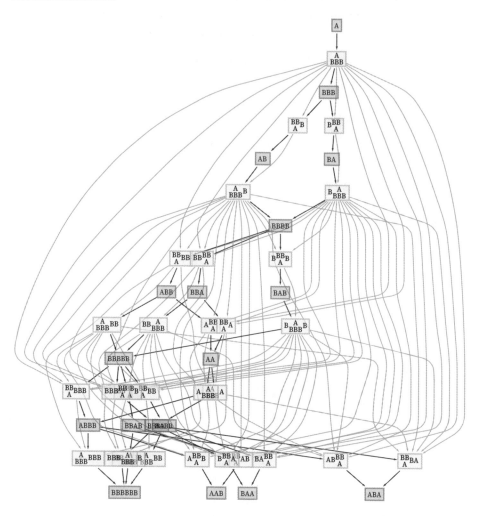

The orange lines in effect show which event has to happen before which other event—or what all the causal relationships in the multiway system are. And, yes, it's complicated. But note that this picture shows the whole multiway system—with all possible paths of history—as well as the whole network of causal relationships within and between these paths.

But here's the crucial thing about causal invariance: it implies that actually the graph of causal relationships is the same regardless of which path of history is followed. And that's why I originally called this property "causal invariance"—because it says that with a rule like this, the causal properties are invariant with respect to different choices of the sequence in which updating is done.

And if one traced through the picture above (and went quite a few more steps), one would find that for every path of history, the causal graph representing causal relationships between events would always be:

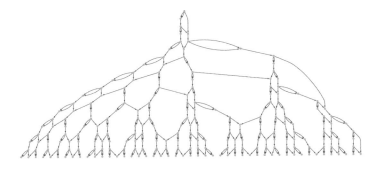

or, drawn differently,

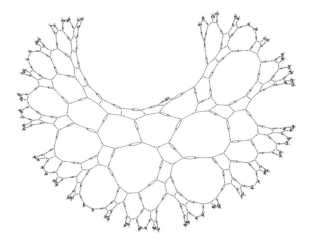

The Importance of Causal Invariance

To understand more about causal invariance, it's useful to look at an even simpler example: the case of the rule BA→AB. This rule says that any time there's a B followed by an A in a string, swap these characters around. In other words, this is a rule that tries to sort a string into alphabetical order, two characters at a time.

Let's say we start with BBBAAA. Then here's the multiway graph that shows all the things that can happen according to the rule:

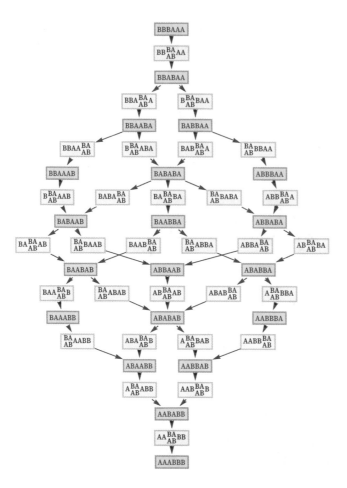

There are lots of different paths that can be followed, depending on which BA in the string the rule is applied to at each step. But the important thing we see is that at the end all the paths merge, and we get a single final result: the sorted string AAABBB. And the fact that we get this single final result is a consequence of the causal invariance of the rule. In a case like this where there's a final result (as opposed to just evolving forever), causal invariance basically says: it doesn't matter what order you do all the updates in; the result you'll get will always be the same.

I've introduced causal invariance in the context of trying to find a model of fundamental physics—and I've said that it's going to be critical to both relativity and quantum mechanics. But actually what amounts to causal invariance has been seen before in various different guises in mathematics, mathematical logic and computer science. (Its most common name is "confluence", though there are some technical differences between this and what I call causal invariance.)

Think about expanding out an algebraic expression, like $(x+(1+x)^2)(x+2)^2$. You could expand one of the powers first, then multiply things out. Or you could multiply the terms first. It doesn't matter what order you do the steps in; you'll always get the same canonical form (which in this case Mathematica tells me is $4+16\,x+17\,x^2+7\,x^3+x^4$). And this independence of orders is essentially causal invariance.

Here's one more example. Imagine you've got some recursive definition, say f[n_]:=f[n−1]+f[n−2] (with f[0]=f[1]=1). Now evaluate f[10]. First you get f[9]+f[8]. But what do you do next? Do you evaluate f[9], or f[8]? And then what? In the end, it doesn't matter; you'll always get 55. And this is another example of causal invariance.

When one thinks about parallel or asynchronous algorithms, it's important if one has causal invariance. Because it means one can do things in any order—say, depth-first, breadth-first, or whatever—and one will always get the same answer. And that's what's happening in our little sorting algorithm above.

OK, but now let's come back to causal relationships. Here's the multiway system for the sorting process annotated with all causal relationships for all paths:

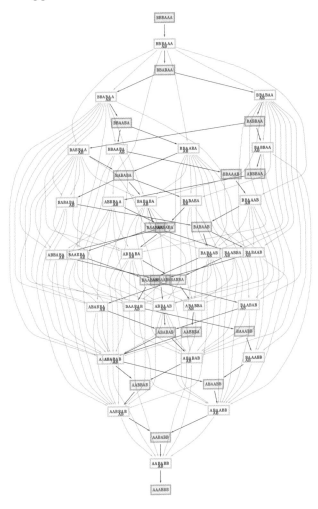

And, yes, it's a mess. But because there's causal invariance, we know something very important: this is basically just a lot of copies of the same causal graph—a simple grid:

(By the way—as the picture suggests—the cross-connections between these copies aren't trivial, and later on we'll see they're associated with deep relations between relativity and quantum mechanics, that probably manifest themselves in the physics of black holes. But we'll get to that later...)

OK, so every different way of applying the sorting rule is supposed to give the same causal graph. So here's one example of how we might apply the rule starting with a particular initial string:

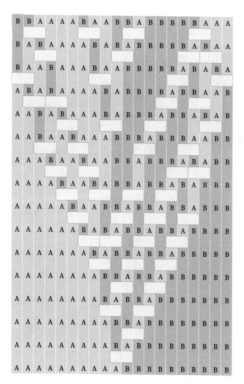

But now let's show the graph of causal connections. And we see it's just a grid:

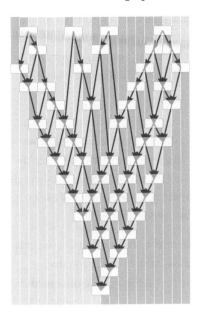

Here are three other possible sequences of updates:

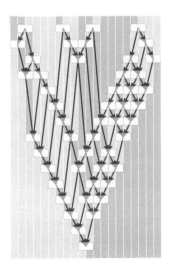 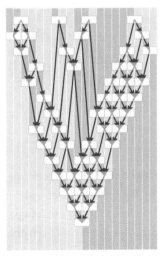 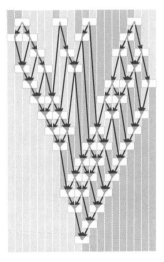

But now we see causal invariance in action: even though different updates occur at different times, the graph of causal relationships between updating events is always the same. And having seen this—in the context of a very simple example—we're ready to talk about special relativity.

Deriving Special Relativity

It's a typical first instinct in thinking about doing science: you imagine doing an experiment on a system, but you—as the "observer"—are outside the system. Of course if you're thinking about modeling the whole universe and everything in it, this isn't ultimately a reasonable way to think about things. Because the "observer" is inevitably part of the universe, and so has to be modeled just like everything else.

In our models what this means is that the "mind of the observer", just like everything else in the universe, has to get updated through a series of updating events. There's no absolute way for the observer to "know what's going on in the universe"; all they ever experience is a series of updating events, that may happen to be affected by updating events occurring elsewhere in the universe. Or, said differently, all the observer can ever observe is the network of causal relationships between events—or the causal graph that we've been talking about.

So as toy model let's look at our BA→AB rule for strings. We might imagine that the string is laid out in space. But to our observer the only thing they know is the causal graph that represents causal relationships between events. And for the BA→AB system here's one way we can draw that:

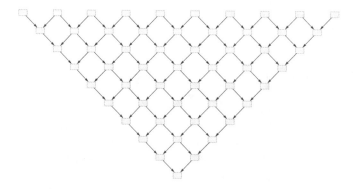

But now let's think about how observers might "experience" this causal graph. Underneath, an observer is getting updated by some sequence of updating events. But even though that's "really what's going on", to make sense of it, we can imagine our observers setting up internal "mental" models for what they see. And a pretty natural thing for observers like us to do is just to say "one set of things happens all across the universe, then another, and so on". And we can translate this into saying that we imagine a series of "moments" in time, where things happen "simultaneously" across the universe—at least with some convention for defining what we mean by simultaneously. (And, yes, this part of what we're doing is basically following what Einstein did when he originally proposed special relativity.)

Here's a possible way of doing it:

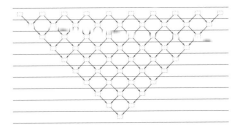

One can describe this as a "foliation" of the causal graph. We're dividing the causal graph into leaves or slices. And each slice our observers can consider to be a "successive moment in time".

It's important to note that there are some constraints on the foliation we can pick. The causal graph defines what event has to happen before what. And if our observers are going to have a chance of making sense of the world, it had better be the case that their notion of the progress of time aligns with what the causal graph says. So for example this foliation wouldn't work—because basically it says that the time we assign to events is going to disagree with the order in which the causal graph says they have to happen:

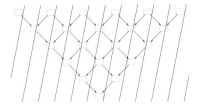

But, so given the foliation above, what actual order of updating events does it imply? It basically just says: as many events as possible happen at the same time (i.e. in the same slice of the foliation), as in this picture:

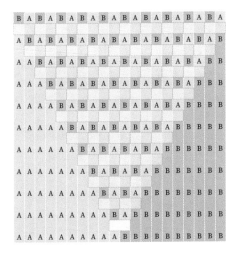

OK, now let's connect this to physics. The foliation we had above is relevant to observers who are somehow "stationary with respect to the universe" (the "cosmological rest frame"). One can imagine that as time progresses, the events a particular observer experiences are ones in a column going vertically down the page:

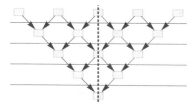

But now let's think about an observer who is uniformly moving in space. They'll experience a different sequence of events, say:

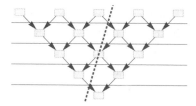

And that means that the foliation they'll naturally construct will be different. From the "outside" we can draw it on the causal graph like this:

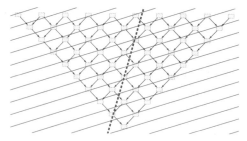

But to the observer each slice just represents a successive moment of time. And they don't have any way to know how the causal graph was drawn. So they'll construct their own version, where the slices are horizontal:

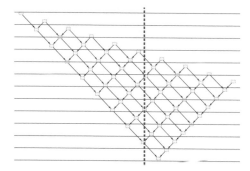

But now there's a purely geometrical fact: to make this rearrangement, while preserving the basic structure (and here, angles) of the causal graph, each moment of time has to sample fewer events in the causal graph, by a factor of $\sqrt{1-\beta^2}$ where β is the angle that represents the velocity of the observer.

If you know about special relativity, you'll recognize a lot of this. What we've been calling foliations correspond directly to relativity's "reference frames". And our foliations that represent motion are the standard inertial reference frames of special relativity.

But here's the special thing that's going on here: we can interpret all this discussion of foliations and reference frames in terms of the actual rules and evolution of our underlying system. So here now is the evolution of our string-sorting system in the "boosted reference frame" corresponding to an observer going at a certain speed:

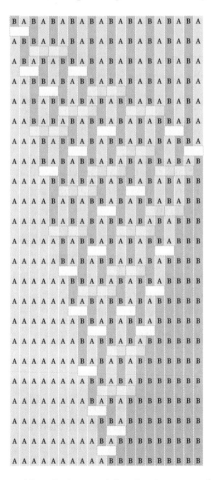

And here's the crucial point: because of causal invariance it doesn't matter that we're in a different reference frame—the causal graph for the system (and the way it eventually sorts the string) is exactly the same.

In special relativity, the key idea is that the "laws of physics" work the same in all inertial reference frames. But why should that be true? Well, in our systems, there's an answer: it's a consequence of causal invariance in the underlying rules. In other words, from the property of causal invariance, we're able to derive relativity.

Normally in physics one puts in relativity by the way one sets up the mathematical structure of spacetime. But in our models we don't start from anything like this, and in fact space and time are not even at all the same kind of thing. But what we can now see is that—because of causal invariance—relativity emerges in our models, with all the relationships between space and time that that implies.

So, for example, if we look at the picture of our string-sorting system above, we can see relativistic time dilation. In effect, because of the foliation we picked, time operates slower. Or, said another way, in the effort to sample space faster, our observer experiences slower updating of the system in time.

The speed of light c in our toy system is defined by the maximum rate at which information can propagate, which is determined by the rule, and in the case of this rule is one character per step. And in terms of this, we can then say that our foliation corresponds to a speed 0.3 c. But now we can look at the amount of time dilation, and it's exactly the amount $\gamma = 1/\sqrt{1-\frac{v^2}{c^2}}$ that relativity says it should be.

By the way, if we imagine trying to make our observer go "faster than light", we can see that can't work. Because there's no way to tip the foliation at more than 45° in our picture, and still maintain the causal relationships implied by the causal graph.

OK, so in our toy model we can derive special relativity. But here's the thing: this derivation isn't specific to the toy model; it applies to any rule that has causal invariance. So even though we may be dealing with hypergraphs, not strings, and we may have a rule that shows all kinds of complicated behavior, if it ultimately has causal invariance, then (with various technical caveats, mostly about possible wildness in the causal graph) it will exhibit relativistic invariance, and a physics based on it will follow special relativity.

What Is Energy? What Is Mass?

In our model, everything in the universe—space, matter, whatever—is supposed to be represented by features of our evolving hypergraph. So within that hypergraph, is there a way to identify things that are familiar from current physics, like mass, or energy?

I have to say that although it's a widespread concept in current physics, I'd never thought of energy as something fundamental. I'd just thought of it as an attribute that things (atoms, photons, whatever) can have. I never really thought of it as something that one could identify abstractly in the very structure of the universe.

So it came as a big surprise when we recently realized that actually in our model, there is something we can point to, and say "that's energy!", independent of what it's the energy of. The technical statement is: energy corresponds to the flux of causal edges through spacelike hypersurfaces. And, by the way, momentum corresponds to the flux of causal edges through timelike hypersurfaces.

OK, so what does this mean? First, what's a spacelike hypersurface? It's actually a standard concept in general relativity, for which there's a direct analogy in our models. Basically it's what forms a slice in our foliation. Why is it called what it's called? We can identify two kinds of directions: spacelike and timelike.

A spacelike direction is one that involves just moving in space—and it's a direction where one can always reverse and go back. A timelike direction is one that involves also progressing through time—where one can't go back. We can mark spacelike (—) and timelike (- -) hypersurfaces in the causal graph for our toy model:

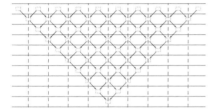

(They might be called "surfaces", except that "surfaces" are usually thought of as 2-dimensional, and our 3-space + 1-time dimensional universe, these foliation slices are 3-dimensional: hence the term "hypersurfaces".)

OK, now let's look at the picture. The "causal edges" are the causal connections between events, shown in the picture as lines joining the events. So when we talk about a "flux of causal edges through spacelike hypersurfaces", what we're talking about is the net number of causal edges that go down through the horizontal slices in the pictures.

In the toy model that's trivial to see. But here's a causal graph from a simple hypergraph model, where it's already considerably more complicated:

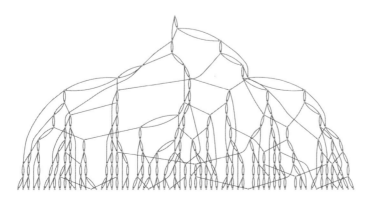

(Our toy-model causal graph starts from a line of events because we set up a long string as the initial condition; this starts from a single event because it's starting from a minimal initial condition.)

But when we put a foliation on this causal graph (thereby effectively defining our reference frame) we can start counting how many causal edges go down through successive ("spacelike") slices:

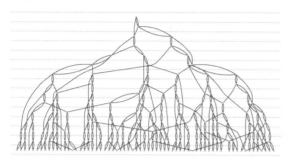

We can also ask how many causal edges go "sideways", through timelike hypersurfaces:

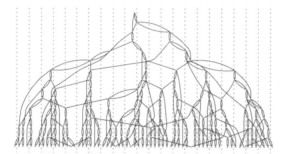

OK, so why do we think these fluxes of edges correspond to energy and momentum? Imagine what happens if we change our foliation, say tipping it to correspond to motion at some velocity, as we did in the previous section. It takes a little bit of math, but what we find out is that our fluxes of causal edges transform with velocity basically just like we saw distance and time transform in the previous section.

In the standard derivation of relativistic mechanics, there's a consistency argument that energy has to transform with velocity like time does, and momentum like distance. But now we actually have a structural reason for this to be the case. It's a fundamental consequence of our whole setup, and of causal invariance. In traditional physics, one often says that position is the conjugate variable to momentum, and energy to time. And that's something that's burnt into the mathematical structure of the theory. But here it's not something we're burning in; it's something we're deriving from the underlying structure of our model.

And that means there's ultimately a lot more we can say about it. For example, we might wonder what the "zero of energy" is. After all, if we look at one of our causal graphs, a lot of the causal edges are really just going into "maintaining the structure of space". So if in a sense space is uniform, there's inevitably a uniform "background flux" of causal edges associated with that. And whatever we consider to be "energy" corresponds to the fluctuations of that flux around its background value.

By the way, it's worth mentioning what a "flux of causal edges" corresponds to. Each causal edge represents a causal connection between events, that is in a sense "carried" by some element in the underlying hypergraph (the "spatial hypergraph"). So a "flux of causal edges" is in effect the communication of activity (i.e. events), either in time (i.e. through spacelike hypersurfaces) or in space (i.e. through timelike hypersurfaces). And at least in some approximation we can then say that energy is associated with activity in the hypergraph that propagates information through time, while momentum is associated with activity that propagates information in space.

There's a fundamental feature of our causal graphs that we haven't mentioned yet—that's related to information propagation. Start at any point (i.e. any event) in a causal graph. Then trace the causal connections from that event. You'll get some kind of cone (here just in 2D):

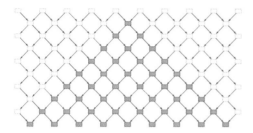

The cone is more complicated in a more complicated causal graph. But you'll always have something like it. And what it corresponds to physically is what's normally called a light cone (or "forward light cone"). Assuming we've drawn our causal network so that events are somehow laid out in space across the page, then the light cone will show how information (as transmitted by light) can spread in space with time.

When the causal graph gets complicated, the whole setup with light cones gets complicated, as we'll discuss for example in connection with black holes later. But for now, we can just say there are cones in our causal graph, and in effect the angle of these cones represents the maximum rate of information propagation in the system, which we can identify with the physical speed of light.

And in fact, not only can we identify light cones in our causal graph: in some sense we can think of our whole causal graph as just being a large number of "elementary light cones" all knitted together. And, as we mentioned, much of the structure that's built necessarily goes into, in effect, "maintaining the structure of space".

But let's look more closely at our light cones. There are causal edges on their boundaries that in effect correspond to propagation at the speed of light—and that, in terms of the underlying hypergraph, correspond to events that "reach out" in the hypergraph, and "entrain" new elements as quickly as possible. But what about causal edges that are "more vertical"? These causal edges are associated with events that in a sense reuse elements in the hypergraph, without involving new ones.

And it looks like these causal edges have an important interpretation: they are associated with mass (or, more specifically, rest mass). OK, so the total flux of causal edges through spacelike hypersurfaces corresponds to energy. And now we're saying that the flux of causal edges specifically in the timelike direction corresponds to rest mass. We can see what happens if we "tip our reference" frames just a bit, say corresponding to a velocity $v \ll c$. Again, there's a small amount of math, but it's pretty easy to derive formulas for momentum (p) and energy (E). The speed of light c comes into the formulas because it defines the ratio of "horizontal" (i.e. spacelike) to "vertical" (i.e timelike) distances on the causal graph. And for v small compared to c we get:

$$p = m\,v + \ldots$$

$$E = m\,c^2 + \frac{1}{2}\,m\,v^2 + \ldots$$

So from these formulas we can see that just by thinking about causal graphs (and, yes, with a backdrop of causal invariance, and a whole host of detailed mathematical limit questions that we're not discussing here), we've managed to derive a basic (and famous) fact about the relation between energy and mass:

$$E = m\,c^2$$

Sometimes in the standard formalism of physics, this relation by now seems more like a definition than something to derive. But in our model, it's not just a definition, and in fact we can successfully derive it.

General Relativity & Gravity

Earlier on, we talked about how curvature of space can arise in our models. But at that point we were just talking about "empty space". Now we can go back and also talk about how curvature interacts with mass and energy in space.

In our earlier discussion, we talked about constructing spherical balls by starting at some point in the hypergraph, and then following all possible sequences of r connections. But now we can do something directly analogous in the causal graph: start at some point, and follow possible sequences of t connections. There's quite a bit of mathematical trickiness, but essentially this gets us "volumes of light cones".

If space is effectively d-dimensional, then to a first approximation this volume will grow like t^{d+1}. But like in the spatial case, there's a correction term, this time proportional to the so-called Ricci tensor $R_{\mu\nu}$. (The actual expression is roughly $t^{d+1}(1 - \frac{1}{6}\,t_i\,t_j\,R_{ij} + \ldots)$ where the t_i are timelike vectors, etc.)

OK, but we also know something else about what is supposed to be inside our light cones: not only are there "background connections" that maintain the structure of space, there are also "additional" causal edges that are associated with energy, momentum and mass. And in the limit of a large causal graph, we can identify the density of these with the so-called energy-momentum tensor $T_{\mu\nu}$. So in the end we have two contributions to the "volumes" of our light cones: one from "pure curvature" and one from energy-momentum.

Again, there's some math involved. But the main thing is to think about the limit when we're looking at a very large causal graph. What needs to be true for us to have d-dimensional space, as opposed to something much wilder? This puts a constraint on the growth rates of our light cone volumes, and when one works everything out, it implies that the following equation must hold:

$$R_{\mu\nu} - \frac{1}{2} R\, g_{\mu\nu} = \sigma\, T_{\mu\nu}$$

But this is exactly Einstein's equation for the curvature of space when matter with a certain energy-momentum is present. We're glossing over lots of details here. But it's still, in my view, quite spectacular: from the basic structure of our very simple models, we're able to derive a fundamental result in physics: the equation that for more than a hundred years has passed every test in describing the operation of gravity.

There's a footnote here. The equation we've just given is without a so-called cosmological term. And how that works is bound up with the question of what the zero of energy is, which in our model relates to what features of the evolving hypergraph just have to do with the "maintenance of space", and what have to do with "things in space" (like matter).

In existing physics, there's an expectation that even in the "vacuum" there's actually a formally infinite density of pairs of virtual particles associated with quantum mechanics. Essentially what's happening is that there are always pairs of particles and antiparticles being created, that annihilate quickly, but that in aggregate contribute a huge effective energy density. We'll discuss how this relates to quantum mechanics in our models later. But for now let's just recall that particles (like electrons) in our models basically correspond to locally stable structures in the hypergraph.

But when we think about how "space is maintained" it's basically through all sorts of seemingly random updating events in the hypergraph. But in existing physics (or, specifically, quantum field theory) we're basically expected to analyze everything in terms of (virtual) particles. So if we try to do that with all these random updating events, it's not surprising that we end up saying that there are these infinite collections of things going on. (Yes, this can be made much more precise; I'm just giving an outline here.)

But as soon as we say this, there is an immediate problem: we're saying that there's a formally infinite—or at least huge—energy density that must exist everywhere in the universe. But if we then apply Einstein's equation, we'll conclude that this must produce enough curvature to basically curl the universe up into a tiny ball.

One way to get out of this is to introduce a so-called cosmological term, that's just an extra term in the Einstein equations, and then posit that this term is sized so as to exactly cancel (yes, to perhaps one part in 10^{60} or more) the energy density from virtual particles. It's certainly not a pretty solution.

But in our models, the situation is quite different. It's not that we have virtual particles "in space", that are having an effect on space. It's that the same stuff that corresponds to the virtual particles is actually "making the space", and maintaining its structure. Of course, there are lots of details about this—which no doubt depend on the particular underlying rule. But the point is that there's no longer a huge mystery about why "vacuum energy" doesn't basically destroy our universe: in effect, it's because it's what's making our universe.

Black Holes, Singularities, etc.

One of the big predictions of general relativity is the existence of black holes. So how do things like that work in our models? Actually, it's rather straightforward. The defining feature of a black hole is the existence of an event horizon: a boundary that light signals can't cross, and where in effect causal connection is broken.

In our models, we can explicitly see that happen in the causal graph. Here's an example:

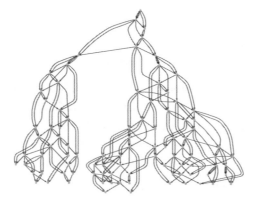

At the beginning, everything is causally connected. But at some point the causal graph splits—and there's an event horizon. Events happening on one side can't influence ones on the other, and so on. And that's how a region of the universe can "causally break off" to form something like a black hole.

But actually, in our models, the "breaking off" can be even more extreme. Not only can the causal graph split; the spatial hypergraph can actually throw off disconnected pieces—each of which in effect forms a whole "separate universe":

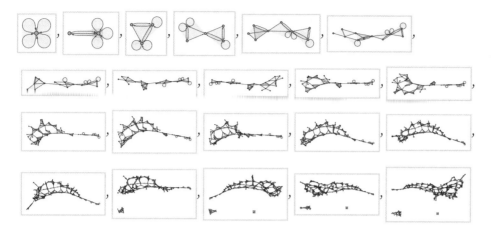

By the way, it's interesting to look at what happens to the foliations observers make when there's an event horizon. Causal invariance says that paths in the causal graph that diverge should always eventually merge. But if the paths go into different disconnected pieces of the causal graph, that can't ever happen. So how does an observer deal with that? Well, basically they have to "freeze time". They have to have a foliation where successive time slices just pile up, and never enter the disconnected pieces.

It's just like what happens in general relativity. To an observer far from the black hole, it'll seem to take an infinite time for anything to fall into the black hole. For now, this is just a phenomenon associated with the structure of space. But later we'll see that it's also the direct analog of something completely different: the process of measurement in quantum mechanics.

Coming back to gravity: we can ask questions not only about event horizons, but also about actual singularities in spacetime. In our models, these are places where lots of paths in a causal graph converge to a single point. And in our models, we can immediately study questions like whether there's always an event horizon associated with any singularity (the "cosmic censorship hypothesis").

We can ask about other strange phenomena from general relativity. For example, there are closed timelike curves, sometimes viewed as allowing time travel. In our models, closed timelike curves are inconsistent with causal invariance. But we can certainly invent rules that produce them. Here's an example:

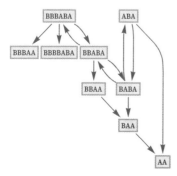

We start from one "initial" state in this multiway system. But as we go forward we can enter a loop where we repeatedly visit the same state. And this loop also occurs in the causal graph. We think we're "going forward in time". But actually we're just in a loop, repeatedly returning to the same state. And if we tried to make a foliation where we could describe time as always advancing, we just wouldn't be able to do it.

Cosmology

In our model, the universe can start as a tiny hypergraph—perhaps a single self-loop. But then—as the rule gets applied—it progressively expands. With some particularly simple rules, the total size of the hypergraph has to just uniformly increase; with others it can fluctuate.

But even if the size of the hypergraph is always increasing, that doesn't mean we'd necessarily notice. It could be that essentially everything we can see just expands too—so in effect the granularity of space is just getting finer and finer. This would be an interesting resolution to the age-old debate about whether the universe is discrete or continuous. Yes, it's structurally discrete, but the scale of discreteness relative to our scale is always getting smaller and smaller. And if this happens fast enough, we'd never be able to "see the discreteness"—because every time we tried to measure it, the universe would effectively have subdivided before we got the result. (Somehow it'd be like the ultimate calculus epsilon-delta proof: you challenge the universe with an epsilon, and before you can get the result, the universe has made a smaller delta.)

There are some other strange possibilities too. Like that the whole hypergraph for the universe is always expanding, but pieces are continually "breaking off", effectively forming black holes of different sizes, and allowing the "main component" of the universe to vary in size.

But regardless of how this kind of expansion works in our universe today, it's clear that if the universe started with a single self-loop, it had to do a lot of expanding, at least early on. And here there's an interesting possibility that's relevant for understanding cosmology.

Just because our current universe exhibits three-dimensional space, in our models there's no reason to think that the early universe necessarily also did. There are very different things that can happen in our models:

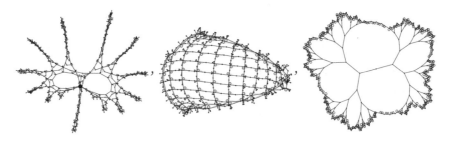

In the first example here, different parts of space effectively separate into non-communicating "black hole" tree branches. In the second example, we have something like ordinary—in this case 2-dimensional—space. But in the third example, space is in a sense very connected. If we work out the volume of a spherical ball, it won't grow like r^d; it'll grow exponentially with r (e.g. like 2^r).

If we look at the causal graph, we'll see that you can effectively "go everywhere in space", or affect every event, very quickly. It'd be as if the speed of light is infinite. But really it's because space is effectively infinite dimensional.

In typical cosmology, it's been quite mysterious how different parts of the early universe managed to "communicate" with each other, for example, to smooth out perturbations. But if the universe starts effectively infinite-dimensional, and only later "relaxes" to being finite-dimensional, that's no longer a mystery.

So, OK, what might we see in the universe today that would reflect what happened extremely early in its history? The fact that our models deterministically generate behavior that seems for all practical purposes random means that we can expect that most features of the initial conditions or very early stages of the universe will quickly be "encrypted", and effectively not reconstructable.

But it's just conceivable that something like a breaking of symmetry associated with the first few hypergraphs might somehow survive. And that suggests the bizarre possibility that—just maybe—something like the angular structure of the cosmic microwave background or the very large-scale distribution of galaxies might reflect the discrete structure of the very early universe. Or, in other words, it's just conceivable that what amounts to the rule for the universe is, in effect, painted across the whole sky. I think this is extremely unlikely, but it'd certainly be an amazing thing if the universe were "self-documenting" that way.

Elementary Particles—Old and New

We've talked several times about particles like electrons. In current physics theories, the various (truly) elementary particles—the quarks, the leptons (electron, muon, neutrinos, etc.), the gauge bosons, the Higgs—are all assumed to intrinsically be point particles, of zero size. In our models, that's not how it works. The particles are all effectively "little lumps of space" that have various special properties.

My guess is that the precise list of what particles exist will be something that's specific to a particular underlying rule. In cellular automata, for example, we're used to seeing complicated sets of possible localized structures arise:

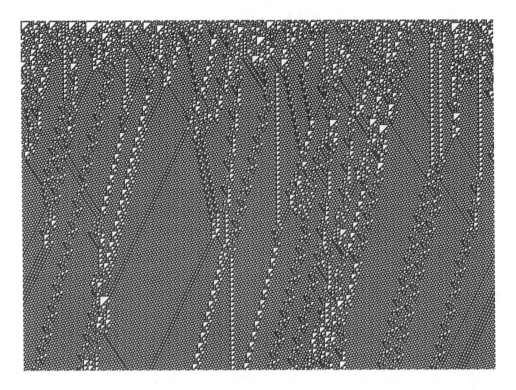

In our hypergraphs, the picture will inevitably be somewhat different. The "core feature" of each particle will be some kind of locally stable structure in the hypergraph (a simple analogy might be that it's a lump of nonplanarity in an otherwise planar graph). But then there'll be lots of causal edges associated with the particle, defining its particular energy and momentum.

Still, the "core feature" of the particles will presumably define things like their charge, quantum numbers, and perhaps spin—and the fact that these things are observed to occur in discrete units may reflect the fact that it's a small piece of hypergraph that's involved in defining them.

It's not easy to know what the actual scale of discreteness in space might be in our models. But a possible (though potentially unreliable) estimate might be that the "elementary length" is around 10^{-93} meters. (Note that that's very small compared to the Planck length ~10^{-35} meters that arises essentially from dimensional analysis.) And with this elementary length, the radius of the electron might be 10^{-81} meters. Tiny, but not zero. (Note that current experiments only tell us that the size of the electron is less than about 10^{-22} meters.)

One feature of our models is that there should be a "quantum of mass"—a discrete amount that all masses, for example of particles, are multiples of. With our estimate for the elementary length, this quantum of mass would be small, perhaps 10^{-30}, or 10^{36} times smaller than the mass of the electron.

And this raises an intriguing possibility. Perhaps the particles—like electrons—that we currently know about are the "big ones". (With our estimates, an electron would have 10^{35} hypergraph elements in it.) And maybe there are some much smaller, and much lighter ones. At least relative to the particles we currently know, such particles would have few hypergraph elements in them—so I'm referring to them as "oligons" (after the Greek word ὀλίγος for "few").

What properties would these oligons have? They'd probably interact very very weakly with other things in the universe. Most likely lots of oligons would have been produced in the very early universe, but with their very weak interactions, they'd soon "drop out of thermal equilibrium", and be left in large numbers as relics—with energies that become progressively lower as the universe expands around them.

So where might oligons be now? Even though their other interactions would likely be exceptionally weak, they'd still be subject to gravity. And if their energies end up being low enough, they'd basically collect in gravity wells around the universe—which means in and around galaxies.

And that's interesting—because right now there's quite a mystery about the amount of mass seen in galaxies. There appears to be a lot of "dark matter" that we can't see but that has gravitational effects. Well, maybe it's oligons. Maybe even lots of different kinds of oligons: a whole shadow physics of much lighter particles.

The Inevitability of Quantum Mechanics

"But how will you ever get quantum mechanics?", physicists would always ask me when I would describe earlier versions of my models. In many ways, quantum mechanics is the pinnacle of existing physics. It's always had a certain "you-are-not-expected-to-understand-this" air, though, coupled with "just-trust-the-mathematical-formalism". And, yes, the mathematical formalism has worked well—really well—in letting us calculate things. (And it almost seems more satisfying because the calculations are often so hard; indeed, hard enough that they're what first made me start using computers to do mathematics 45 years ago.)

Our usual impression of the world is that definite things happen. And before quantum mechanics, classical physics typically captured this in laws—usually equations—that would tell one what specifically a system would do. But in quantum mechanics the formalism involves any particular system doing lots of different things "in parallel", with us just seeing samples—ultimately with certain probabilities—of these possibilities.

And as soon as one hears of a model in which there are definite rules, one might assume that it could never reproduce quantum mechanics. But, actually, in our models, quantum mechanics is not just possible; it's absolutely inevitable. And, as we'll see, in something I consider quite beautiful, the core of what leads to it turns out to be the same as what leads to relativity.

OK, so how does this work? Let's go back to what we discussed when we first started talking about time. In our models there's a definite rule for updates to make in our hypergraphs, say:

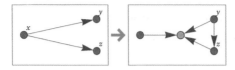

But if we've got a hypergraph like this:

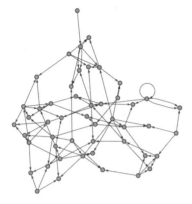

there will usually be many places where this rule can be applied. So which update should we do first? The model doesn't tell us. But let's just imagine all the possibilities. The rule tells us what they all are—and we can represent them (as we discussed above) as a multiway system— here illustrated using the simpler case of strings rather than hypergraphs:

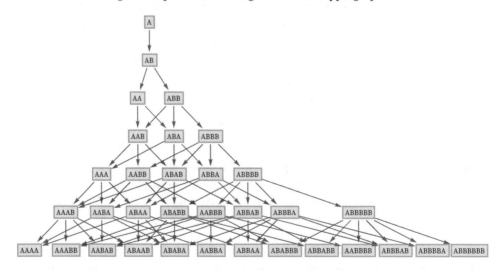

Each node in this graph now represents a complete state of our system (a hypergraph in our actual models). And each node is joined by arrows to the state or states that one gets by applying a single update to it.

If our model had been operating "like classical physics" we would expect it to progress in time from one state to another, say like this:

But the crucial point is that the structure of our models leaves us no choice but to consider multiway systems. The form of the whole multiway system is completely determined by the rules. But—in a way that is already quite reminiscent of the standard formalism of quantum mechanics—the multiway system defines many different possible paths of history.

But now there is a mystery. If there are always all these different possible paths of history, how is it that we ever think that definite things happen in the world? This has been a core mystery of quantum mechanics for a century. It turns out that if one's just using quantum mechanics to do calculations, the answer basically doesn't matter. But if one wants to "really understand what's going on" in quantum mechanics, it's something that definitely does matter.

And the exciting thing is that in our models, there's an obvious resolution. And actually it's based on the exact same phenomenon—causal invariance—that gives us relativity.

Here's roughly how this works. The key point is to think about what an observer who is themselves part of the multiway system will conclude about the world. Yes, there are different possible paths of history. But—just as in our discussion of relativity—the only aspect of them that an observer will ever be aware of is the causal relationships between the events they involve. But the point is that—even though when looked at from "outside" the paths are different—causal invariance implies that the network of relationships between causal events (which is all that's relevant when one's inside the system) will always be exactly the same.

In other words—much as in the case of relativity—even though from outside the system there may seem to be many possible "threads of time", from inside the system causal invariance implies that there's in a sense ultimately just one thread of time, or, in effect, one objective reality.

How does this all relate to the detailed standard formalism of quantum mechanics? It's a little complicated. But let me make at least a few comments here. (There's some more detail in my technical document; Jonathan Gorard has given even more.)

The states in the multiway system can be thought of as possible states of the quantum system. But how do we characterize how observers experience them? In particular, which states is the observer aware of when? Just like in the relativity case, the observer can in a sense make a choice of how they define time. One possibility might be through a foliation of the multiway system like this:

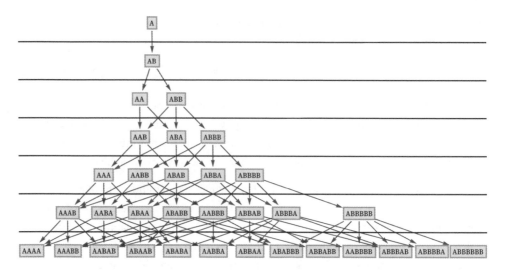

In the formalism of quantum mechanics, one can then say that at each time, the observer experiences a superposition of possible states of the system. But now there's a critical point. In direct analogy to the case of relativity, there are many different possible choices the observer can make about how to define time—and each of them corresponds to a different foliation of the multiway graph.

Again by analogy to relativity, we can then think of these choices as what we can call different "quantum observation frames". Causal invariance implies that as long they respect the causal relationships in the graph, these frames can basically be set up in any way we want. In talking about relativity, it was useful to just have "tipped parallel lines" ("inertial frames") representing observers who are moving uniformly in space.

In talking about quantum mechanics, other frames are useful. In particular, in the standard formalism of quantum mechanics, it's common to talk about "quantum measurement": essentially the act of taking a quantum system and determining some definite (essentially classical) outcome from it. Well, in our setup, a quantum measurement basically corresponds to a particular quantum observation frame.

Here's an example:

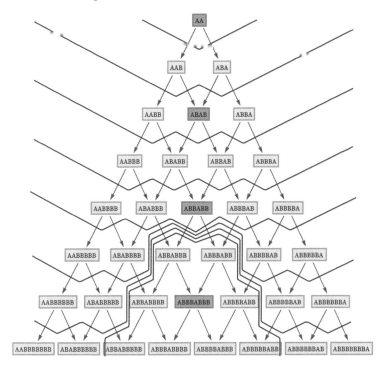

The successive pink lines effectively mark off what the observer is considering to be successive moments in time. So when all the lines bunch up below the state ABBABB what it means is that the observer is effectively choosing to "freeze time" for that state. In other words, the observer is saying "that's the state I consider the system to be in, and I'm sticking to it". Or, put another way, even though in the full multiway graph there's all sorts of other "quantum mechanical" evolution of states going on, the observer has set up their quantum observation frame so that they pick out just a particular, definite, classical-like outcome.

OK, but can they consistently do that? Well, that depends on the actual underlying structure of the multiway graph, which ultimately depends on the actual underlying rule. In the example above, we've set up a foliation (i.e. a quantum observation frame) that does the best possible job in this rule at "freezing time" for the ABBABB state. But just how long can this "reality distortion field" be maintained?

The only way to keep the foliation consistent in the multiway graph above is to have it progressively expand over time. In other words, to keep time frozen, more and more quantum states have to be pulled into the "reality distortion field", and so there's less and less coherence in the system.

The picture above is for a very trivial rule. Here's a corresponding picture for a slightly more realistic case:

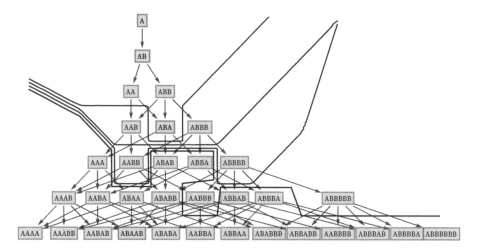

And what we see here is that—even in this still incredibly simplified case—the structure of the multiway system will force the observer to construct a more and more elaborate foliation if they are to successfully freeze time. Measurement in quantum mechanics has always involved a slightly uncomfortable mathematical idealization—and this now gives us a sense of what's really going on. (The situation is ultimately very similar to the problem of decoding "encrypted" thermodynamic initial conditions that I mentioned above.)

Quantum measurement is really about what an observer perceives. But if you are for example trying to construct a quantum computer, it's not just a question of having a qubit be perceived as being maintained in a particular state; it actually has to be maintained in that state. And for this to be the case we actually have to freeze time for that qubit. But here's a very simplified example of how that can happen in a multiway graph:

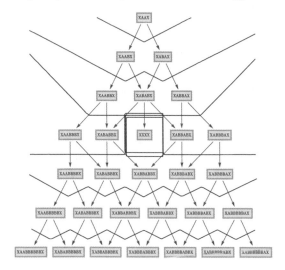

All this discussion of "freezing time" might seem weird, and not like anything one usually talks about in physics. But actually, there's a wonderful connection: the freezing of time we're talking about here can be thought of as happening because we've got the analog in the space of quantum states of a black hole in physical space.

The picture above makes it plausible that we've got something where things can go in, but if they do, they always get stuck. But there's more to it. If you're an observer far from a black hole, then you'll never actually see anything fall into the black hole in finite time (that's why black holes are called "frozen stars" in Russian). And the reason for this is precisely because (according to the mathematics) time is frozen at the event horizon of the black hole. In other words, to successfully make a qubit, you effectively have to isolate it in quantum space like things get isolated in physical space by the presence of the event horizon of a black hole.

General Relativity and Quantum Mechanics Are the Same Idea!

General relativity and quantum mechanics are the two great foundational theories of current physics. And in the past it's often been a struggle to reconcile them. But one of the beautiful outcomes of our project so far has been the realization that at some deep level general relativity and quantum mechanics are actually the same idea. It's something that (at least so far) is only clear in the context of our models. But the basic point is that both theories are consequences of causal invariance—just applied in different situations.

Recall our discussion of causal graphs in the context of relativity above. We drew foliations and said that if we looked at a particular slice, it would tell us the arrangement of the system in space at what we consider to be a particular time. So now let's look at multiway graphs. We saw in the previous section that in quantum mechanics we're interested in foliations of these. But if we look at a particular slice in one of these foliations, what does it represent? The foliation has got a bunch of states in it. And it turns out that we can think of them as being laid out in an abstract kind of space that we're calling "branchial space".

To make sense of this space, we have to have a way to say what's near what. But actually the multiway graph gives us that. Take a look at this multiway graph:

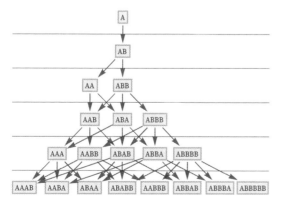

At each slice in the foliation, let's draw a graph where we connect two states whenever they're both part of the same "branch pair", so that—like AA and ABB here—they both come from the same state on the slice before. Here are the graphs we get by doing this for successive slices:

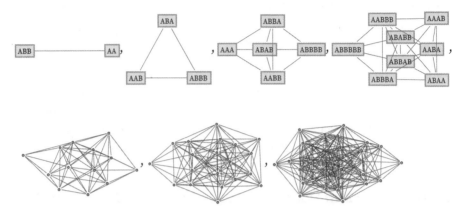

We call these branchial graphs. And we can think of them as representing the correlation—or entanglement—of quantum states. Two states that are nearby in the graph are highly entangled; those further away, less so. And we can imagine that as our system evolves, we'll get larger and larger branchial graphs, until eventually, just like for our original hypergraphs, we can think of these graphs as limiting to something like a continuous space.

But what is this space like? For our original hypergraphs, we imagined that we'd get something like ordinary physical space (say close to three-dimensional Euclidean space). But branchial space is something more abstract—and much wilder. And typically it won't even be finite-dimensional. (It might approximate a projective Hilbert space.) But we can still think of it mathematically as some kind of space.

OK, things are getting fairly complicated here. But let me try to give at least a flavor of how things work. Here's an example of a wonderful correspondence: curvature in physical space is like the uncertainty principle of quantum mechanics. Why do these have anything to do with each other?

The uncertainty principle says that if you measure, say, the position of something, then its momentum, you'll get a different answer than if you do it in the opposite order. But now think about what happens when you try to make a rectangle in physical space by going in direction x first, then y, and then you do these in the opposite order. In a flat space, you'll get to the same place. But in a curved space, you won't:

And essentially what's happening in the uncertainty principle is that you're doing exactly this, but in branchial space, rather than physical space. And it's because branchial space is wild—and effectively very curved—that you get the uncertainty principle.

Alright, so the next question might be: What's the analog of the Einstein equations in branchial space? And again, it's quite wonderful: at least in some sense, the answer is that it's the path integral—the fundamental mathematical construct of modern quantum mechanics and quantum field theory.

This is again somewhat complicated. But let me try to give a flavor of it. Just as we discussed geodesics as describing paths traversed through physical space in the course of time, so also we can discuss geodesics as describing paths traversed through branchial space in the course of time. In both cases these geodesics are determined by curvature in the corresponding space. In the case of physical space, we argued (roughly) that the presence of excess causal edges—corresponding to energy—would lead to what amounts to curvature in the spatial hypergraph, as described by Einstein's equations.

OK, so what about branchial space? Just like for the spatial hypergraph, we can think about the causal connections between the updating events that define the branchial graph. And we can once again imagine identifying the flux of causal edges—now not through spacelike hypersurfaces, but through branchlike ones—as corresponding to energy. And—much like in the spatial hypergraph case—an excess of these causal edges will have the effect of producing what amounts to curvature in branchial space (or, more strictly, in branchtime—the analog of spacetime). But this curvature will then affect the geodesics that traverse branchial space.

In general relativity, the presence of mass (or energy) causes curvature in space which causes the paths of geodesics to turn—which is what is normally interpreted as the action of the force of gravity. But now we have an analog in quantum mechanics, in our branchial space. The presence of energy effectively causes curvature in branchial space which causes the paths of geodesics through branchial space to turn.

What does turning correspond to? Basically it's exactly what the path integral talks about. The path integral (and the usual formalism of quantum mechanics) is set up in terms of complex numbers. But it can just as well be thought of in terms of turning through an angle. And that's exactly what's happening with our geodesics in branchial space. In the path integral there's a quantity called the action—which is a kind of relativistic analog of energy— and when one works things out more carefully, our fluxes of causal edges correspond to the action, but are also exactly what determine the rate of turning of geodesics.

It all fits together beautifully. In physical space we have Einstein's equations—the core of general relativity. And in branchial space (or, more accurately, multiway space) we have Feynman's path integral—the core of modern quantum mechanics. And in the context of our models they're just different facets of the same idea. It's an amazing unification that I have to say I didn't see coming; it's something that just emerged as an inevitable consequence of our simple models of applying rules to collections of relations, or hypergraphs.

Branchial Motion and the Entanglement Horizon

We can think of motion in physical space as like the process of exploring new elements in the spatial hypergraph, and potentially becoming affected by them. But now that we're talking about branchial space, it's natural to ask whether there's something like motion there too. And the answer is that there is. And it's basically exactly the same kind of thing: but instead of exploring new elements in the spatial hypergraph, we're exploring new elements in the branchial graph, and potentially becoming affected by them.

There's a way of talking about it in the standard language of quantum mechanics: as we move in branchial space, we're effectively getting "entangled" with more and more quantum states.

OK, so let's take the analogy further. In physical space, there's a maximum speed of motion—the speed of light, c. So what about in branchial space? Well, in our models we can see that there's also got to be a maximum speed of motion in branchial space. Or, in other words, there's a maximum rate at which we can entangle with new quantum states.

In physical space we talk about light cones as being the regions that can be causally affected by some event at a particular location in space. In the same way, we can talk about entanglement cones that define regions in branchial space that can be affected by events at some position in branchial space. And just as there's a causal graph that effectively knits together elementary light cones, there's something similar that knits together entanglement cones.

That something similar is the multiway causal graph: a graph that represents causal relationships between all events that can happen anywhere in a multiway system. Here's an example of a multiway causal graph for just a few steps of a very simple string substitution system—and it's already pretty complicated:

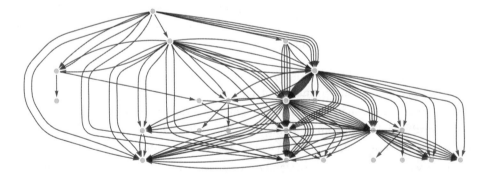

But in a sense the multiway causal graph is the most complete description of everything that can affect the experience of observers. Some of the causal relationships it describes represent spacelike connections; some represent branchlike connections. But all of them are there. And so in a sense the multiway causal graph is where relativity and quantum mechanics come together. Slice one way and you'll see relationships in physical space; slice another way and you'll see relationships in branchial space, between quantum states.

To help see how this works here's a very toy version of a multiway causal graph:

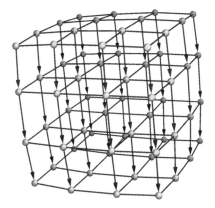

Each point is an event that happens in some hypergraph on some branch of a multiway system. And now the graph records the causal relationship of that event to other ones. In this toy example, there are purely timelike relationships—indicated by arrows pointing down—in which basically some element of the hypergraph is affecting its future self. But then there are both spacelike and branchlike relationships, where the event affects elements that are either "spatially" separated in the hypergraph, or "branchially" separated in the multiway system.

But in all this complexity, there's something wonderful that happens. As soon as the underlying rule has causal invariance, this implies all sorts of regularities in the multiway causal graph. And for example it tells us that all those causal graphs we get by taking different branchtime slices are actually the same when we project them into spacetime—and this is what leads to relativity.

But causal invariance has other consequences too. One of them is that there should be an analog of special relativity that applies not in spacetime but in branchtime. The reference frames of special relativity are now our quantum observation frames. And the analog of speed in physical space is the rate of entangling new quantum states.

So what about a phenomenon like relativistic time dilation? Is there an analog of that for motion in branchial space? Well, actually, yes there is. And it turns out to be what's sometimes called the quantum Zeno effect: if you repeatedly measure a quantum system fast enough it won't change. It's a phenomenon that's implied by the add-ons to the standard formalism of quantum mechanics that describe measurement. But in our models it just comes directly from the analogy between branchial and physical space.

Doing new measurements is equivalent to getting entangled with new quantum states—or to moving in branchial space. And in direct analogy to what happens in special relativity, as you get closer to moving at the maximum speed you inevitably sample things more slowly in time—and so you get time dilation, which means that your "quantum evolution" slows down.

OK, so there are relativistic phenomena in physical space, and quantum analogs in branchial space. But in our models these are all effectively facets of one thing: the multiway causal graph. So are there situations in which the two kinds of phenomena can mix? Normally there aren't: relativistic phenomena involve large physical scales; quantum phenomena tend to involve small ones.

But one example of an extreme situation where they can mix is black holes. I've mentioned several times that the formation of an event horizon around a black hole is associated with disconnection in the causal graph. But it's more than that. It's actually disconnection not only in the spacetime causal graph, but in the full multiway causal graph. And that means that there's not only an ordinary causal event horizon—in physical space—but also an "entanglement horizon" in branchial space. And just as a piece of the spatial hypergraph can get disconnected when there's a black hole, so can a piece of the branchial graph.

What does this mean? There are a variety of consequences. One of them is that quantum information can be trapped inside the entanglement horizon even when it hasn't crossed the causal event horizon—so that in effect the black hole is freezing quantum information "at its surface" (at least its surface in branchial space). It's a weird phenomenon implied by our models, but what's perhaps particularly interesting about it is that it's very much aligned with conclusions about black holes that have emerged in some of the latest work in physics on the so-called holographic principle in quantum field theory and general relativity.

Here's another related, weird phenomenon. If you pass the causal event horizon of a black hole, it's an inevitable fact that you'll eventually get infinitely physically elongated (or "spaghettified") by tidal forces. Well, something similar happens if you pass the entanglement horizon—except now you'll get elongated in branchial space rather than physical space. And in our models, this eventually means you won't be able to make a quantum measurement—so in a sense as an observer you won't be able to "form a classical thought", or, in other words, beyond the entanglement horizon you'll never be able to "come to a definite conclusion" about, for example, whether something fell into the black hole or didn't.

The speed of light c is a fundamental physical constant that relates distance in physical space to time. In our models, there's now a new fundamental physical constant: the maximum entanglement speed, that relates distance in branchial space to time. I call this maximum entanglement speed ζ (zeta) (ζ looks a bit like a "tangled c"). I'm not sure what its value is, but a possible estimate is that it corresponds to entangling about 10^{102} new quantum states per second. And in a sense the fact that this is so big is why we're normally able to "form classical thoughts".

Because of the relation between (multiway) causal edges and energy, it's possible to convert ζ to units of energy per second, and our estimate then implies that ζ is about 10^5 solar masses per second. It's a big value, although conceivably not irrelevant to something like a merger of galactic black holes. (And, yes, this would mean that for an intelligence to "quantum grok" our galaxy would take maybe six months.)

Finding the Ultimate Rule

I'm frankly amazed at how much we've been able to figure out just from the general structure of our models. But to get a final fundamental theory of physics we've still got to find a specific rule. A rule that gives us 3 (or so) dimensions of space, the particular expansion rate of the universe, the particular masses and properties of elementary particles, and so on. But how should we set about finding this rule?

And actually even before that, we need to ask: if we had the right rule, would we even know it? As I mentioned earlier, there's potentially a big problem here with computational irreducibility. Because whatever the underlying rule is, our actual universe has applied it perhaps 10^{500} times. And if there's computational irreducibility—as there inevitably will be—then there won't be a way to fundamentally reduce the amount of computational effort that's needed to determine the outcome of all these rule applications.

But what we have to hope is that somehow—even though the complete evolution of the universe is computationally irreducible—there are still enough "tunnels of computational reducibility" that we'll be able to figure out at least what's needed to be able to compare with what we know in physics, without having to do all that computational work. And I have to say that our recent success in getting conclusions just from the general structure of our models makes me much more optimistic about this possibility.

But, OK, so what rules should we consider? The traditional approach in natural science (at least over the past few centuries) has tended to be: start from what you know about whatever system you're studying, then try to "reverse engineer" what its rules are. But in our models there's in a sense too much emergence for this to work. Look at something like this:

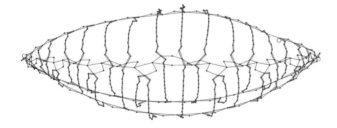

Given the overall form of this structure, would you ever figure that it could be produced just by the rule:

$$\{\{x, y, y\}, \{y, z, u\}\} \to \{\{u, z, z\}, \{u, x, v\}, \{y, u, v\}\}$$

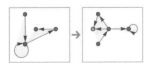

Having myself explored the computational universe of simple programs for some forty years, I have to say that even now it's amazing how often I'm humbled by the ability of extremely simple rules to give behavior I never expected. And this is particularly common with the very structureless models we're using here. So in the end the only real way to find out what can happen in these models is just to enumerate possible rules, and then run them and see what they do.

But now there's a crucial question. If we just start enumerating very simple rules, how far are we going to have to go before we find our universe? Or, put another way, just how simple is the rule for our universe going to end up being?

It could have been that in a sense the rule for the universe would have a special case in it for every element of the universe—every particle, every position in space, etc. But the very fact that we've been able to find definite scientific laws—and that systematic physics has even been possible—suggests that the rule at least doesn't have that level of complexity. But how simple might it be? We don't know. And I have to say that I don't think our recent discoveries shed any particular light on this—because they basically say that lots of things in physics are generic, and independent of the specifics of the underlying rule, however simple or complex it may be.

Why This Universe? The Relativity of Rules

But, OK, let's say we find that our universe can be described by some particular rule. Then the obvious immediate question would be: why that rule, and not another? The history of science—certainly since Copernicus—has shown us over and over again evidence that we're "not special". But if the rule we find to describe our universe is simple, wouldn't that simplicity be a sign of "specialness"?

I have long wondered about this. Could it for example be that the rule is only simple because of the way that we, as entities existing in our particular universe, choose to set up our ways of describing things? And that in some other universe, with some other rule, the entities that exist there would set up their ways of describing things so that the rule for their universe is simple to them, even though it might be very complex to us?

Or could it be that in some fundamental sense it doesn't matter what the rules for the universe are: that to observers embedded in a universe, operating according to the same rules as that universe, the conclusions about how the universe works will always be the same?

Or could it be that this is a kind of question that's just outside the realm of science?

To my considerable surprise, the paradigm that's emerging from our recent discoveries potentially seems to suggest a definite—though at first seemingly bizarre—scientific answer.

In what we've discussed so far we're imagining that there's a particular, single rule for our universe, that gets applied over and over again, effectively in all possible ways. But what if there wasn't just one rule that could be used? What if all conceivable rules could be used?

What if every updating event could just use any possible rule? (Notice that in a finite universe, there are only ever finitely many rules that can ever apply.)

At first it might not seem as if this setup would ever lead to anything definite. But imagine making a multiway graph of absolutely everything that can happen—including all events for all possible rules. This is a big, complicated object. But far from being structureless, it's full of all kinds of structure.

And there's one very important thing about it: it's basically guaranteed to have causal invariance (basically because if there's a rule that does something, there's always another rule somewhere that can undo it).

So now we can make a rule-space multiway causal graph—which will show a rule-space analog of relativity. And what this means is that in the rule-space multiway graph, we can expect to make different foliations, but have them all give consistent results.

It's a remarkable conceptual unification. We've got physical space, branchial space, and now also what we can call rulial space (or just rule space). And the same overall ideas and principles apply to all of them. And just as we defined reference frames in physical space and branchial space, so also we can define reference frames in rulial space.

But what kinds of reference frames might observers set up in rulial space? In a typical case we can think of different reference frames in rulial space as corresponding to different description languages in which an observer can describe their experience of the universe.

In the abstract, it's a familiar idea that given any particular description language, we can always explicitly program any universal computer to translate it to another description language. But what we're saying here is that in rulial space it just takes choosing a different reference frame to have our representation of the universe use a different description language.

And roughly the reason this works is that different foliations of rulial space correspond to different choices of sequences of rules in the rule-space multiway graph—which can in effect be set up to "compute" the output that would be obtained with any given description language. That this can work ultimately depends on the fact that sequences of our rules can support universal computation (which the Principle of Computational Equivalence implies they ubiquitously will)—which is in effect why it only takes "choosing a different reference frame in rule space" to "run a different program" and get a different description of the observed behavior of the universe.

It's a strange but rather appealing picture. The universe is effectively using all possible rules. But as entities embedded in the universe, we're picking a particular foliation (or sequence of reference frames) to make sense of what's happening. And that choice of foliation corresponds to a description language which gives us our particular way of describing the universe.

But what is there to say definitely about the universe—independent of the foliation? There's one immediate thing: that the universe, whatever foliation one uses to describe it, is just a universal computer, and nothing more. And that hypercomputation is never possible in the universe.

But given the structure of our models, there's more. Just like there's a maximum speed in physical space (the speed of light c), and a maximum speed in branchial space (the maximum entanglement speed ζ), so also there must be a maximum speed in rulial space, which we can call ρ—that's effectively another fundamental constant of nature. (The constancy of ρ is in effect a reflection of the Principle of Computational Equivalence.)

But what does moving in rulial space correspond to? Basically it's a change of rule. And to say that this can only happen at a finite speed is to say that there's computational irreducibility: that one rule cannot emulate another infinitely fast. And given this finite "speed of emulation" there are "emulation cones" that are the analog of light cones, and that define how far one can get in rulial space in a certain amount of time.

What are the units of ρ? Essentially they are program length divided by time. But whereas in the theory of computation one typically imagines that program length can be scaled almost arbitrarily by different models of computation, here this is a measure of program length that's somehow fundamentally anchored to the structure of the rule-space multiway system, and of physics. (By the way, there'll be an analog of curvature and Einstein's equations in rulial space too—and it probably corresponds to a geometrization of computational complexity theory and questions like P?=NP.)

There's more to say about the structure of rulial space. For example, let's imagine we try to make a foliation in which we freeze time somewhere in rulial space. That'll correspond to trying to describe the universe using some computationally reducible model—and over time it'll get more and more difficult to maintain this as emulation cones effectively deliver more and more computational irreducibility.

So what does all this mean for our original goal—of finding a rule to describe our universe? Basically it's saying that any (computation universal) rule will do—if we're prepared to craft the appropriate description language. But the point is that we've basically already defined at least some elements of our description language: they are the kinds of things our senses detect, our measuring devices measure, and our existing physics describes. So now our challenge is to find a rule that successfully describes our universe within this framework.

For me this is a very satisfactory solution to the mystery of why some particular rule would be picked for our universe. The answer is that there isn't ultimately ever a particular rule; basically any rule capable of universal computation will do. It's just that—with some particular mode of description that we choose to use—there will be some definite rule that describes our universe. And in a sense whatever specialness there is to this rule is just a reflection of the specialness of our mode of description. In effect, the only thing special about the universe to us is us ourselves.

And this suggests a definite answer to another longstanding question: could there be other universes? The answer in our setup is basically no. We can't just "pick another rule and get another universe". Because in a sense our universe already contains all possible rules, so there can only be one of it. (There could still be other universes that do various levels of hypercomputation.)

But there is something perhaps more bizarre that is possible. While we view our universe—and reality—through our particular type of description language, there are endless other possible description languages which can lead to descriptions of reality that will seem coherent (and even in some appropriate definition "meaningful") within themselves, but which will seem to us to correspond to utterly incoherent and meaningless aspects of our universe.

I've always assumed that any entity that exists in our universe must at least "experience the same physics as us". But now I realize that this isn't true. There's actually an almost infinite diversity of different ways to describe and experience our universe, or in effect an almost infinite diversity of different "planes of existence" for entities in the universe—corresponding to different possible reference frames in rulial space, all ultimately connected by universal computation and rule-space relativity.

The Challenge of Language Design for the Universe

What does it mean to make a model for the universe? If we just want to know what the universe does, well, then we have the universe, and we can just watch what it does. But when we talk about making a model, what we really mean is that we want to have a representation of the universe that somehow connects it to what we humans can understand. Given computational irreducibility, it's not that we expect a model that will in any fundamental sense "predict in advance" the precise behavior of the universe down to every detail (like that I am writing this sentence now). But we do want to be able to point to the model—whose structure we understand—and then be able to say that this model corresponds to our universe.

In the previous section we said that we wanted to find a rule that we could in a sense connect with the description language that we use for the universe. But what should the description language for the rule itself be? Inevitably there is a great computational distance between the underlying rule and features of the universe that we're used to describing. So—as I've said several times here in different ways—we can't expect to use the ordinary concepts with which we describe the world (or physics) directly in the construction of the rule.

I've spent the better part of my life as a language designer, primarily building what's now the full-scale computational language that is the Wolfram Language. And I now view the effort to find a fundamental theory of physics as in many ways just another challenge in language design—perhaps even the ultimate such challenge.

In designing a computational language what one is really trying to do is to create a bridge between two domains: the abstract world of what is possible to do computationally, and the "mental" world of what people understand and are interested in doing. There are all sorts of computational processes that one can invent (say running randomly picked cellular automaton rules), but the challenge in language design is to figure out which ones people care about at this point in human history, and then to give people a way to describe these.

Usually in computational language design one is leveraging human natural language—or the more formal languages that have been developed in mathematics and science—to find words or their analogs to refer to particular "lumps of computation". But at least in the way I have done it, the essence of language design is to try to find the purest primitives that can be expressed this way.

OK, so let's talk about setting up a model for the universe. Perhaps the single most important idea in my effort to find a fundamental theory of physics is that the theory should be based on the general computational paradigm (and not, for example, specifically on mathematics). So when we talk about having a language in which to describe our model of the universe we can see that it has to bridge three different domains. It has to be a language that humans can understand. It has to be a language that can express computational ideas. And it has to be a language that can actually represent the underlying structure of physics.

So what should this language be like? What kinds of primitives should it contain? The history that has led me to what I describe here is in many ways the history of my attempts to formulate an appropriate language. Is it trivalent graphs? Is it ordered graphs? Is it rules applied to abstract relations?

In many ways, we are inevitably skating at the edge of what humans can understand. Maybe one day we will have built up familiar ways of talking about the concepts that are involved. But for now, we don't have these. And in a sense what has made this project feasible now is that we've come so far in developing ways to express computational ideas—and that through the Wolfram Language in particular those forms of expression have become familiar, at the very least to me.

And it's certainly satisfying to see that the basic structure of the models we're using can be expressed very cleanly and succinctly in the Wolfram Language. In fact, in what perhaps can be viewed as some sort of endorsement of the structure of the Wolfram Language, the models are in a sense just a quintessential example of transformation rules for symbolic expressions, which is exactly what the Wolfram Language is based on. But even though the structure is well represented in the Wolfram Language, the "use case" of "running the universe" is different from what the Wolfram Language is normally set up to do.

In the effort to serve what people normally want, the Wolfram Language is primarily about taking input, evaluating it by doing computation, and then generating output. But that's not what the universe does. The universe in a sense had input at the very beginning, but now it's just running an evaluation—and with all our different ideas of foliations and so on, we are sampling certain aspects of that ongoing evaluation.

It's computation, but it's computation sampled in a different way than we've been used to doing it. To a language designer like me, this is something interesting in its own right, with its own scientific and technological spinoffs. And perhaps it will take more ideas before we can finish the job of finding a way to represent a rule for fundamental physics.

But I'm optimistic that we actually already have pretty much all the ideas we need. And we also have a crucial piece of methodology that helps us: our ability to do explorations through computer experiments. If we based everything on the traditional methodology of mathematics, we would in effect only be able to explore what we somehow already understood. But in running computer experiments we are in effect sampling the raw computational universe of possibilities, without being limited by our existing understanding.

Of course, as with physical experiments, it matters how we define and think about our experiments, and in effect what description language we use. But what certainly helps me, at least, is that I've now been doing computer experiments for more than forty years, and over that time I've been able to slowly refine the art and science of how best to do them.

In a way it's very much like how we learn from our experience in the physical world. From seeing the results of many experiments, we gradually build up intuition, which in turn lets us start creating a conceptual framework, which then informs the design of our language for describing things. One always has to keep doing experiments, though. In a sense computational irreducibility implies that there will always be surprises, and that's certainly what I constantly find in practice, not least in this project.

Will we be able to bring together physics, computation and human understanding to deliver what we can reasonably consider to be a final, fundamental theory of physics? It is difficult to know how hard this will be. But I am extremely optimistic that we are finally on the right track, and may even have effectively already solved the fascinating problem of language design that this entails.

Let's Go Find the Fundamental Theory!

OK, so given all this, what's it going to take to find the fundamental theory of physics? The most important thing—about which I'm extremely excited—is that I think we're finally on the right track. Of course, perhaps not surprisingly, it's still technically difficult. Part of that difficulty comes directly from computational irreducibility and from the difficulty of working out the consequences of underlying rules. But part of the difficulty also comes from the very success and sophistication of existing physics.

In the end our goal must be to build a bridge that connects our models to existing knowledge about physics. And there is difficult work to do on both sides. Trying to frame the conse quences of our models in terms that align with existing physics, and trying to frame the (usually mathematical) structures of existing physics in terms that align with our models.

For me, one of the most satisfying aspects of our discoveries over the past couple of months has been the extent to which they end up resonating with a huge range of existing—sometimes so far seemingly "just mathematical"—directions that have been taken in physics in recent years. It almost seems like everyone has been right all along, and it just takes adding a new substrate to see how it all fits together. There are hints of string theory, holographic principles, causal set theory, loop quantum gravity, twistor theory, and much more. And not only that, there are also modern mathematical ideas—geometric group theory, higher-order category theory, non-commutative geometry, geometric complexity theory, etc.—that seem so well aligned that one might almost think they must have been built to inform the analysis of our models.

I have to say I didn't expect this. The ideas and methods on which our models are based are very different from what's ever been seriously pursued in physics, or really even in mathematics. But somehow—and I think it's a good sign all around—what's emerged is something that aligns wonderfully with lots of recent work in physics and mathematics. The foundations and motivating ideas are different, but the methods (and sometimes even the results) often look to be quite immediately applicable.

There's something else I didn't expect, but that's very important. In studying things (like cellular automata) out in the computational universe of simple programs, I have normally found that computational irreducibility—and phenomena like undecidability—are everywhere. Try using sophisticated methods from mathematics; they will almost always fail. It is as if one hits the wall of irreducibility almost immediately, so there is almost nothing for our sophisticated methods, which ultimately rely on reducibility, to do.

But perhaps because they are so minimal and so structureless our models for fundamental physics don't seem to work this way. Yes, there is computational irreducibility, and it's surely important, both in principle and in practice. But the surprising thing is that there's a remarkable depth of richness before one hits irreducibility. And indeed that's where many of our recent discoveries come from. And it's also where existing methods from physics and mathematics have the potential to make great contributions. But what's important is that it's realistic that they can; there's a lot one can understand before one hits computational irreducibility. (Which is, by the way, presumably why we are fundamentally able to form a coherent view of physical reality at all.)

So how is the effort to try to find a fundamental theory of physics going to work in practice? We plan to have a centralized effort that will push forward with the project using essentially the same R&D methods that we've developed at Wolfram Research over the past three decades, and that have successfully brought us so much technology—not to mention what exists of this project so far. But we plan to do everything in a completely open way. We've already posted the full suite of software tools that we've developed, along with nearly a thousand archived working notebooks going back to the 1990s, and soon more than 400 hours of videos of recent working sessions.

We want to make it as easy for people to get involved as possible, whether directly in our centralized effort, or in separate efforts of their own. We'll be livestreaming what we do, and soliciting as much interaction as possible. We'll be running a variety of educational programs. And we also plan to have (livestreamed) working sessions with other individuals and groups, as well as providing channels for the computational publishing of results and intermediate findings.

I have to say that for me, working on this project both now and in past years has been tremendously exciting, satisfying, and really just fun. And I'm hoping many other people will be able to share in this as the project goes forward. I think we've finally got a path to finding the fundamental theory of physics. Now let's go follow that path. Let's have a blast. And let's try to make this the time in human history when we finally figure out how this universe of ours works!

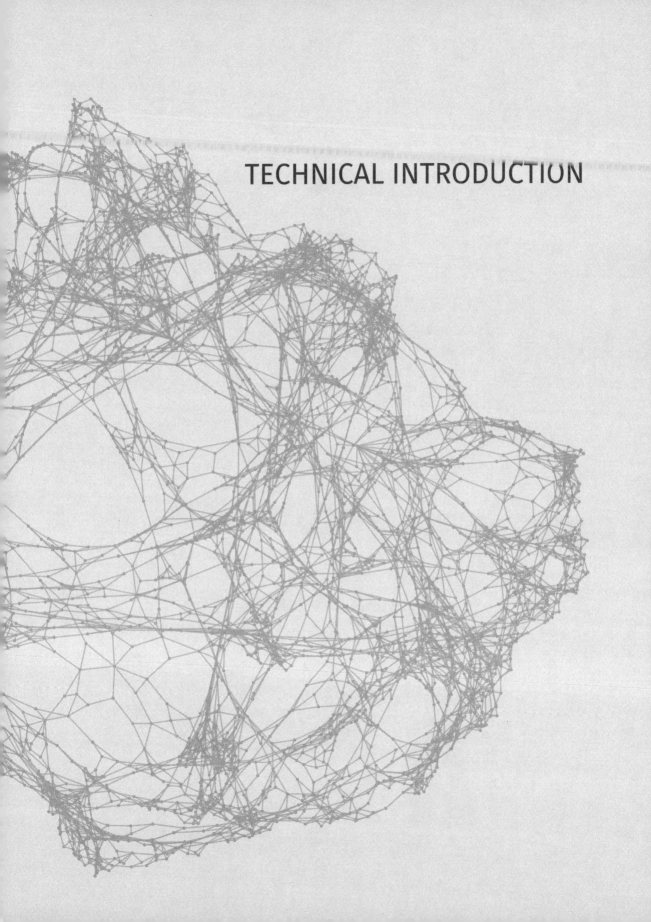

TECHNICAL INTRODUCTION

A Class of Models with the Potential to Represent Fundamental Physics

A class of models intended to be as minimal and structureless as possible is introduced. Even in cases with simple rules, rich and complex behavior is found to emerge, and striking correspondences to some important core known features of fundamental physics are seen, suggesting the possibility that the models may provide a new approach to finding a fundamental theory of physics.

1 | Introduction

Quantum mechanics and general relativity—both introduced more than a century ago—have delivered many impressive successes in physics. But so far they have not allowed the formulation of a complete, fundamental theory of our universe, and at this point it seems worthwhile to try exploring other foundations from which space, time, general relativity, quantum mechanics and all the other known features of physics could emerge.

The purpose here is to introduce a class of models that could be relevant. The models are set up to be as minimal and structureless as possible, but despite the simplicity of their construction, they can nevertheless exhibit great complexity and structure in their behavior. Even independent of their possible relevance to fundamental physics, the models appear to be of significant interest in their own right, not least as sources of examples amenable to rich analysis by modern methods in mathematics and mathematical physics.

But what is potentially significant for physics is that with exceptionally little input, the models already seem able to reproduce some important and sophisticated features of known fundamental physics—and give suggestive indications of being able to reproduce much more.

Our approach here is to carry out a fairly extensive empirical investigation of the models, then to use the results of this to make connections with known mathematical and other features of physics. We do not know *a priori* whether any model that we would recognize as simple can completely describe the operation of our universe—although the very existence of physical laws does seem to indicate some simplicity. But it is basically inevitable that if a simple model exists, then almost nothing about the universe as we normally perceive it—including notions like space and time—will fit recognizably into the model.

And given this, the approach we take is to consider models that are as minimal and structure-less as possible, so that in effect there is the greatest opportunity for the phenomenon of emergence to operate. The models introduced here have their origins in network-based models studied in the 1990s for [1], but the present models are more minimal and structure-less. They can be thought of as abstracted versions of a surprisingly wide range of types of mathematical and computational systems, including combinatorial, functional, categorical, algebraic and axiomatic ones.

In what follows, sections 2 through 7 describe features of our models, without specific reference to physics. Section 8 discusses how the results of the preceding sections can potentially be used to understand known fundamental features of physics.

An informal introduction to the ideas described here is given in [2].

2 | Basic Form of Models

2.1 Basic Structure

At the lowest level, the structures on which our models operate consist of collections of relations between identical (but labeled) discrete elements. One convenient way to represent such structures is as graphs (or, in general, hypergraphs). The elements are the nodes of the graph or hypergraph. The relations are the (directed) edges or hyperedges that connect these elements.

For example, the graph

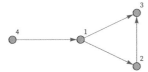

corresponds to the collection of relations

{{1, 2}, {1, 3}, {2, 3}, {4, 1}}

The order in which these relations are stated is irrelevant, but the order in which elements appear within each relation is considered significant (and is reflected by the directions of the edges in the graph). The specific labels used for the elements (here 1, 2, 3, 4) are arbitrary; all that matters is that a particular label always refer to the same element.

2.2 First Example of a Rule

The core of our models are rules for rewriting collections of relations. A very simple example of a rule is:

$\{\{x, y\}\} \rightarrow \{\{x, y\}, \{y, z\}\}$

Here x, y and z stand for any elements. (The elements they stand for need not be distinct; for example, x and y could both stand for the element 1.) The rule states that wherever a relation that matches $\{x,y\}$ appears, it should be replaced by $\{\{x ,y\},\{y,z\}\}$, where z is a new element. So given $\{\{1, 2\}\}$ the rule will produce $\{\{1,2\},\{2,\square\}\}$ where $\square$ is a new element. The label for the new element could be anything—so long as it is distinct from 1 and 2. Here we will use 3, so that the result of applying the rule to $\{\{1,2\}\}$ becomes:

$\{\{1, 2\}, \{2, 3\}\}$

If one applies the rule again, it will now operate again on {1,2}, and also on {2,3}. On {1,2} it again gives {{1,2},{2,□}}, but now the new node □ cannot be labeled 3, because that label is already taken—so instead we will label it 4. When the rule operates on {2,3} it gives {{2,3},{3,□}}, where again □ is a new node, which can now be labeled 5. Combining these gives the final result:

{{1, 2}, {2, 4}, {2, 3}, {3, 5}}

(We have written this so that the results from {{1,2}} are followed by those from {{2,3}}—but there is no significance to the order in which the relations appear.)

In graphical terms, the rule we have used is

and the sequence of steps is:

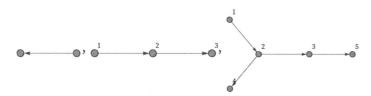

It is important to note that all that matters in these graphs is their connectivity. Where nodes are placed on the page in drawing the graph has no fundamental significance; it is usually just done to make the graphs as easy to read as possible.

Continuing to apply the same rule for three more steps gives:

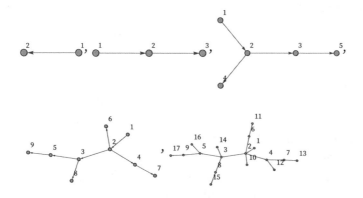

Laying out nodes differently makes it easier to see some features of the graphs:

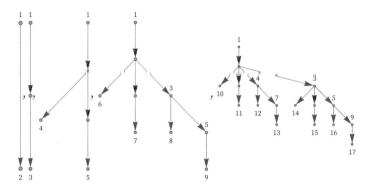

Continuing for a few more steps with the original layout gives the result:

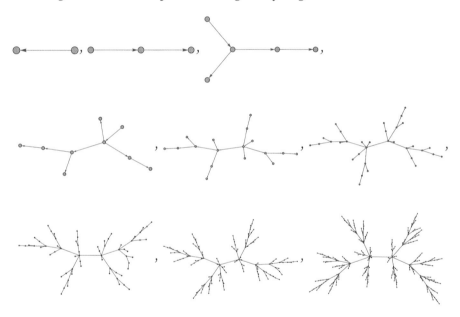

Showing the last 3 steps with the other layout makes it a little clearer what is going on:

The rule is generating a binomial tree, with 2^n edges (relations) and 2^{n+1} nodes (distinct elements) at step n (and with Binomial[n, $s-1$] nodes at level s).

2.3 A Slightly Different Rule

Since order within each relation matters, the following is a different rule:

$$\{\{x, y\}\} \rightarrow \{\{z, y\}, \{y, x\}\}$$

This rule can be represented graphically as:

Like the previous rule, running this rule also gives a tree, but now with a somewhat different structure:

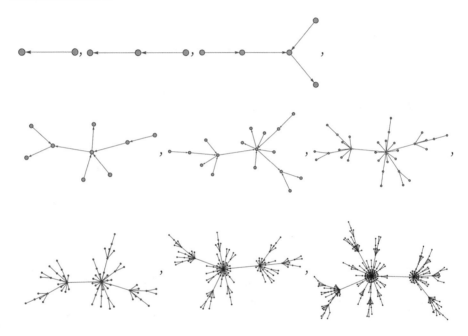

With the other rendering from above, the last 3 steps here are:

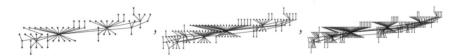

2.4 Self-Loops

A relation can contain two identical elements, as in {0,0}, corresponding to a self-loop in a graph. Starting our first rule from a single self-loop, the self-loop effectively just stays marking the original node:

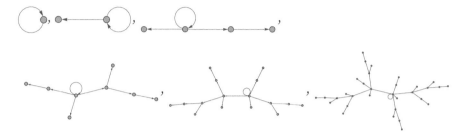

However, with for example the rule:

$$\{\{x, y\}\} \to \{\{y, z\}, \{z, x\}\}$$

the self-loop effectively "takes over" the system, "inflating" to a 2^n – gon:

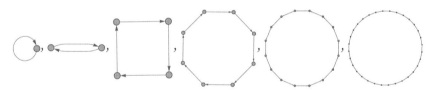

The rule can also contain self-loops. An example is

$$\{\{x, x\}\} \to \{\{y, y\}, \{y, y\}, \{x, y\}\}$$

represented graphically as:

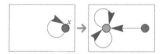

Starting from a single self-loop, this rule produces a simple binary tree:

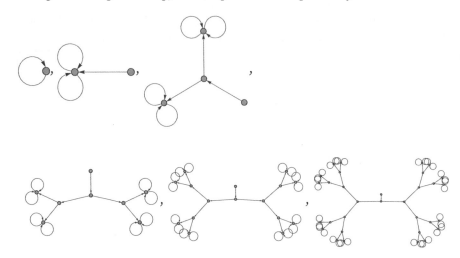

2.5 Multiedges

Rules can involve several copies of the same relation, corresponding to multiedges in a graph. A simple example is the rule:

$$\{\{x, y\}\} \rightarrow \{\{x, z\}, \{x, z\}, \{y, z\}\}$$

Running this rule produces a structure with 3^n edges and $\frac{1}{6}(3^{n+1} + 3)$ nodes at step n:

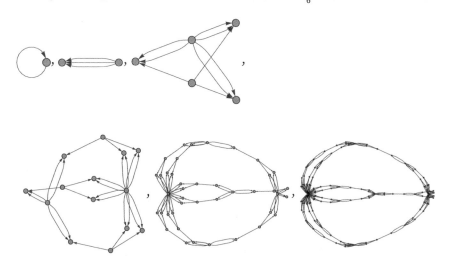

Rules can both create and destroy multiedges. The rule

$$\{\{x, y\}\} \rightarrow \{\{x, z\}, \{z, w\}, \{y, z\}\}$$

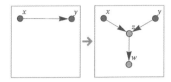

generates a multiedge after one step, but then destroys it:

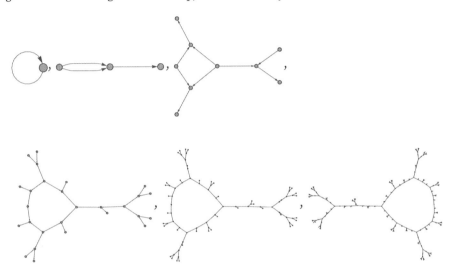

2.6 The Representation of Rules

The examples we have discussed so far all contain only relations involving two elements, which can readily be represented as ordinary directed graphs. But in the class of models we consider, it is also possible to have relations involving other numbers of elements, say three.

As an example, consider:

$$\{\{1, 2, 3\}, \{3, 4, 5\}\}$$

which consists of two ternary relations. Such an object can be represented as a hypergraph consisting of two ternary hyperedges:

Because our relations are ordered, the hypergraph is directed, as indicated by the arrows around each hyperedge.

Note that hypergraphs can contain full or partial self-loops, as in the example of

{{1, 1, 1}, {1, 2, 3}, {3, 4, 4}}

which can be drawn as:

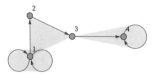

Rules can involve *k*-ary relations. Here is an example with ternary relations:

{{*x*, *y*, *z*}} → {{*x*, *y*, *w*}, {*y*, *w*, *z*}}

This rule can be represented as:

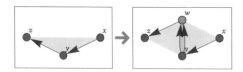

Starting from a single ternary self-loop, here are the first few steps obtained with this rule:

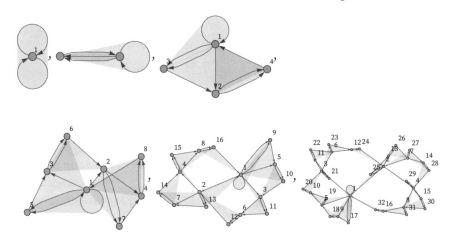

Continuing with this rule gives the following result:

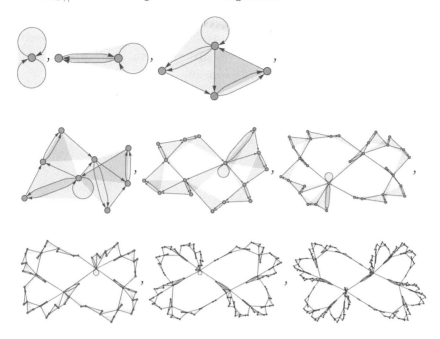

It is worth noting that in addition to having relations involving 3 or more elements, it is also possible to have relations with just one element. Here is an example of a rule involving unary relations:

$$\{\{x\}\} \rightarrow \{\{x, y\}, \{y\}, \{y\}\}$$

Starting from a unary self-loop, this rule leads to a binary tree with double-unary self-loops as leaves:

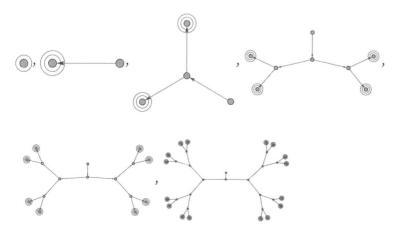

2.7 Rules Depending on More Than One Relation

A crucial simplifying feature of the rules we have considered so far is that they depend only on one relation, so that in a collection of relations, the rule can be applied separately to each relation (cf. [1:p82]). Put another way, this means that all the rules we have considered always transform single edges or hyperedges independently.

But consider a rule like:

$\{\{x, y\}, \{x, z\}\} \to \{\{x, y\}, \{x, w\}, \{y, w\}, \{z, w\}\}$

This can be represented graphically as:

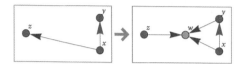

Here is the result of running the rule for several steps:

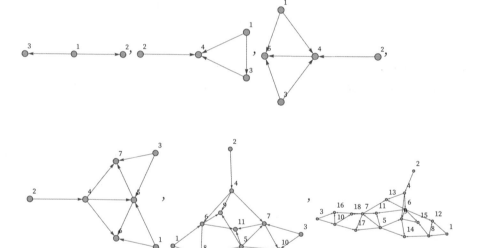

Here is the result for 10 steps:

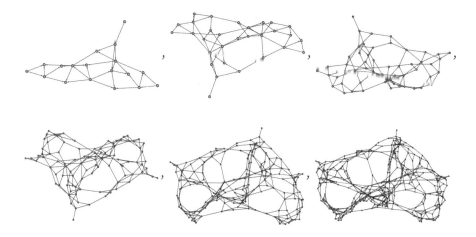

Despite the simplicity of the underlying rule, the structure that is built (here after 15 steps, and involving 6974 elements and 13,944 relations) is complex:

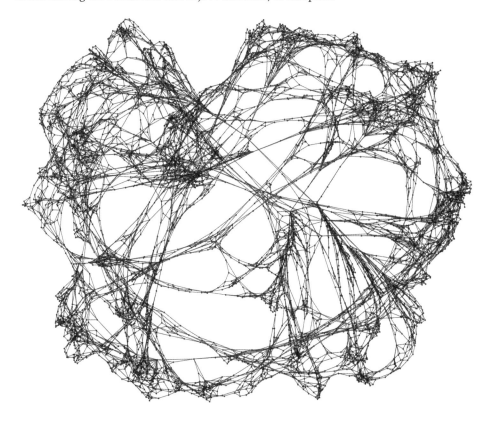

In getting this result, we are, however, glossing over an important issue that will occupy us extensively in later sections, and that potentially seems intimately connected with foundational features of physics.

With a rule that just depends on a single relation, there is in a sense never any ambiguity in where the rule should be applied: it can always separately be used on any relation. But with a rule that depends on multiple relations, ambiguity is possible.

Consider the configuration:

$$\{\{1, 2\}, \{1, 3\}, \{1, 4\}, \{1, 4\}\}$$

The rule

$$\{\{x, y\}, \{x, z\}\} \rightarrow \{\{x, y\}, \{x, w\}, \{y, w\}, \{z, w\}\}$$

can be applied here in two distinct, but overlapping, ways. First, one can take

$$\{x \rightarrow 1, y \rightarrow 2, z \rightarrow 3\}$$

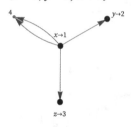

giving the result:

$$\{\{1, 2\}, \{1, 5\}, \{2, 5\}, \{3, 5\}, \{1, 4\}, \{1, 4\}\}$$

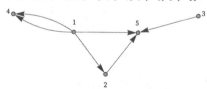

But one can equally well take

$$\{x \rightarrow 1, y \rightarrow 3, z \rightarrow 4\}$$

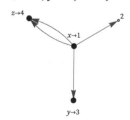

giving the inequivalent result:

{{1, 2}, {1, 4}, {1, 3}, {1, 5}, {3, 5}, {4, 5}}

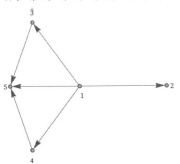

With a rule that just depends on a single relation, there is an obvious way to define a single complete step in the evolution of the system: just make it correspond to the result of applying the rule once to each relation. But when the rule involves multiple relations, we have seen that there can be ambiguity in how it is applied (cf. [1:p501]), and one consequence of this is that there is no longer an obvious unique way to define a single complete step of evolution. For our purposes at this point, however, we will take each step to be what is obtained by scanning the configuration of the system, and finding the largest number of non-overlapping updates that can be made (cf. [1:p487]). In other words, in a single step, we update as many edges (or hyperedges) as possible, while never updating any edge more than once.

For now, this will give us a good indication of what kind of typical behavior different rules can produce. Later, we will study the results of all possible updating orders. And while this will not affect our basic conclusions about typical behavior, it will have many important consequences for our understanding of the models presented here, and their potential relevance to fundamental physics.

2.8 Termination

We have seen that there can be several ways to apply a particular rule to a configuration of one of our systems. It is also possible that there may be no way to apply a rule. This can happen trivially if the evolution of the system reduces the number of relations it contains, and at some point there are simply no relations left. It can also happen if the rule involves, say, only k-ary relations, but there are no k-ary relations in the configuration of the system.

In general, however, a rule can continue for any number of steps, but then get to a configuration where it can no longer apply. The rule below, for example, takes 9 steps to go from {{0,0,0},{0,0}} to a configuration that contains only a single 3-edge, and no 2-edges that match the pattern for the rule:

$$\{\{x, y, z\}, \{u, x\}\} \rightarrow \{\{x, u, v\}, \{z, y\}, \{z, u\}\}$$

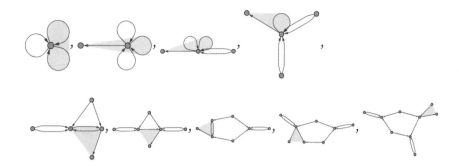

It can be arbitrarily difficult to predict if or when a particular rule will "halt", and we will see later that this is to be expected on the basis of computational irreducibility [1:12.6].

2.9 Connectedness

All the rules we have seen so far maintain connectedness. It is, however, straightforward to set up rules that do not. An obvious example is:

$$\{\{x, y\}\} \rightarrow \{\{y, y\}, \{x, z\}\}$$

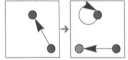

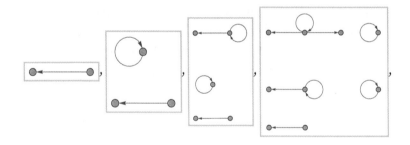

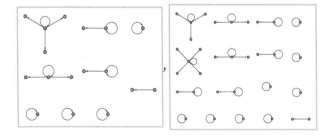

At step n, there are 2^{n+1} components altogether, with the largest component having $n + 1$ relations.

Rules that are themselves connected can produce disconnected results:

$\{\{x, y\}\} \rightarrow \{\{x, x\}, \{z, x\}\}$

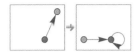

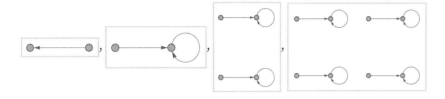

Rules whose left-hand sides are connected in a sense operate locally on hypergraphs. But rules with disconnected left-hand sides (such as $\{\{x\},\{y\}\} \rightarrow \{\{x,y\}\}$) can operate non-locally and in effect knit together elements from anywhere—though such a process is almost inevitably rife with ambiguity.

3 | Typical Behaviors

3.1 The Representation of Rules

Having introduced our class of models, we now begin to study the general distribution of behavior in them. Like with cellular automata [1:c2] and other kinds of systems defined by what can be thought of as simple computational rules [1:c3, c4, c5], we will find great diversity in behavior as well as unifying trends.

Any one of our models is defined by a rule that specifies transformations between collections of relations. It is convenient to introduce the concept of the "signature" of a rule, defined as the number of relations of each arity that appear on the left and right of each transformation.

Thus, for example, the rule

$$\{\{x, y\}, \{x, z\}\} \rightarrow \{\{x, y\}, \{x, w\}, \{y, w\}, \{z, w\}\}$$

has signature $2_2 \rightarrow 4_2$ (and involves a total of 4 distinct elements). Similarly, the rule

$$\{\{a, a, b\}, \{c, d\}\} \rightarrow \{\{b, b, d\}, \{a, e, d\}, \{b, b\}, \{c, a\}\}$$

has signature $1_3 1_2 \rightarrow 2_3 2_2$ (and involves 5 distinct elements).

So far, we have always used letters to indicate elements in a rule, to highlight the fact that these are merely placeholders for the particular elements that appear in the configuration to which the rule is applied. But in systematic studies it is often convenient just to use integers to represent elements in rules, even though these are still to be considered placeholders (or pattern variables), not specific elements. So as a result, the rule just mentioned can be written:

$$\{\{1, 1, 2\}, \{3, 4\}\} \rightarrow \{\{2, 2, 4\}, \{1, 5, 4\}, \{2, 2\}, \{3, 1\}\}$$

It is important to note that there is a certain arbitrariness in the way rules are written. The names assigned to elements, and the order in which relations appear, can both be rearranged without changing the meaning of the rule. In general, determining whether two presentations of a rule are equivalent is essentially a problem of hypergraph isomorphism. Here we will give rules in a particular canonical form obtained by permuting names of elements and orders of relations in all possible ways, numbering elements starting at 1, and using the lexicographically first form obtained. (This form has the property that DeleteDuplicates[Flatten[{*lhs,rhs*}]] is always a sequence of successive integers starting at 1.)

Thus for example, both

$$\{\{1, 1\}, \{2, 4, 5\}, \{7, 5\}\} \rightarrow \{\{3, 8\}, \{2, 7\}, \{5, 4, 1\}, \{4, 6\}, \{5, 1, 7\}\}$$

and

$\{\{7, 3\}, \{4, 4\}, \{8, 5, 3\}\} \to \{\{3, 4, 7\}, \{5, 6\}, \{8, 7\}, \{3, 5, 4\}, \{1, 2\}\}$

would be given in the canonical form:

$\{\{1, 2, 3\}, \{4, 4\}, \{5, 3\}\} \to \{\{3, 2, 4\}, \{3, 4, 5\}, \{1, 5\}, \{2, 6\}, \{7, 8\}\}$

From the canonical form, it is possible to derive a single integer to represent the rule. The basic idea is to get the sequence Flatten[{*lhs,rhs*}] (in this case $\{1, 2, 3, 4, 4, 5, 3, 3, 2, 4, 3, 4, 5, 1, 5, 2, 6, 7, 8\}$) and then find out (through a generalized pairing or "tupling" function [3]) where in a list of all possible tuples of this length this sequence occurs [4]. In this example, the result is 310528242279018009.

But unlike for systems like cellular automata [5][1:p53][6] or Turing machines [1:p888][7] where it is straightforward to set up a dense sequence of rule numbers, only a small fraction of integers constructed like this represent inequivalent rules (most correspond to non-canonical rule specifications).

In addition—for example for applications in physics—one is usually not even interested in all possible rules, but instead in a small number of somehow "notable" rules. And it is often convenient to refer to such notable rules by "short codes". These can be obtained by hashing the canonical form of the rule, but since hashes can collide, it is necessary to maintain a central repository to ensure that short codes remain unique. In our Registry of Notable Universes [8], the rule just presented has short code wm8678.

3.2 The Number of Possible Rules

Given a particular signature, one may ask how many distinct possible canonical rules there are with that signature. As a first step, one can ask how many distinct elements can occur in the rule. If the rule signature has terms n_{ik_i} on both left and right, the maximum conceivable number of distinct elements is $\sum_i n_i\, k_i$. (For example, a possible canonical $2_2 \to 2_2$ rule is $\{\{1,2\},\{3,4\}\} \to \{\{5,6\},\{7,8\}\}$.)

But for many purposes we will want to impose connectivity constraints on the rule. For example, we may want the hypergraph corresponding to the relations on the left-hand side of the rule to be connected [9], and for elements in these relations to appear in some way on the right. Requiring this kind of "left connectivity" reduces the maximum conceivable number of distinct elements to $\sum_{i \in \text{LHS}} n_i(k_i-1) + \sum_{i \in \text{RHS}} n_i\, k_i$ (or 6 for $2_2 \to 2_2$). (If the right-hand side is also required to be a connected hypergraph, the maximum number of distinct elements is $1 + \sum n_i(k_i-1)$, or 5 for $2_2 \to 2_2$.)

Given a maximum number of possible elements m, an immediate upper bound on the number of rules is $m^{\sum n_i\, k_i}$. But this is usually a dramatic overestimate, because most rules are not canonical. For example, it would imply 1,679,616 left-connected $2_2 \to 2_2$ rules, but actually there are only 562 canonical such rules.

The following gives the number of left-connected canonical rules for various rule signatures (for $n_1 \rightarrow$ *anything* there is always only one inequivalent left-connected rule):

$1_2 \rightarrow 1_2$	11	$1_3 \rightarrow 1_3$	178	$1_4 \rightarrow 1_4$	3915
$1_2 \rightarrow 2_2$	73	$1_3 \rightarrow 2_3$	9373	$1_4 \rightarrow 2_4$	2 022 956
$1_2 \rightarrow 3_2$	506	$1_3 \rightarrow 3_3$	637 568	$1_4 \rightarrow 3_4$	1.7×10^9
$1_2 \rightarrow 4_2$	3740	$1_3 \rightarrow 4_3$	53 644 781	$1_4 \rightarrow 4_4$	2.1×10^{12}
$1_2 \rightarrow 5_2$	28 959	$1_3 \rightarrow 5_3$	5.4×10^9	$1_4 \rightarrow 5_4$	$\approx 4 \times 10^{15}$
$2_2 \rightarrow 1_2$	64	$2_3 \rightarrow 1_3$	8413	$2_4 \rightarrow 1_4$	1 891 285
$2_2 \rightarrow 2_2$	562	$2_3 \rightarrow 2_3$	772 696	$2_4 \rightarrow 2_4$	2.3×10^9
$2_2 \rightarrow 3_2$	4702	$2_3 \rightarrow 3_3$	79 359 764	$2_4 \rightarrow 3_4$	3.5×10^{12}
$2_2 \rightarrow 4_2$	40 405	$2_3 \rightarrow 4_3$	9.2×10^9	$2_4 \rightarrow 4_4$	$\approx 9 \times 10^{15}$
$2_2 \rightarrow 5_2$	353 462	$2_3 \rightarrow 5_3$	1.2×10^{12}	$2_4 \rightarrow 5_4$	$\approx 3 \times 10^{19}$
$3_2 \rightarrow 1_2$	416	$3_3 \rightarrow 1_3$	568 462	$3_4 \rightarrow 1_4$	1.6×10^9
$3_2 \rightarrow 2_2$	4688	$3_3 \rightarrow 2_3$	8.4×10^7	$3_4 \rightarrow 2_4$	3.8×10^{12}
$3_2 \rightarrow 3_2$	48 554	$3_3 \rightarrow 3_3$	1.4×10^{10}	$3_4 \rightarrow 3_4$	$\approx 1 \times 10^{16}$
$4_2 \rightarrow 1_2$	3011	$4_3 \rightarrow 1_3$	4.9×10^7	$4_4 \rightarrow 1_4$	2.1×10^{12}
$4_2 \rightarrow 2_2$	42 955	$4_3 \rightarrow 2_3$	1.1×10^{10}	$4_4 \rightarrow 2_4$	$\approx 9 \times 10^{15}$
$5_2 \rightarrow 1_2$	23 211	$5_3 \rightarrow 1_3$	5.3×10^9	$5_4 \rightarrow 1_4$	$\approx 4 \times 10^{15}$

Although the exact computation of these numbers seems to be comparatively complex, it is possible to obtain fairly accurate lower-bound estimates in terms of Bell numbers [10]. If one ignores connectivity constraints, the number of canonical rules is bounded below by BellB$[\sum_i k_i]/\prod n_i!$. Here are some examples comparing the estimate with exact results both for the unconstrained and left-connected cases:

	estimate	unconstrained	left–connected
$1_1 \rightarrow 2_1$	2.5	4	1
$1_2 \rightarrow 2_2$	102	117	73
$1_2 \rightarrow 3_2$	690	877	506
$1_3 \rightarrow 2_3$	10 574	10 848	9373
$2_2 \rightarrow 2_2$	1035	1252	562
$2_2 \rightarrow 3_2$	9665	12 157	4702
$2_2 \rightarrow 4_2$	87 783	117 121	40 405

Based on the estimates, we can say that the number of canonical rules typically increases faster than exponentially as either n_i or k_i increase. (For $5 \leq n \leq 10\,874$, one finds $2^n < $ BellB$[n] < 2^{n \log n}$, and for larger n, $2^n < $ BellB$[n] < n^n$.)

Note that given an estimate for unconstrained rules, an estimate for the number of left-connected rules can be found from the fraction of randomly sampled unconstrained rules that are left connected. For signature $1_p \rightarrow 1_q$, the number of unconstrained canonical rules is $\mathsf{BellB}[p+q]$, but given the constraint of left-connectedness there is only ever one canonical rule in this case. When there are no connectivity constraints, the number of canonical rules for signature $a \rightarrow b$ is the same as for signature $b \rightarrow a$. With the constraint of left connectivity, the number of $1_2 \rightarrow 5_2$ rules is slightly larger than $5_2 \rightarrow 1_2$ rules, because there are fewer constraints in the former case.

For any given signature, we can ask how many distinct elements occur in different canonical rules. Here are histograms for a few cases:

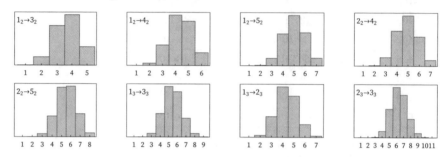

There are a number of features of rules that are important when using them in our models. First, if there are relations of arity k on the left-hand side of the rule, there must be relations of the same arity on the right-hand side if those relations are not just going to be inert under that rule. Thus, for example, a rule with signature $a_2 \rightarrow b_3$ will never (on its own) apply more than once, regardless of the values of a and b.

In addition, if a rule is going to have a chance of leading to growth, the number of relations of some arity on the right-hand side must be greater than the number of that arity on the left.

These two constraints, however, do not always apply if a complete rule involves several individual rules. Thus, for example, a complete rule containing individual rules with signatures $2_2 \rightarrow 3_2\,2_1$, $2_2\,1_1 \rightarrow 1_2$ can show growth, and can involve all relations. Note that since canonicalization is independent between different individual rules, the total number of possible inequivalent complete rules is just the product of the number of possible individual inequivalent rules.

When investigating cases where a large number of inequivalent rules are possible, it will often be convenient to do random sampling. If one picks a random rule first, and then canonicalizes it, some canonical rules will be significantly more common than others. But it is possible to pick with equal probability among canonical rules by choosing an integer between 1 and the total number of rules, then decoding this integer as discussed above to give the canonical rule.

3.3 Initial Conditions

In addition to enumerating rules, we can also consider enumerating possible initial conditions. Like each side of a rule, these can be characterized by sequences $n_1{}^{k_1} n_2{}^{k_2}$... which give the number of relations n_i of arity k_i.

The only possible inequivalent 1_2 initial conditions are $\{\{1,1\}\}$, corresponding a graph consisting of a single self-loop, and $\{\{1,2\}\}$, consisting of a single edge. The possible inequivalent connected 2_2 initial conditions are:

$\{\{1, 1\}, \{1, 1\}\}, \{\{1, 1\}, \{1, 2\}\}, \{\{1, 1\}, \{2, 1\}\},$
$\{\{1, 2\}, \{1, 2\}\}, \{\{1, 2\}, \{2, 1\}\}, \{\{1, 2\}, \{1, 3\}\}, \{\{1, 2\}, \{2, 3\}\}, \{\{1, 2\}, \{3, 2\}\}\}$

These correspond to the graphs:

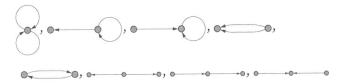

The possible inequivalent 1_3 initial conditions are:

$\{\{\{1, 1, 1\}\}, \{\{1, 1, 2\}\}, \{\{1, 2, 1\}\}, \{\{1, 2, 2\}\}, \{\{1, 2, 3\}\}\}$

These correspond to the hypergraphs:

There are 102 inequivalent connected 2_3 initial conditions. Ignoring ordering of relations, these correspond to hypergraphs with the following structures:

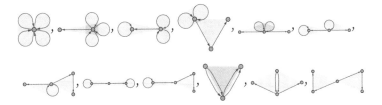

Ignoring connectivity, the number of possible inequivalent n_1 initial conditions is PartitionsP[n], the number of 1_n ones is BellB[n], while the number of n_2 ones can be derived using cycle index polynomials (see also [11:A137975]). The number of inequivalent connected initial conditions for various small signatures is as follows (with essentially the same Bell number estimates applying as for rules) [12]:

1_2	2	7_2	40211	3_3	3268	2_4	2032	3_5	2.3×10^8
2_2	8	8_2	293370	4_3	164391	3_4	678358	4_5	2.1×10^{12}
3_2	32	9_2	2255406	5_3	1.1×10^7	4_4	4.2×10^8	1_6	203
4_2	167	10_2	18201706	6_3	9.0×10^8	5_4	4.1×10^{11}	2_6	2089513
5_2	928	1_3	5	7_3	7.1×10^{10}	1_5	52	3_6	1.1×10^{11}
6_2	5924	2_3	102	1_4	15	2_5	57109	1_7	877

A rule can only apply to a given initial condition if the initial condition contains at least enough relations to match all elements of the left-hand side of the rule. In other words, for a rule with signature $n_k \to \ldots$ there must be at least n k-ary relations in the initial condition.

One way to guarantee that a rule will be able to apply to an initial condition is to make the initial condition in effect be a copy of the left-hand side of the rule, for example giving an initial condition {{1,2},{1,3}} for a rule with left-hand side {{x,y},{x,z}}. But the initial condition that in effect has the most chance to match is what is in many ways the simplest possible initial condition: the "self-loop" one where all elements are identical, or in this case {{0,0},{0,0}}. In what follows we will usually use such self-loop initial conditions Table[0,n,k].

3.4 Rules Depending on a Single Unary Relation

The very simplest possible rules are ones that transform a single unary relation, for example the $1_1 \to 2_1$ rule:

$$\{\{x\}\} \to \{\{x\}, \{y\}\}$$

This rule generates a disconnected hypergraph, containing 2^n disconnected unary hyperedges at step n:

To get less trivial behavior, one must introduce at least one binary relation. With the $1_1 \to 1_2 1_1$ rule

$$\{\{x\}\} \to \{\{x, y\}, \{x\}\}$$

one just gets a figure with progressively more binary-edge "arms" being added to central unary hyperedge:

The rule

$$\{\{x\}\} \to \{\{x, y\}, \{y\}\}$$

produces a growing linear structure, progressively "extruding" binary edges from the unary hyperedge:

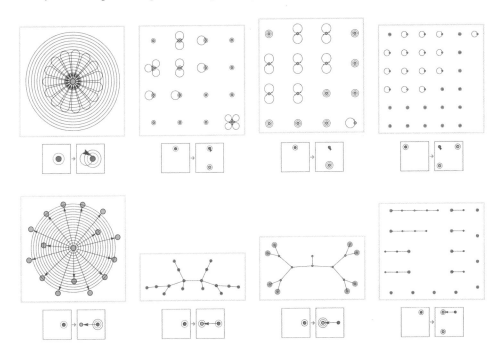

With two unary relations and one binary relation (signature $1_1 \to 1_2 2_1$) there are 16 possible rules; after 4 steps starting from a single unary relation, these give:

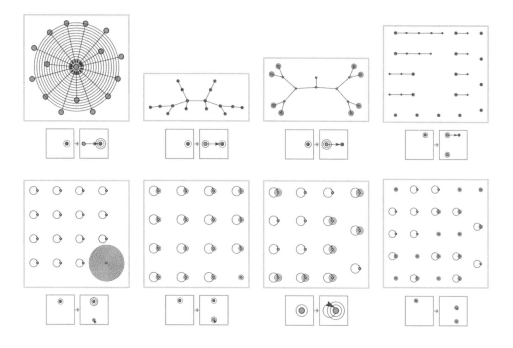

Many lead to disconnected hypergraphs; four lead to binary trees with structures we have already seen. ($\{\{x\}\} \to \{\{x,y\},\{x\},\{y\}\}$ is a $1_2 \to 1_2 2_1$ rule that gives the same result as the very first $1_2 \to 2_2$ rule we saw.

Rules for a single unary relation can never give structures more complex than trees, though the morphology of the trees can become slightly more elaborate:

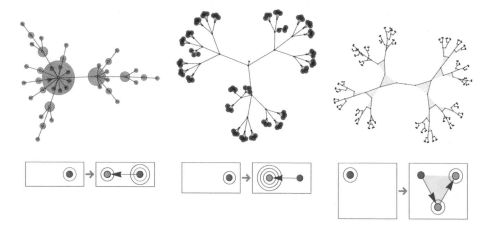

3.5 Rules Depending on a Single Binary Relation

There are 73 inequivalent left-connected $1_2 \to 2_2$ rules, but none lead to structures more complex than trees. Starting each from a single self-loop, the results after 5 steps are (note that even a connected rule like $\{\{x,y\}\} \to \{\{x,z\},\{z,x\}\}$ can give a disconnected result):

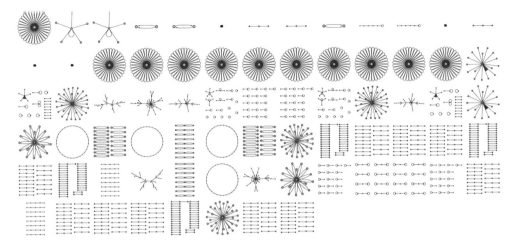

With an initial condition consisting of a square graph, the following very similar results are obtained:

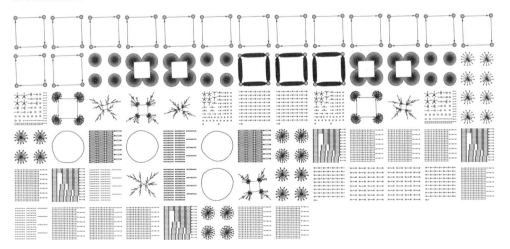

There are 506 inequivalent left-connected $1_2 \to 3_2$ rules. Running all these rules for 5 steps starting from a single self-loop, and keeping only distinct connected results, one gets (note that similar-looking results can differ in small-scale details):

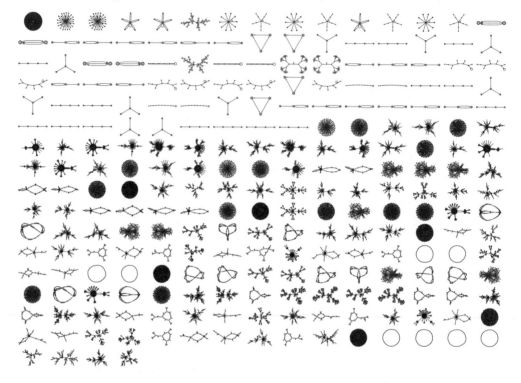

Several distinct classes of behavior are visible. Beyond simple lines, loops, trees and radial "bursts", there are nested ("cactus-like") graphs such as obtained from the rule:

$$\{\{x, y\}\} \rightarrow \{\{z, z\}, \{x, z\}, \{y, z\}\}$$

The only slightly different rule

$$\{\{x, y\}\} \rightarrow \{\{x, x\}, \{x, y\}, \{z, x\}\}$$

gives a rather different structure:

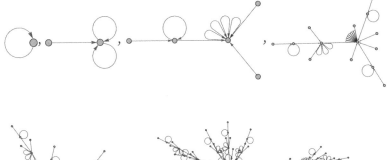

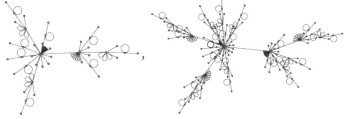

A layered rendering makes the behavior slightly clearer:

Another notable rule similar to one we saw in the previous section is:

$$\{\{x, y\}\} \rightarrow \{\{x, z\}, \{x, z\}, \{z, y\}\}$$

From a single edge this gives:

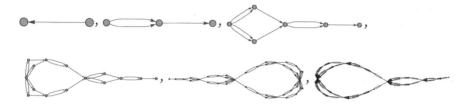

Starting from a single self-loop gives a more complex topological structure (and copies of this structure appear when the initial condition is more complex):

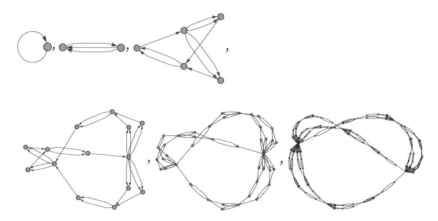

Another notable $1_2 \to 2_2$ rule is

$$\{\{x, y\}\} \to \{\{x, y\}, \{y, z\}, \{z, x\}\}$$

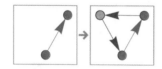

which produces an elaborately filled-in structure:

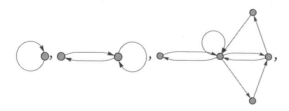

After 8 steps, the structure has the form:

After t steps, there are 3^{t-1} nodes, and $\frac{1}{6}(3^t + 1)$ edges. The graph diameter is $2\,t - 1$ if directions of edges are taken into account, and $t - 1$ if they are not. The maximum degree of any vertex is 2^t—and all vertices have degrees of the form 2^s, with the number of vertices of degree 2^s being proportional to 3^{t-s}.

Starting from a single edge makes it slightly easier to understand what is going on:

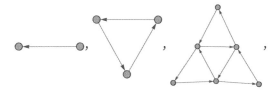

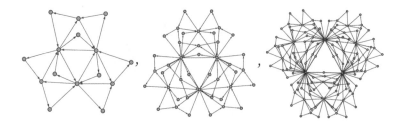

As the rule indicates, every edge of every triangle "sprouts" a new triangle at every step, in effect producing a sequence of "frills upon frills". But even though this may seem complicated, the whole structure basically corresponds just to a ternary tree in which each node is replaced by a triangle:

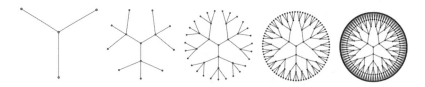

Starting from a single self loop, all $1_2 \to 3_2$ rules give after n steps a number of relations that is either constant, or goes like $2t - 1$, $2^t - 1$ or 3^{t-1}.

For $1_2 \to 4_2$, there are 3740 distinct left-connected rules. As suggested by the random cases below, their behavior is typically similar to $1_2 \to 3_2$ rules, though the forms obtained can be somewhat more elaborate:

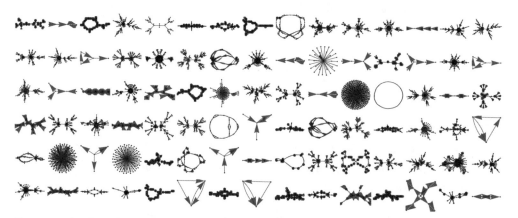

For example, the rule

$$\{\{x, y\}\} \to \{\{y, z\}, \{y, z\}, \{z, y\}, \{z, x\}\}$$

gives the following:

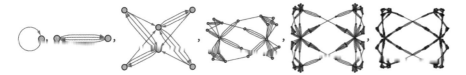

The rule

$$\{\{x, y\}\} \rightarrow \{\{z, w\}, \{w, z\}, \{z, x\}, \{z, y\}\}$$

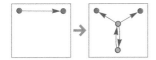

gives a nested form:

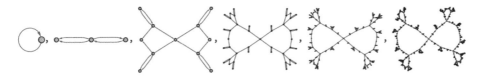

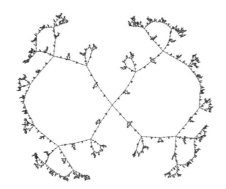

The rule

$$\{\{x, y\}\} \rightarrow \{\{y, z\}, \{y, w\}, \{z, w\}, \{z, x\}\}$$

gives

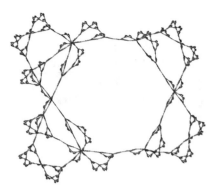

while the similar rule

$$\{\{x, y\}\} \rightarrow \{\{x, z\}, \{x, w\}, \{z, w\}, \{z, y\}\}$$

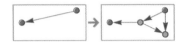

gives:

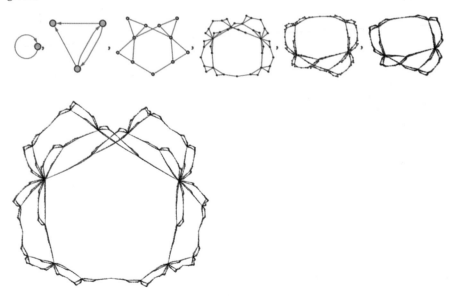

Successive steps in effect just fill in this shape, which seems somewhat irregular when rendered in 2D, but appears more regular if rendered in 3D.

Another rule with a simple structure when rendered in 3D is

$$\{\{x, y\}\} \rightarrow \{\{y, z\}, \{y, z\}, \{z, x\}, \{z, x\}\}$$

which yields:

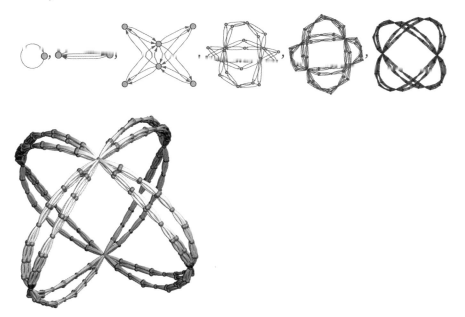

The outputs from $1_2 \rightarrow 4_2$ rules all grow either linearly (for example, like $3\,t - 2$), or exponentially, asymptotically like 2^t, 3^t or 4^t. The number of relations after t steps is always given by a linear recurrence relation; for the rule $\{\{x,x\}\} \rightarrow \{\{x,x\},\{x,x\},\{x,y\},\{x,y\}\}$ the recurrence is f[t]=3f[t−1]−2f[t−2] (with f[1]=1, f[2]=4), giving size $\frac{1}{2}\,(3 \times 2^t - 4)$.

3.6 Rules Depending on One Ternary Relation

There are 9373 inequivalent left-connected $1_3 \rightarrow 2_3$ rules. Here are typical examples of their behavior after 5 steps, starting from a single ternary self-loop:

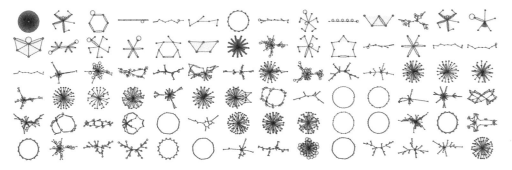

Here are results from a few of these rules after 10 steps:

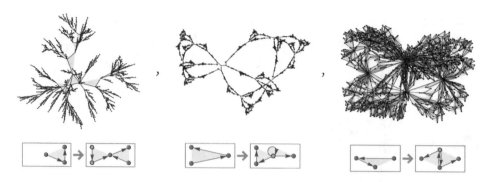

The number of relations in the evolution of $1_3 \rightarrow 2_3$ rules can grow in a slightly more compli-cated way than for $1_2 \rightarrow n_2$ rules. In addition to linear and 2^t growth, there is also, for example, quadratic growth: in the rule

$$\{\{x, x, y\}\} \rightarrow \{\{y, y, z\}, \{x, y, x\}\}$$

each existing "arm" effectively grows by one element each step, and there is one new arm generated, yielding a total size of $\sum_{k=2}^{t} k = \frac{1}{2}(t^2 + t - 2)$:

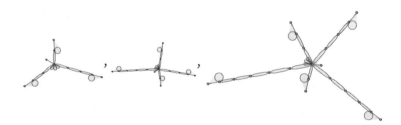

The rule

$$\{\{x, x, y\}\} \rightarrow \{\{y, y, y\}, \{x, y, z\}\}$$

yields a Fibonacci tree, with size Fibonacci$[t+2]-1 \sim \phi^t$:

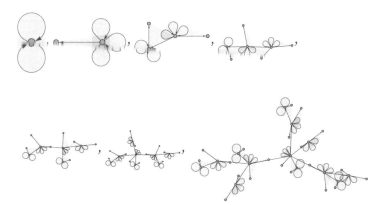

$1_3 \rightarrow 2_3$ rules can produce results that look fairly complex. But it is a consequence of their dependence only on a single relation that once such rules have established a large-scale structure, later updates (which are necessarily purely local) can in a sense only embellish it, not fundamentally change it:

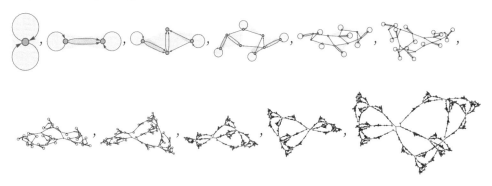

There are 637,568 inequivalent left-connected $1_3 \rightarrow 3_3$ rules; here are samples of their behavior:

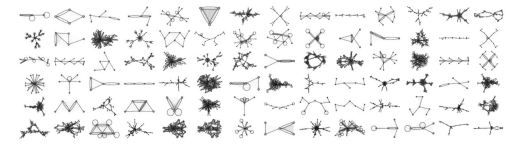

The results can be more elaborate than for $1_3 \to 2_3$ rules—as the following examples illustrate—but remain qualitatively similar:

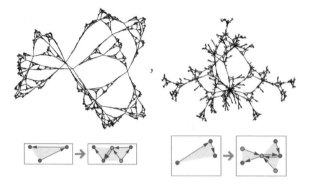

One notable $1_3 \to 3_3$ rule (that we will discuss below) in a sense directly implements the recursive formation of a nested Sierpiński pattern:

$$\{\{x, y, z\}\} \to \{\{x, u, v\}, \{z, v, w\}, \{y, w, u\}\}$$

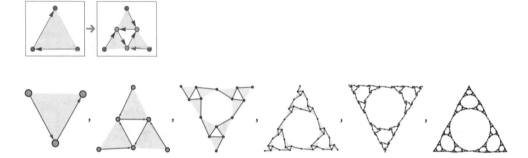

3.7 Rules Depending on More Than One Relation: The $2_2 \to 3_2$ Case

The smallest nontrivial signature that can lead to growth (and therefore unbounded evolution) is $2_2 \to 3_2$. There are 4702 distinct left-connected rules with this signature. Here is a random sample of the behavior they generate, starting from a double self-loop $\{\{0,0\},\{0,0\}\}$ and run for 8 steps:

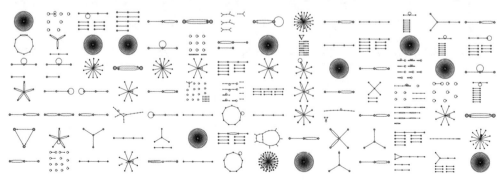

Restricting to connected cases, there are 291 distinct outputs involving more than 10 relations after 8 steps:

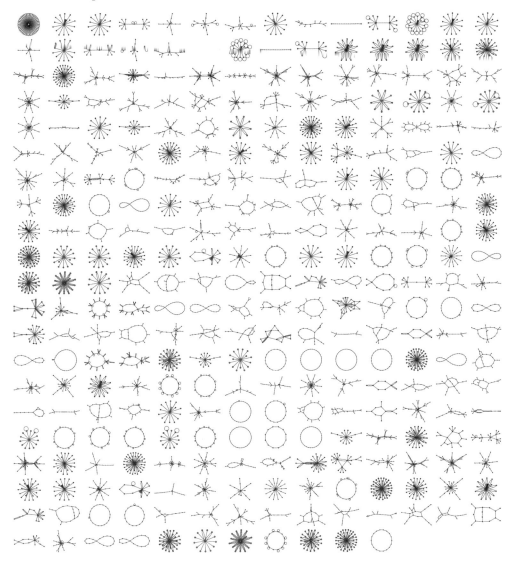

The overall behavior we see here is very similar to what we saw with rules depending only on a single relation. But there is a new issue now to be addressed. With rules depending only on a single relation there is never any ambiguity about where the rule should be applied. But with rules that depend on more than one relation, there can be ambiguity, and the results one gets can potentially depend on the order in which updating is done.

Consider the rule

$$\{\{x, y\}, \{x, z\}\} \rightarrow \{\{x, w\}, \{y, w\}, \{z, w\}\}$$

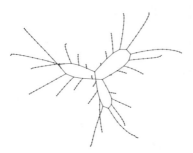

With our standard updating order, the result of running this rule for 30 steps is:

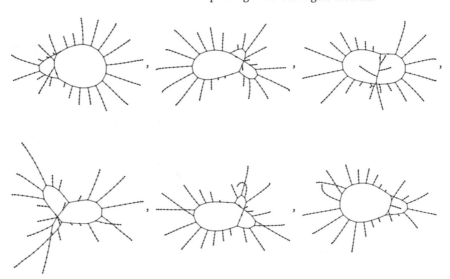

But with 6 different choices of random updating orders one gets instead:

None of these graphs are isomorphic, but all of them are qualitatively similar. Later on, we will discuss in detail the consequences of different updating orders, and their potentially important implications for physics. But for now, suffice it to say that at a qualitative level different updating orders typically lead to similar behavior.

As an example of something of an exception, consider the $2_2 \rightarrow 3_2$ rule shown in the array above:

$$\{\{x, y\}, \{y, z\}\} \rightarrow \{\{x, w\}, \{w, z\}, \{z, x\}\}$$

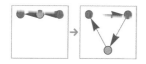

With our standard updating order, this rule behaves as follows, yielding complicated-looking results with about 1.5^n relations after n steps:

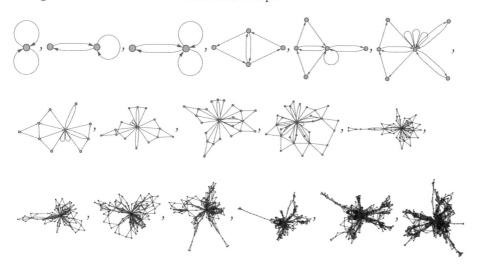

But with random updating order, the behavior is typically quite different. Here are six examples of results obtained after 10 steps—and all of them are disconnected:

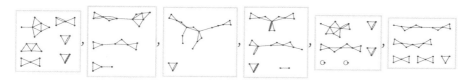

3.8 Rules with Signature $2_2 \rightarrow 4_2$

For $2_2 \rightarrow 4_2$, there are 40,405 inequivalent left-connected rules. Of these, about 36% stay connected when they evolve. Starting from two self-loops $\{\{0,0\},\{0,0\}\}$, and running for 8 steps, here is a sample of the 4000 or so distinct behaviors that are produced:

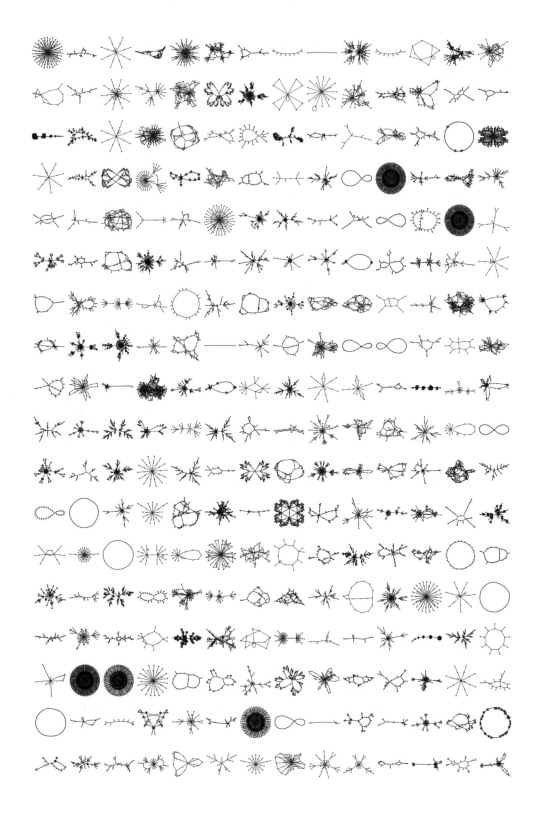

Most of these rules show the same kinds of behaviors we have seen before. But there is one major new kind of behavior that is observed: in a little less than 1% of all cases, the rules produce globular structures that in effect continually add various forms of cross-connections. Here are a few examples (notably, even though $2_2 \rightarrow 4_2$ rules can involve up to 7 distinct elements, these rules all involve just 4):

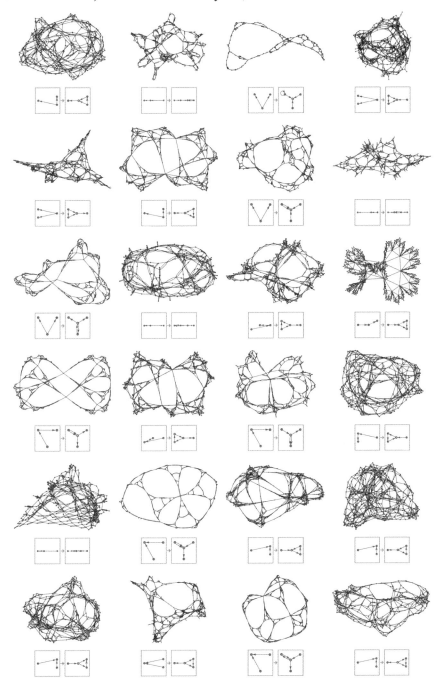

We will study these kinds of structures in more detail later. Note that the specific forms shown here depend on the underlying updating order used—though for example random orders typically seem to give similar results. It is also the case that the detailed visual layout of graphs can affect the impression of these structures; we will address this in the next section when we discuss various forms of quantitative analysis.

It is remarkable how complex the structures are that can be created even from very simple rules. Here are three examples (with short codes wm5583, wm4519, wm2469) shown in more detail:

$$\{\{x, y\}, \{x, z\}\} \rightarrow \{\{y, z\}, \{y, w\}, \{z, w\}, \{w, x\}\}$$

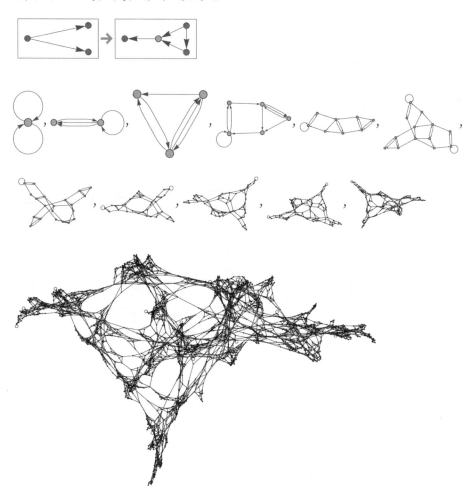

$$\{\{x, y\}, \{y, z\}\} \rightarrow \{\{x, y\}, \{y, x\}, \{w, x\}, \{w, z\}\}$$

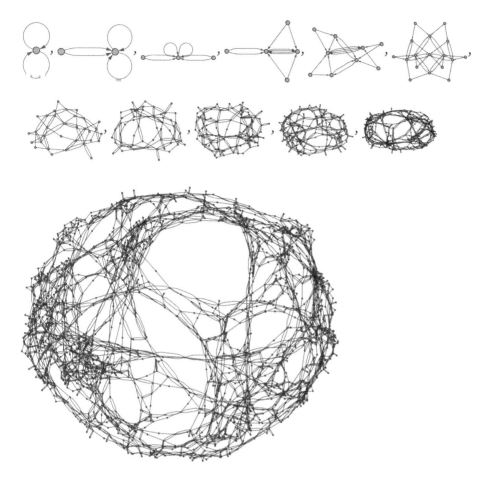

$$\{\{x, y\}, \{y, z\}\} \rightarrow \{\{w, y\}, \{y, z\}, \{z, w\}, \{x, w\}\}$$

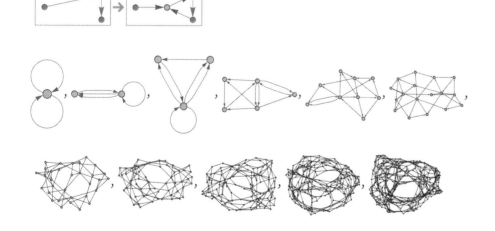

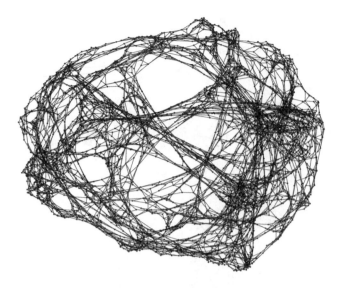

Much as we have seen in other systems such as cellular automata [1], there seems to be no simple way to deduce from the rules from our systems here what their behavior will be. And indeed even seemingly very similar rules can give dramatically different behavior, sometimes simple, and sometimes complex.

3.9 Binary Rules with Signatures Beyond $2_2 \rightarrow 4_2$

Going from signature $2_2 \rightarrow 3_2$ to signature $2_2 \rightarrow 4_2$ brought us the phenomenon of globular structures. Going to signature $2_2 \rightarrow 5_2$ and beyond does not seem to bring us any similarly widespread significant new form of behavior. The fraction of rules that yield connected results decreases, but among connected results, similar fractions of globular structures are seen, with examples from $2_2 \rightarrow 5_2$ including:

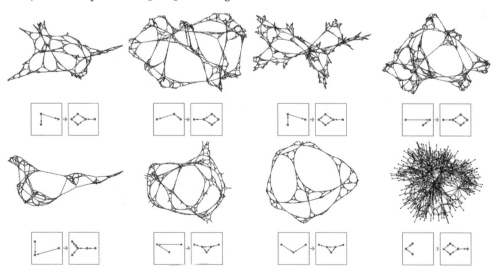

The last rule shown here has a feature that is seen in a few $2_2 \to 4_2$ rules, but is more prominent in $2_2 \to 5_2$ rules: the presence of many "dangling ends" that at least visually obscure the structure. To see the structure better, one can take the evolution of this rule

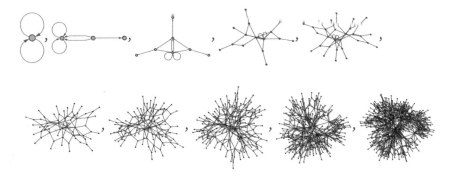

and effectively just "edit" the graphs obtained at each step, removing all dangling ends:

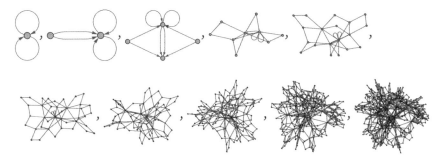

In addition to increasing the number of relations on the right-hand side of the rule, one can also increase the number on the left. For example, one can consider $3_2 \to 4_2$ rules. These much more often lead to termination than $2_2 \to \ldots$ rules, and appear to produce results generally similar to $2_2 \to 3_2$ rules.

$3_2 \to 5_2$ rules also produce globular structures, though more rarely than $2_2 \to 4_2$ rules, and with slower growth. A few examples are:

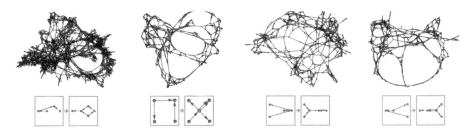

3.10 Rules Depending on Two Ternary Relations: the $2_3 \rightarrow 3_3$ Case

There are 79,359,764 inequivalent left-connected $2_3 \rightarrow 3_3$ rules. The fraction of these rules showing continued growth is considerably smaller than for $2_2 \rightarrow \ldots$ rules. But here is a typical sample of growth rules (note that different rules are run for different numbers of steps to achieve a roughly balanced level of detail):

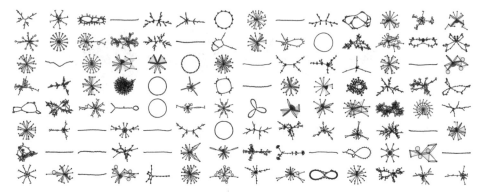

And even though there are only 3 relations on the right-hand side (rather than the 4 in $2_2 \rightarrow 4_2$) these rules can produce globular structures. Some examples are:

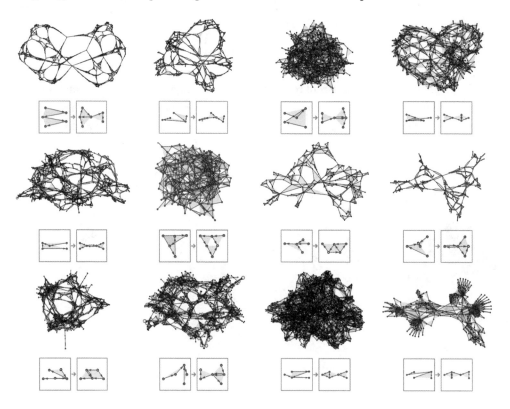

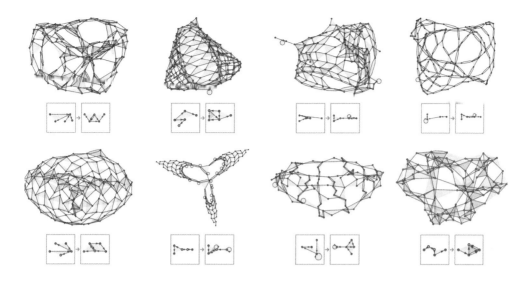

A new phenomenon exhibited by $2_3 \to 3_3$ rules is the formation of globular structures by what amounts to slow grow. This is exemplified by a rule like:

$$\{\{x, y, z\}, \{x, u, v\}\} \to \{\{x, w, u\}, \{v, w, y\}, \{w, y, z\}\}$$

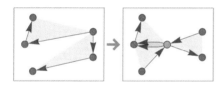

This rule progressively builds up a structure by growing only in one place at a time (the position of the surviving self-loop):

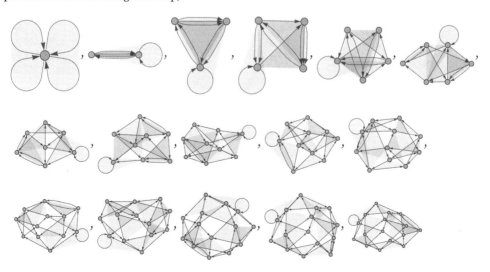

After 1000 steps the rule has produced this structure containing 1000 ternary relations (plus the 2 already present in the initial condition):

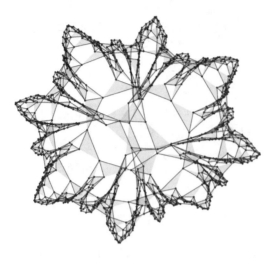

Another example of slow growth occurs in the rule

$$\{\{x, x, y\}, \{z, u, x\}\} \rightarrow \{\{u, u, z\}, \{v, u, v\}, \{v, y, x\}\}$$

which after 1000 steps generates:

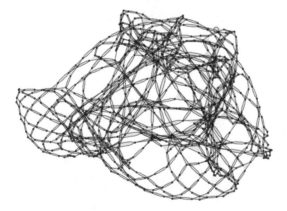

Note the presence here of regions of square grids. These occur even more prominently in the rule

$$\{\{x, y, z\}, \{u, y, v\}\} \rightarrow \{\{w, z, x\}, \{z, w, u\}, \{x, y, w\}\}$$

which after 500 steps produces:

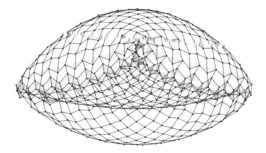

As we will discuss in the next section, the grid here becomes quite explicit when the hypergraph is rendered in 3D. Notice that the grid is not evident even after 20 steps in the evolution of the rule; it takes longer to emerge:

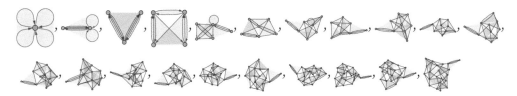

Once again, though, the rule adds just a single relation at each generation; in effect the grid is being "knitted" one node at a time.

The emergence of a grid is still easier to see in the rule

$$\{\{x, y, z\}, \{x, u, v\}\} \rightarrow \{\{z, z, w\}, \{w, w, v\}, \{u, v, w\}\}$$

which after 200 steps yields:

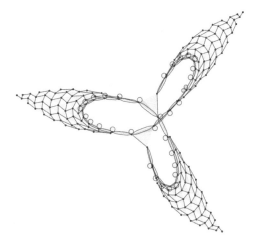

Once again, the "knitting" of this form is far from obvious in the first 20 steps of evolution:

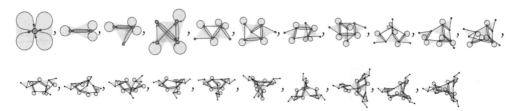

Just sometimes, however, the behavior is quite easy to trace, as in this particularly direct example of "knitting"

$$\{\{x, y, y\}, \{z, x, u\}\} \rightarrow \{\{y, v, y\}, \{y, z, v\}, \{u, v, v\}\}$$

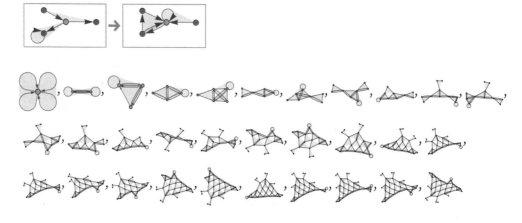

which after 200 steps yields:

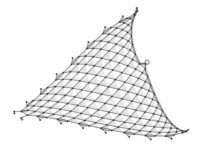

As a different example of slow growth, consider the rule:

$$\{\{x, y, y\}, \{y, z, u\}\} \rightarrow \{\{u, z, z\}, \{u, x, v\}, \{y, u, v\}\}$$

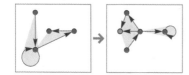

After 200 steps this rule gives

while after 500 steps it gives:

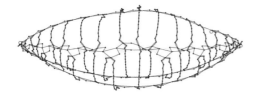

Looking at all 79 million or so $2_3 \rightarrow 3_3$ rules in canonical order, one finds that rules with slow growth are quite rare and are strongly localized to about 10 broad regions in the space of possible rules. Of rules with slow growth, only a few percent form nontrivial globular structures. And of these, perhaps 10% exhibit obvious lattice-like patterns.

The pictures below show additional examples. Note that—as we will discuss later—many of the patterns here are best visualized in 3D.

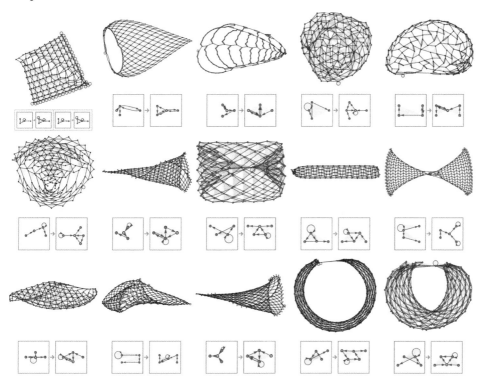

3.11 Rules Involving More Ternary Relations

There are about 9 billion inequivalent left-connected $2_3 \rightarrow 4_3$ rules. About 20% lead to connected results, and of these about half show continued growth. Here is a random sampling of the behavior of such rules:

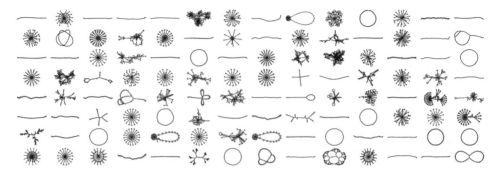

The fraction of complex behavior appears to be no higher than for $2_3 \rightarrow 3_3$ rules, and no obvious major new phenomena are seen. Much like in systems such as cellular automata (and as suggested by the Principle of Computational Equivalence [1:c12]), above some low threshold, adding complexity to the rules does not appear to add complexity to the typical behavior produced.

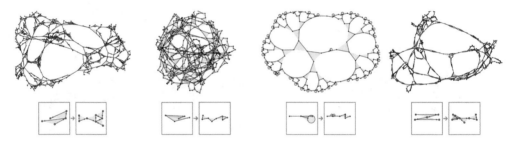

The trend continues with $3_3 \rightarrow 4_3$ rules, with one notable feature here being an increased propensity for rules to yield results that become disconnected, though only after many steps. The general difficulty of predicting long-term behavior is illustrated for example by the evolution of this $3_3 \rightarrow 5_3$ rule, sampled every 10 steps:

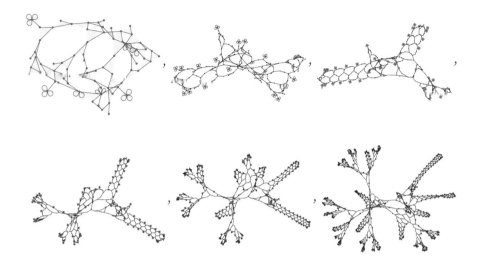

3.12 Rules with Mixed Arity

So far essentially all the rules we have considered have "pure signatures" of the form $m_k \to n_k$ for some arity k. Continued growth is never possible unless the right-hand side of a rule contains some relations with the same arity as appear on the left. But, for example, it is perfectly possible to have growth in rules with signatures like $1_2 \to 2_2 2_1$. Such rules produce unary relations, which can serve as "markers" for the application of the rule, but cannot themselves affect how or where the rule is used:

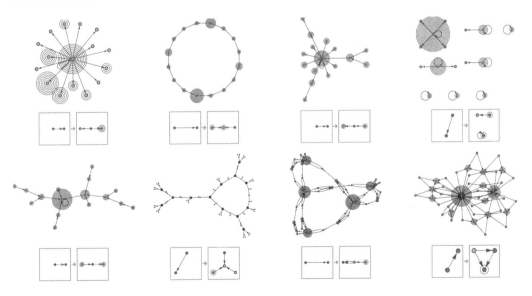

The 634 rules with signature $1_2 \to 1_3 1_2$ all show very simple behavior (as do the 2212 rules with signature $1_2 \to 1_3 1_2 1_1$), with not even trees being possible. But among the 7652 $1_2 \to 1_3 2_2$ rules there are not only many trees, but also closed structures such as:

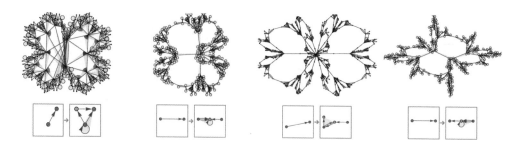

Previously we had only seen structures like the first one above in rules that depend on more than one relation. But as this illustrates, such structures can be produced even with just a single relation on the left:

$$\{\{x, y\}\} \rightarrow \{\{x, x, y\}, \{x, z\}, \{z, y\}\}$$

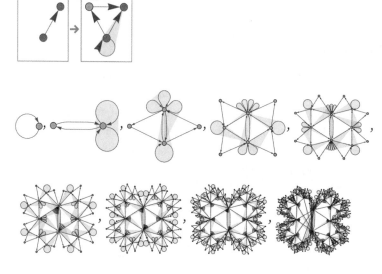

The 44,686 rules with signature $1_2 \rightarrow 2_3 1_2$ cannot even produce trees. Rules with signature $1_3 \rightarrow 2_3 1_2$ can produce trees, as well as closed structures similar to those seen in $1_2 \rightarrow 1_3 2_2$ rules.

A minimal way to add mixed arity to the left-hand sides of rule is to introduce unary relations— but the presence of these seems to inhibit the production of any more complex forms of behavior.

Looking at mixed binary and ternary left-hand sides, none of the 1,141,692 rules with signature $1_3 1_2 \rightarrow 1_3 2_2$ seem to produce even trees. But rules with signature $1_3 1_2 \rightarrow 2_3 2_2$ readily produce structures such as:

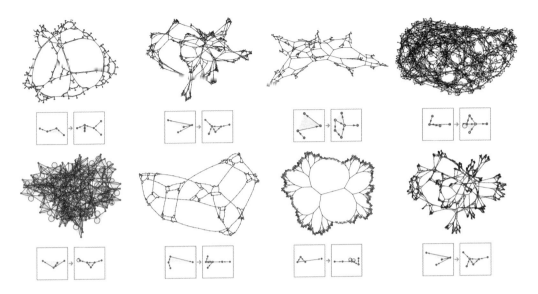

One can go on and look at rules with higher signatures, and probably the most notable finding is that—in keeping with the Principle of Computational Equivalence [1:c12]—the overall behavior seen does not appear to change at all. Here are nevertheless a few examples of slightly unusual behavior found in $2_31_2 \rightarrow 3_32_2$ and $2_31_2 \rightarrow 4_34_2$ rules:

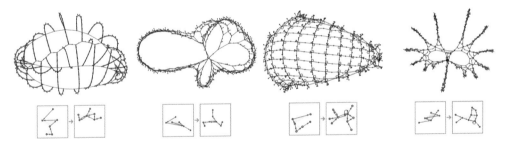

3.13 Multiple Transformation Rules

So far we have always considered having just a single possible transformation rule which can be used wherever it applies. It is also possible to have multiple transformation rules which are used wherever they apply. A single transformation rule can either increase or decrease the number of relations, but must do the same every time it is used. With multiple transformations, some can increase the number of relations while others decrease it.

As a minimal example, consider the rule:

$$\{\{\{x, x\}\} \rightarrow \{\{y, x\}, \{x, z\}\}, \{\{x, y\}, \{y, z\}\} \rightarrow \{\{x, x\}\}\}$$

On successive steps, this rule simply alternates between two cases:

As another example, consider the rule:

$$\{\{\{x, x\}\} \to \{\{y, x\}, \{y, x\}, \{z, x\}\}, \{\{x, y\}, \{z, y\}\} \to \{\{y, y\}\}\}$$

This rule produces results that alternately grow and shrink on successive steps:

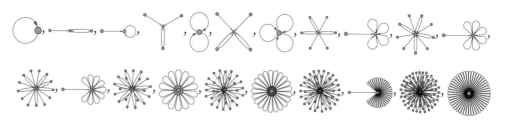

It is fairly common with multiple transformation rules to find that one transformation is occasionally applied. But at least with our standard updating order, it is difficult to find rules in which, for example, the total size of the results varies in anything but a fairly regular way from step to step.

3.14 Rules Involving Disconnected Pieces

We have mostly restricted ourselves so far to cases where the results generated by a rule remain connected. But in fact if one looks at all possible rules the majority generate disconnected pieces, or at least can do so for certain initial conditions. Among the 73 rules with signature $1_2 \to 2_2$, only 33 generate connected results starting from initial condition $\{\{0,0\}\}$ (and a further 10 terminate from this initial condition).

(Note that we are ignoring order in determining connectivity, so that, for example, the relation $\{1,2\}$ is considered connected not only to $\{2,3\}$ but also to $\{1,3\}$. Translating binary relations like these into directed edges in a graph, this means we are considering weak connectivity, or, equivalently, we are looking only at the undirected version of the graph.)

Most $1_2 \to 2_2$ rules that yield disconnected results essentially just produce exponentially more copies of the same structure:

$$\{\{x, y\}\} \to \{\{y, z\}, \{y, z\}\}$$

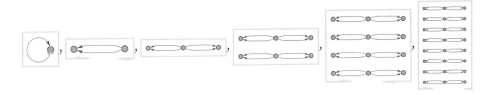

(Note that this rule is an example of one that yields disconnected results even though the rule itself is not disconnected.)

A few rules show slightly more complicated behavior. Examples are (wm575, wm879):

$$\{\{x, y\}\} \to \{\{y, y\}, \{x, z\}\}$$

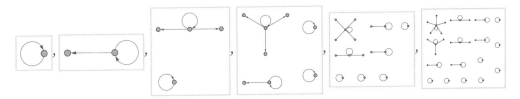

$$\{\{x, y\}\} \to \{\{x, x\}, \{y, z\}\}$$

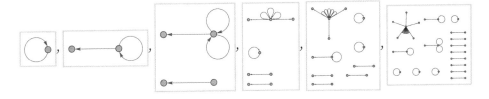

Both these rules still show exponentially increasing numbers of connected components. In the first case, at step t there are components of all sizes 1 through t, in exponentially decreasing numbers. In the second case, the size of the largest component is

1, 2, 2, 3, 4, 6, 9, 14, 22, 35, 56, 90, 145, 234, 378, ...

or asymptotically $\sim \phi^n$ (it follows the recurrence $f[n]=2f[n-1]-f[n-3]$).

Note that if one tracks only the largest component, one gets a sequence of results that could only be generated by a rule involving several separate transformations (in this case $\{\{x,x\}\} \to \{\{x,y\},\{x,x\}\}$ and $\{\{x,y\}\} \to \{\{x,x\}\}$). In general, with a single transformation, the total number of relations must either always increase or always decrease. But if there are disconnected pieces, and one tracks, say, only the largest component, one can get a sequence of results that can both increase and decrease in size.

As an example, consider the rule:

$$\{\{x, y\}, \{x, z\}\} \rightarrow \{\{y, z\}, \{z, y\}, \{x, w\}\}$$

Evolving this rule with our standard updating order gives:

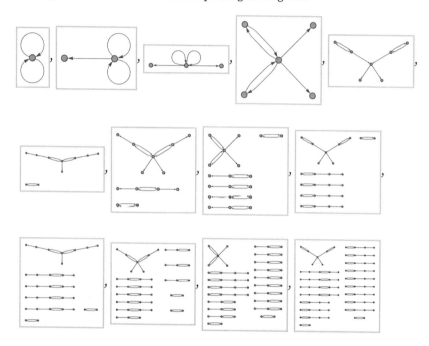

The total number of relations increases roughly exponentially. But tracing only the largest component, we see that it oscillates in size, eventually settling into the cycle 5,8,9,8:

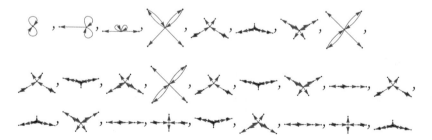

Note that this result is quite specific to the use of our standard updating order. A random updating order, for example, will typically give larger results for the largest component, and no cycle will normally be seen.

It is quite common to see rules that sometimes yield connected results, and sometimes do not. (In fact, proving that a given rule in a given case can never generate disconnected components can be arbitrarily difficult.) Sometimes there can be a large component with a complex structure, with small disconnected pieces occasionally getting "thrown off". Consider for example the rule.

$\{\{x, y\}, \{y, z\}\} \rightarrow \{\{x, w\}, \{w, x\}, \{z, x\}\}$

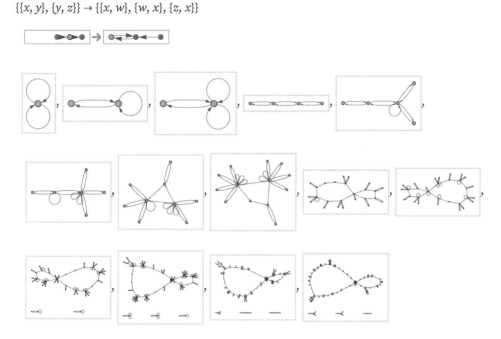

With the standard updating order, it remains connected for 10 steps, then suddenly starts throwing off small disconnected pieces.

As a more elaborate example, consider the rule:

$\{\{x, y, z\}, \{u, v, z\}\} \rightarrow \{\{y, w, u\}, \{w, x, y\}, \{u, y, x\}\}$

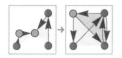

This remains connected for 16 steps, then starts throwing off disconnected pieces:

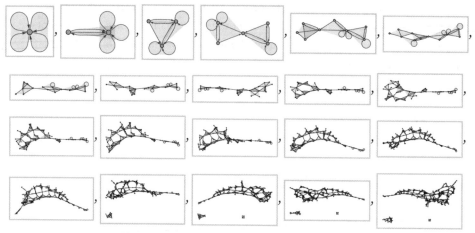

With a rule like this, once components become disconnected, they can in a sense never interact again; their evolutions become completely separate. The only way for disconnected components to interact is to have a rule which itself has a disconnected left-hand side.

For example, a rule like

$$\{\{x\}, \{y\}\} \rightarrow \{\{x, y\}\}$$

will collect even completely disconnected unary relations, and connect pairs of them into binary relations:

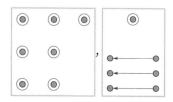

Connected unary relations (i.e. such as {1}, {1}, ...) can end up in the same component, but the result depends critically on the order in which updates are done:

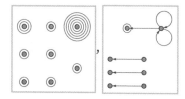

For now, we will not consider any further rules with disconnected left-hand sides—and the extreme nonlocality they represent.

3.15 Termination

Not all rules continue to evolve forever from a given initial state. Instead they can reach a fixed point where the rule no longer applies. If the rule depends only on a single relation, this can only happen at the very first step. But if the rule depends on multiple relations, it can happen after multiple steps. Among the 4702 rules with signature $2_2 \to 3_2$, 1788 rules eventually reach a fixed point starting from a self-loop initial condition, at least using our standard updating order. Their "halting time" decreases roughly exponentially, with the maximum being 7 steps, achieved by the rule:

$$\{\{x, y\}, \{z, y\}\} \to \{\{y, u\}, \{u, x\}, \{v, z\}\}$$

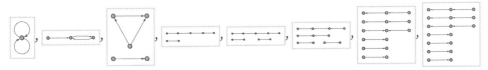

The longest halting time for which connectedness is maintained is 3 steps, achieved for example by:

$$\{\{x, y\}, \{y, z\}\} \to \{\{y, z\}, \{y, u\}, \{v, z\}\}$$

Among the 40,405 $2_2 \to 4_2$ rules, 10,480 evolve to fixed points starting from self-loops. The maximum halting time is 13 steps; the maximum maintaining connectedness is 6 steps, achieved by:

$$\{\{x, x\}, \{y, x\}\} \to \{\{y, y\}, \{y, z\}, \{z, x\}, \{w, z\}\}$$

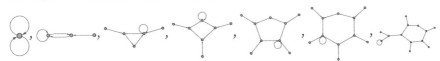

Among the 353,462 $2_2 \to 5_2$ rules, 67,817 (or about 19%) evolve to fixed points. The maximum halting time is 24 steps; the maximum maintaining connectedness is 10 steps, achieved for example by:

$$\{\{x, x\}, \{y, x\}\} \to \{\{y, y\}, \{y, z\}, \{y, z\}, \{z, x\}, \{w, z\}\}$$

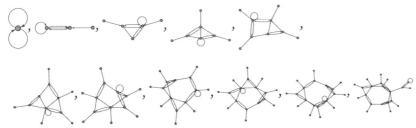

Among $2_3 \rightarrow 3_3$ rules

$$\{\{x, y, z\}, \{x, u, v\}\} \rightarrow \{\{y, x, w\}, \{w, u, s\}, \{v, z, u\}\}$$

has halting time 20:

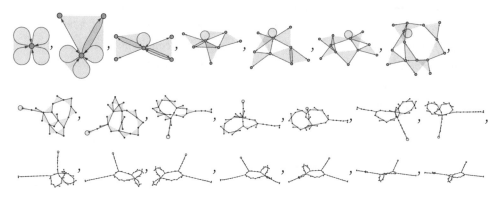

3.16 The Effect of Initial Conditions

For rules that depend on only a single relation, adding relations to initial conditions always just leads to replication of identical structures, as in these examples for the rule:

$$\{\{x, y\}\} \rightarrow \{\{y, z\}, \{z, x\}\}$$

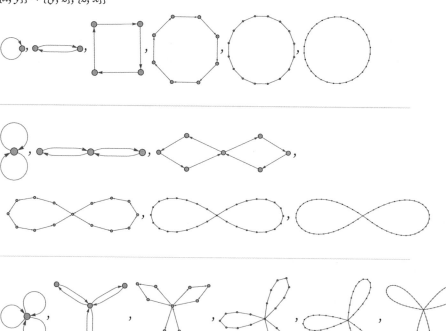

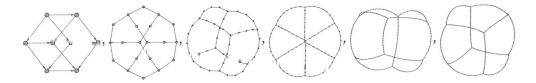

Sometimes, however, the layout of hypergraphs for visualization can make the replication of structures a little less obvious, as in this example for the rule:

$$\{\{x, y\}\} \rightarrow \{\{x, z\}, \{x, z\}, \{z, y\}\}$$

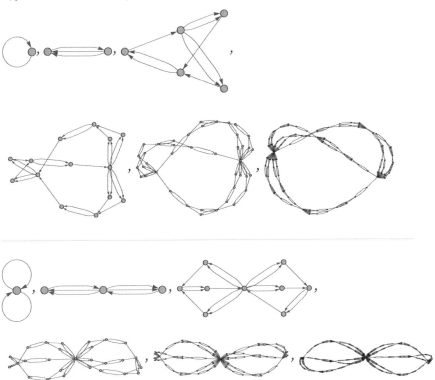

For rules depending on more than one relation, initial conditions can have more important effects. Starting with the rule

$$\{\{x, y\}, \{y, z\}\} \rightarrow \{\{w, z\}, \{w, z\}, \{x, w\}, \{y, z\}\}$$

from all 8 inequivalent 2-relation and all 32 inequivalent 3-relation initial conditions, one sees quite a range of behavior:

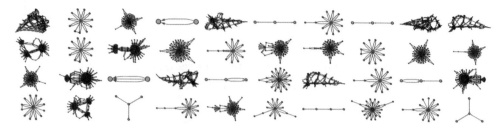

But in other rules—particularly many of those such as

$$\{\{x, y\}, \{x, z\}\} \rightarrow \{\{x, y\}, \{x, w\}, \{y, w\}, \{z, w\}\}$$

that yield globular structures—different initial conditions (so long as they lead to growth at all) produce behavior that is different in detail but similar in overall features, a bit like what happens in class 3 cellular automata such as rule 30 [1:p251]):

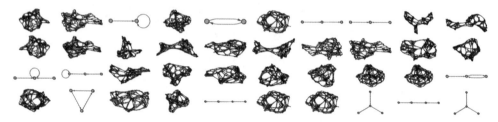

For the evolution of a rule to not just immediately terminate, the left-hand side of the rule must be able to match the initial conditions given (and so must be a sub-hypergraph of the initial conditions). This is guaranteed if the initial conditions are in effect just a copy of the left-hand side. But the most "fertile" initial conditions, with the most possibility for different matches, are always self-loops: in particular, n k-ary self-loops for a rule with signature $n_k \rightarrow \ldots$. And in what follows, this is the form of initial conditions that we will most often use.

One practical issue with self-loop initial conditions, however, is that they can make it visually more difficult to tell what is going on. Sometimes, for example, initial conditions that lead to slightly less activity, or enforce some particular symmetry, can help. Note, however, that in the evolution of rules that depend on more than one relation, there may be no way to preserve symmetry, at least with any specific updating order (see section 6). Thus, for example, the rule

$$\{\{x, y\}, \{x, z\}\} \rightarrow \{\{x, y\}, \{x, w\}, \{y, w\}, \{z, w\}\}$$

with our standard updating order gives:

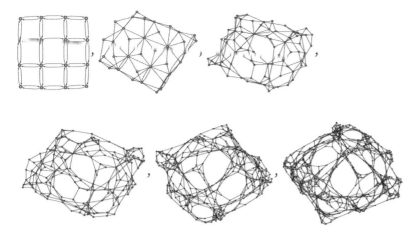

Another feature of initial conditions is that they can affect the connectivity of the results from a rule. Thus, for example, even in the case of the rule above that generates a grid, initial conditions consisting of different numbers of 3-ary self-loops lead to differently connected results:

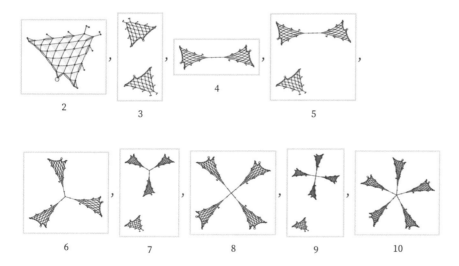

3.17 Behavior without Growth

Essentially all the rules we have considered so far have been set up to add relations. But with extended initial conditions, it makes sense also to consider rules that maintain a fixed number of relations.

Rules with signatures like $1_2 \to 1_2$ that depend only on one relation cannot give rise to nontrivial behavior. But rules with signature $2_2 \to 2_2$ (of which a total of 562 are inequivalent) already can.

Consider the rule:

$$\{\{x, y\}, \{y, z\}\} \rightarrow \{\{y, x\}, \{z, x\}\}$$

Starting from a chain of 5 binary relations, this is the behavior of the rule:

Given that only a finite number of elements and relations are involved, the total number of possible states of the system is finite, so it is inevitable that the evolution of the system must eventually repeat. In the particular case shown here, the repetition period is only 3 steps. (Note that the detailed behavior—and the repetition period—can depend on the updating order used.)

In general, the total number of possible states of the system is given by the number of distinct hypergraphs of a certain size. One can then construct a state transition graph for these states under a rule. Here is the result for the rule above with the 32 distinct connected 3_2 hypergraphs (note that with this rule, the hypergraphs always remain connected):

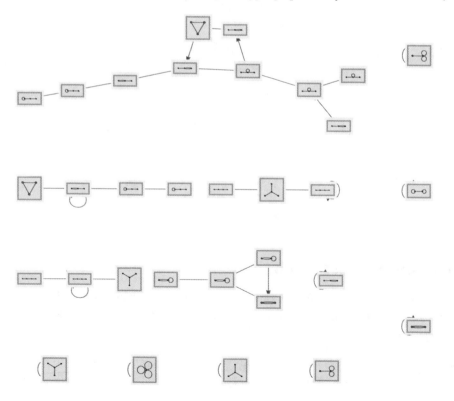

The result for all 928 5_2 hypergraphs is:

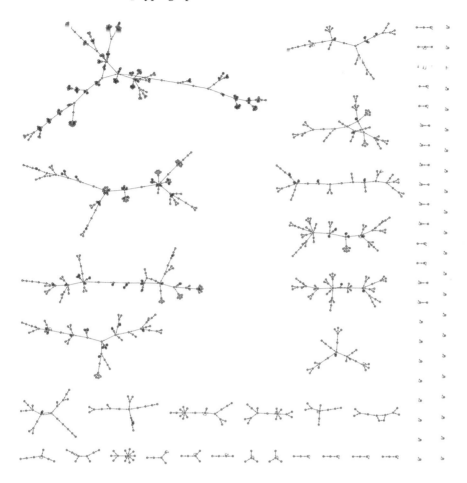

This graph contains trees corresponding to transients, leading into cycles. The maximum cycle length in this case is 5. But when the size of the system increases, the lengths of cycles can increase rapidly (cf. [1:6.4]). The length is bounded by the number of distinct n_k hypergraphs, which grows faster than exponentially with n. The plot below shows the lengths of cycles and transients in the rule above for initial conditions consisting of progressively longer chains of relations:

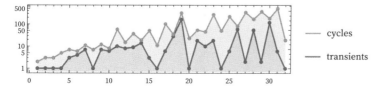

3.18 Random Rules and Overall Classification of Behavior

Here are samples of random rules with various signatures (only connected results are included):

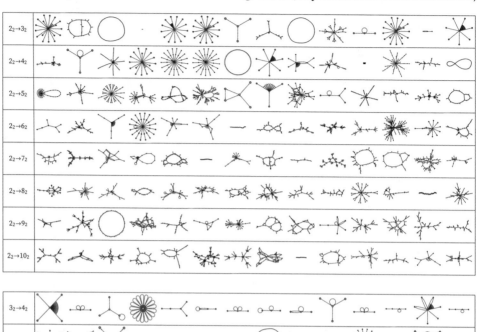

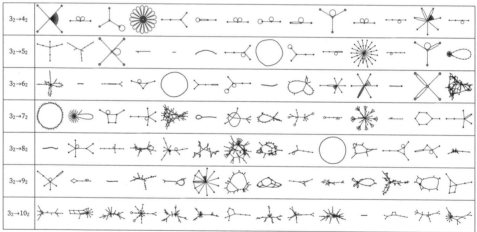

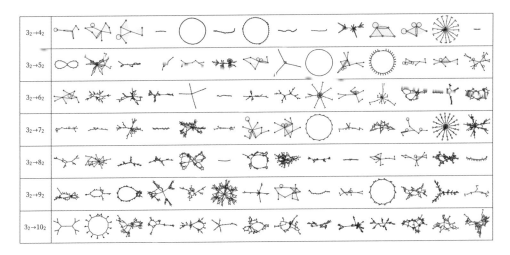

As expected from the Principle of Computational Equivalence [1:c12], above a low threshold more complex rules do not generally lead to more complex behavior, although the frequencies of different kinds of behavior do change somewhat.

At a basic visual level, one can identify several general types of behavior:

- Line-like: elements are connected primarily in sequences (lines, circles, etc.)
- Radial: most elements are connected to just a few core elements
- Tree-like: elements repeatedly form independent branches
- Globular: more complex, closed structures

Inevitably, these types of behavior are neither mutually exclusive, nor precisely defined. There are certainly specific graph-theoretic and other methods that could be used to discriminate different types, but there will always be ambiguous cases (and sometimes it will even be formally undecidable what category something is in). But just like for cellular automata— or for many systems in the empirical sciences—classifications can still be useful in practice even if their definitions are not unique or precise.

As an alternative to categorical classification, one can also consider systematically arranging behaviors in a continuous feature space (e.g. [13]). The results inevitably depend on how features are extracted. Here is what happens if one takes images like the ones above, and directly applies a feature extractor trained on images of picturable nouns in human language [14]:

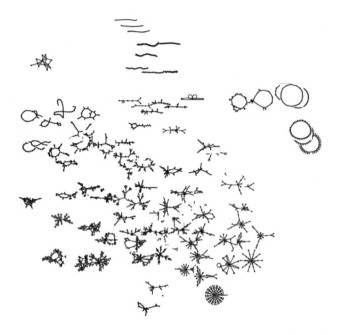

Here is the fairly similar result based on feature extraction of underlying adjacency matrices:

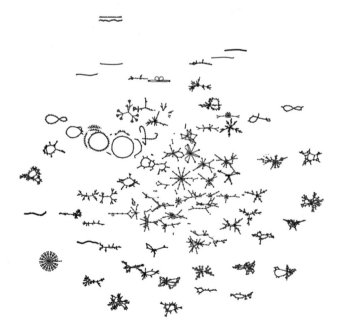

In addition to characterizing the behavior of individual rules, one can also ask to what extent behavior is clustered in rule space. Here are samples of what happens if one starts from particular $2_2 \rightarrow 7_2$ rules, then looks at a collection of "nearby" rules that differ by one element in one relation:

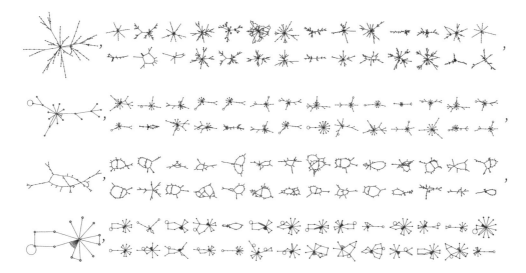

And what we see is that even though there are only 68 million or so $2_2 \rightarrow 7_2$ rules, changing one element (out of 14) still usually gives a rule whose overall behavior is similar.

4 | Limiting Behavior and Emergent Geometry

4.1 Recognizable Geometry

Particularly for potential applications to fundamental physics, it will be of great importance to understand what happens if we run our models for many steps—and to find ways to characterize overall behavior that emerges. Sometimes the characterization is easy. One gets a loop with progressively more links:

$\{\{x, y\}\} \rightarrow \{\{y, z\}, \{z, x\}\}$

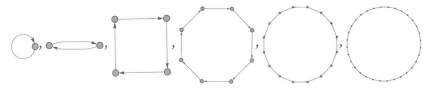

Or one gets a tree with progressively more levels of branching:

$\{\{x\}\} \rightarrow \{\{x, y\}, \{y\}, \{y\}\}$

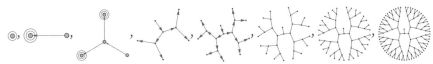

But what about a case like the following? Is there any way to characterize the limiting behavior here?

$\{\{x, y\}, \{x, z\}\} \rightarrow \{\{x, y\}, \{x, w\}, \{y, w\}, \{z, w\}\}$

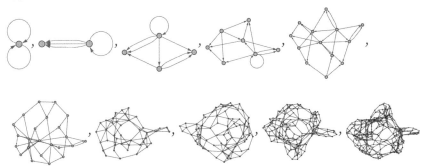

It turns out that a rare phenomenon that we saw in the previous section gives a critical clue. Consider the rule:

$\{\{x, y, y\}, \{z, x, u\}\} \rightarrow \{\{y, v, y\}, \{y, z, v\}, \{u, v, v\}\}$

Looking at the first 10 steps it is not clear what it will do:

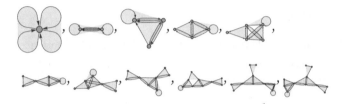

But showing the results every 10 steps thereafter it starts to become clearer:

And after 1000 steps it is very clear: the rule has basically produced a simple grid:

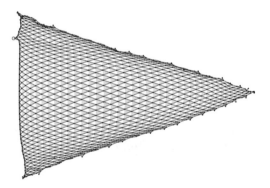

Geometrical though this looks, it is important to understand that at a fundamental level there is no geometry in our model: it just involves abstract collections of relations. Our visualization methods make it evident, however, that the pattern of these relations corresponds to the pattern of connections in a grid.

In other words, from the purely combinatorial structure of the model, what we can interpret as geometrical structure has emerged. And if we continue running the model, the grid in our picture will get finer and finer, until eventually it approximates a triangular piece of continuous two-dimensional space.

Consider now the rule:

$$\{\{x, x, y\}, \{x, z, u\}\} \rightarrow \{\{u, u, z\}, \{y, v, z\}, \{y, v, z\}\}$$

Looking at the first 10 steps of evolution it is again not clear what will happen:

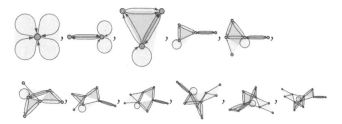

But after 1000 steps a definite geometric structure has emerged:

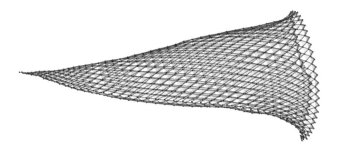

There is evidence of a grid, but now it is no longer flat. Visualizing in 3D makes it clearer what is going on: the grid is effectively defining a 2D surface in 3D:

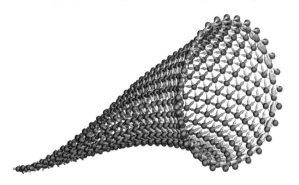

To make its form clearer, we can go for 2000 steps, and include an approximate surface reconstruction [15]:

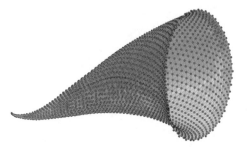

The result is that we can identify that in the limit this rule can be characterized as creating what is essentially a cone.

Other rules produce other shapes. For example, the rule

$$\{\{x, y, z\}, \{u, y, v\}\} \rightarrow \{\{w, z, x\}, \{z, w, u\}, \{x, y, w\}\}$$

gives after 1000 steps:

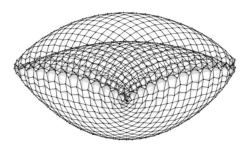

The structure is clearer when visualized in 3D:

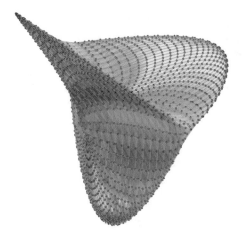

Despite its smooth form, there does not seem to be a simple mathematical characterization of this surface. (Its three-lobed structure means it cannot be an ordinary algebraic surface [16]; it is similar but not the same as the surface $r = \sin(\phi)$ in spherical coordinates.)

Changing the initial condition from  to  yields the rather different surface:

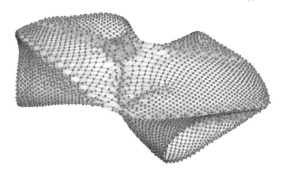

This rule gives a closer approximation to a sphere, though there is a definite threefold structure to be seen:

$$\{\{x, y, y\}, \{x, z, u\}\} \rightarrow \{\{u, v, v\}, \{v, z, y\}, \{x, y, v\}\}$$

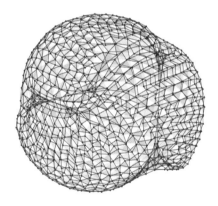

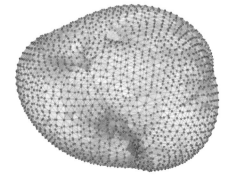

Simpler forms, such as cylindrical tubes, also appear:

$\{\{x, x, y\}, \{z, u, y\}\} \to \{\{u, u, y\}, \{x, v, y\}, \{x, v, z\}\}$

It is worth pausing for a moment to consider in what sense the limiting object here "is" a tube. What we ultimately have is a collection of relations which define a hypergraph. But there is an obvious measure of distance on the hypergraph: how many relations you have to follow to go from one element to another. So now one can ask whether there is a way to make this hypergraph distance between elements correspond to an ordinary geometrical distance. Can one assign positions in space to the elements so that the spatial distances between them agree with the hypergraph distances?

The answer in this case is that one can—by placing the elements at a lattice of positions on the surface of a cylinder in three-dimensional space. (And, conveniently, it so happens that our visualization method for hypergraphs basically automatically does this.) But it is important to realize that such a direct correspondence with an easy-to-describe surface is a rare and special feature of the particular rule used here.

Consider the rule:

$\{\{x, x, y\}, \{x, z, u\}\} \to \{\{u, u, v\}, \{v, u, y\}, \{z, y, v\}\}$

After 1000 steps, this rule produces:

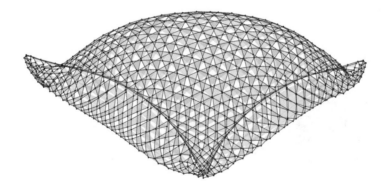

In 3D, this can be visualized as:

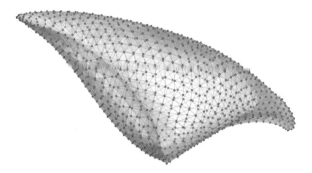

There are many subtle issues here. First, at every step the rule adds more elements, and in principle this could change the emergent geometry. But it appears that after enough steps, there is a definite limiting shape. Unlike in the case of a cylinder, however, it is much less clear how to assign spatial coordinates to different elements. It does not help that the limiting shape does not appear to have a completely smooth surface; instead there are places at which it appears to form cusps (reminiscent of an orbifold [17]).

There are rules that give more obvious "singularities"; an example is:

$$\{\{x, x, y\}, \{y, z, u\}\} \rightarrow \{\{v, v, u\}, \{v, u, x\}, \{z, y, v\}\}$$

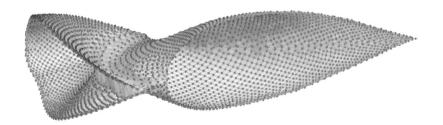

Some rules produce surfaces with complex folds:

$$\{\{x, x, y\}, \{z, u, x\}\} \rightarrow \{\{z, z, v\}, \{y, v, x\}, \{y, w, v\}\}$$

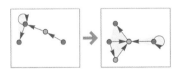

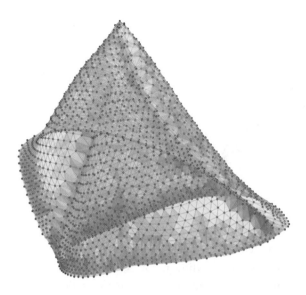

It is also perfectly possible for the emergent geometry to have nontrivial topology. This rule produces a (strangely twisted) torus:

$$\{\{x, x, y\}, \{z, u, x\}\} \rightarrow \{\{x, x, z\}, \{u, v, x\}, \{y, v, z\}\}$$

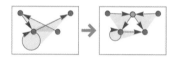

All the emergent geometries we have seen so far in effect involve a regular mesh. But this rule, instead uses a mixture of triangles, quadrilaterals and pentagons to cover a region:

$$\{\{x, y, x\}, \{x, z, u\}\} \rightarrow \{\{u, v, u\}, \{v, u, z\}, \{x, y, v\}\}$$

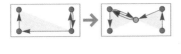

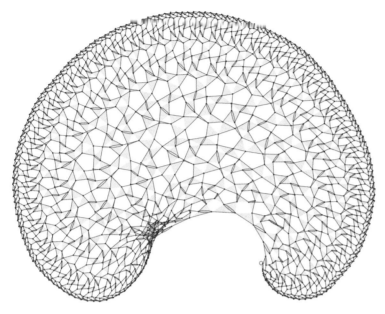

4.2 Hyperbolic Space

Among all possible rules, the formation of geometrical shapes of the kind we have just been discussing is very rare. Slightly more common is the type of behavior that we see in a rule like:

$$\{\{x, y\}, \{y, z\}\} \to \{\{w, x\}, \{w, y\}, \{x, y\}, \{y, z\}\}$$

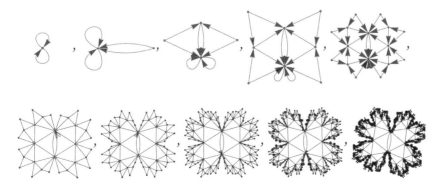

Essentially the same behavior also occurs in a mixed-arity rule with a single relation on the left-hand side:

$$\{\{x, y\}\} \to \{\{z, y, x\}, \{y, z\}, \{z, x\}\}$$

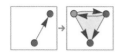

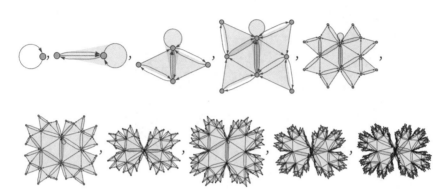

We can think of the structure that is produced as being like a binary tree of triangles:

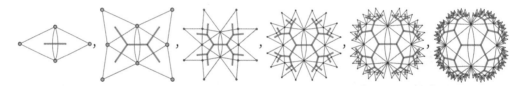

The same structure can be produced from an Apollonian circle packing (e.g. [18][1: p985]):

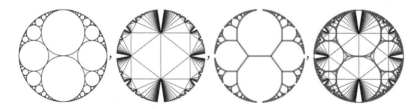

If each triangle is required to have the same area, the structure can be rendered in 2D as:

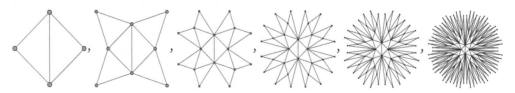

If we tried to render this with every triangle roughly the same size, then even in 3D the best we could do would be to have something that crinkles up more and more at the edge, like an idealized lettuce leaf:

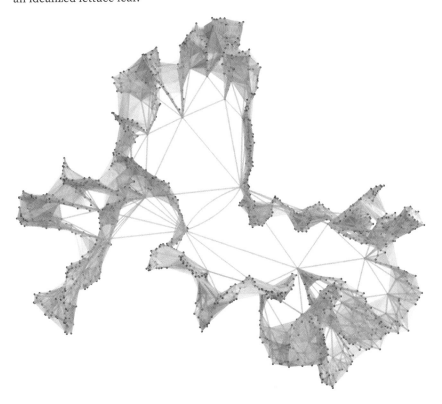

But just as we can think of the grids we discussed before as being regularly laid out in ordinary 2D or 3D space, so now we can think of the object we have here as being regularly laid out in a hyperbolic space [19][20] of constant negative curvature.

In particular, the object corresponds to an infinite-order triangular tiling of the hyperbolic plane (with Schläfli symbol {3,∞}). There are a variety of ways to visualize the hyperbolic plane. One example is the Poincaré disk model in which hyperbolic-space straight lines are rendered as arcs of circles orthogonal to the boundary:

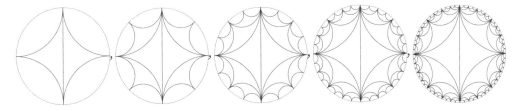

(The particular graph here happens to be the Farey graph [21].)

4.3 Geometry from Subdivision

The grids and surfaces that we saw above were all produced by rules that end up executing a laborious "knitting" process in which they add just a single relation at each step. But it is also possible to generate recognizable geometric forms more quickly—in effect by a process of repeated subdivision.

Consider the $2_31_2 \rightarrow 4_34_2$ rule:

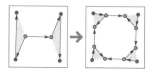

At each step, this rule doubles the number of relations—and quickly produces a structure with a definite emergent geometrical form:

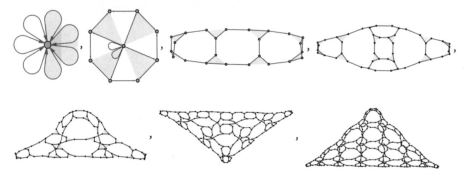

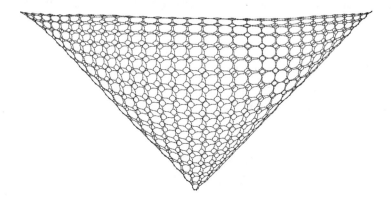

After 10 steps the rule has generated 2560 relations, in the following structure:

Visualized in 3D, this becomes:

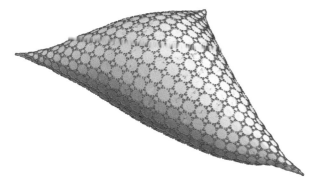

Once again, this corresponds to a smooth surface, but with 3 cusps. The surface is defined not by a simple triangular grid, but instead by an octagon-square ("truncated square") tiling—that in this case becomes twice as fine at every step.

Changing the initial conditions can give a somewhat different structure:

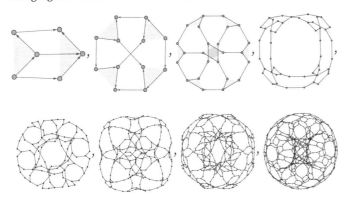

Visualized in 3D after 10 steps (and reconstructing less of the surface), this becomes:

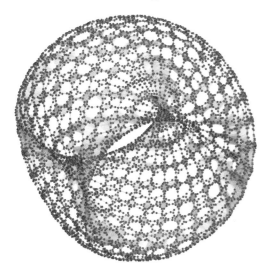

4.4 Nested Patterns

Consider the $1_3 \to 3_3$ rule:

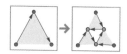

Starting from a single ternary relation with three distinct elements {{1,2,3}}, this gives a classic Sierpiński triangle structure:

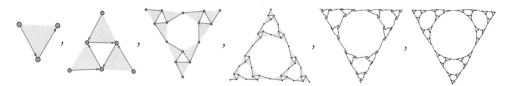

Starting instead from a ternary self loop {{0,0,0}} one gets what amounts to a tetrahedron of Sierpiński triangles:

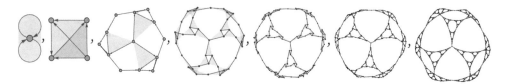

This is exactly the same as one would get by starting with a tetrahedron graph, and repeatedly replacing every trivalent vertex with a triangle of vertices [1:p509]:

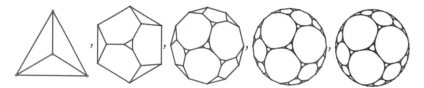

In an ordinary Sierpiński triangle, the points on the edges have different neighborhoods from those in the interior. But in the structure shown here, all points have the same neighborhoods (so there is an isometry).

Many of the rules we have used have completely different behavior if the order of elements in their relations are changed. But in this case the limiting shape is always the same, regardless of ordering, as in these examples:

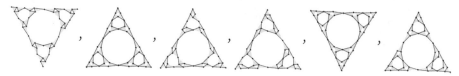

The rule we have discussed so far in this section in a sense directly implements the recursive construction of nested patterns [1:5.4]. But the formation of nested patterns is also a common feature of the limiting behavior of many rules that do not exhibit any such obvious construction.

As an example, consider the $1_3 \to 2_3$ rule:

$$\{\{x, y, z\}\} \to \{\{z, w, w\}, \{y, w, x\}\}$$

This rule effectively constructs a nested sequence of self-similar "segments":

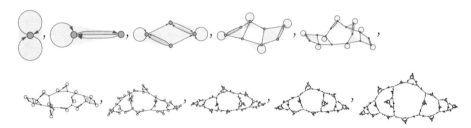

Similar behavior is seen in rules with binary relations, such as the $1_2 \to 4_2$ rule:

$$\{\{x, y\}\} \to \{\{z, w\}, \{z, x\}, \{w, x\}, \{y, w\}\}$$

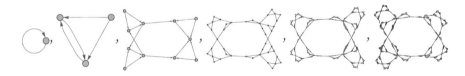

A clear "naturally occurring" Sierpiński pattern appears in the limiting behavior of the $2_2 \to 4_2$ rule:

$$\{\{x, y\}, \{z, y\}\} \to \{\{y, w\}, \{y, w\}, \{w, x\}, \{z, w\}\}$$

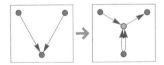

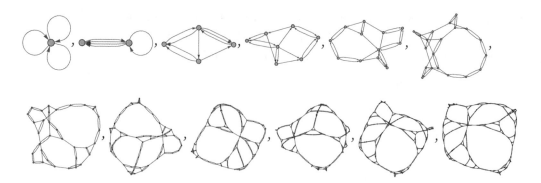

After 15 steps, the rule yields:

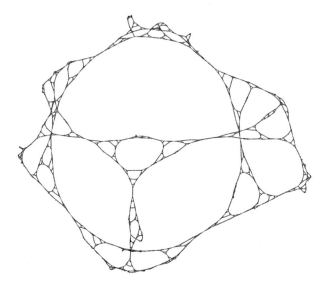

4.5 The Notion of Dimension

In traditional geometry, a basic feature of any continuous space is its dimension. And we have seen that at least in certain cases we can characterize the limiting behavior of our models in terms of the emergence of recognizable geometry—with definite dimension. So this suggests that perhaps we might be able to use a notion of dimension to characterize the limiting behavior of our models even when we do not readily recognize traditional geometrical structure in them.

For standard continuous spaces it is straightforward to define dimension, normally in terms of the number of coordinates needed to specify a position. If we make a discrete approximation to a continuous space, say with a progressively finer grid, we can still identify dimension in terms of the number of coordinates on the grid. But now imagine we only have a connectivity graph for a grid. Can we deduce what dimension it corresponds to?

We might choose to draw the grids so they lay out according to coordinates, here in 1-, 2- and 3-dimensional Euclidean space:

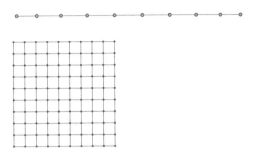

But these are all the same graph, with the same connectivity information:

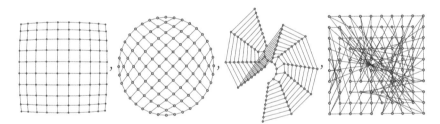

So just from intrinsic information about a graph—or, more accurately, from information about a sequence of larger and larger graphs—can we deduce what dimension of space it might correspond to?

The procedure we will follow is straightforward (cf. [1:p479][22]). For any point X in the graph define $V_r(X)$ to be the number of points in the graph that can be reached by going at most graph distance r. This can be thought of as the volume of a ball of radius r in the graph centered at X.

For a square grid, the region that defines $V_r(X)$ for successive r starting at a point in the center is:

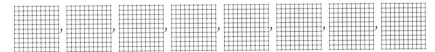

For an infinite grid we then have:

$$V_r = 2\,r^2 + 2\,r + 1$$

For a 1D grid the corresponding result is:

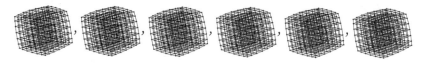

$$V_r = 2\,r + 1$$

And for a 3D grid it is:

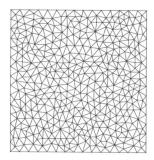

$$V_r = \frac{4\,r^3}{3} + 2\,r^2 + \frac{8\,r}{3} + 1$$

In general, for a d-dimensional cubic grid (cf. [1:p1031]) the result is a terminating hypergeometric series (and the coefficient of z^d in the expansion of $(z+1)^r/(z-1)^{r+1}$):

$$_2F_1(-d, r+1; -d+r+1; -1)\binom{r}{d} = \frac{2^d}{d!}\,r^d + \frac{2^{d-1}}{(d-1)!}\,r^{d-1} + \frac{2^{d-2}\,(d+1)}{3\,(d-2)!}\,r^{d-2} + \ldots$$

But the important feature for us is that the leading term—which is computable purely from connectivity information about the graph—is proportional to r^d.

What will happen for a graph that is less regular than a grid? Here is a graph made by random triangulation of a 2D region:

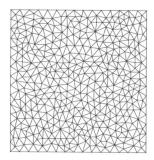

And once again, the number of points reached at graph distance r grows like r^2:

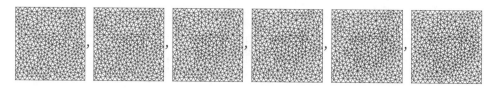

In ordinary d-dimensional continuous Euclidean space, the volume of a ball is exactly

$$\frac{\pi^{d/2}}{(d/2)!} r^d$$

And we should expect that if in some sense our graphs limit to d-dimensional space, then in correspondence with this, V_r should always show r^d growth.

There are, however, many subtle issues. The first—immediately evident in practice—is that if our graph is finite (like the grids above) then there are edge effects that prevent r^d growth in V_r when the radius of the ball becomes comparable to the radius of the graph. The pictures below show what happens for a grid with side length 11, compared to an infinite grid, and the r^d term on its own:

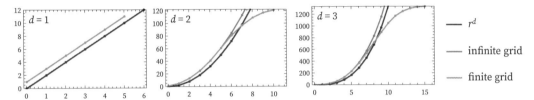

One might imagine that edge effects would be avoided if one had a toroidal grid graph such as:

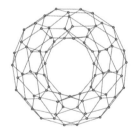

But actually the results for $V_r(X)$ for any point on a toroidal graph are exactly the same as those for the center point in an ordinary grid; it is just that now finite-size effects come from paths in the graph that wrap around the torus.

Still, so long as r is small compared to the radius of the graph—but large enough that we can see overall r^d growth—we can potentially deduce an effective dimension from measurements of V_r.

In practice, a convenient way to assess the form of V_r, and to make estimates of dimension, is to compute log differences as a function of r:

$$\Delta(r) = \frac{\log(V_{r+1}) - \log(V_r)}{\log(r + 1) - \log(r)}$$

Here are results for the center points of grid graphs (or for any point in the analogous toroidal graphs):

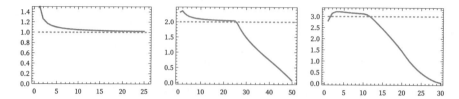

The results are far from perfect. For small r one is sensitive to the detailed structure of the grid, and for large r to the finite overall size of the graph. But, for example, for a 2D grid graph, as the size of the graph is progressively increased, we see that there is an expanding region of values of r at which our estimate of dimension is accurate:

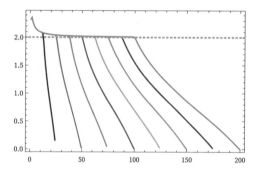

A notable feature of measuring dimension from the growth rate of $V_r(X)$ is that the measurement is in some sense local: it starts from a particular position X. Of course, in looking at successively larger balls, $V_r(X)$ will be sensitive to parts of the graph progressively further away from X. But still, the results can depend on the choice of X. And unless the graph is homogeneous (like our toroidal grids above), one will often want to average over at least a range of possible positions X. Here is an example of doing such averaging for a collection of starting points in the center of the random 2D graph above. The error bars indicate 1σ ranges in the distribution of values obtained from different points X.

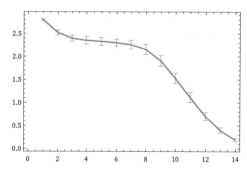

So far we have looked at graphs that approximate standard integer-dimensional spaces. But what about fractal spaces [23]? Let us consider a Sierpiński graph, and look at the growth of a ball in the graph:

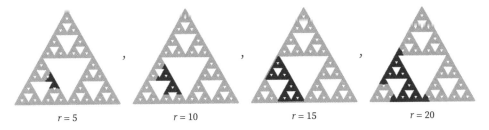

Estimating dimension from $V_r(X)$ averaged over all points we get (for graphs made from 6 and 7 recursive subdivisions):

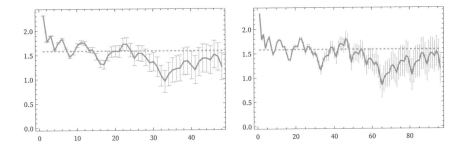

The dotted line indicates the standard Hausdorff dimension $\log_2(3) \approx 1.58$ for a Sierpiński triangle [23]. And what the pictures suggest is that the growth rate of V_r approximates this value. But to get the exact value we see that in addition to everything else, we will need average estimates of dimension over different values of r.

In the end, therefore, we have quite a collection of limits to take. First, we need the overall size of our graph to be large. Second, we need the range of values of r for measuring V_r to be small compared to the size of the graph. Third, we need these values to be large relative to individual nodes in the graph, and to be large enough that we can readily measure the leading order growth of V_r—and that this will be of the form r^d. In addition, if the graph is not homogeneous we need to be averaging over a region X that is large compared to the size of inhomogeneities in the graph, but small compared to the values of r we will use in estimating the growth of V_r. And finally, as we have just seen, we may need to average over different ranges of r in estimating overall dimension.

If we have something like a grid graph, all of this will work out fine. But there are certainly cases where we can immediately tell that it will not work. Consider, for example, first the case of a complete graph, and second of a tree:

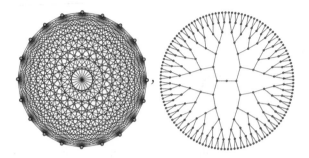

For a complete graph there is no way to have a range of r values "smaller than the radius of graph" from which to estimate a growth rate for V_r. For a tree, V_r grows exponentially rather than as a power of r, so our estimate of dimension $\Delta(r)$ will just continually increase with r:

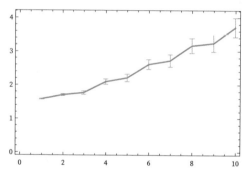

But notwithstanding these issues, we can try applying our approach to the objects generated by our models. As constructed, these objects correspond to directed graphs or hypergraphs. But for our current purposes, we will ignore directedness in determining distance, effectively taking all elements in a particular k-ary relation—regardless of their ordering—to be at unit distance from each other.

As a first example, consider the $2_3 \to 3_3$ rule we discussed above that "knits" a simple grid:

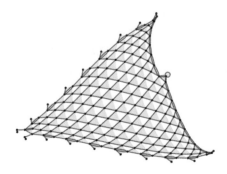

As we run the rule, the structure it produces gets larger, so it becomes easier to estimate the growth rate of V_r. The picture below shows $\Delta(r)$ (starting at the center point) computed after successively more steps. And we see that, as expected, the dimension estimate appears to converge to value 2:

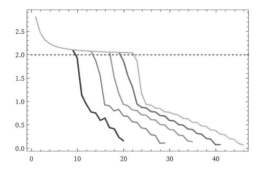

It is worth mentioning that if we did not compute $V_r(X)$ by starting at the center point, but instead averaged over all points, we would get a less useful result, dominated by edge effects:

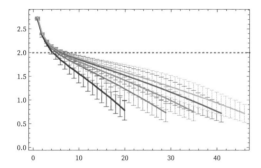

As a second example, consider the $2_3 \rightarrow 3_3$ rule that slowly generates a somewhat complex kind of surface:

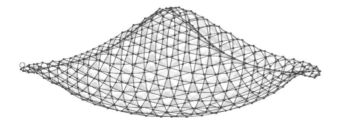

As we run this longer, we see what appears to be increasingly close approximation to dimension 2, reflecting the fact that even though we can best draw this object embedded in 3D space, its intrinsic surface is two-dimensional (though, as we will discuss later, it also shows the effects of curvature):

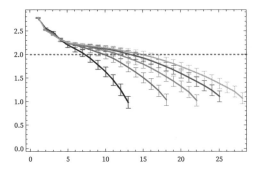

The successive dimension estimates shown above are spaced by 500 steps in the evolution of the rule. As another example, consider the $2_3 1_2 \rightarrow 4_3 4_2$ rule, in which geometry emerges rapidly through a process of subdivision:

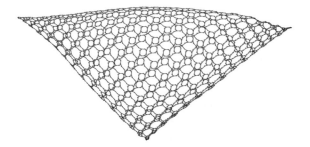

These are dimension estimates for all of the first 10 steps in the evolution of this rule:

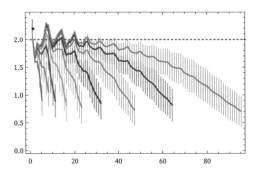

We can also validate our approach by looking at rules that generate obviously nested structures. An example is the $2_2 \to 4_2$ rule that produces:

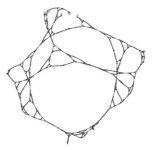

The results for each of the first 15 steps show good correspondence to dimension $\log_2(3) \approx 1.58$:

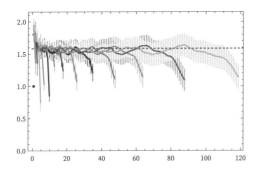

4.6 Dimension-Related Characterizations

Having seen how our notion of dimension works in cases where we can readily recognize emergent geometry, we now turn to using it to study the more general limiting behavior of our models.

As a first example, consider the $2_2 \to 4_2$ rule

$$\{\{x, y\}, \{x, z\}\} \to \{\{x, y\}, \{x, w\}, \{y, w\}, \{z, w\}\}$$

which generates results such as (with about 1.84^t relations at step t):

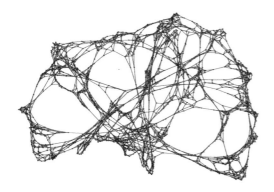

If we attempt to reconstruct a surface from successive steps in the evolution of this rule, no clearly recognizable geometry emerges:

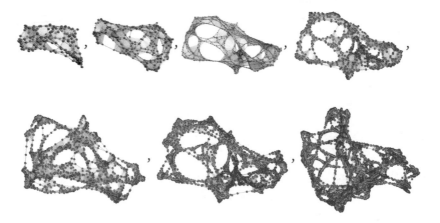

But instead we can try to characterize the results using $V_r(X)$ and our notion of dimension. We compute $V_r(X)$ as we do elsewhere: by starting at a point in the structure and constructing successively larger balls:

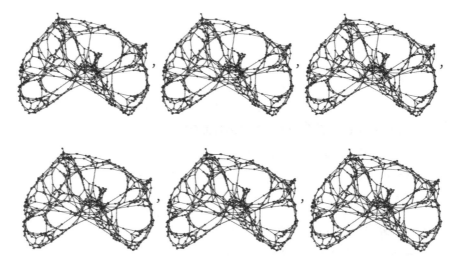

Computing the $\Delta(r)$ for all points over the first 16 steps of evolution gives:

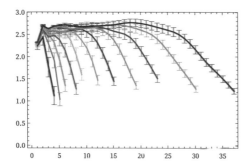

The most important feature of this plot is that it suggests $\Delta(r)$ might approach a definite limit as the number of steps increases. And from the increasing region of flatness there is some evidence that perhaps V_r might approach a stable r^d form, with $d \approx 2.7$, suggesting that in the limit this rule might produce some kind of emergent geometry with dimension around 2.7.

What about other rules? Here are some examples for rules we have discussed above:

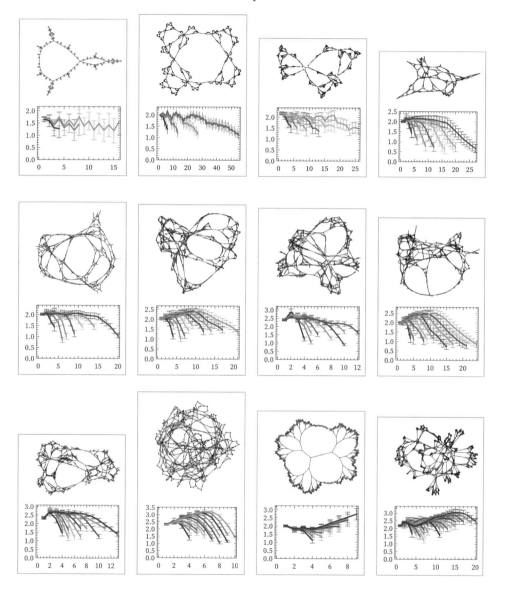

Some rules do not show convergence, at least over the number of steps sampled here. Other rules show quite stable limiting forms, often with a flat region which suggests a structure with definite dimension. Sometimes this dimension is an integer, like 1 or 2; often it is not. Still other rules seem to show linear increase in log differences of V_r, implying an exponential form for V_r itself, characteristic of tree-like behavior.

4.7 Curvature

In ordinary plane geometry, the area of a circle is πr^2. But if the circle is drawn on the surface of a sphere of radius a, the area of the spherical region enclosed by the circle is instead:

$$2\pi a^2 \left(1 - \cos\left(\frac{r}{a}\right)\right) = \pi r^2 \left(1 - \frac{r^2}{12\,a^2} + \frac{r^4}{360\,a^4} - \ldots\right)$$

In other words, curvature in the underlying space introduces a correction to the growth rate for the area of the circle as a function of radius. And in general there is a similar correction for the volume of a d-dimensional ball in a curved space (e.g. [24][1:p1050])

$$\frac{\pi^{d/2}}{(d/2)!}\, r^d \left(1 - \frac{r^2}{6\,(d+2)}\, R + O(r^4)\right)$$

where here R is the Ricci scalar curvature of the space [25][26][27]. (For example, for the d-dimensional surface of a $(d+1)$-dimensional sphere of radius a, $R = \frac{(d-1)\,d}{a^2}$.)

Now consider the sequence of "sphere" graphs:

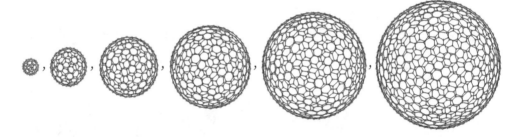

We can compute V_r for each of these graphs. Here are the log differences $\Delta(r)$ (the error bars come from the different neighborhoods associated with hexagonal and pentagonal "faces" in the graph):

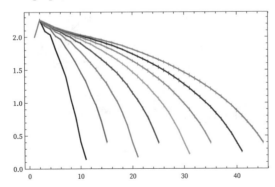

We immediately see the effect of curvature: even though in the limit the graphs effectively define 2D surfaces, the presence of curvature introduces a negative correction to pure r^2 growth in V_r. (Somewhat confusingly, there is only one scale defined for the kind of "pure sphere" graphs shown here, so they all have the same curvature, independent of size.)

A torus, unlike a sphere, has no intrinsic surface curvature. So torus graphs of the form

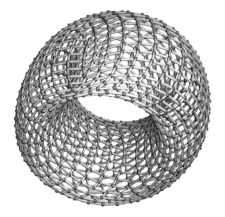

give flat log differences for V_r:

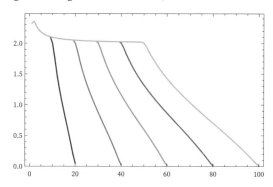

A graph based on a tiling in hyperbolic space

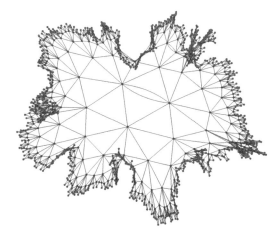

has negative curvature, so leads to a positive correction to V_r:

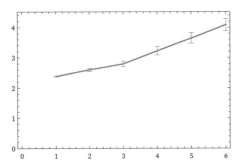

(One can imagine getting other examples by taking 3D objects and putting meshes on their surfaces. And indeed if the meshes are sufficiently faithful to the intrinsic geometry of the surfaces—say based on their geodesics—then the $V_r(X)$ for the connectivity graphs of these meshes [28] will reflect the intrinsic curvatures of the surfaces. In practical computational geometry, though, meshes tend to be based on things like coordinate parametrizations, and so do not reflect intrinsic geometry.)

Many structures produced by our models exhibit curvature. There are cases of negative curvature:

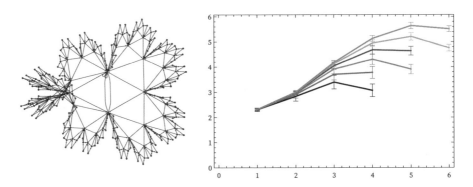

As well as positive curvature:

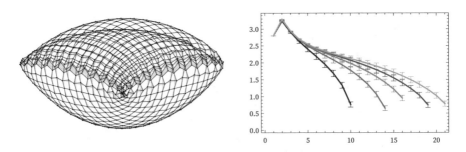

The most obvious examples of nested structures have fractional dimension, but no curvature:

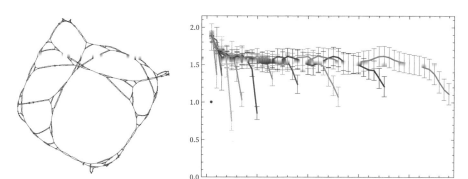

But even though it is not well characterized using ideas from traditional calculus, there is every reason to expect that the limits of our models can exhibit a combination of fractional dimension and curvature.

In general, though, there is no obvious constraint on the possible limiting form of V_r. Curvature can be thought of as associated with the $O(r^2)$ term in a Taylor expansion of V_r about $r = 0$, after factoring out r^d. But there is nothing to say that the leading behavior of V_r should match a form like r^d. In addition to exponentials like λ^r it could show an infinite collection of intermediate asymptotic scales, like $2^{r \log(r)}$ or $r^{\sqrt{r}}$ [29][30].

4.8 Homogeneity and Local Graph Neighborhoods

In studying V_r we are looking at the total size of the neighborhood up to distance r around a point in a graph. But what about the actual local structure of the neighborhood?

In general, it can be different for every point on the graph. Thus, for example, in

obtained from 10 steps of the rule $\{\{x,y\},\{x,z\}\} \rightarrow \{\{x,z\},\{x,w\},\{y,w\},\{z,w\}\}$ the collection of distinct range-1 neighborhoods (with their counts) is:

$$\{ \ \triangleright\!\!-\!\!- \rightarrow 139, \ \triangleright\!\!\!\triangleleft \rightarrow 29, \ \perp\!\!\!\!\diagdown \rightarrow 25, \ \triangleleft\!\triangleright \rightarrow 19, \ \curlyvee \rightarrow 19, \ \triangleright\!\!\!\prec\!\!\triangleleft \rightarrow 14, \ \ominus\!\!- \rightarrow 10, \ \triangleright\!\!\!\triangleleft\!\!\!\triangleleft \rightarrow 10, \ \triangleright\!\!\!\triangleleft\!\!\triangleleft \rightarrow 7, $$

$$\divideontimes \rightarrow 7, \ \ominus\!\!\!- \rightarrow 7, \ \bowtie\!\!\!\times \rightarrow 7, \ \divideontimes \rightarrow 5, \ \divideontimes \rightarrow 4, \ \divideontimes \rightarrow 3, \ \divideontimes \rightarrow 2, \ \divideontimes \rightarrow 2, \ \divideontimes \rightarrow 2, \ \triangledown \rightarrow 2, $$

$$\divideontimes \rightarrow 1, \ \divideontimes \rightarrow 1, \ \divideontimes \rightarrow 1, \ \divideontimes \rightarrow 1, \ \divideontimes \rightarrow 1, \ \divideontimes \rightarrow 1, \ \divideontimes \rightarrow 1, \ \divideontimes \rightarrow 1, \ \divideontimes \rightarrow 1, \ \!-\!\!\!-\!\!\!-\!\!\!- \rightarrow 1 \}$$

The corresponding result after 12 steps is:

$$\{ \ \triangleright\!\!-\!\!- \rightarrow 478, \ \triangleright\!\!\!\triangleleft \rightarrow 94, \ \perp\!\!\!\!\diagdown \rightarrow 79, \ \triangleleft\!\triangleright \rightarrow 67, \ \curlyvee \rightarrow 62, \ \triangleright\!\!\!\prec\!\!\triangleleft \rightarrow 55, \ \bowtie \rightarrow 36, $$

$$\ominus\!\!- \rightarrow 26, \ \ominus\!\!\!- \rightarrow 24, \ \bowtie\!\!\triangleleft \rightarrow 23, \ \times\!\!\!\times \rightarrow 20, \ \divideontimes \rightarrow 18, \ \divideontimes \rightarrow 13, \ \divideontimes \rightarrow 13, \ \divideontimes \rightarrow 10, $$

$$\divideontimes \rightarrow 9, \ \divideontimes \rightarrow 7, \ \divideontimes \rightarrow 7, \ \divideontimes \rightarrow 6, \ \divideontimes \rightarrow 4, \ \divideontimes \rightarrow 3, \ \divideontimes \rightarrow 3, \ \divideontimes \rightarrow 2, \ \divideontimes \rightarrow 2, $$

$$\divideontimes \rightarrow 2, \ \divideontimes \rightarrow 2, \ \divideontimes \rightarrow 2, \ \triangledown \rightarrow 2, \ \divideontimes \rightarrow 1, \ \divideontimes \rightarrow 1, \ \divideontimes \rightarrow 1, \ \divideontimes \rightarrow 1, \ \divideontimes \rightarrow 1, $$

$$\divideontimes \rightarrow 1, \ \divideontimes \rightarrow 1, \ \divideontimes \rightarrow 1, \ \divideontimes \rightarrow 1, \ \bowtie\!\!\triangleleft \rightarrow 1, \ \bowtie \rightarrow 1, \ \triangleright\!\!\!\prec \rightarrow 1, \ \!-\!\!\!-\!\!\!-\!\!\!- \rightarrow 1 \}$$

And it seems that for this rule the distribution of different forms for a given range of neighborhood generally stabilizes as the number of steps increases. (It may be possible to characterize it as limiting to an invariant measure in the space of possible hypergraphs, perhaps with some related entropy (cf. [1:p958][31]).)

One sees the same kind of stabilization for most rules, though, for example, in a case like

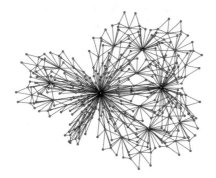

from the rule $\{\{x,y\}\}\rightarrow\{\{x,y\},\{y,z\},\{z,x\}\}$ one always gets some neighborhoods with new forms at each step:

$$\{\ \cdot\!\bigtriangledown \rightarrow 6,\ \bigtriangledown\!\!\!\!\!/ \rightarrow 2,\ \bigtriangledown \rightarrow 2,\ \bigstar \rightarrow 1,\ \bigstar \rightarrow 1,\ \bigstar \rightarrow 1,\ \circ\!\!-\!\! \rightarrow 1\}$$

$$\{\ \bigtriangledown\!\!\!\!/ \rightarrow 14,\ \bigtriangledown \rightarrow 12,\ \cdots \rightarrow 0,\ \cdots \rightarrow 2,\ \cdots \rightarrow 2,\ \bigstar \rightarrow 1,\ \bigstar \rightarrow 1,\ \bigstar \rightarrow 1,\ \bigstar \rightarrow 1,\ \circ\!\!-\!\! \rightarrow 1\}$$

$$\{\ \bigtriangledown \rightarrow 50,\ \cdot\!\bigtriangledown \rightarrow 30,\ \bigtriangledown\!\!\!\!/ \rightarrow 14,\ \bigtriangledown\!\!\!\!/ \rightarrow 12,\ \bigstar \rightarrow 6,$$
$$\bigstar \rightarrow 2,\ \bigstar \rightarrow 2,\ \bigstar \rightarrow 1,\ \bigstar \rightarrow 1,\ \bigstar \rightarrow 1,\ \bigstar \rightarrow 1,\ \bigstar \rightarrow 1,\ \circ\!\!-\!\! \rightarrow 1\}$$

$$\{\ \bigtriangledown \rightarrow 180,\ \cdot\!\bigtriangledown \rightarrow 62,\ \bigtriangledown\!\!\!\!/ \rightarrow 50,\ \bigtriangledown\!\!\!\!/ \rightarrow 30,\ \bigstar \rightarrow 14,\ \bigstar \rightarrow 12,\ \bigstar \rightarrow 6,$$
$$\bigstar \rightarrow 2,\ \bigstar \rightarrow 2,\ \bullet \rightarrow 1,\ \bigstar \rightarrow 1,\ \bigstar \rightarrow 1,\ \bigstar \rightarrow 1,\ \bigstar \rightarrow 1,\ \bigstar \rightarrow 1,\ \circ\!\!-\!\! \rightarrow 1\}$$

In general, the presence of many identical neighborhoods reflects a certain kind of approximate symmetry or isometry of the emergent geometry of the system.

In a torus graph, for example, the symmetry is exact, and all local neighborhoods of a given range are the same:

$$\{\{\times\},\{\boxtimes\},\{\boxtimes\},\{\boxtimes\},\{\boxtimes\}\}$$

The same is true for a 3D torus graph:

$$\{\{\times\},\{\boxtimes\},\{\boxtimes\},\{\bullet\},\{\boxtimes\}\}$$

For a sphere graph not every point has the exact same local neighborhood, but there are a limited number of neighborhoods of a given range:

$$\{\{\curlyvee \rightarrow 500\},\ \{\curlyvee \rightarrow 440,\ \diamondsuit\!<\ \rightarrow 60\},$$
$$\{\text{⬡} \rightarrow 380,\ \text{⬡} \rightarrow 60,\ \text{⬡} \rightarrow 60\},\ \{\text{⬡} \rightarrow 260,\ \text{⬡} \rightarrow 120,\ \text{⬡} \rightarrow 60,\ \text{⬡} \rightarrow 60\}\}$$

And from the dual graph it becomes clear that these are associated with hexagonal and pentagonal "faces":

$$\{\{\hexagon \rightarrow 240,\ \pentagon \rightarrow 12\},\ \{\hexagon \rightarrow 180,\ \hexagon \rightarrow 60,\ \hexagon \rightarrow 12\},$$
$$\{\hexagon \rightarrow 60,\ \hexagon \rightarrow 60,\ \hexagon \rightarrow 60,\ \hexagon \rightarrow 60,\ \hexagon \rightarrow 12\}\}$$

For a (spherical) Sierpiński graph, there are also a limited number of neighborhoods of a given range:

$$\{\{\triangleright\!\!-\!\! \rightarrow 108\},\ \{\triangleright\!\!-\!\!\triangleleft \rightarrow 108\},\ \{\triangleright\!\!-\!\!\triangleleft \rightarrow 72,\ \triangleright\!\!-\!\!\triangleleft \rightarrow 36\},\ \{\triangle \rightarrow 72,\ \triangleright\!\!-\!\!\triangleleft \rightarrow 36\}\}$$

Whenever every local neighborhood is essentially identical, $V_r(X)$ will have the same form for every point X in a graph or hypergraph. But in general $V_r(X)$ (and the log differences $\Delta_r(X)$) will depend on X. The picture below shows the relative values of $\Delta_r(X)$ at each point in the structure we showed above:

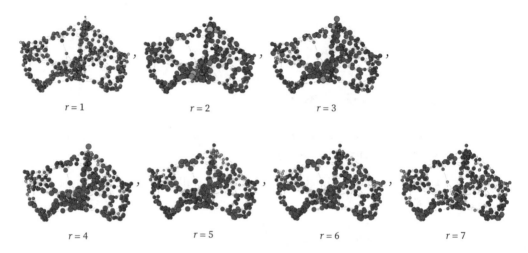

We can also compute the distribution of values for $\Delta_r(X)$ across the structure, as a function of r:

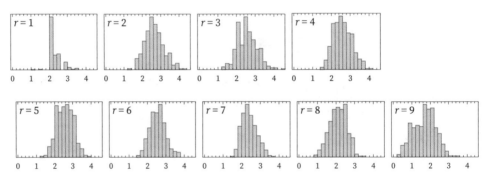

Both these pictures indicate a certain statistical uniformity in $V_r(X)$. This is also seen if we look at the evolution of the distribution of $\Delta_r(X)$, here shown for the specific value $r = 6$, for steps 8 through 16:

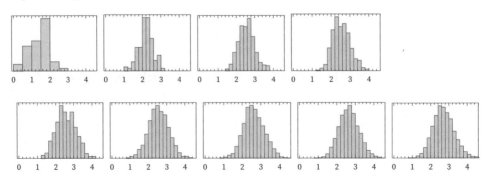

4.9 Adjacency Matrices and Age Distributions

We have made explicit visualizations of the connectivity structures of the graphs (and hypergraphs) generated by our models. But an alternative approach is to look at adjacency matrices (or tensors). In our models, there is a natural way to index the nodes in the graph: the order in which they were created. Here are the adjacency matrices for the first 14 steps in the evolution of the rule $\{\{x,y\},\{x,z\}\}\to\{\{x,z\},\{x,w\},\{y,w\},\{z,w\}\}$ discussed above:

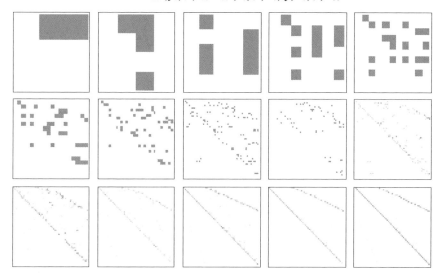

It is notable that even though these adjacency matrices grow by roughly a factor of 1.84 at each step, they maintain many consistent features—and something similar is seen in many other rules.

Our models evolve by continually adding new relations, and for example in the rule we are currently considering, there are roughly exponentially more relations at each step. The result, as shown below for step 14, is that at a given step the relations that exist will almost all be from the most recent step (shown in red):

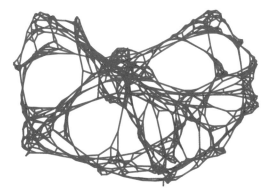

Other rules can show quite different age distributions. Here are age distributions for a few rules that "knit" their structures one relation at a time:

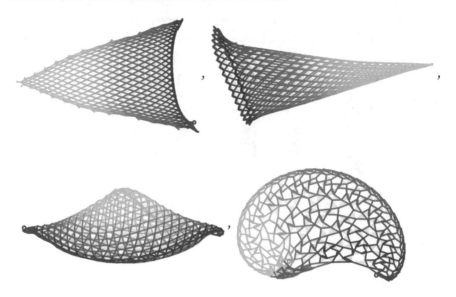

,

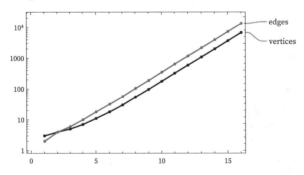

,

4.10 Other Graph Properties

There are many graph and hypergraph properties that can be studied for the output of our models. Here we primarily give examples for the rule $\{\{x,y\},\{x,z\}\}\rightarrow\{\{x,z\},\{x,w\},\{y,w\},\{z,w\}\}$ discussed above.

A basic question is how the numbers of vertices and edges (elements and relations) grow with successive steps. Plotting on a logarithmic scale suggests eventually roughly exponential growth in this case:

We can also compute the growth of the graph diameter (greatest distance between vertices) and graph radius:

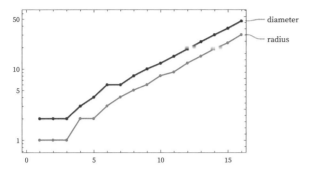

If one assumes that the total vertex count V is related to diameter D by $V = D^d$, then plotting d gives (to be compared to dimension approaching ≈ 2.68 computed from the growth of V_r):

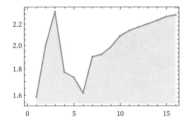

There are many measures of graph structure which basically support the expectation that after many steps, the outputs from the model somehow converge to a kind of statistically invariant "equilibrium" state:

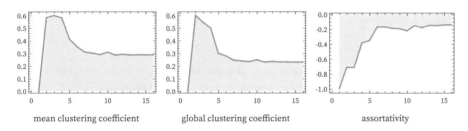

| mean clustering coefficient | global clustering coefficient | assortativity |

Some centrality measures [32][33] start (here at step 10) somewhat concentrated, but rapidly diffuse to be much more broadly distributed:

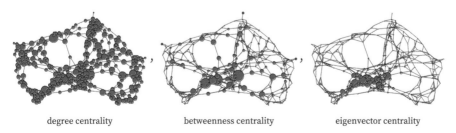

| degree centrality | betweenness centrality | eigenvector centrality |

There are local features of the graph that are closely related to $V_1(X)$ and $V_2(X)$:

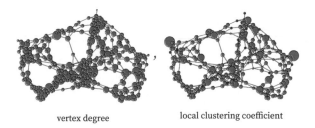

vertex degree   local clustering coefficient

Another feature of our graphs to study is their cycle structure. At the outset, our graphs give us only connectivity information. But one way to imagine identifying "faces" that could be used to infer emergent topology is to look at the fundamental cycles in the graph:

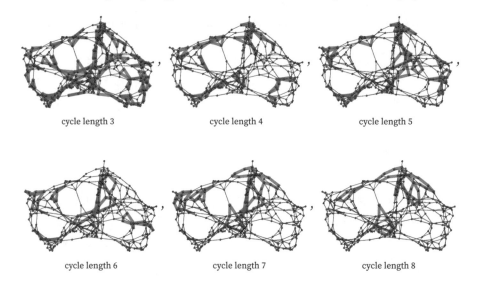

cycle length 3   cycle length 4   cycle length 5

cycle length 6   cycle length 7   cycle length 8

In this particular graph, there are altogether 320 fundamental cycles, with the longest one being of length 24. The distribution of cycle lengths on successive steps once again seems to approach an "equilibrium" form:

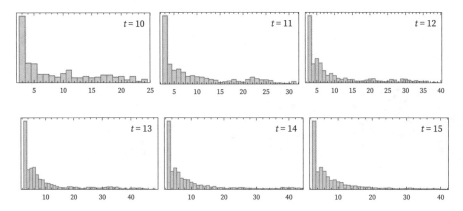

One way to probe overall properties of a graph is to consider the evolution of some dynamical process on the graph. For example, one could run a totalistic cellular automaton with values at nodes of the graph. Another possibility is to solve a discretized PDE. For example, having computed a graph Laplacian [34] (or its higher order analogs) one can determine the distribution of eigenvalues, or the eigenmodes, for a particular graph [35]. The density of eigenvalues is then closely related to V_r and our estimates of dimension and curvature.

4.11 Graph Properties Conserved by Rules

Many rules (at least when they exhibit complex behavior) seem to lead to statistically similar behavior, independent of their initial conditions. But there could still be disjoint families of states that can be reached from different initial conditions, perhaps characterized by different graph or hypergraph invariants.

As one example, we can ask whether there are rules that preserve the planarity of graphs. All rules with signature $1_2 \to 2_2$ inevitably do this. A rule like

$$\{\{x, y\}\} \to \{\{x, y\}, \{y, z\}, \{z, x\}\}$$

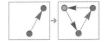

might not at first appear to:

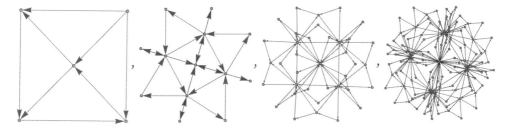

But a different graph layout shows that actually all these graphs are planar [36]:

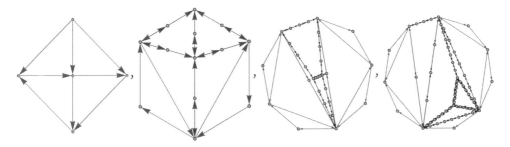

Among larger rules, many still preserve planarity. But for example, $\{\{x,y\},\{x,z\}\}\to\{\{x,z\},\{x,w\},\{y,w\},\{z,w\}\}$ does not, since it transforms the planar graph

to the nonplanar one:

In general, a graph is planar so long as it does not contain as a subgraph either of [37]

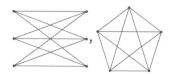

so a rule preserves planarity if (and only if) it never generates either of these subgraphs.

Planarity is one of a class of properties of graphs that are preserved under deletion of vertices and edges, and contraction of edges. Another such property is whether a graph can be drawn without crossings on a 2D surface of any specific genus g [38]. It turns out [38] that for any such property it is known that there are in principle only a finite number of subgraphs that can "obstruct" the property—so if a rule never generates any of these, it must preserve the property.

4.12 Apparent Randomness and Growth Rates

The phenomenon of intrinsic randomness generation is an important and ubiquitous feature of computational systems [1:7.5][39]—the rule 30 cellular automaton [1:2.1] being a quintessential example. In our models the phenomenon definitely often occurs, but two issues make it slightly more difficult to identify.

First, there is considerable arbitrariness in the way we choose to present or visualize graphs or hypergraphs—so it is more difficult to tell whether apparent randomness we see is a genuine feature of our system, or just a reflection of some aspect of our presentation or visualization method.

And second, there may be many possible choices of updating orders, and the specific results we get may depend on the order we choose. Later we will discuss the phenomenon of causal invariance, and we will see that there are causal graphs that can be independent of updating order. But for now, we can consider our updating process to just be another deterministic procedure added to the rules of our system, and we can ask about apparent randomness for this combined system.

And to avoid the arbitrariness of different graph or hypergraph presentations, we can look at graph or hypergraph invariants, which are the same for all isomorphic graphs or hypergraphs, independent of their presentation or visualization.

The most obvious invariants to start with are the total numbers of elements and relations (nodes and edges) in the system. For rules that involve only a single relation on the left-hand side, it is inevitable that these numbers must be determined by a linear recurrence (cf. [1:p890]). (For $1_k \to n_k$ rules, up to a k-term linear recurrence may be involved.)

For rules that involve more than one relation more complicated behavior is common. Consider for example the rule:

$$\{\{x, y\}, \{x, z\}\} \to \{\{y, w\}, \{w, x\}, \{z, w\}\}$$

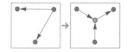

The number of relations generated over the first 50 steps (using our standard updating order) is:

{2, 3, 4, 5, 6, 7, 9, 11, 13, 15, 18, 22, 26, 30, 35, 42, 50, 58, 67, 79, 94, 110, 127, 148, 175, 206, 239, 277, 325, 383, 447,
 518, 604, 710, 832, 967, 1124, 1316, 1544, 1801, 2093, 2442, 2862, 3347, 3896, 4537, 5306, 6211, 7245, 8435, 9845}

Taking third differences yields:

{0, 0, 0, 1, −1, 0, 0, 1, 0, −1, 0, 1, 1, −1, −1, 1, 2, 0, −2, 0, 3, 2, −2,
 −2, 3, 5, 0, −4, 1, 8, 5, −4, −3, 9, 13, 1, −7, 6, 22, 14, −6, −1, 28, 36, 8, −7, 27, 64}

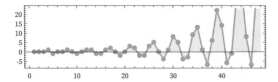

One can consider many other invariants, including counts of in and out degrees of elements, and counts of cycles. In general, one can construct invariant "fingerprints" of hypergraphs— and the typical observation is that for rules whose behavior seems complex, almost all of these will exhibit extensive apparent randomness.

4.13 Statistical Mechanics

Features like dimension and curvature can be used to probe the consistent large-scale structure of the limiting behavior of our models. But particularly insofar as our models generate apparent randomness, it also makes sense to study their statistical features. We discussed above the overall distribution of values of $V_r(X)$ and $\Delta_r(X)$. But we can also consider fluctuations and correlations.

For example, we can look at a 2-point correlation function
$S_r(s) = (\langle V_r(X)\, V_r(Y)\rangle - \langle V_r(X)\rangle^2)/\langle V_r(X)\rangle^2$ for points X and Y separated by graph distance s.
For a uniform graph such as the torus graph, $S_r(s)$ always vanishes. For the buckyball approximation to the sphere that we used above, $S_r(s)$ shows peaks at the distances between "pentagons" in the graph.

For the rule $\{\{x,y\},\{x,z\}\}\rightarrow\{\{x,z\},\{x,w\},\{y,w\},\{z,w\}\}$, $S_r(s)$ steadily expands the region of s over which it shows positive correlations, and perhaps (at least for larger r, indicated by redder curves) approaches a limiting form:

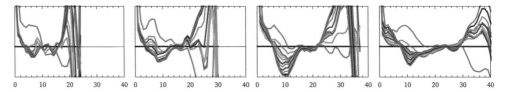

It is conceivable that for this or other rules there might be systematic rescalings of distance and number of steps that would lead to fixed limiting forms.

In statistical mechanics, it is common to think about the ensemble of all possible states of a system—and for example to discuss evolution from all possible initial conditions. But typical systems in statistical mechanics can basically be discussed in terms of a fixed number of degrees of freedom (either coordinates or values).

For our models, there is no obvious way to apply the rules but, for example, to limit the total number of relations—making it difficult to do analysis in terms of ensembles of states.

One can certainly imagine the set of all possible hypergraphs (and even have Ramsey-theory-style results about it), but this set does not appear to have the kind of geometry or structure that has typically been necessary for results in statistical mechanics or dynamical systems theory. (One could however potentially think in terms of a distribution of adjacency matrices, limiting to graphon-like functions [40] for infinite graphs.)

4.14 The Effect of Perturbations

Imagine that at some step in the evolution of a rule one reverses a single relation. What effect will it have? Here is an example for the rule $\{\{x,y\},\{x,z\}\}\rightarrow\{\{x,z\},\{x,w\},\{y,w\},\{z,w\}\}$. The first row is the original evolution; the second is the evolution after reversing the relation:

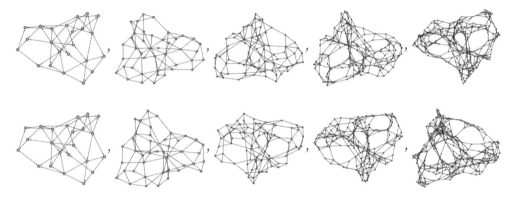

We can illustrate the effect by coloring edges in the first row of graphs that are different in the second one (taking account of graph isomorphism) [41]:

Visualizing the second and third graphs in 3D makes it more obvious that the changed edges are mostly connected:

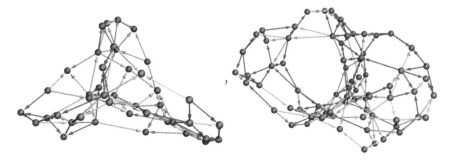

It takes only a few steps before the effect of the change has spread to essentially all parts of the system. (In this particular case, with the updating order used, about 20% of edges are still unaffected after 5 steps, with the fraction slowly decreasing, even as the number of new edges increases.)

In rules with fairly simple behavior, it is common for changes to remain localized:

However, when complex behavior occurs, changes tend to spread. This is analogous to what is seen, for example, in the much simpler case of class 2 versus class 3 cellular automata [31][1:6.3]:

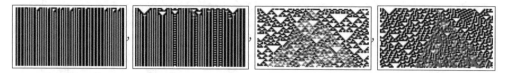

Cellular automata are also known [31] to exhibit the important phenomenon of class 4 behavior—in which there is a discrete set of localized "particle-like" structures through which changes typically propagate:

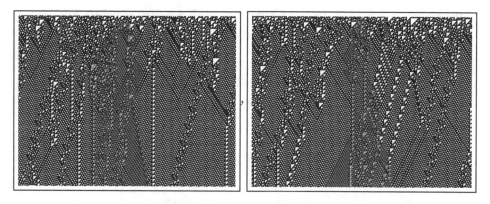

In cellular automata, there is a fixed lattice on which local rules operate, making it straight-forward [1:6.3] to identify the region that can in principle be affected by a change in initial conditions. In the models here, however, everything is dynamic, and so even the question of what parts can in principle be affected by a change in initial conditions is nontrivial.

As we will discuss at length later, however, it is always possible to trace which updating events in a particular evolution depend on which others, and which relations are associated with these. The result will always be a superset of the actual effect of a change in the initial condition:

We discussed above the quantity $V_r(X)$ obtained by "statically" looking at the number of nodes in a hypergraph reached by going graph distance r—in effect computing the volume of a ball of radius r in the hypergraph. By looking at the dependence of updating events in t successive steps of evolution, we can define another quantity $C_t(X)$ which in effect measures the volume of a cone of dependencies in the evolution of the system.

$V_r(X)$ is in a sense a quantity that is "applied" to the system from outside; $C_t(X)$ is in a sense intrinsic. But as we will discuss later, $V_r(X)$ is in some sense an approximation to $C_t(X)$—and particularly when we can reasonably consider the evolution of a model to have reached some kind of "equilibrium", $V_r(X)$ will provide a useful characterization of the "state" of a model.

4.15 Geodesics

Given any two points in a graph or hypergraph one can find a (not necessarily unique) shortest path (or "geodesic") between them, as measured by the number of edges or hyper-edges traversed to go from one point to the other. Here are a few examples of such geodesics:

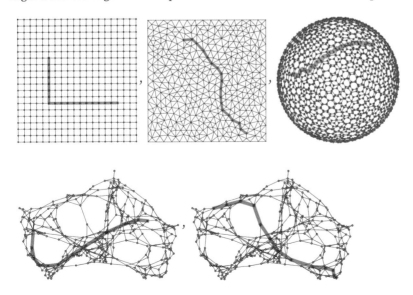

A geodesic in effect defines the analog of a straight line in a graph or hypergraph, and by analogy with the way geodesics work in continuous spaces, we can use them to probe emergent geometry.

For example, in the case of positive curvature, we can expect that nearby geodesics diverge, while in the case of negative curvature they converge:

One can see the same effect in sufficiently large graphs (although it can be obscured by regularities in graphs which lead to large numbers of "degenerate" geodesics, all of the same length):

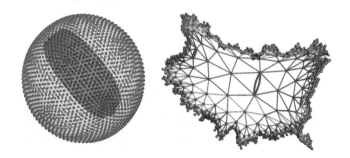

We saw before that the growth rate of the volume $V_r(X)$ of a ball centered at some point X in a graph could be identified as giving a measure of the Ricci scalar curvature R at X. But we can now consider tubes formed from balls centered at each point on a geodesic. And from the growth rates of volumes of these tubes we will be able to measure what can be identified as different components of curvature associated with the Ricci tensor (cf. [1:p1048][27][42]).

In a continuous space (or, more precisely, on a Riemannian manifold) the infinitesimal volume element at a point X is given in terms of the metric tensor g by $\sqrt{\det g(X)}$. If we look at a nearby point $X + \delta x$ we can expand in a power series in δx (e.g. [43])

$$\sqrt{\det g(X + \delta x)} = \sqrt{\det g(X)} \left(1 - \frac{1}{6} \sum R_{ij}(X) \, \delta x^i \, \delta x^j + O(\delta x^3) + ...\right)$$

where R_{ij} is the Ricci tensor and the δ^i (contravariant vectors) are orthogonal components of δx (say along axes defined by some coordinate system).

If we integrate over a ball of radius r in d dimensions, we recover our previous formula for the volume of a ball

$$V_r(X) = \int \sqrt{\det g(X + \delta x)} \; d^d \delta x = \frac{\pi^{d/2}}{(d/2)!} \, r^\mu (1 - \frac{r^2}{6 \, (d+2)} \; \sum R_i{}^i + O(r^4) \,)$$

where $R = \sum R_i{}^i$ is the Ricci scalar curvature.

But now let us consider integrating over a tube of radius r that goes a distance δ along a geodesic starting at X. Then we get a formula for the volume of the tube (cf. [44])

$$\bar{V}_{r,\delta x}(X) = \frac{\pi^{\frac{d-1}{2}}}{(\frac{d-1}{2})!} \, r^{d-1} \, \delta x \, (1 - \left(\frac{d-1}{d+1} \right) (R - \sum R_{ij} \, \hat{\delta x}^i \, \hat{\delta x}^j) \, r^2 + O(r^3 + r^2 \delta x) + ...)$$

where the $\hat{\delta x}^i$ are components of unit vectors along the geodesic.

There is now a direct analog in our hypergraphs: just as we measured the growth rates of geodesic balls to find Ricci scalar curvature, we can now measure growth rates of geodesic tubes to probe full Ricci curvature.

To construct an example, consider a graph formed from a mesh on the surface of an ellipsoid. (It is important that this mesh is intrinsic to the surface, with each mesh element corresponding to about the same surface area—and that the mesh does not just come from, say, a standard θ, ϕ coordinate grid.)

As a first step, consider balls of progressively larger radii at different points on the ellipsoid mesh graph:

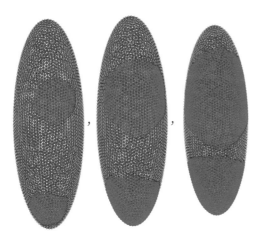

In the region of higher curvature near the tip, the area of the ball for a given radius is smaller, reflecting higher values of the Ricci scalar curvature R there:

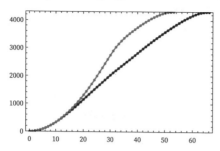

But now consider tubes around geodesics on the ellipsoid mesh graph. Instead of measuring the scalar curvature R, these instead in effect measure components of the Ricci tensor along these geodesics.

To measure all the components of the Ricci tensor, we could consider not just a tube but a bundle of geodesics, and we could look at the sectional curvature associated with deformations of the shape of this bundle. Or, as an alternative, we could consider tubes along not just one, but two geodesics through a given point. But in both cases, the analogy with the continuous case is easiest if we can identify something that we can consider an orthogonal direction.

One way to do this on a graph is to start from a particular geodesic through a given point, then to look at all other geodesics through that point, and work out which ones are the largest graph distance away. These show sequences of progressively more distant geodesics (as measured by the graph distance to the original geodesic of their endpoints):

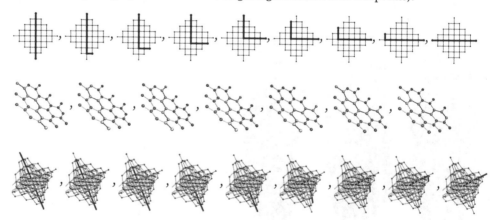

In general there may be many choices of these geodesics—and in a sense these correspond to different local choices of coordinates. But given particular choices of geodesics we can imagine using them to form a grid.

Looking at growth rates of volumes on this grid then gives us results not just about the Ricci tensor, but also about the Riemann tensor, about parallel transport and about covariant derivatives (cf. [27]).

The examples we have shown so far all involve graphs that have a straightforward correspondence with familiar geometry. But exactly the same methods can be used on the kinds of graphs and hypergraphs that arise from our models. This shows tubes of successively larger radii along two different geodesics:

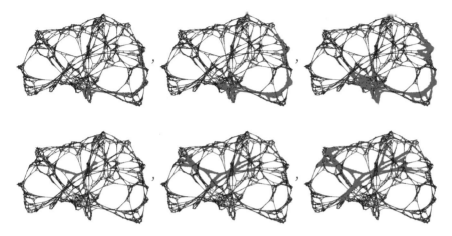

In the limit of a large number of steps, we can measure the volumes of tubes like these to compute approximations to projections of the Ricci tensor—and for example determine the level of isotropy of the emergent geometry of our models.

4.16 Functions on Graphs

Traditional Riemannian manifolds are full of structure that our hypergraphs do not have. Nevertheless, we are beginning to see that there are analogs of many ideas from geometry and calculus on manifolds that can be applied to our hypergraphs—at least in some appropriate limit as they become sufficiently large.

To continue the analogy, consider trying to define a function on a hypergraph. For a scalar function, we might just assign a value to each node of the hypergraph. And if we want the function to be somehow smooth, we should make sure that nearby nodes are assigned similar values.

But what about a vector function? An obvious approach is just to assign values to each directed edge of the hypergraph. And given this, we can find the component in a direction corresponding to a particular geodesic just by averaging over all edges of the hypergraph along that geodesic. (To recover results for continuous spaces, we must take all sorts of potentially intricate limits.)

(At a slightly more formal mathematical level, to define vectors in our system, we need some analog of a tangent space. On manifolds, the tangent space at a point can be defined in terms of the equivalence class of geodesics passing through that point. In our systems, the obvious analog is to look at the edges around a point, which are exactly what any geodesic through that point must traverse.)

For a rank-p tensor function, we can assign values to p edges associated either with a single node, or with a neighborhood of nearby nodes. And, once again, we can compute "projections" of the tensor in particular "directions" by averaging values along p geodesics.

The gradient of a scalar function ∇f at a particular point X can be defined by starting at X and seeing along what geodesic the (suitably averaged) values decrease fastest, and at what rate. The results of this can then be assigned to the edges along the geodesic so as to specify a vector function.

The divergence of a vector function $\nabla . \vec{f}$ can be defined by looking at a ball in the hypergraph, and asking for the total of the values of the function on all hyperedges in the ball. The analog of Gauss's theorem then becomes a fairly straightforward "continuity equation" statement about sums of values on edges inside and at the surface of part of a hypergraph.

4.17 Manifolds and Model Spaces

We saw above a rule which generates a sequence of hypergraphs like this:

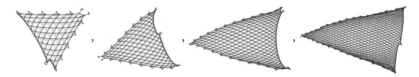

We can think of this after an infinite number of steps as giving an infinitely fine mesh—or in effect a structure which limits to a two-dimensional manifold. In standard mathematics, the defining feature of a manifold is that it is locally like Euclidean space (in some number of dimensions d) [45]. By using Euclidean space as a model many things can be defined and computed about manifolds (e.g. [26]).

Some of our models here yield emergent geometry whose limit is an ordinary manifold. But the question arises of what mathematical structures might be appropriate for describing the limiting behavior of other cases. Is there perhaps some other kind of model space whose properties can be transferred?

It is tempting to try to start from Euclidean space (or $\mathbb{R}^n$), and define some subset such as a Cantor set. But it seems more likely to be fruitful to start from convenient discrete structures, and see how their limits might correspond to what we have. One important feature of Euclidean space is its uniformity: every point is in a sense like every other, even if different points can be labeled by different coordinates.

So this suggests that by analogy we could consider graphs (and hypergraphs) whose vertices all have the same graph neighborhood (vertex transitive graphs). Several obvious infinite examples are the limits of:

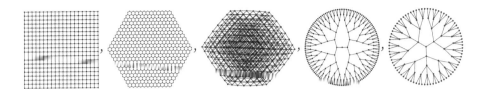

Any uniform tessellation or regular tree provides an example. One might think that another example would be graphs formed by uniform application of a vertex substitution rule—such as "spherical Sierpiński graphs" starting from a tetrahedron, dodecahedron or buckyball graph:

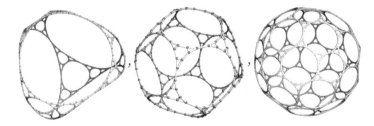

But (as mentioned in 4.8) in these graphs not every vertex has exactly the same neighborhood, at least if one goes beyond geodesic distance 2. The number of distinct neighborhoods does, however, grow fairly slowly, suggesting that it may be possible to consider such graphs "quasi vertex transitive" (in rough analogy to quasiconformal).

But one important class of graphs that are precisely vertex transitive are Cayley graphs of groups—and indeed the infinite tessellation and tree graphs above are all examples of these. (Note that not all vertex-transitive graphs are Cayley graphs; the Petersen graph is an example [46]. It is also known that there are infinite vertex-transitive graphs that are not Cayley graphs [47], and are not even "close" to any such graphs [48].)

In a Cayley graph for a group, each node represents an element of the group, and each edge is labeled with a generator of the group. (Different presentations of the group—with different choices of generators and relations—can have slightly different Cayley graphs, but their infinite limits can be considered the same.) Each point in the Cayley graph can then be labeled (typically not uniquely) by a word in the group, specified as a product of generators of the group.

One can imagine progressively building up a Cayley graph by looking at longer and longer words. In the case of a free group with two generators A and B, this yields:

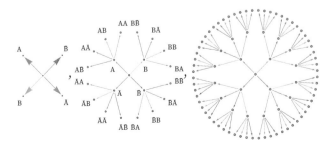

If one adds the relation AB = BA, defining an Abelian group, the Cayley graph is instead a grid, with "coordinates" given by the numbers of As and Bs (or their inverses):

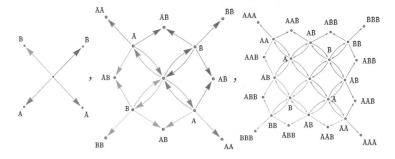

Here are the Cayley graphs for the first few symmetric and alternating (finite) groups:

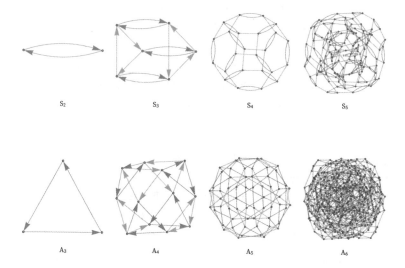

For a given infinite Cayley graph, one can compute a limiting V_r just as we have for hypergraphs. If one picks a finite number of generators and relations at random, one will usually get a Cayley graph that has a basically tree-like structure, with a V_r that grows exponentially. For nilpotent groups, however, V_r always has polynomial growth—an example being the Heisenberg group H_3 whose Cayley graph is the limit of [49]:

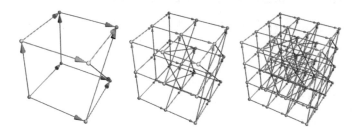

There are also groups known that yield growth intermediate between polynomial and exponential [50]. There do not, however, appear to be groups that yield fractional-power growth, corresponding to finite but fractional dimension.

It is possible that one could view the evolution of one of our models as being directly analogous to the growth of the Cayley graph for a group—or at least somehow approximated by it. As we discussed above, the hypergraphs generated by most of our systems are not, however, uniform, in the sense that the structures of the neighborhoods around different points in the hypergraph can be different. But this does not mean that a Cayley graph could not provide a good (at least approximate) local model for a part of the hypergraph. And if this connection could be made, there might be useful results from modern geometric group theory that could be applied, for example in classifying different kinds of limiting behaviors of our systems.

On a sufficiently small scale, any manifold is defined to be like Euclidean space. But if one goes to a slightly larger scale, one needs to represent deviations from Euclidean space. And a convenient way to do this is again to consider model spaces. The most obvious is a sphere (or in general a hyperellipsoid)—and this is what gives the notion of curvature. Quite what the appropriate analog even of this is in fractional dimensional space is not clear, but it would potentially be useful in studying our systems. And when there is a possibility for change in dimension as well as change in curvature, the situation is even less clear.

5 | The Updating Process for String Substitution Systems

5.1 String Substitution Systems

The basic concept of our models is to define rules for updating collections of relations. But for a particular collection of relations, there are often multiple ways in which a given rule can be applied, and there is considerable subtlety in the question of what effects different choices can have.

To begin exploring this, we will first consider in this section the somewhat simpler case of string substitution systems (e.g. [1:3.5][51]). String substitution systems have arisen in many different settings under many different names [1:p893], but in all cases they involve strings whose elements are repeatedly replaced according to fixed substitution rules.

As a simple example, consider the string substitution system with rules {A → AB, B → BA}. Starting with A and repeatedly applying these rules wherever possible gives a sequence of results beginning with:

{A, AB, ABBA, ABBABAAB, ABBABAABBAABABBA,
ABBABAABBAABABBABAABABBAABBABAAB}

The application of these particular rules is simple and unambiguous. At each step, every occurrence of A or B is independently replaced, in a way that does not depend on its neighbors. One can visualize the process as a tree:

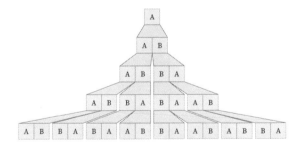

At step n, there are 2^n elements, and the kth element is determined by whether the number of 1s in the base-2 decomposition of k is even or odd. (This particular case corresponds to the Thue–Morse sequence.)

The evolution of the string substitution system can still be represented by a tree even if the replacements are not the same length. The rules {A → B, B → AB} yield the "Fibonacci tree":

In this case, the number of elements on the tth step is the tth Fibonacci number. For any neighbor-independent substitution system, the number of elements on the nth step is determined by a linear recurrence, and usually, but not always, grows exponentially. (Equivalently, the number of elements of each type on the nth step can be determined from the nth power of the transition matrix.)

But consider now a substitution system with rules {A → BBB, BB → A}. If one starts with A, the first step is unambiguous: just replace A by BBB. But now there are two possible replacements for BBB: either replace the first BB to get AB, or replace the second one to get BA.

We can represent all the different possibilities as a multiway system [1:5.6] in which there can be multiple outcomes at each step, and there are multiple possible paths of evolution (here shown over the course of 5 steps):

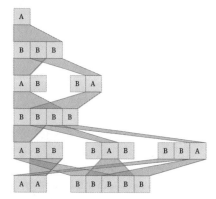

We can represent the possible paths of 5 steps of evolution between states of the system by a graph:

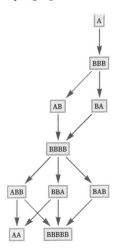

In effect each path through this graph represents a different possible history for the system, based on applying a different sequence of possible updates.

By adding something extra to our model, we can of course force a particular history. For example, we could consider sequential substitution systems (analogous to search-and-replace in a text editor) in which we always do only the first possible replacement in a left-to-right scan of the state reached at each step. With this setup we get the following history for the system shown above:

{A, BBB, AB, BBBB, ABB, BBBBB, ABBB, BBBBBB, ABBBB, BBBBBBB, ABBBBB}

An alternative strategy (analogous, for example, to the operation of **StringReplace** in the Wolfram Language) is to scan from left to right, but rather than just doing the first possible replacement at each step, instead keep scanning after the first replacement, and also carry out every subsequent replacement that can independently be done. With this "maximum scan" strategy, the sequence of states reached in the example above becomes:

{A, BBB, AB, BBBB, AA, BBBBBB, AAA, BBBBBBBBB, AAAAB, BBBBBBBBBBBBB, AAAAAAB}

(The first deviation occurs at BBBB. After replacing the first BB, the maximum scan strategy can continue and replace the second BB as well, thereby in effect "skipping a step" in the multiway evolution graph shown above.)

Note that in both the strategies just described, the evolution obtained can depend on the order in which different replacements are stated in the rule. With the rule {BB → A, A → BBB} instead of {A → BBB, BB → A}, the sequential substitution system updating scheme yields:

{A, BBB, AB, BBBB, ABB, AA, BBBA, ABA, BBBBA, ABBA, AAA}

instead of:

{A, BBB, AB, BBBB, ABB, BBBBB, ABBB, BBBBBB, ABBBB, BBBBBBB, ABBBBB}

Given a particular multiway system, one can ask whether it can ever generate a given string. In other words, does there exist any sequence of replacements that leads to a given string? In the case of {A → BBB, BB → Λ}, starting from A, the strings B and BB cannot be generated, though with this particular rule, all other strings eventually can be generated (it takes $5(k-1)$ steps to get all 2^k strings of length k).

One of the applications of multiway systems is as an idealization of derivations in equational logic [1:p777], in which the rules of the multiway system correspond to axioms that define transformations between equivalent expressions in the logical system. Starting from a state corresponding to a particular expression, the states generated by the multiway system are expressions that are ultimately equivalent to the original expression. The paths in the multiway system are then chains of transformations that represent proofs of equivalences between expressions—and the problem of whether a particular equivalence between expression holds is reduced to the (still potentially very difficult) problem of determining whether there is a path in the multiway system that connects the states corresponding to these expressions.

Thus, for example, with the transformations {A → BBB, BB → A}, it is possible to see that A can be transformed to AAA, but the path required is 10 steps long:

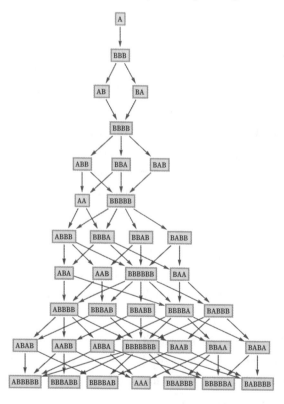

In general, there is no upper bound on how long a path may be required to reach a particular string in a multiway system, and the question of whether a given string can ever be reached is in general undecidable [52][53][1:p778].

5.2 The Phenomenon of Causal Invariance

Consider the rule {BA → AB}, starting from BABABA:

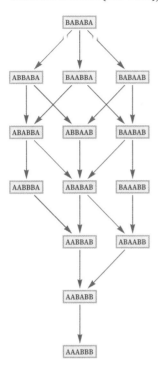

As before, there are different possible paths through this graph, corresponding to different possible histories for the system. But now all these paths converge to a single final state. And in this particular case, there is a simple interpretation: the rule is effectively sorting As in front of Bs by repeatedly doing the transposition BA → AB. And while there are multiple different possible sequences of transpositions that can be used, all of them eventually lead to the same answer: the sorted state AAABBB.

There are many practical examples of systems that behave in this kind of way, allowing operations to be carried out in different orders, generating different intermediate states, while always leading to the same final answer. Evaluation or simplification of (parenthesized) arithmetic (e.g. [54]), algebraic or Boolean expressions are examples, as is lambda function evaluation [55].

Many substitution systems, however, do not have this property. For example, consider the rule {AB → AA, AB → BA}, again starting from BABABA. Like the sorting rule, after a limited number of steps this rule gets into a final state that no longer changes. But unlike the sorting rule, it does not have a unique final state. Depending on what path is taken, it goes in this case to one of three possible final states:

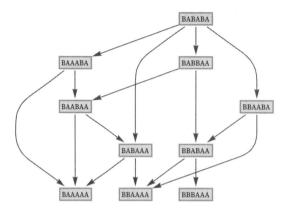

But what about systems that do not "terminate" at particular final states? Is there some way to define a notion of "path independence" [55]—or what we will call "causal invariance" [1:9.10]—for these?

Consider again the rule {A → BBB, BB → A} that we discussed above:

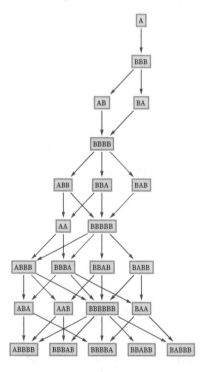

The state BBB at step 2 has two possible successors: AB and BA. But after another step, AB and BA converge again to the state BBBB. And in fact the same kind of thing happens throughout the graph: every time two paths diverge, they always reconverge after just one more step. This means that the graph in effect consists of a collection of "diamonds" of edges [56]:

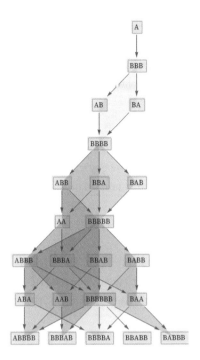

There is no need, however, for reconvergence to happen in just one step. Consider for example the rule {A → AA, AA → AB}:

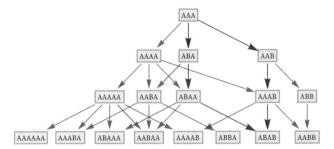

As the picture indicates, there are paths from AAA leading to both ABA and AAB—but these only reconverge again (to ABAB) after two more steps. (In general, it can take an arbitrary number of steps for reconvergence to occur.)

Whether a system is causal invariant may depend on its initial conditions. Consider, for example, the rule AA → AAB. With initial condition AABAA the rule is causal invariant, but with initial condition AAA it is not

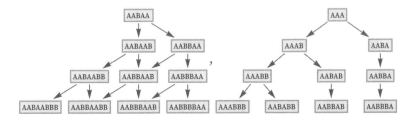

When a system is causal invariant for all possible initial conditions, we will say that it is totally causally invariant. (This is essentially the confluence property discussed in the theory of term-rewriting systems.) Later, we will discuss how to systematically test for causal invariance—and we will see that it is often easier to test for total causal invariance than for causal invariance for specific initial conditions.

Causal invariance may at first seem like a rather obscure property. But in the context of our models, we will see in what follows that it may in fact be the key to a remarkable range of fundamental features of physics, including relativistic invariance, general covariance, and local gauge invariance, as well as the possibility of objective reality in quantum mechanics.

5.3 States Graphs

If there are multiple successors to a particular state in a substitution system one thing to do would be just to assume that each of these successors is a new, unique state. The result of this will always be to produce a tree of states, here shown for the rule {A → BBB, BB → A}:

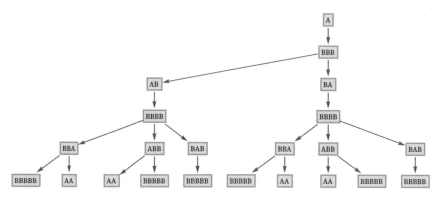

But in our construction of multiway systems, we assume that actually the states produced are not all unique, and instead that states at a given step consisting of the same string can be merged, thereby reducing the tree above to the directed graph:

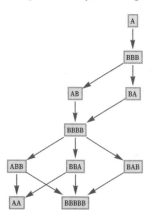

But if we are going to merge identical states, why do so only at a given step? Why not merge identical states whenever they occur in the evolution of the system? After all, given the setup, a particular state—wherever it occurs—will always evolve in the same way, so in some sense it is redundant to show it multiple times.

The particular rule {A → BBB, BB → A} that we have just used as an example has the special feature that it always "makes progress" and never repeats itself—with the result that a given string only ever appears once in its evolution. Most rules, however, do not have this property.

Consider for example the rule {AB → BAB, BA → A}. Starting from ABA, here is our normal "evolution graph":

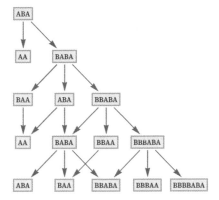

Notice that in this evolution even the original state ABA appears again, both at step 3 and at step 5—and each time it appears, it necessarily makes a complete repeat of the same evolution graph. To remove this redundancy, we can make a graph in which we effectively merge all instances of a given state, so that we show each state only once, connecting it to whatever states it evolves to under the rule:

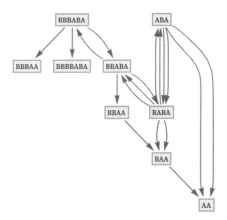

But in this graph there are, for example, two connections from ABA to BABA, because this transformation happens twice in the 4 steps of evolution that we are considering. But in a sense this multiplicity again always gives redundant information, so in what we will call our "states graph" [1:p209], we only ever keep one connection between any given pair of states, so that in this case we get:

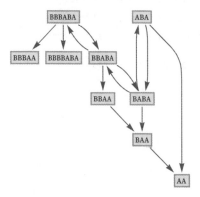

There is one further subtlety in the construction of a states graph. The graph only records which state can be transformed into which other: it does not record how many different replacements could be applied to achieve this. In the rule we just showed, it is never possible to have different replacements on a single string yield the same result.

Consider the rule {A → AA, A → B} starting with AA. There are, for example, two different ways that this rule can be applied to AA to get AAA:

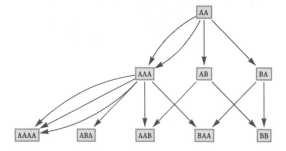

In our standard states graph, however, we show only that AA is transformed to AAA, and we do not record how many different possible replacements can achieve this:

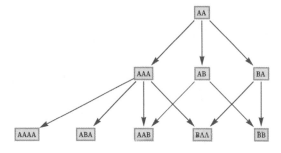

The degree of compression achieved in going from evolution graphs to states graphs can be quite dramatic. For example, for the rule {BA → AB, AB → BA} the evolution graph is

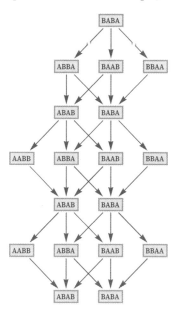

and the states graph is

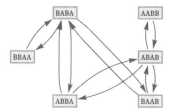

or in our standard rendering:

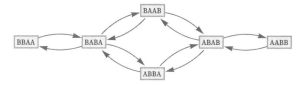

Note that causal invariance works the same in states graphs as it does in evolution graphs: if a rule is causal invariant, any two paths that diverge must eventually reconverge.

5.4 Typical Multiway Graph Structures

Before considering further features of the updating process, it is helpful to discuss the typical kinds of multiway graphs that are generated from string substitution systems. Much as for our primary models based on general relations (hypergraphs), we can assign signatures to string substitution system rules based on the lengths of the strings in each transformation. For example, we will say that the rule {A → BBB, BB → A} has signature 2: 1→3, 2→1, where the initial 2 indicates the number of distinct possible elements (here A and B) that occur in the rule.

With a signature of the form k: $n_1 \to n_2$, $n_3 \to n_4$, ... there are nominally $k^{\sum n_i}$ possible rules. However, many of these rules are equivalent under renaming of elements or reversal of strings. Taking this into account, the number of inequivalent possible rules for various cases is:

	$k{=}2$	$k{=}3$	$k{=}4$
1 → 1	2	2	2
1 → 2	3	4	4
1 → 3	6	10	11
2 → 2	6	10	11
1 → 1, 1 → 1	8	14	15
1 → 4	10	25	31
2 → 3	10	25	31
1 → 1, 1 → 2	12	28	35
1 → 5	20	70	107
2 → 4	20	70	107
3 → 3	20	70	107
1 → 1, 1 → 3	24	82	123
1 → 1, 2 → 2	20	70	107
1 → 2, 1 → 2	20	70	107
1 → 2, 2 → 1	20	70	107
1 → 1, 1 → 1, 1 → 1	32	122	187

	$k{=}2$	$k{=}3$	$k{=}4$
1 → 6	36	196	379
2 → 5	36	196	379
3 → 4	36	196	379
1 → 1, 1 → 4	40	205	395
1 → 1, 2 → 3	40	205	395
1 → 2, 1 → 3	40	205	395
1 → 2, 3 → 1	40	205	395
1 → 3, 2 → 1	40	205	395
1 → 2, 2 → 2	36	196	379
1 → 1, 1 → 1, 1 → 2	48	244	459
1 → 7	72	574	1451
2 → 6	72	574	1451
3 → 5	72	574	1451
1 → 1, 1 → 5	80	610	1515
4 → 4	72	574	1451
1 → 1, 2 → 4	72	574	1451

	$k{=}2$	$k{=}3$	$k{=}4$
1 → 2, 1 → 4	72	574	1451
1 → 2, 4 → 1	72	574	1451
1 → 4, 2 → 1	72	574	1451
1 → 1, 3 → 3	80	610	1515
1 → 3, 1 → 3	80	610	1515
1 → 3, 3 → 1	80	610	1515
1 → 2, 2 → 3	72	574	1451
1 → 2, 3 → 2	72	574	1451
1 → 3, 2 → 2	72	574	1451
2 → 1, 2 → 3	72	574	1451
1 → 1, 1 → 1, 1 → 3	96	730	1771
2 → 2, 2 → 2	72	574	1451
1 → 1, 1 → 1, 2 → 2	80	610	1515
1 → 1, 1 → 2, 1 → 2	80	610	1515
1 → 1, 1 → 2, 2 → 1	80	610	1515
1 → 1, 1 → 1, 1 → 1, 1 → 1	128	1094	2795

Rules with signature k: 1→n must always be totally causal invariant. If they are started from strings of length 1, their states graphs can never branch. However, with strings of length more than 1, branching can (but may not) occur, as in this example of A → AB started from three strings of length 2:

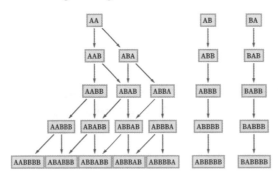

With initial conditions AAA and AAAA, this rule produces the following states graphs:

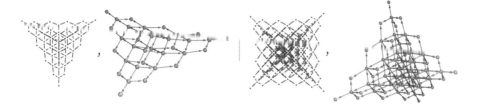

Even the rule A → AA can produce states graphs like these if it has initial conditions that contain Bs as "separators":

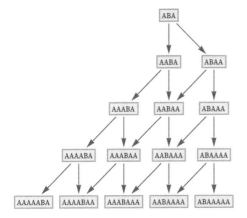

And as a seemingly even more trivial example, the rule A → B with an initial condition containing n As gives a states graph corresponding to an n-dimensional cube (with a total of 2^n nodes):

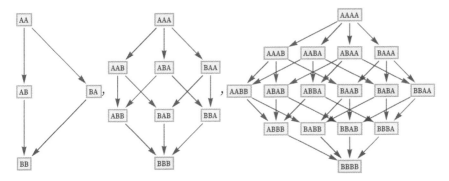

With multiple rules, one can get tree-like structures, with exponentially increasing numbers of states. The simplest case is the 2: 0→1, 0→1 rule { → A, → B} starting with the null string:

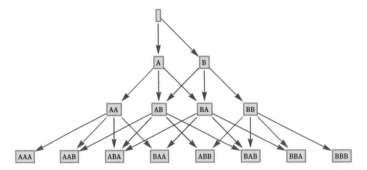

With multiple rules, even with single-symbol left-hand sides, causal invariance is no longer guaranteed. Of the 8 inequivalent 2: 1→1, 1→1 rules, all are totally causal invariant, although the rule {A → B, B → A} achieves this through cyclic behavior:

Among the 14 inequivalent 3: 1→1, 1→1 rules, all but two are totally causal invariant. The exceptions are the cyclic rule, and also the rule {A → B, A → C}, which in effect terminates before its B and C branches can reconverge:

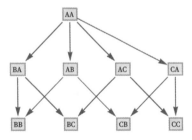

The 12 inequivalent 2: 1→2, 1→1 rules yield the following states graphs when run for 4 steps starting from all possible length-3 strings of As and Bs:

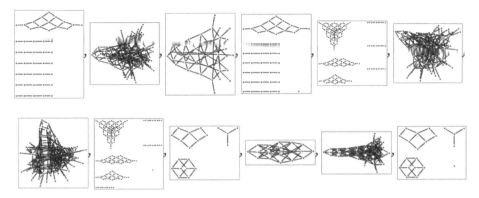

All but three of these rules are totally causal invariant. Among causal invariant ones are:

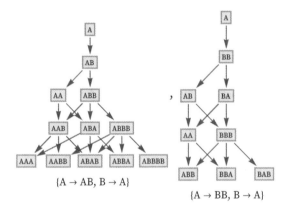

$\{A \to AB, B \to A\}$

$\{A \to BB, B \to A\}$

After more steps these yield:

Examples of non-causal invariant 2: 1→2, 1→1 rules are:

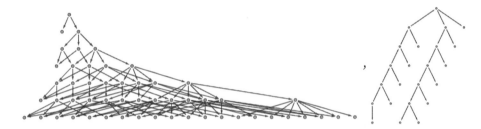

$\{A \to AA, A \to B\}$, $\{A \to AB, A \to B\}$

After more steps these yield:

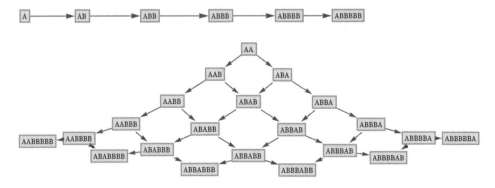

,

When we look at rules with larger signatures, the vast majority at least superficially show the same kinds of behavior that we have already seen.

Like for the hypergraphs from our models that we considered in previous sections, we can study the limiting structure of states graphs generated in multiway systems, and see what emergent geometry they may have. And in analogy to $V_r(X)$ for hypergraphs, we can define a quantity $M_t(S)$ which specifies the total number of distinct states reached in the multiway system after t steps of evolution starting from a state S.

For the rule $\{A \to AB\}$ mentioned above, the geometry of the multiway graph obtained by starting from n As is effectively a regular n-dimensional grid:

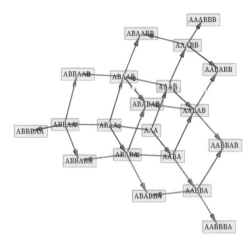

$M_t(A^n)$ in this case is then an n-fold nested sum of t 1s:

$$M_t(A^n) = \prod_{k=0}^{n-1} \frac{(t-k)}{n!} \sim \frac{t^n}{n!}\left(1 - \binom{n}{2}\frac{n}{t} + \ldots\right)$$

Some rules create states graphs that are trees, with $M_t \sim m^t$. Other rules do not explicitly give trees, but still give exponentially increasing M_t. An example is $\{A \to AB, B \to A\}$, for which M_t is a sum of Fibonacci numbers, and successive states graphs can be rendered as:

Note that rules with both polynomial and exponential growth in M_t can exhibit causal invariance.

It is not uncommon to find rules with fairly long transients. A simple example is the totally causal invariant rule $\{A \to BBB, BBBB \to A\}$. When started from n As this stabilizes after $7n$ steps, with $\sim 2.8^n$ states, with a states graph like:

Rules typically seem to have either asymptotically exponential or asymptotically polynomial M_t. (This may have some analogy with what is seen in the growth of groups [57][58][22].) Among rules with polynomial growth, it is typical to see fairly regular grid-like structures. An example is the rule

$\{AB \to A, ABA \to BBAABB\}$

which from initial condition ABAA gives states graph:

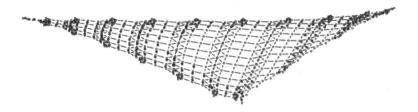

With the slightly different initial condition ABAAA, the states graph has a more elaborate structure

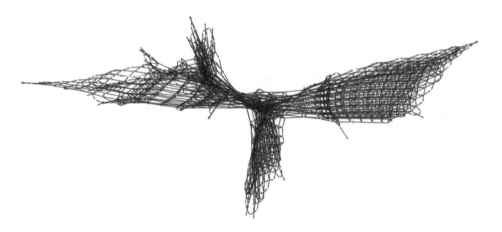

and the form of M_t is more complicated (though $\sim t^2$ and ultimately quasiperiodic); the second differences of M_t in this case are:

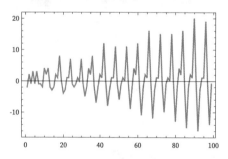

Another example of a somewhat complex structure occurs in the rule

{ABA → BBAA, BAA → AAB}

that was discussed in [1:p 205]. Starting from BABBAAB it gives the states graph:

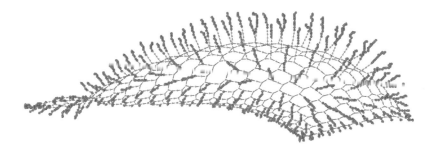

5.5 Testing for Causal Invariance

Causal invariance implies that regardless of the order in which updates are made, it is always possible to get to the same outcome. One way this can happen is if different updates can never interfere with each other. Consider the rule {A → AA, B → BB}. Every time one sees an A, it can be "doubled", and similarly with a B. But these doublings can happen independently, in any order. Looking at an evolution graph for this rule we see that at each state there can be an "A replacement" applied, or a "B replacement". There are two branches of evolution depending on which replacement is chosen, but one can always eventually reach the same outcome, regardless of which choice was made—and as a result the rule is causal invariant:

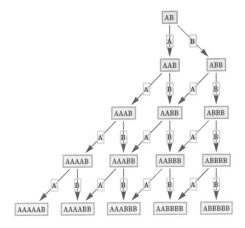

The replacements A → AA and B → BB trivially cannot interfere because their left-hand sides involve different elements. But a more general way to guarantee that interference cannot occur is for the left-hand sides of replacements not to be able to overlap with each other—or with themselves.

In general, the set of strings of As and Bs up to length 5 that do not overlap themselves are (up to A,B interchange and reversal): [1:p1033][59]

{A, AB, AAB, AAAB, AABB, AAAAB, AAABB, AABAB}

These can be formed into pairs in the following ways:

{{A, B}, {AABAB, AABB}, {AABB, ABABB}, {AAABB, AABAB}, {AAABB, ABABB}}

The first triples with no overlaps are of length 6. An example is {AAABB, ABAABB, ABABB}. And whenever there is a set of strings with no overlaps being used as the left-hand side of replacements, one is guaranteed to have a system that is totally causal invariant.

It is also perfectly possible for the right-hand sides of rules to be such that the system is totally causal invariant even though their left-hand sides overlap. An example is the simple rule {A → AA, AA → A}:

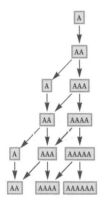

At every branch point in a multiway system, one can identify all pairs of strings that can be generated. We will call such pairs of strings branch pairs (they are often called "critical pairs" [60]). And the question of whether a system is causal invariant is then equivalent to the question of whether all branch pairs that can be generated will eventually resolve, in the sense that there is a common successor for both members of the pair [61][62][63][64].

Consider for example the rule {A → AB, B → A}:

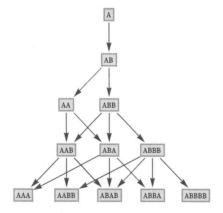

After two steps, a branch pair appears: {AA, ABB}. But after just one more step it resolves. However, two more branch pairs are generated: {AAB, ABA} and {ABA, ABBB}. But after another step, these also resolve. And in fact in this system all branch pairs that are ever generated resolve (actually always in just one step), and so the system is causal invariant.

In general, it can, however, take more than one step for a branch pair to resolve. The simplest case involving resolution after two steps involves the rule:

{A → B, AB → AA}

The state AB generates the branch pair {BB, AA}:

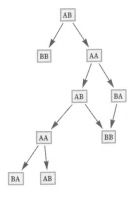

In the evolution graph, we do not see a resolution of this branch pair. But looking at the states graph, we see that the branch pair does indeed resolve in two steps, though with BB being a terminating state:

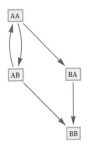

The same kind of thing can also happen without a terminating state. Consider for example

{A → AA, AB → BA}

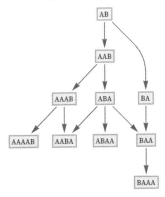

where the branch pair {AAB, BA} takes 2 steps to resolve.

In the rule

{A → AA, AAB → BA}

it takes 3 steps for the branch pair {AAAB, BA} to resolve:

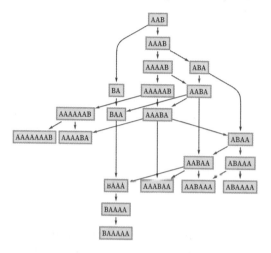

Things can get quite complicated even with simple rules. For example, in the rule

{A → AA, AA → BAB}

the branch pair {AAA, BAB} resolves after 4 steps. The following is essentially a proof of this:

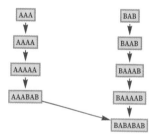

But finding this in the 67-node 4-step states graph is quite complicated:

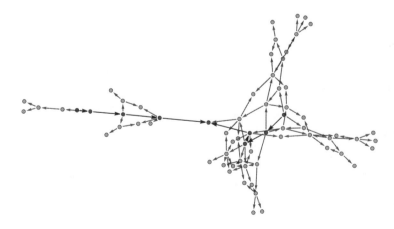

In the rule

{A → AAB, ABBA → A}

it takes 7 steps for the branch pair

{A, AABBBA}

to resolve to the common successor AAAABBBAAB. The 7-step states graph involved has 5869 nodes, and the proof that the branch pair resolves is:

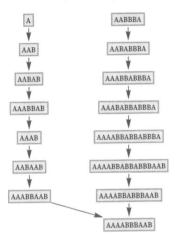

In general, there is no upper bound on how long it may take a branch pair to resolve, or for example how long its common successor—or intermediate strings involved in reaching it— may be. Here are the simplest rules with two distinct elements that take successively longer to resolve (the last column gives the size of the states graph when resolution is found):

1	{A → A}	A → {A, A} → A	2
2	{A → B, AB → AA}	AB → {BB, AA} → BB	5
3	{A → AA, A → BAB}	A → {AA, BAB} → BABABAB	22
4	{A → AA, A → BAAB}	A → {AA, BAAB} → BAABAABAAB	121
5	{A → AA, A → BAABB}	A → {AA, BAABB} → BAABBAABBAABBABB	515
6	{A → AAB, ABAA → A}	ABAA → {AABBAA, A} → AABBAABB	1664
7	{A → AAB, ABBA → A}	ABBA → {AABBBA, A} → AAAABBBAAB	2401
8	{A → AA, AA → BABBB}	AA → {AAA, BABBB} → BABBBABBBABBBBBBBBB	759
9	{A → B, BB → A, AAAA → B}	AAAA → {BAAA, B} → B	30
10	{A → AA, AA → BABBBB}	AA → {AAA, BABBBB} → BABBBBABBBBABBBBBBBBBBBBBBBB	4020
11	{A → AA, AAA → BABBB}	AAA → {AAAA, BABBB} → BABBBABBBABBBBBBBBBB	2294
12	{A → AA, AA → B, BBBB → A}	AA → {AAA, B} → B	405
13	{A → B, BB → A, AAAAAB → A}	AAAAAB → {BAAAAB, A} → A	94
14	{A → AB, BAA → A, BBB → A}	BBBAA → {AAA, BBA} → AA	2698
15	{A → AA, BBB → A, AAAA → B}	AAAA → {AAAAA, B} → B	430
16	{A → AA, AAA → B, BBBB → A}	AAA → {AAAA, B} → B	906

Note that—like the first case of a 2-step resolution that we showed above—quite a few of these longest-to-resolve rules actually terminate, with a member of the branch pair being their final output. Thus, for example, the last case listed is really just a reflection of the fact that with this rule, AAAA takes 16 steps to reach the termination state B:

{AAAA, AAAAA, AAAAAA, AAAAAAA, AAAAAAAA, AAAAAAAAA, AAAAAAAAAA,
AAAAAAAAAAA, AAAAAAAAAAAA, AAAAAAAAAAAAA, AAAAAAAAAAAAAA,
AAAAAAAAAAAAB, AAAAAAAABB, AAAAABBB, AABBBB, AAA, B}

(With 3 distinct elements similar results are seen; the first time a shorter example is seen is {A → BAC, A → AABA} at resolution-length 6.)

Despite the existence of long-to-resolve cases, most branch pairs in most rules in practice resolve quickly: the fraction that take τ steps seems to decrease roughly like $2^{-\tau}$. But there is still in a sense an arbitrarily long tail—and the general problem of determining whether a branch pair will resolve is known to be formally undecidable (e.g. [65]).

One interesting feature of causal invariance testing is that (while still in principle undecidable) it is in some ways easier to test for total causal invariance than to test for partial causal invariance for specific initial conditions. The reason is that if a rule is going to be totally causal invariant then there is a certain core set of branch pairs that must resolve, and if all these resolve then the rule is guaranteed to be totally causal invariant. This core set of branch pairs is derived from the possible overlaps between left-hand sides of replacements, and are the successors of the minimal "unifications" of these left-hand sides, formed by minimally overlapping the strings.

Consider the rule:

{AA → A, AB → BAA}

The only possible overlap between the left-hand sides is A. This leads to the minimal unification AAB, which yields the branch pair {ABAA, AB}:

From this branch pair we construct a states graph:

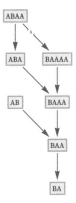

And from this we see that the branch pair resolves in 3 steps. And because this is the only branch pair that can arise through overlaps between the left-hand sides, this resolution now establishes the total causal invariance of this rule.

In the rule

{AB → BA, BAA → A}

there are two possible overlaps between the left-hand sides: A and B. These lead to two different minimal unifications: BAAB and ABAA. And these two unifications yield two branch pairs, {BABA, AB} and {BAAA, AA}. But now we can establish that both of these resolve, thus showing the total causal invariance of the original rule.

In general, one might in principle have to continue for arbitrarily many steps to determine if a given branch pair resolves. But the crucial point here is that because the number of possible overlaps (and therefore unifications) is fine, there are only a finite number of branch pairs one needs to consider in order to determine if a rule is totally causal invariant. There is no need to look at branch pairs that arise from larger strings than the unifications; any additional elements are basically just "padding" that cannot affect the basic interference between replacements that leads to a breakdown of causal invariance.

Looking at branch pairs from all possible unifications is a way to determine total causal invariance—and thus to determine whether a rule will be causal invariant from all possible initial conditions. But even if a rule is not totally causal invariant, it may still be causal invariant for particular initial conditions—effectively because whatever branch pairs might break causal invariance simply never occur in evolution from those initial conditions.

In practice, it is fairly common to have rules that are causal invariant for some initial conditions, but not others. In effect, there is some "conservation law" that keeps the rule away from branch pairs that would break causal invariance—and that keeps the rule operating with some subset of its possible states that happen to yield causal invariance.

5.6 The Frequency of Causal Invariance

The plots below show the fractions of rules found to be totally causal invariant [66], as a function of the total number of elements they involve, for the cases of $k = 2$ (A, B) and $k = 3$ (A, B, C):

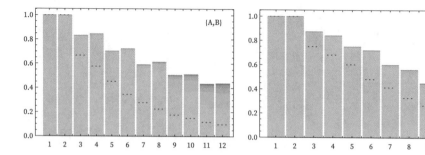

The darker colors indicate larger numbers of steps to resolve branch pairs. (There is some uncertainty in these plots—conceivably as much as 9% for 10 total elements with $k = 3$—since in some cases the states graph became too big to compute before it could be determined whether all branch pairs resolved.)

The dotted lines indicate rules are in a sense inevitably causal invariant because their left-hand sides involve strings that do not overlap themselves or each other, thereby guaranteeing total causal invariance. Rules such as AA → AAA are causal invariant despite having overlapping left-hand sides because their right-hand sides in a sense give the same result whatever overlap occurs.

Ignoring the structure of rules, one can just ask what fraction of strings are non-overlapping [67]. Out of the total of k^n possible strings with length n containing k distinct elements the number that do not overlap themselves is given by [1:p1033]:

a[0] = 1; a[n_] := k a[n − 1] − If[EvenQ[n], a[n/2], 0]

This yields the following fractions (for the limit see e.g. [68][11:A003000]):

n	$k = 2$	$k = 3$	$k = 4$	$k = 5$
2	0.500	0.667	0.750	0.800
3	0.500	0.667	0.750	0.800
4	0.375	0.593	0.703	0.768
5	0.375	0.593	0.703	0.768
6	0.313	0.568	0.691	0.762
7	0.313	0.568	0.691	0.762
8	0.289	0.561	0.689	0.760
9	0.289	0.561	0.689	0.760
10	0.277	0.558	0.688	0.760
∞	0.268	0.557	0.688	0.760

One can also look at how many possible sets of s strings of length up to n allow no overlaps with themselves or each other [1:p1033]. The numbers and fractions for $k = 2$ are as follows:

n	$s = 1$	$s = 2$	$s = 3$	$s = 4$	$s = 5$
2	2 (0.5)	2 (0.2)	2 (0.1)	2 (0.057)	2 (0.036)
3	4 (0.5)	4 (0.11)	4 (0.033)	4 (0.012)	4 (0.0051)
4	6 (0.38)	6 (0.044)	6 (0.0074)	6 (0.0015)	6 (0.00039)
5	12 (0.38)	20 (0.038)	28 (0.0047)	36 (0.00069)	44 (0.00012)
6	20 (0.31)	54 (0.026)	104 (0.0023)	170 (0.00022)	252 (0.000024)
7	40 (0.31)	220 (0.027)	728 (0.002)	1788 (0.00015)	3672 (0.000012)
8	74 (0.29)	798 (0.024)	4806 (0.0017)	19 708 (0.00011)	62 668 (6.6×10^{-6})

To get a sense of the distribution of non-overlapping strings, one can make an array that shows which pairs of strings (ordered lexicographically) do not allow overlaps. Here are the results for $k = 2$ and $k = 3$ for strings respectively up to length 6 and length 4, showing clear structure in the space of possible strings [51]:

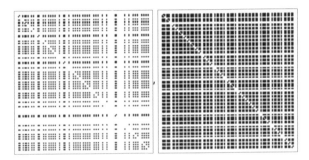

5.7 Events and Their Causal Relationships

So far the nodes in our graphs have always been states generated by substitution systems. But we can also introduce nodes to represent the "updating events" associated with replacements performed on strings. Here is the result for evolution according to the rule {AB → BAB, BA → A} starting from ABA—with each event node indicating the string replacement to which it corresponds:

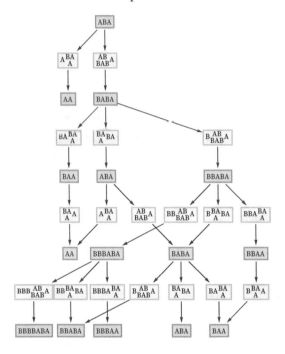

We can also show this as a states graph, where we have merged instances of the same state that occur at different steps:

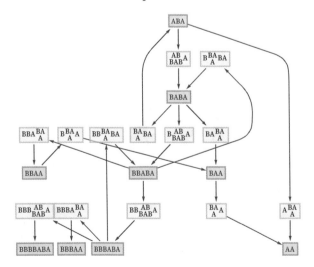

States are connected through events. But how are events connected? Given two events the key question to ask is whether they are causally related. Does one event depend on the other—in the sense that all or part of its input comes from the output of the other event?

Looking at the graph above, for example, the event $\underset{BAB}{\overset{AB}{}}A$ depends on $\overset{BA}{\underset{A}{}}BA$ because $\underset{BAB}{\overset{AB}{}}A$ uses as input the A that arises as output from $\overset{BA}{\underset{A}{}}BA$. On the other hand, $A\overset{BA}{\underset{A}{}}$ does not depend on $\overset{BA}{\underset{A}{}}BA$ because the BA it consumes was not generated by $\overset{BA}{\underset{A}{}}BA$.

We can add this dependency information to the evolution graph by putting orange lines between events that are causally related:

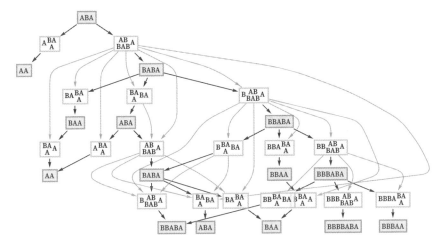

We can also do this in the states graph, in which we have merged instances of states from different steps:

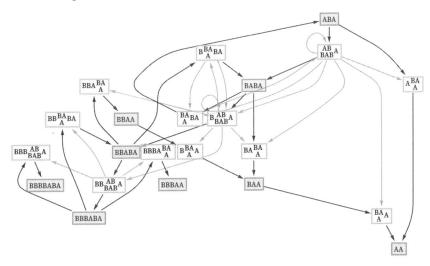

We can redraw this graph without the layering that puts the initial state at the top. We have added an "initialization event" $_{ABA}$ to indicate the creation of the initial condition:

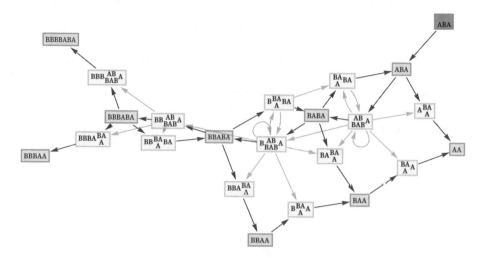

If we want to focus on causal relationships, we can now drop the state nodes altogether, and get a multiway causal graph that represents possible causal relationships between events:

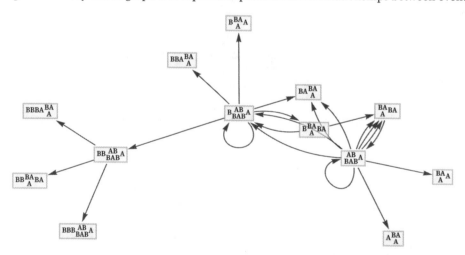

This causal graph is dual to our original evolution graph in the sense that edges in the original evolution graph correspond to events—which now become nodes in the causal graph. Similarly, each edge in the causal graph is associated with some state which appears as a node in the evolution graph.

We can get a sense of "possible causal histories" of our system by arranging the multiway causal graph in layers:

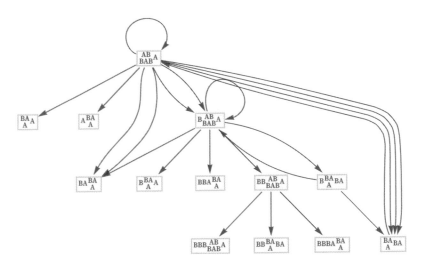

Just like every possible path through the multiway evolution graph gives a possible sequence of states that can occur in the evolution of a system, so also every possible path through the multiway causal graph gives a possible sequence of events that can occur in the evolution of the system.

After 10 steps, the graph in our example has become quite complicated:

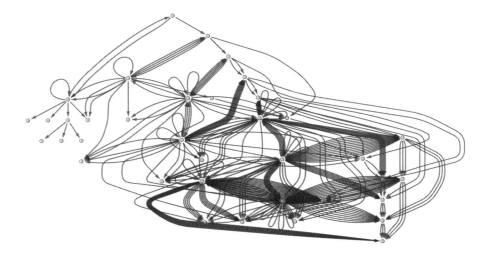

5.8 Causal Graphs for Particular Updating Sequences

The multiway causal graph that we have just constructed shows the causal relationships for all possible paths of evolution in a multiway system. But what if we just pick a single path of evolution? Instead of looking at the results for every possible updating order, let us pick a particular updating order.

For example, for the rule above we could pick "sequential updating", in which at each step, first for AB → BAB and then for BA → A, we scan the string from left to right, doing the first replacement we can [1:3.6]. This leads to a specific single path of evolution for the system (now drawn across the page):

We can show the causal relationships between the events in this evolution:

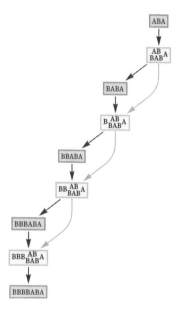

And we can generate a causal graph—which is very simple:

But now let us consider a different updating scheme, in which now as we scan the string, we try at each position both AB → BAB and BA → A, then do the first replacement we can. This procedure again leads to a specific single path of evolution, but it is a different one from before:

This particular path just involves an alternation between the states ABA and BABA, so the states graph is a cycle:

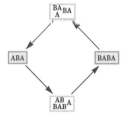

Including causal relationships here we get:

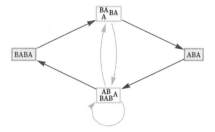

The resulting causal graph is then:

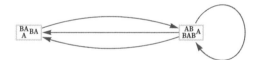

This causal graph is quite different from the one we got for the previous updating scheme. But both individual causal graphs necessarily occur in the whole multiway causal graph:

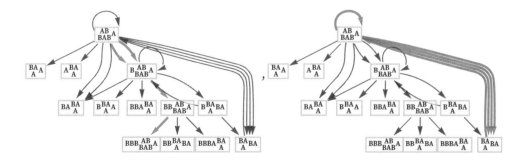

Given the multiway causal graph, we can explicitly find all possible individual causal graphs (not showing individual loop configurations separately):

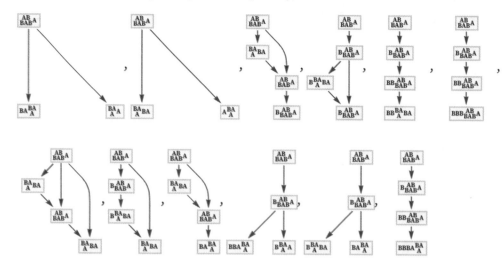

And what this shows is that at least with the particular rule we are looking at, there are many different classes of evolution paths, that can lead to distinctly different individual causal graphs—and therefore causal histories.

5.9 The Significance of Causal Invariance

One might think that all rules would work like the one we just studied, and would give different causal graphs depending on what specific path of evolution one chose, or what updating scheme one used. But a crucial fact that will be central to the potential application of our models to physics is this is not the case.

Instead, whenever a rule is causal invariant, it does not produce many different causal graphs. Instead, whatever specific path of evolution one choses, the rule always yields an exactly equivalent causal graph.

The rule we just studied is not causal invariant. But consider instead the simple causal invariant rule {BA → AB} evolving from the state BBBAA:

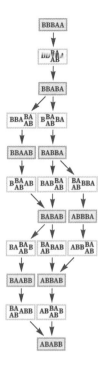

Adding in causal relationships this becomes:

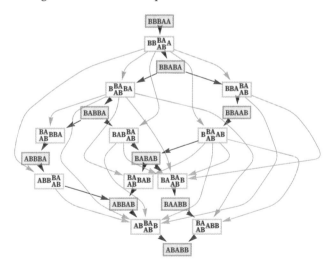

The corresponding multiway causal graph is:

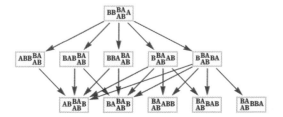

But now consider the individual causal graphs, corresponding to different possible paths of evolution. From the multiway causal graph we can extract all of these, and the result is:

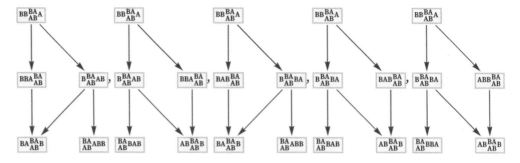

There are five different cases. But the remarkable fact is that they all correspond to isomorphic graphs. In other words. even though the specific sequence of states that the system visits is different in each case, the network of causal relationships is always exactly the same, regardless of what path is followed.

And this is a general feature of any causal invariant system. The underlying evolution rules for the system may allow many different paths of evolution—and many different sequences of states. But when the rules for the system are causal invariant, it means that the network of relationships between updating events is always the same. Depending on the particular order in which updates are done, one can see different paths of evolution; but if one looks only at event updates and their relationships, there is just one thing the system does.

Here is a slightly larger example for the rule {BA → AB} starting from BBBBAAAA. In each case a different random updating order is used, leading to a different sequence of states. But the final causal graphs representing the causal relationships between events are exactly the same:

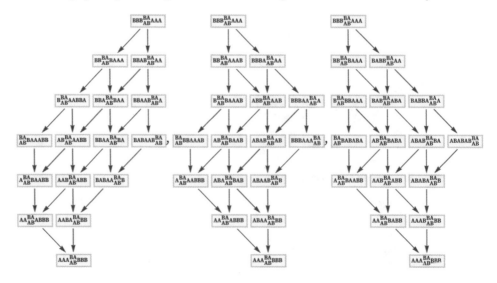

5.10 Causal Foliations and Causal Cones

We have discussed causal invariance in terms of path independence in multiway systems. But we can also explore it in terms of specific evolution histories for the underlying substitution system. Consider the rule {BA → AB}. Here is a representation of one way it can act on a particular initial string:

In a multiway system, each path represents a particular sequence of updates that occur one after another. But here in showing the action of {BA → AB} we are choosing to draw several updates on the same row. If we want, we can think of these updates as being done in sequence, but since they are all independent, it is consistent to show them as we do.

If we annotate the picture by showing causal connections between updates, we see the causal graph for the evolution—and we see that the updates we have drawn on the same row are indeed independent: they are not connected in the causal graph:

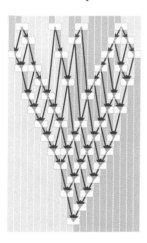

The picture above in effect uses a particular updating order. The pictures below show three possible random choices of updating orders. In each case, the final result of the evolution is the same. The intermediate steps, however, are different. But because our rule is causal invariant, the causal graph of causal relationships always has exactly the same form:

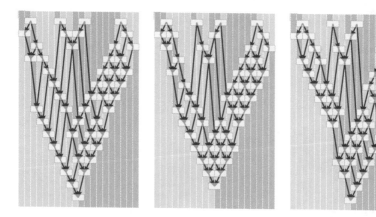

In picking updating orders there is always one constraint: no update can happen until the input for it is ready. In other words, if the input for update V comes from the output of update U, then U must already have happened before V can be done. But so long as this constraint is satisfied, we can pick whatever order of updates we want (cf. [1:9.10]).

It is sometimes convenient, however, to think in terms of "complete steps of evolution" in which all updates that could yet be done have been done. And for the particular rule we are currently discussing, we can readily do this, separating each "complete step" in the pictures below with a red line:

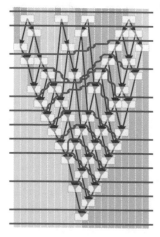

Where the red lines go depends on the update order we choose. But because of causal invariance it is always possible to draw them to delineate steps in which a collection of independent updates occur.

Each choice of how to assign updates to steps in effect defines a foliation of the evolution. We will call foliations in which the updates at each step are causally independent "causal foliations". Such causal foliations are in effect orthogonal to the connections defined by the causal graph. (In physics, the analogy is that the causal foliations are like foliations of spacetime defined by a sequence of spacelike hypersurfaces, with connections in the causal graph being timelike.)

The fact that our underlying substitutions (in this case just BA → AB) involve neighboring elements implies a certain locality to the process of evolution. The consequence of this is that we can meaningfully discuss the "spatial" spreading of causal effects. For example, consider tracing the causal connections from one event in our system:

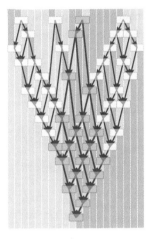

In effect there is a cone (here just two-dimensional) of elements in the system that can be affected. We will call this the causal cone for the evolution. (In physics, the analogy is a light cone.) If we pick a different updating order, the causal cone is distorted. But viewed in terms of the causal foliations, it is exactly the same:

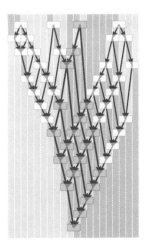

This is the result purely in terms of the causal graph:

Now let us turn things around. Imagine we have a causal graph. Then we can ask how it relates to an actual sequence of states generated by a particular path of evolution. The pictures below show how we can arrange a causal graph so that its nodes—corresponding to events—appear at positions down the page that correspond to a particular causal foliation and thus a particular path of evolution:

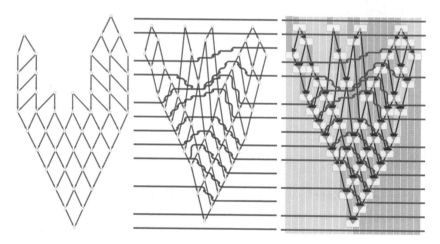

It is worth noticing that at least for the rule we are using here the intrinsic structure of the causal graph defines a convenient foliation in which successive events are simply arranged in layers:

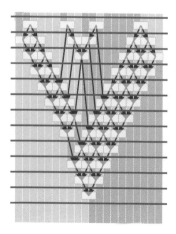

The rule BA → AB that we are using has many simplifying features. But the concepts of causal foliations and causal cones are general, and will be important in much of what follows.

As it happens, we have already implicitly seen both ideas. The "standard updating order" for our main models defines a foliation (similar, in fact, to the last one we showed here, in which in some sense "as much gets done as possible" at each step)—though the foliation is only a causal one if the rule used is causal invariant.

In addition, in 4.14 we discussed how the effect of a small change in the state in one of our models can spread on subsequent steps, and this is just like the causal cone we are discussing here.

5.11 Causal Graphs for Infinite Evolutions

One of the simplifying features of the rule BA → AB discussed in the previous subsection is that for any finite initial condition, it always evolves to a definite final state after a finite number of steps—so it is possible to construct a complete multiway causal graph for it, and for example to verify that all the causal graphs for specific paths of evolution are identical.

But consider the rule {A → BB, B → A}:

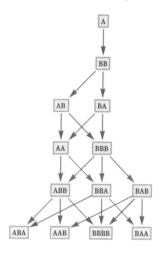

This rule is causal invariant, but never evolves to a definite state, and instead keeps growing forever. Including events in the evolution we get:

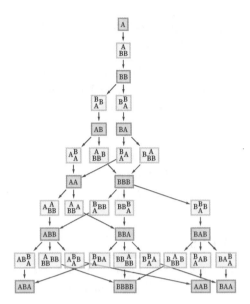

The corresponding multiway causal graph is:

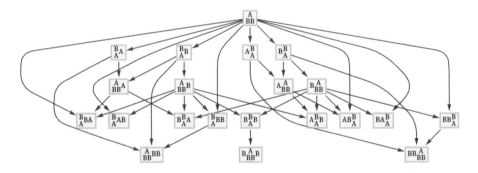

And now if we extract possible individual causal graphs from this, we get:

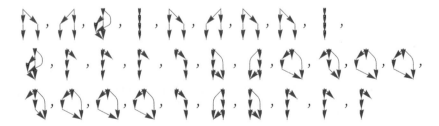

These look somewhat similar, but they are not directly equivalent. And the reason for this has to do with how we are "counting steps" in the evolution of our system. If we evolve for longer, the effect becomes progressively less important. Here are causal graphs generated by a few different randomly chosen specific sequences of updates (each corresponding to a specific path through the multiway system):

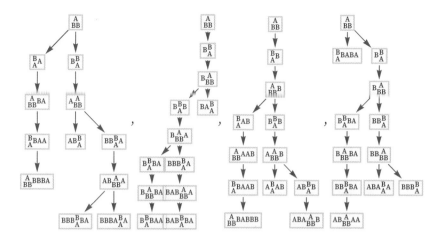

Here are the corresponding results after a few more updates:

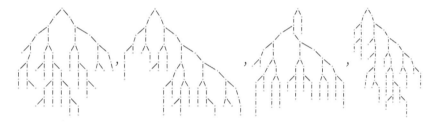

This is a different rendering:

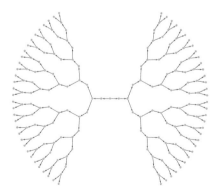

And this is what happens after many more updates (with a somewhat more systematic ordering):

If we continued for an infinite number of updates, all these would give the same result—and the same infinite causal graph, just as we expect from causal invariance. But in the particular cases we are showing, they are being cut off in different ways. And this is directly related to the causal foliations we discussed in the previous subsection.

Here are examples of evolution with specific choices of updating orders:

Adding causal graphs we get:

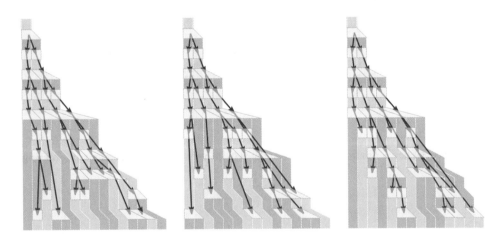

Here is what happens if we continue these for longer:

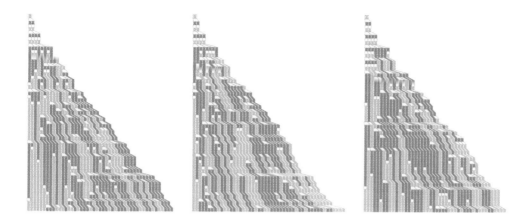

And here are the causal graphs that correspond to these evolutions:

5.12 Typical Causal Graphs

Any causal invariant system always ultimately has a unique causal graph. The graph can be found by analyzing any possible evolution for the system, with any updating scheme—though for visualization purposes, it is usually useful to use an updating scheme where as much happens as possible at each step.

The trivial causal invariant rule A → A starting from A has causal graph:

Starting from a string of 10 As it has causal graph:

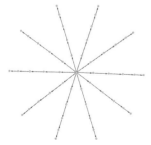

A → AA has a causal graph starting from A that is a binary tree

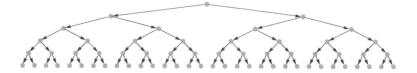

which can also be rendered:

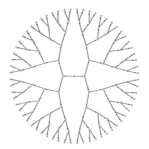

The rule

{A → A, A → AA}

starting from A gives a "two-step binary tree" with $2^{\frac{t}{2}}$ nodes at level t:

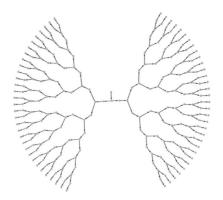

One does not have to go beyond rules involving just a single element (all of which are causal invariant) to find a range of causal graph structures. For example, here are all the forms obtained by rules allowing up to 6 instance of a single element A, with initial condition AA:

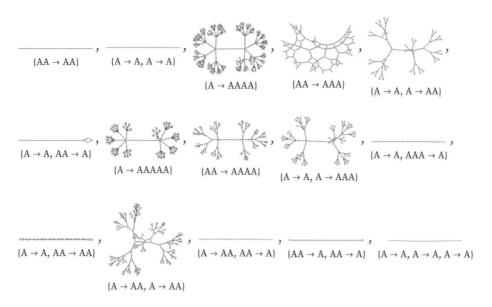

A notable case is the rule:

{AA → AAA}

Shown in layered form, the first few steps give:

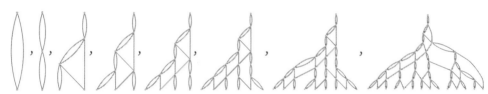

After a few more steps, this can be rendered as:

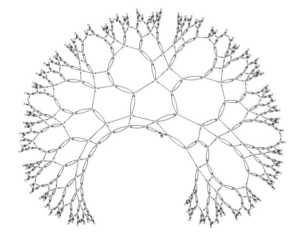

Running the underlying substitution system AA → AAA updating as much as possible at each step (the StringReplace scheme), one gets strings with successive lengths

{2, 3, 4, 6, 9, 13, 19, 28, 42, 63, 94, 141, 211, 316, 474, 711,
    1066, 1599, 2398, 3597, 5395, 8092, 12 138, 18 207, 27 310, 40 965}

which follow the recurrence:

a[1] = 2; a[n_] := If[EvenQ[n], 3 n / 2, (3 n − 1) / 2]

Other rules of the form $A^p \to A^q$ for non-commensurate p and q give similar results, analogous to tessellations in hyperbolic space:

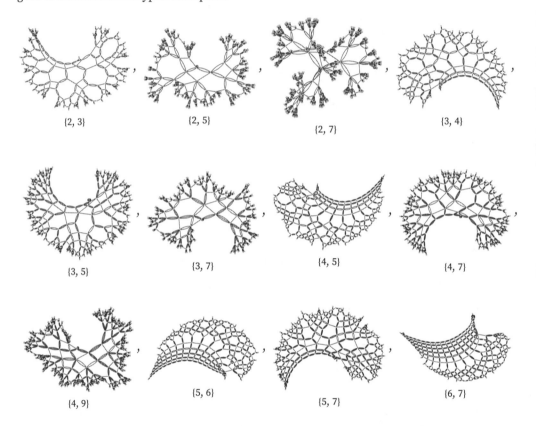

{2, 3} , {2, 5} , {2, 7} , {3, 4} ,

{3, 5} , {3, 7} , {4, 5} , {4, 7} ,

{4, 9} , {5, 6} , {5, 7} , {6, 7}

Rules that involve multiple replacements can give similar behavior even starting from a single A:

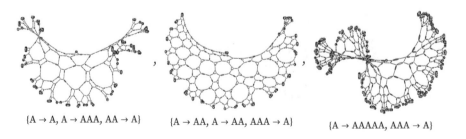

{A → A, A → AAA, AA → A} , {A → AA, A → AA, AAA → A} , {A → AAAAA, AAA → A}

Rules just containing only As cannot progressively grow to produce ordinary tilings. One can get these with the "sorting rule"

{BA → AB}

which when started with 20 BAs yields:

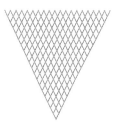

There are also rules which "grow" grid-like tilings. For example, the rule

{A → AB, BB → BB}

starting from a single A produces

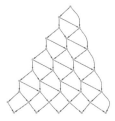

which is equivalent to a square grid:

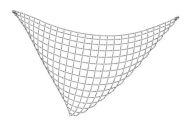

There is also a simple rule that generates essentially a hexagonal grid:

{A → B, B → AB, BA → A}

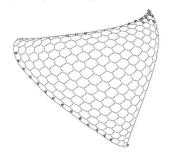

Other forms of causal graphs produced by simple causal invariant substitution systems include (starting from A, AB or ABA):

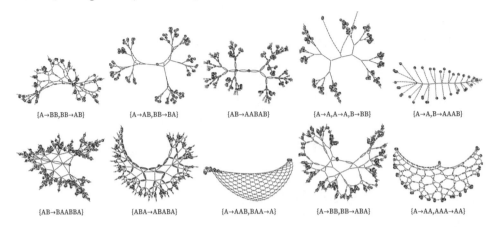

| {A→BB,BB→AB} | {A→AB,BB→BA} | {AB→AABAB} | {A→A,A→A,B→BB} | {A→A,B→AAAB} |

| {AB→BAABBA} | {ABA→ABABA} | {A→AAB,BAA→A} | {A→BB,BB→ABA} | {A→AA,AAA→AA} |

When rules terminate they yield finite causal graphs. But these can often be quite complicated. For example, the rule

{A → BBB, BBBB → A}

started from strings consisting of from 1 to 6 As yields the following finite causal graphs:

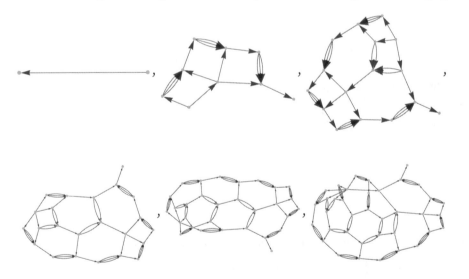

With a string of 50 As, the rule gives the finite causal graph:

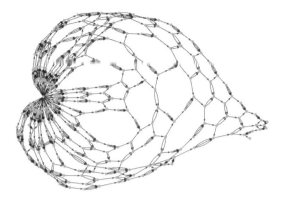

Compared to the hypergraphs we studied in previous sections, or even the multiway graphs from earlier in this section, the causal graphs here may seem to have rather simple structures. But there is a good reason for this. While there can be many updating events in the evolution of a string substitution system, all of them are in a sense arranged on the same one-dimensional structure that is the underlying string. And since the updating rules we consider involve strings of limited length, there is inevitably a linear ordering to the events along the string. This greatly simplifies the possible forms of causal graphs that can occur, for example requiring them always to remain planar. In the next section, we will see that for our hypergraph-based models—which have no simplifying underlying structure—causal graphs can be considerably more complex.

5.13 Limits of Causal Graphs

Much as we did for hypergraphs in section 4, we can consider the limiting structures of causal graphs after a large number of steps. And much as for hypergraphs, we can potentially describe these limiting structures in terms of emergent geometry. But one difference from what we did for hypergraphs is that for causal graphs, it is essential to take account of the directedness of their edges. It is still perfectly possible to have a limit that is like a manifold, but now to measure its properties we must generate the analog of cones, rather than balls.

Consider for example the simple directed grid graph:

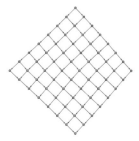

Now consider starting from a particular node, and constructing progressively larger "cones":

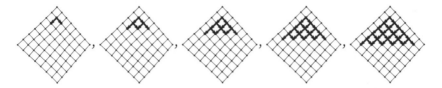

We can call the number of nodes in this cone after t steps C_t. In this case the result (for t below the diameter of the graph) is:

$$C_t = \frac{1}{2} t(1 + t)$$

And in the limit of large graphs, we will have:

$$C_t \sim t^2$$

We can also set up a 3D directed grid graph

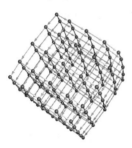

and generate a similar cone

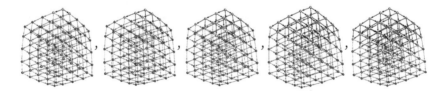

for which now $C_t \sim t^3$.

In general, we can think about the limits of these grid graphs as generating a d-dimensional "directed space". There is also nothing to prevent having cyclic versions, such as

and in general a family of graphs that are going to behave like d-dimensional directed space in the limit will have $C_t \sim t^d$.

In direct analogy to what we did with hypergraphs in section 4, we can compute C_t for causal graphs, and then estimate effective dimension by looking at its growth rate. (There are some additional subtleties, though, because whereas at any given step in the evolution of the system, V_r can be computed for any r for any point in a hypergraph, C_t can be computed only until t "reaches the edge of the causal graph" from that starting point—and later we will see that the cutoff can also depend on the foliation one uses.)

Consider the substitution system:

{A → AB, BB → BB}

This generates the causal graph:

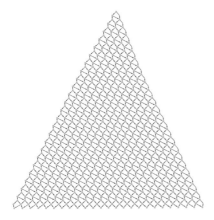

The log differences of C_t averaged over all points for causal graphs obtained from 10 through 100 steps of evolution have the form (the larger error bars for larger t in each case are the result of fewer starting points being able to contribute):

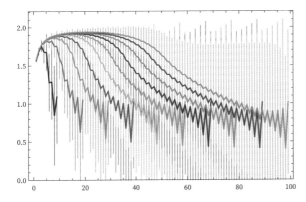

As expected, for t small compared to the number of steps, the limiting estimated dimension is 2.

Most of the other causal graphs shown in the previous subsection do not have finite dimension, however. For example, for the rule AA → AAA the causal graph has the form

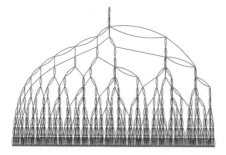

which increases exponentially, with $C_t \sim \left(\frac{3}{2}\right)^t$.

The limits of the grid graphs we showed above essentially correspond to flat d-dimensional directed space. But we can also consider d-dimensional directed space with curvature. Although we cannot construct a complete sphere graph that is consistently directed, we can construct a partial sphere graph:

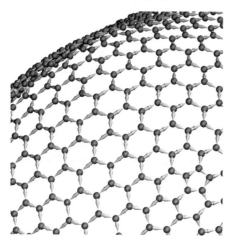

In a layered rendering, this is:

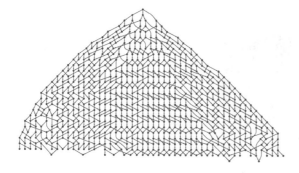

Once again, we can compute the log differences of C_t (the similarity of sphere graphs means that using larger versions does not change the result):

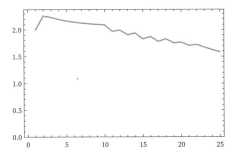

The systematic deviation from the $d = 2$ result is—like in the hypergraph case—a reflection of curvature.

5.14 Foliations and Coordinates on Causal Graphs

One way to describe a causal graph is to say that it defines the partial ordering of events in a system—or, in other words, it is a representation of a poset. (The actual graph is essentially the Hasse diagram of the poset (e.g. [69]).) Any particular sequence of updating events can then be thought of as a particular total ordering of the events.

As a simple example, consider a grid causal graph (as generated, for example, by the rule BA → AB):

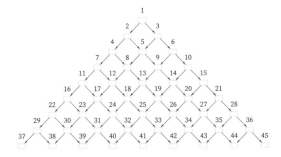

One total ordering of events consistent with all the causal relations in the graph is a "breadth-first scan" [70]:

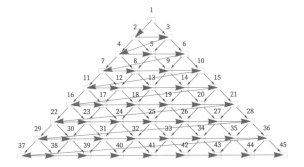

But another possible ordering is a "depth-first scan" [71]:

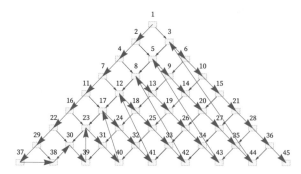

Another conceivable ordering would be:

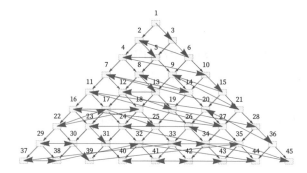

And in general there are many orderings consistent with the relations defined by the causal graph. For the particular graph shown here, out of the $n!$ conceivable orderings of nodes 1 through n, the orderings consistent with the causal relations correspond to possible Young tableaux, and the number of them is equal to the number of involutions (self-inverse permutations) of n elements (e.g. [11:A000085]) which is asymptotically a little larger than $(\frac{n}{e})^{-\frac{n}{2}}$ times $n!$.

Here are the possible causal orderings that visit nodes 1 through 6 above (out of all 6! = 720 orderings):

And here are all 76 possible causal orderings that visit any six nodes starting with node 1:

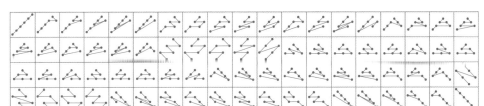

But while a great many total orderings are in principle possible, if one wants, for example, to think about large-scale limits, one usually wants to restrict oneself to orderings that can specified by ("reasonable") foliations.

The idea of a foliation is to define a sequence of slices with the property that events on successive slices must occur in the order of the slices, but that events within a slice can occur in any order. So, for example, an immediate possible foliation of the causal graph above is just:

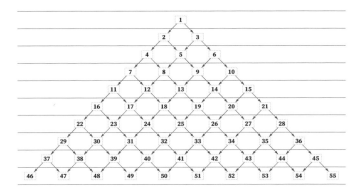

This foliation specifies that event 1 must happen first, but then events 2 and 3 can happen in any order, followed by events 4, 5 and 6 in order, and so on.

But another consistent foliation takes diagonal slices (with actual locations of events in the diagram being thought of as the centers of the boxes):

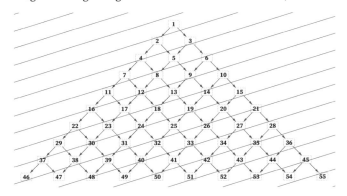

And so long as the diagonals are not steeper than the connections in the causal graph, this foliation will again lead to orderings that are consistent with the partial order defined by the causal graph. (For example, here event 1 must occur first, followed by event 2, followed by events 3 and 4 in any order, and so on.)

Particularly if the diagonals are steeper, multiple events will often happen in a single slice (as we see with events 4 and 7 here):

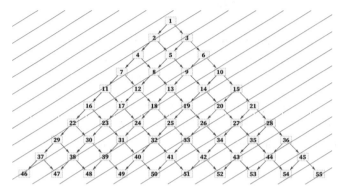

Now let us consider how this relates to taking the limit of a large number of events. If it were not for the directedness of the graph, we could do as we did in 4.17, and just imagine a process of refinement that leads to a manifold. But the Euclidean space that is the model for the manifold does not immediately have a way to capture the directedness of the graph, and so we need to do a little more.

But this is a place where foliations help. Because within a slice of a foliation we have events that can happen in any order. And at least for our string substitution system, the events can be thought of in the limit as being on a one-dimensional manifold, with a coordinate related to position on the string. And then there is just a second coordinate that is the index of the slices in the foliation.

But if the limit of our causal graph is a continuous space, we should be able to have a consistent notion of "distance between events". For events that are "out of order", the distance should be undefined (or perhaps infinite). But for other events, we should be able to compute the distance in terms of the coordinate (say t) that indexes the slices in the foliation and the coordinate (say x) within the slices.

Given the particular setup of diagonal slices on a causal graph that is a grid, there is a unique distance function that is independent of the angle of the slices, which can be expressed in terms of the coordinate differences Δt and Δx:

$$\sqrt{\Delta t^2 - \Delta x^2}$$

This function is exactly the standard Minkowski metric for a Lorentzian manifold [72][73], and we will encounter it again in section 8 when we discuss potential connections to physics. But here the metric is simply an abstract way to express distance in the limit of our causal graphs for string substitution systems.

What happens if we use a different foliation? For example, a foliation like the following also leads to orderings of events that are consistent with the partial ordering required by the causal graph:

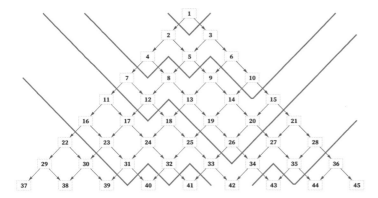

The process of limiting to a manifold is more complicated here. We can start by defining a "lapse function" $\alpha(t,x)$ (in analogy with the ADM formalism of general relativity [74][75]) which effectively says "how thick" each slice of the foliation is at each position. (If we also wanted to skew our foliations, we could include a "shift vector" as well.) And in the limit we can potentially define a distance by integrating $\sqrt{\alpha(t,x)^2\,\delta t^2 - \delta x^2}$ along the shortest path from one point to another.

In a sense, however, even by imagining that there is a reasonable function $\alpha(t,x)$ that depends on real variables t and x we are implicitly assuming that our foliation has a certain simplicity and structure—and is not trying to reproduce some of the more circuitous total orderings at the beginning of this subsection.

But in a sense the question of what type of foliation we need to consider depends on what we want to use it for. And in making potential connections with physics, foliations will in effect be how we parametrize observers. And as soon as we assume that observers are limited in their computational capabilities, this puts constraints on the types of foliations we need to consider.

5.15 The Concept of Branchial Graphs

Causal graphs provide one kind of summary of the evolution of a system, based on capturing the causal relationships between events. What we call branchial graphs provide another kind of summary, based on capturing relationships between states on different branches of a multiway system. And whereas causal graphs capture relationships between events at different steps in the evolution of a system, branchial graphs capture relationships between states on different branches at a given step. And in a sense they define a map for exploring branchial space in a multiway system.

One might perhaps have imagined that states on different branches of a multiway system would be completely independent. But when causal invariance is present they are definitely not—because for example whenever they split (to form a branch pair), they will always merge again.

Consider the multiway evolution graph (for the rule $\{A \rightarrow AB, B \rightarrow A\}$):

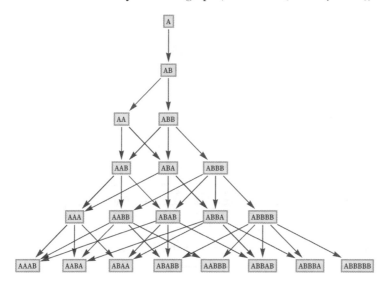

Look at the second-to-last step shown. This contains the following unresolved branch pairs:

{{AAA, AABB}, {AAA, ABAB}, {AAA, ABBA}, {AABB, ABAB}, {AABB, ABBA}, {AABB, ABBBB}, {ABAB, ABBA}, {ABAB, ABBBB}, {ABBA, ABBBB}}

The two states in each of these branch pairs are related, in the sense that they diverged from a common ancestor—and will converge to a common successor. We form the branchial graph by connecting the states that appear in newly unresolved branch pairs at a given step. For the steps shown in the evolution graph above, the successive branchial graphs are:

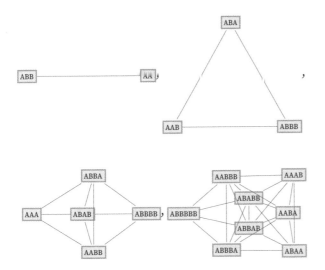

For the next few steps, the states' branchial graphs are:

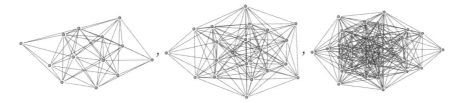

For the rule shown here, the number of nodes at the tth step is the tth Fibonacci number, or $\sim\phi^t$ for large t. The graphs are highly connected, but far from completely so. The number of edges $\sim 2^t$, while the diameter is $\left\lfloor\frac{t}{2}\right\rfloor$. The degree of transitivity (i.e. whether X being connected to Y and Y being connected Z implies X being connected to Z) [76] gradually decreases with t. As a measure of uniformity, one can look at the local clustering coefficient [77] (which measures to what extent there are local complete graphs):

The graphs have somewhat complex vertex degree distributions (here shown after 10 and 15 steps):

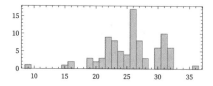 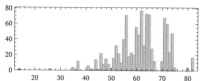

For the rule we are showing here, the branchial graph turns out to have a particularly simple interpretation as a map of the level of common ancestry of states. By definition, if two states are directly connected on the branchial graph, it means they had an immediate common ancestor one step before. But what does it mean if two states are graph distance 2 apart?

The particular rule shown here has the property that it is causal invariant, but also that all branch pairs resolve in just one step. And from this it follows that states that are distance 2 apart on the branchial graph must have a common ancestor 2 steps back. And in general the distance on the branchial graph is equal to the number of steps one must go back before one gets to a common ancestor.

The following histograms show the distribution of graph distances between all pairs of states at steps 10 and 15—or alternatively, the distribution of how many steps it has been since the states had a common ancestor (for this rule the mean increases roughly like $\frac{t}{6}$):

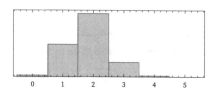 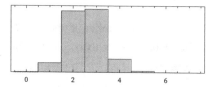

We are defining the branchial graph to be based on looking at branch pairs that are unresolved at a particular step, and are new at that step. But we could generalize to consider a "thickened" branchial graph that includes all branch pairs that have been new within the past m steps. By doing this we can capture common ancestry of states even when they are associated with branch pairs that take up to m steps to resolve—but when we do this it is at the cost of having many additions to the graph associated with branch pairs that have "come and gone" within our thickening depth.

It should be noted that any possible interpretation of branchial graphs in terms of common ancestors depends on having causal invariance. Absent causal invariance, there is no guarantee that states with common ancestors will even be connected in the branchial graph. As an extreme example, consider the rule:

{A → AB, A → AC}

The multiway graph for this rule is a tree

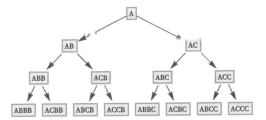

and its branchial graph on successive steps just consists of a collection of disconnected pieces:

By thickening the branchial graph by *m* steps, one could capture *m* steps of common ancestry. And in general one could imagine infinitely thickening the graph, so that one looks all the way back to the initial conditions. But the branchial graph one would get in this way would essentially just be a copy of the whole multiway graph.

When a rule has branch pairs that take several steps to resolve, it is possible for the branchial graph to be disconnected, even when the rule is causal invariant. Consider for example the rule

{A → AA, A → BAB}

in which the branch pair {BAAB, BBABB} takes 3 steps to resolve. The first few branchial graphs for this rule are:

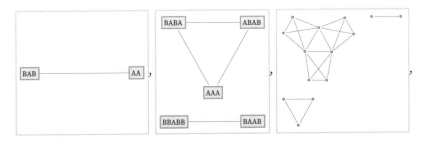

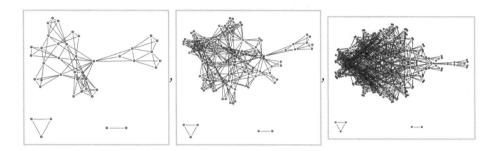

It is fairly common to get branchial graphs in which a few disconnected pieces are "thrown off" in the first few steps, and never recombine. Sometimes, however, disconnected pieces can recombine. The rule

{A → BB, BB → AA}

starting from initial condition A yields the sequence of branchial graphs:

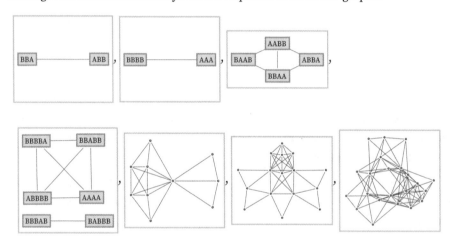

Sometimes the branchial graph can break into many components. This happens for the rule

{AA → AABB}

starting from initial condition AA:

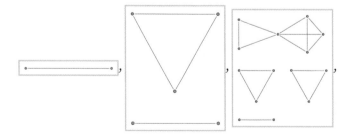

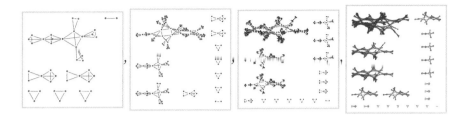

The causal graph for this rule reveals that there is also causal disconnection in this case:

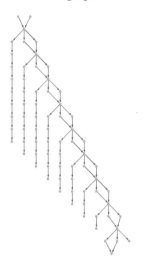

5.16 Typical Forms of Branchial Graphs

As a first example, consider the (causal invariant) rule which effectively just creates either A or B from nothing:

$\{ \to A, \to B\}$

At step t, this rule produces all 2^t possible strings. Its multiway way graph is:

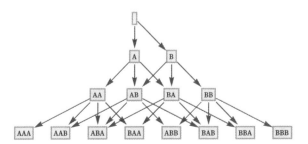

The succession of branchial graphs is then:

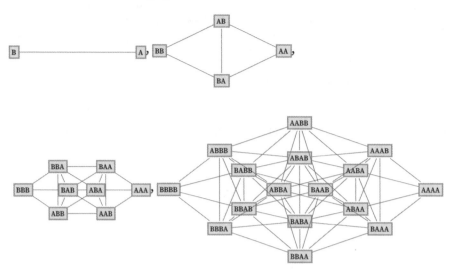

The graph on step t has 2^t nodes and $2^{t-2}(t^2 - t + 4) - 1$ edges. The distance on the graph between two states is precisely the difference in the total number of As (or Bs) between them, plus 1—so combining states which differ only through ordering of A and B the last graph becomes:

With the rule

$$\{ \rightarrow A, \rightarrow B, \rightarrow C\}$$

the sequence of branchial graphs is

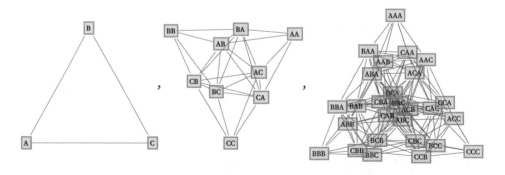

and in the last case combining states which differ only in the order of elements, one gets:

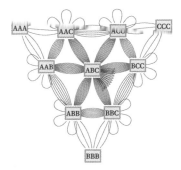

Note that no rule involving only As can have a nontrivial branchial graph, since all branch pairs immediately resolve.

Consider now the rule:

{A → AB}

As mentioned in 5.4, with initial condition AA this rule gives a multiway graph that corresponds to a 2D grid:

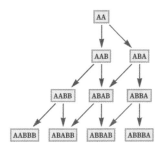

The corresponding branchial graphs are 1D:

With initial condition AAA, the multiway graph is effectively a 3D grid, and the branchial graph is a 2D grid:

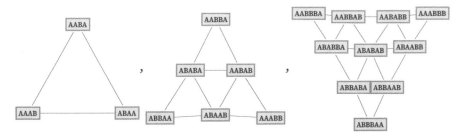

Some rules produce only finite sequences of branchial graphs. For example, the rule

{A → B}

with initial condition AAAA yields what are effectively sections through a cube oriented on its corner:

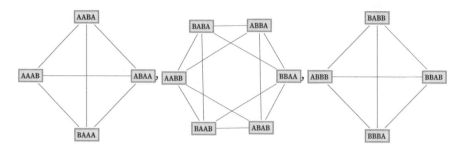

As another example producing a finite sequence of branchial graphs, consider the rule:

{BA → AB}

Starting from BBBAAA it gives:

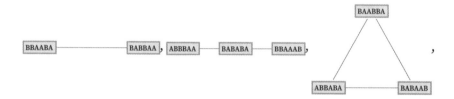

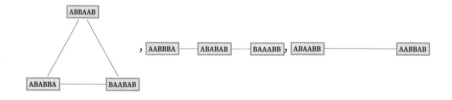

Starting from BBBBBAAAAA it gives:

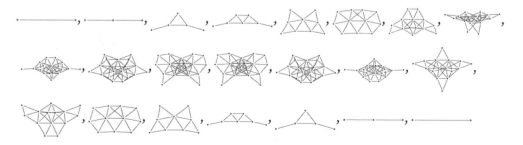

One can think of this as showing the "shapes" of successive slices through the multiway system for the evolution of this rule.

As another example of a rule yielding an infinite sequence of branchial graphs, consider:

$\{A \rightarrow AAB\}$

This yields the following branchial graphs:

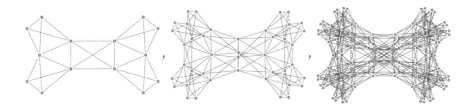

In a 3D rendering, the graph on the next step is:

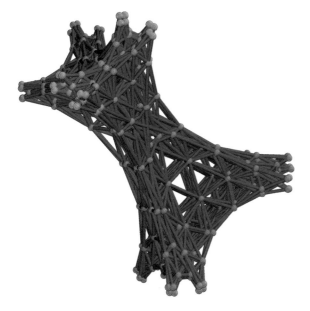

The following are the distinct forms of branchial graphs obtained from rules involving a total of up to 6 As and Bs (starting from a single A):

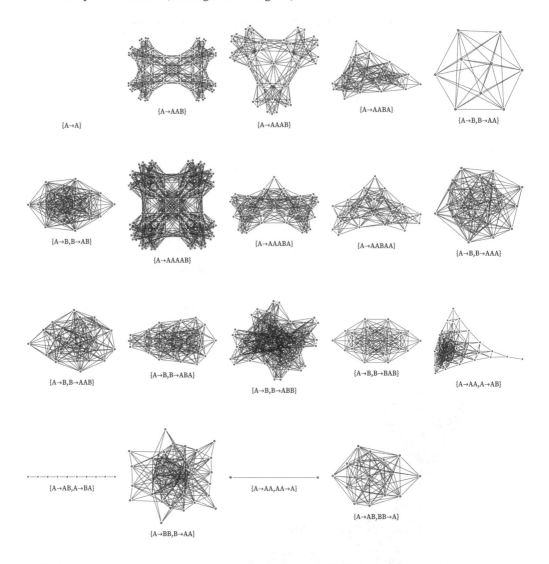

We have seen that branchial graphs can form regular grids. But many branchial graphs have much higher levels of connectivity. No branchial graph can continue to be a complete graph (with all neighbors having distance 1) for more than a limited number of steps. However, the diameters of branchial graphs do tend to grow slowly, and on step t they can be no larger than t. Some branchial graphs show linear or polynomial growth with the number of steps in vertex and edge count, but many show exponential growth.

In analogy to what we did for hypergraphs and causal graphs, we can define a quantity B_b which measures the number of nodes in the branchial graph reached by going out to graph distance b from a given node.

Consider for example the rule:

$\{ \to A, \to B\}$

The sequence of forms for B_b as a function of b on successive steps is:

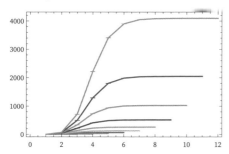

At step t, the diameter of the graph is just t, and $B_{b=t} = 2^t$. For smaller b, the ratios of the B_b for given b at successive steps t steadily decrease, perhaps suggesting ultimately less-than-exponential growth:

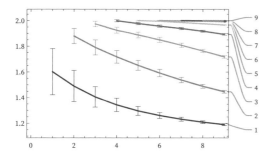

One can ask what the limit of a branchial graph after a large number of steps may be. As an initial possible model, consider graphs representing n-cubes in progressively higher dimensions:

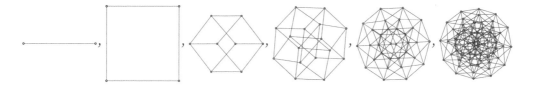

The graph distances between nodes in these graphs are exactly the same as the Euclidean distances between the 2^n possible tuples of 0s and 1s (here shown in distance matrices arranged in lexicographic order):

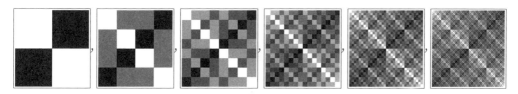

The values of B_b in this case can be found from [11:A008949]:

Accumulate[Table[Binomial[n, k], {k, 0, n}]]

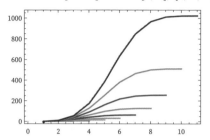

This shows the ratios of B_b for given b for successive n:

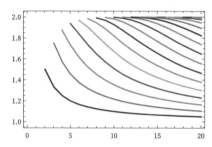

Much as one can consider progressively larger grid graphs as limiting to a manifold, so perhaps one may consider higher and higher "dimensional" cube graphs as limiting to a Hilbert space.

It is also conceivable that limits of branchial graphs may be related to projective spaces [78]. As one potential connection, one can look at discrete models of incidence geometry [79]. For example, with integers representing points and triples representing lines, the Fano plane

{{1, 2, 3}, {1, 4, 5}, {1, 6, 7}, {2, 4, 6}, {2, 5, 7}, {3, 4, 7}, {3, 5, 6}}

is a discrete model of the projective plane. One can consider the sequence of such objects as hypergraphs

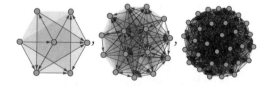

and representing both points and lines here as nodes, these correspond to the graphs:

But for such graphs one finds that B_b has a very different form from typical branchial graphs:

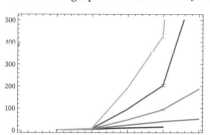

An alternative approach to connecting with discrete models of projective space is to think in terms of lattice theory [69][80][81]. A multiway graph can be interpreted as a lattice (in the algebraic sense), with its evolution defining the partial order in the lattice. The states in the multiway system are elements in the lattice, and the meet and join operations in the lattice correspond to finding the common ancestors and common successors of states.

The analogy with projective geometry is based on thinking of states in the multiway system (which correspond to elements in the lattice) as points, connected by lines that correspond to their evolution in the multiway system. Points are considered collinear if they have the same common successor. But (assuming the multiway system starts from a single state), causal invariance is exactly the condition that any set of points will eventually have a common successor—or in other words, that all lines will eventually intersect, suggesting that the multiway graph is indeed in some sense a discrete model of projective space—so that branchial graphs may also be models of projective Hilbert spaces.

5.17 Foliations of the Multiway Graph and the Structure of Branchial Space

Just as states that occur at successive steps in the evolution of our underlying systems can be thought of as associated with successive slices in a foliation of the causal graph, so also branchial graphs can be thought of as being associated with successive slices in a foliation of the multiway graph.

As we discussed above, different foliations of the causal graph define different relative orderings of updating events within our underlying system. But we can now think about this at a higher level and consider foliations of the multiway graph, that in effect define different relative orders of updating events on different branches of the multiway system. A foliation of the causal graph in effect defines how we should line up our notion of "time" for events in different parts of our underlying system; a foliation of the multiway graph now also defines how we should line up our notion of "time" for events on different branches of the multiway system.

For example, with the rule

{ A → AB}

starting from AA, we can define the following foliation of the multiway graph:

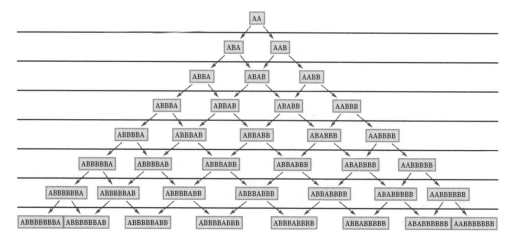

This yields the branchial graphs:

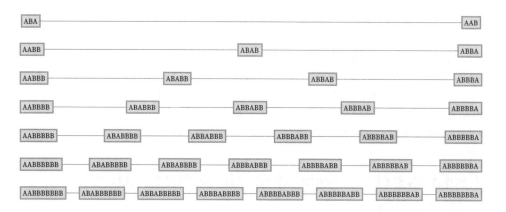

Just as the causal graph defines a partial order for events, so now the multiway graph defines a partial order for states. And so long as it is consistent with this partial order, we can pick any total order for the states. And we can parametrize some of these total orders as foliations.

For the particularly simple case shown here, an alternative foliation consistent with the partial order defined by the multiway system is:

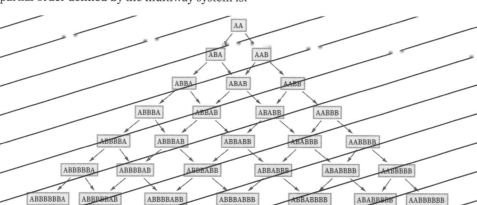

And if we use this foliation, we get a different sequence of branchial graphs, now no longer connected:

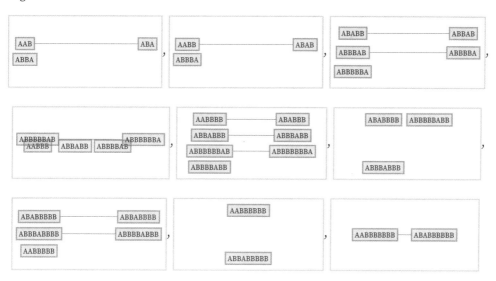

This example is particularly obvious in its analogy with the causal graphs we discussed above. But what makes this work is a special feature of the branchial graphs in this case: the fact that the states that appear in them can in effect be assigned simple 1D "coordinates". In the original foliation with unslanted ("one event per slice") slices, the "coordinate" is effectively just the position of the second A in the string. And with respect to the "space" defined by this "coordinate", the branchial graphs can readily be laid out in one dimension, and we can readily set up "slanted" foliations, just like we did for causal graphs.

With the underlying systems we are discussing in this section being based on strings of elements, it is inevitable that there will be 1D coordinates that can be assigned to the events that occur in the causal graph. But nothing like this need be true of the branchial graph, and indeed most branchial graphs have a significantly more complex structure.

Consider the same rule as above, but now started from AAA. The multiway graph in this case—with a foliation indicated—is then:

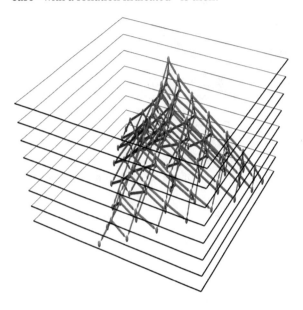

The branchial graphs now have a two-dimensional structure—with the positions of the second and third As in each string providing potential "coordinates":

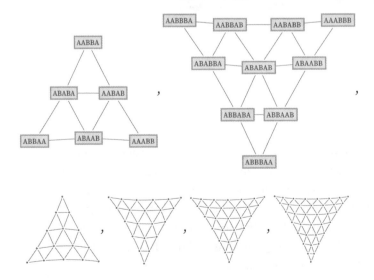

But consider now the rule

{BA → AB}

started from BABABABA. The multiway graph in this case is:

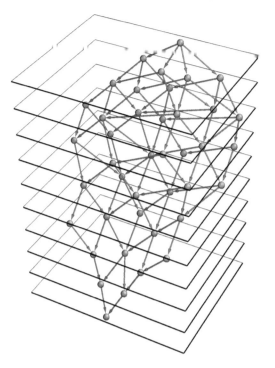

And the sequence of branchial graphs based on the foliation above is now:

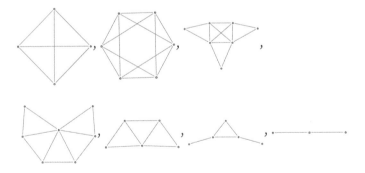

But here it is already much less clear how to assign "coordinates" in "branchial space", or how to create a meaningful family of foliations of the multiway graph.

In thinking about multiway graphs and their foliations there is another complication that can arise for some rules. Consider two versions of the multiway graph for the rule:

{AB → BAB, BA → A}

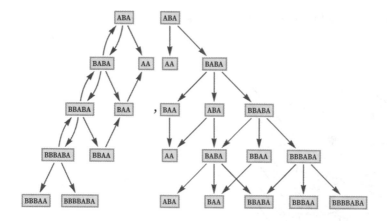

In the first version, every distinct state is shown only once. But in the second case, the evolution is "partially unrolled" to show separately different instances of the same state, produced after different numbers of updating events. With a foliation whose slices correspond to the layers in the renderings above, the first version of the multiway system yields the branchial graphs:

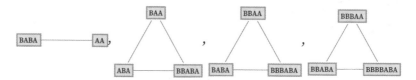

The second version, however, yields different branchial graphs:

To some extent this difference is just like taking a different foliation. But there is more to it, because the second version of the multiway graph actually defines different ordering constraints than the first one. In the second version, there is a true partial ordering, defined by the directed edges in the multiway graph. But in the first version, there can be loops, and so no strict partial order is defined. (We will discuss this phenomenon more in 6.9.)

5.18 The Relationship between Graphs, and the Multiway Causal Graph

In the course of this section, we have seen various ways of describing and relating the possible behaviors of systems. In many ways the most general is the combined multiway evolution and multiway causal graph.

For the rule

{A → AB}

starting from AA this graph has the form:

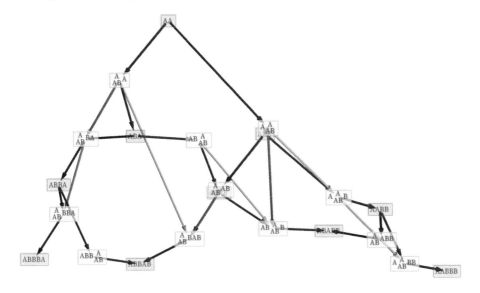

Continuing for another step, we have:

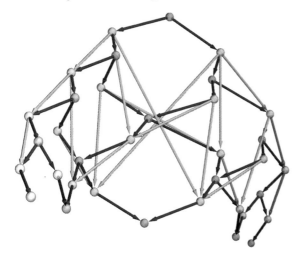

There are several different kinds of descriptions that we can derive from this graph. The standard multiway graph gives the evolution relationship between states:

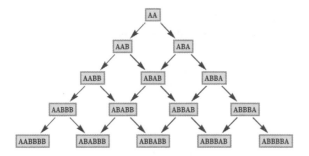

Each possible path through this graph corresponds to a possible evolution history for the system.

The multiway causal graph gives the causal relationships between all events that can happen on any branch. The full multiway causal graph for the rule shown here is infinite. But truncating to show only the part contained in the graph above, one gets:

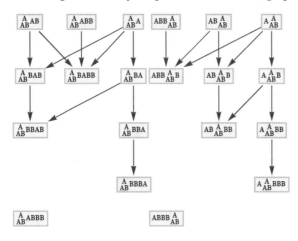

Continuing for more steps one gets:

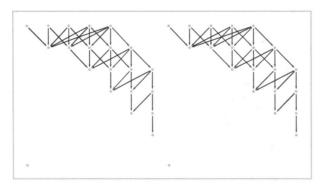

From the multiway causal graph, one can project out the specific causal graph for each possible evolution history, corresponding to each possible branch in the multiway system. But for rules like the one shown here that have the property of causal invariance, every one of these specific causal graphs (at least if extended far enough) must have exactly the same structure. For the particular rule shown here, this structure is extremely simpler

(In effect, the nodes here are "generic events" in the system, and could be labeled just by copies of the underlying local rule.)

The multiway graph and multiway causal graph effectively give two different "vertical views" of the original graph—using respectively states as nodes and and events as nodes. But an alternative is to view the graph in terms of "horizontal slices". To get such slices we have to do foliations.

But now if we look at horizontal slices associated with states, we get the branchial graphs, which for this rule with this initial condition are rather trivial:

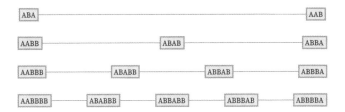

In principle we could also ask about horizontal slices associated with events. But by construction the events analog of the branchial graph must just consist of a collection of complete graphs.

However, a particular sequence of slices through any particular causal graph defines an actual sequence of states for the underlying system, and thus a possible evolution history, such as:

{AA, ABAB, ABBABB, ABBBABBB, ABBBBABBBB}

As a slightly cleaner example with similar behavior, consider the rule:

{A → AB, A → BA}

The combined multiway evolution and multiway causal graph in this case is

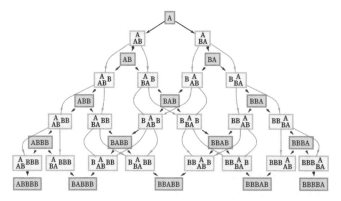

and the individual multiway evolution and causal graphs are both regular 2D grids:

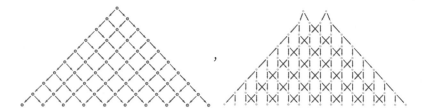

The rules we have used as an example so far have behavior that is in a sense fairly trivial. But consider now the related rule with slightly less trivial behavior:

{A → AB, B → A}

For this rule, the combined multiway evolution and causal graph has the form:

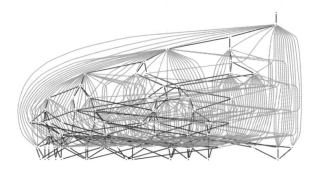

On their own, the state evolution graph and the event causal graph have the forms:

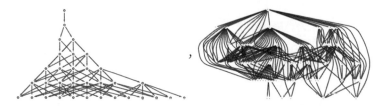

The sequence of branchial graphs is:

This rule is causal invariant, and so the multiway causal graph decomposes into many identical copies of causal graphs for all individual possible paths of evolution. In this case, these graphs all have the form:

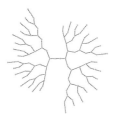

But even though the multiway causal graph can be decomposed into identical pieces, it still contains more information than any of them. Because in effect it describes not only "spatial" causal relationships between events happening in different places in the underlying string, but also "branchial" causal relationships between events happening on different branches of the multiway system.

And just like for other graphs, we can study the large-scale structure of multiway causal graphs. We can define a quantity C_t^M which is the multiway analog of the cone volume C_t for individual causal graphs. For the rule shown here, the various graph growth rates (as computed with our standard foliation) have the forms:

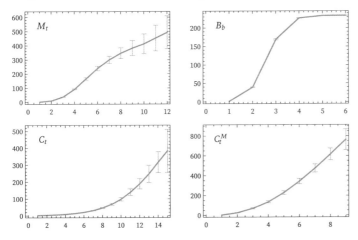

As another example, consider the "sorting" rule

{BA → AB}

starting from BABABABA. The combined multiway evolution and causal graph has the (terminating) form:

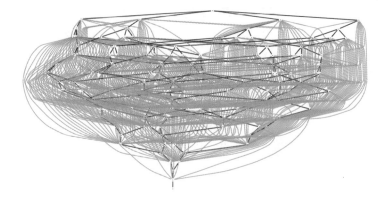

The multiway evolution and causal graphs on their own are:

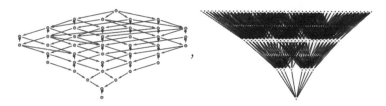

The branchial graphs are

and the causal graph for a single (finite) path of evolution is:

Earlier in this section we looked at the multiway evolution graphs generated by all 12 inequivalent 2: 1→2, 1→1 rules. The pictures below now compare these with the multiway causal graphs for the same rules (starting from all possible length-3 strings of As and Bs, and run for 4 steps of our standard multiway foliation):

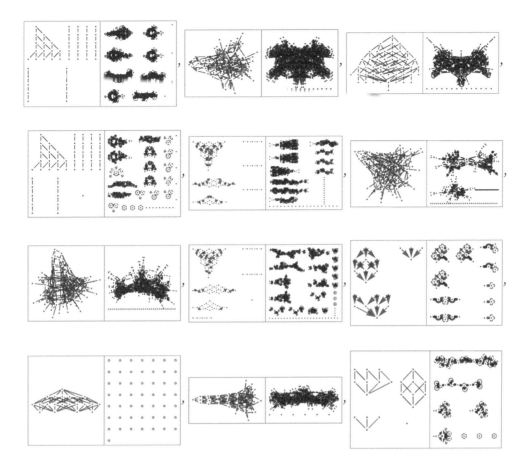

The multiway causal graph is in some ways a kind of dual to the multiway evolution graph—resulting in many similarities among the graphs in the pictures above. Like M_t for multiway evolution graphs, C_t^M for multiway causal graphs typically seems to grow either polynomially or exponentially.

But even in a case like the rule

{AA → AAA}

where the causal graph for a single evolution has the fairly regular form

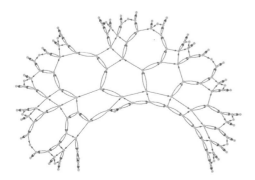

the full multiway causal graph is quite complex. This shows how it builds up over the first few steps (in our standard multiway foliation):

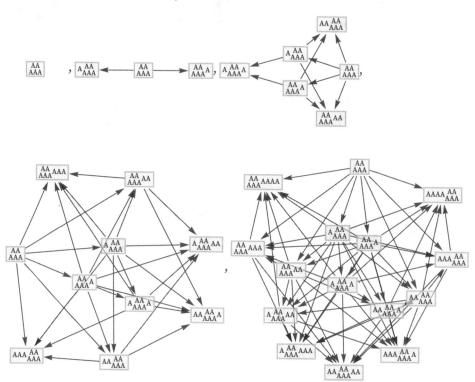

And here are 3D renderings after 8 and 9 steps:

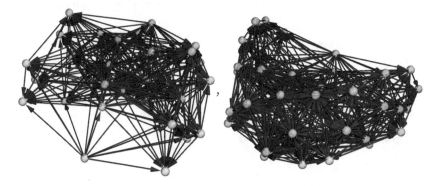

5.19 Weighted Multiway Graphs

In a multiway system, there are in general multiple paths that can produce the same state. But in our usual construction of the multiway graph, we record only what states are produced, not how many paths can do it.

Consider the rule:

{A → AA, A → A}

The full form of its multiway graph—including an edge for every possible event—is:

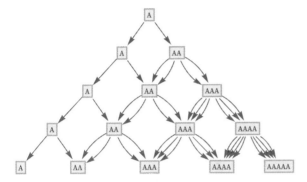

Here is the same graph, with a count included at each node for the number of distinct paths from the root that reach it:

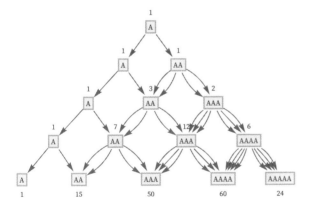

An alternative weighting scheme might be to start with weight 1 for the initial state, then at each state we reach, to distribute the weight to its successors, dividing it equally among possible events:

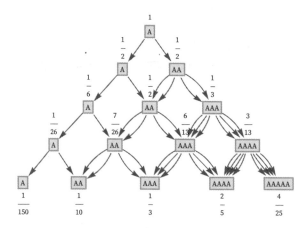

This approach has the feature that it gives normalized weights (summing to 1) at each successive layer in a graph like this. But in general the approach is not robust, and if we even took a different foliation through the graph above, the weights on each slice would no longer be normalized. In addition, if we were to combine identical states from different steps, we would not know what weights to assign. Pure counting of paths, however, still works even in this case, although any normalization has to be done only after all the counts are known:

Note that even the counting of paths becomes difficult to define if there is a loop in the multiway graph—though one can adopt the convention that one counts paths only to the first encounter with any given state:

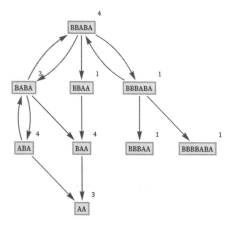

Weights on the multiway graph can also be inherited by branchial graphs. Consider for example the rule:

{A → AB, B → BA}

The multiway graph for this rule, weighted with path counts, is:

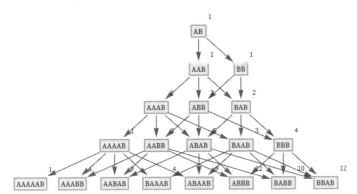

The corresponding weighted branchial graphs are:

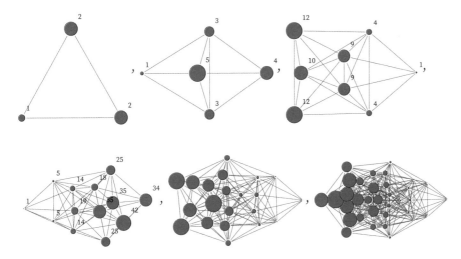

The weights in effect define a measure on the branchial graph. A case with a particular straightforward limiting measure is the rule:

{A → AB}

With initial condition A this gives weights that reproduce Pascal's triangle, and yield a limiting Gaussian:

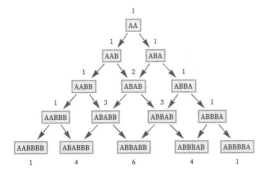

With initial condition AAA, the weights in the branchial graph limit to a 2D Gaussian:

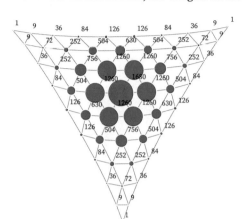

In general, after sufficiently many steps one can expect that the weights will define an invariant measure, although a complexity is that the branchial graph will typically continue to grow. As one indication of the limiting measure, one can compute the distribution of values of the weights.

The results for the rule {A → B, B → AB} above illustrate slow convergence to a limiting form:

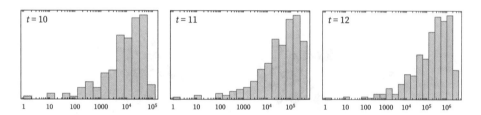

We discussed in a previous subsection probing the structure of the branchial graph by computing the number of nodes B_b at most graph distance b from a given point. We can now generalize this to computing a path-weighted quantity B_b^μ (cf. [1:p959]). At least for simple multiway graphs, this may be related in the limit to the results of solving a PDE on the multiway graph.

5.20 Effective Causal Invariance

In any causal invariant rule, all branch pairs that are generated must eventually resolve. But by looking at how many branch pairs are resolved—and unresolved—at each step, we can get a sense of "how far" a rule is from causal invariance.

Consider the causal invariant rule:

{A → AB, B → A}

With this rule, all branch pairs resolve in one step

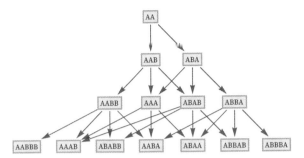

and the total number of branch pairs that have already resolved on successive steps is (roughly 2^t):

{0, 6, 22, 66, 174, 420, 951, 2053, 4273, 8643}

But now consider the slightly different—and non-causal-invariant—rule:

{A → AB, BA → BB}

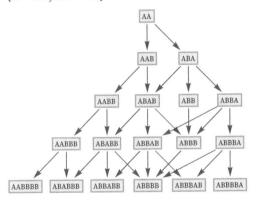

The number of resolved branch pairs goes up on successive steps—in this case quadratically:

{1, 5, 11, 19, 29, 41, 55, 71, 89, 109}

But now there is a "residue" of new unresolved branch pairs at each step that reflect the lack of causal invariance:

{4, 6, 8, 10, 12, 14, 16, 18, 20, 22}

There are other rules in which the deviation from causal invariance is in a sense larger. Consider the rule:

{AA → AAB, AA → B}

The multiway graph for this rule shows various "dead ends"

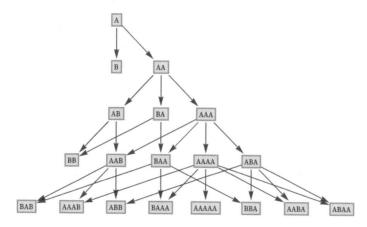

and now the number of resolved branch pairs is

{5, 15, 30, 50, 75, 105, 140, 180, 225, 275}

while the number of unresolved ones grows at a similar rate:

{14, 23, 33, 44, 56, 69, 83, 98, 114, 131}

When a system is not causal invariant, what it means is that in a sense the system can reach states from which it cannot ever "get back" to other states. But this suggests that by extending the rules for the system, one might be able to make it causal invariant.

Consider the rule

{A → AA, A → B}

with multiway graph:

With this rule, the branch pair {B, AA} never resolves. But now let us just extend the rule by adding B → AA:

{A → AA, A → B, B → AA}

The multiway graph becomes

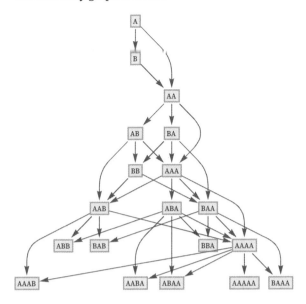

and the rule is now causal invariant.

In general, given a rule that is not causal invariant, we can consider extending it by including transformations that relate strings in branch pairs that do not resolve. For the rule

{AA → AAB, AA → B}

discussed above it turns out that the minimal additions to achieve causal invariance are:

{AB → AAAB, BA → AB}

Having added these transformations, the multiway graph now begins:

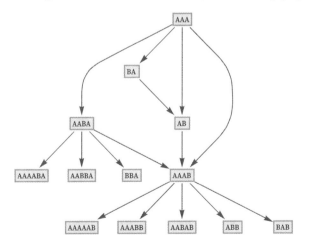

After more steps, the multiway graph is:

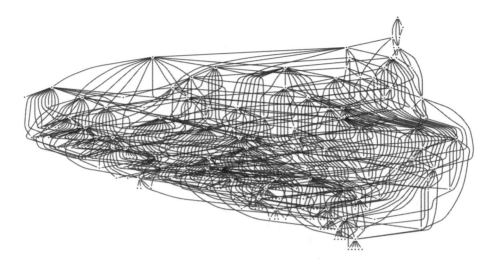

This kind of "completion" procedure of adding "relations" in order to achieve what amounts to causal invariance is familiar in automated theorem proving [82] and related areas [60]. For our purposes we can think of it as a kind of "coarse graining" of our systems, in which the additional rules in effect define equivalences between states that would otherwise be distinct.

If a particular multiway graph terminates after a finite number of steps, then it is always possible to add enough completion rules to the system to ensure causal invariance [63][64]. But if the multiway graph grows without bound, this may not be possible. Sometimes one may succeed in adding enough completions to achieve causal invariance for a certain number of steps, only to have it fail after more steps. And in general, like determining whether branch pairs will resolve, there is ultimately no upper bound on how long one may have to wait, making the problem of completion ultimately formally undecidable [83].

But if (as is often the case) one only has to add a small number of completion rules to make a system causal invariant, then one can take this to mean that the system is not far from causal invariance, so that it is likely that many of the large-scale properties of the completion of the system will be shared by the system itself.

5.21 Generational Evolution

Systems like cellular automata always update every element at every step in their evolution. But in string substitution systems (as well as in our hypergraph-based models), the presence of overlaps between possible updating events typically means that there is no single, consistent way to do this kind of parallel updating. Nevertheless, in studying our models in earlier sections, we often used "steps" of evolution in which we updated as many elements as we consistently could. And we can also apply this kind of "generation based" updating to string substitution systems.

Consider the rule:

{A → AB, B → A}

We can construct the multiway graph for this rule by considering how one state is produced from another by a single updating event, corresponding to a single application of one of the transformations in the rule:

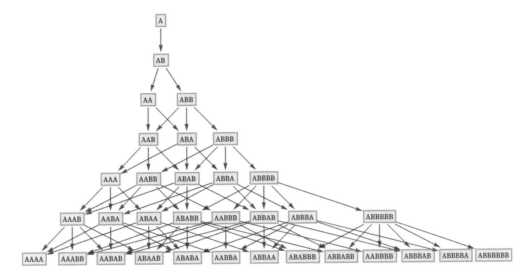

But we can also consider producing a "generational multiway graph" in which we do as many non-overlapping updates as possible on any given string. For this particular rule, doing this is straightforward, since every A and every B in the string can be transformed separately.

But the result is now a radically simplified multiway graph, in which there is just a single path of evolution:

The "generational steps" here involve an increasing number of update events, as we can see from this rendering of the evolution:

All the states obtained at generational steps do appear somewhere in the full multiway graph, but the full graph also contains many additional states—that, among other things, can be thought of as representing all possible intermediate stages of generational steps:

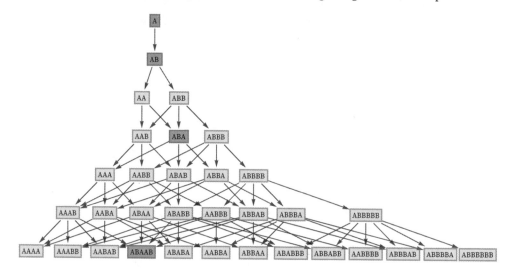

For a rule like

{A → AB}

the generational steps

correspond to a particularly simple trajectory through the full multiway graph:

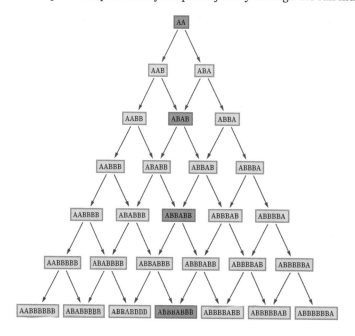

It is not always the case that the generational multiway graph involves just a single path. Consider the rule:

{A → AB, A → B}

The ordinary multiway graph for this rule starting from AA is:

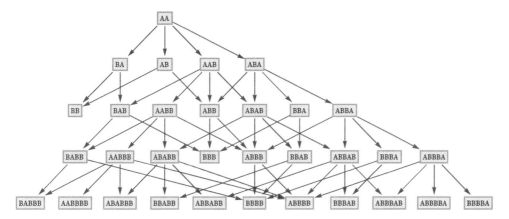

And the generational multiway graph is now:

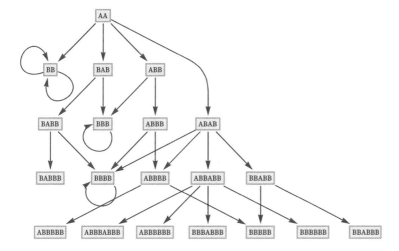

The generational multiway graph is always in a sense a compression of the full multiway graph. And one way to think of it is as being derived from the full multiway graph by combining sequences of edges when they correspond to updating events that do not overlap on the string.

But there is also another view of generational evolution. Consider a branchial graph from the full multiway graph above (this branchial graph is derived from the layered foliation shown):

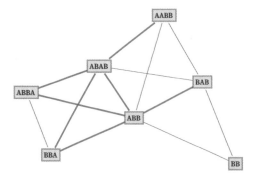

The branch pairs in this branchial graph (shown as adjacent nodes) can be thought of as being of two kinds. The first are produced by applying different rules to a single part of a string (e.g. ABA → {ABBA, BBA}). And the second (highlighted in the graph above) by applying rules to different parts of a string (e.g. ABA → {ABBA, ABAB}).

In the full multiway graph, no distinction is made between these two kinds of branch pairs, and the graph includes both of them. But in a generational multiway system, strings in the second kind of branch pairs can be combined.

And indeed this provides another way to construct a generational multiway system: look at branchial graphs and take pairs of strings corresponding to "spatially" disjoint updating events, and then knit these together to form generational steps. And if there is only one way to do this for each branchial graph, one will get a single path of generational evolution. But if there are multiple ways, then the generational multiway graph will be more complicated.

For the rule

{A → AB, B → A}

that we discussed above, the sequence of branchial graphs is

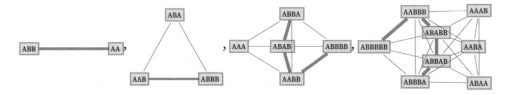

and it is readily possible to assemble "string fragments" (such as those highlighted) to produce the states at successive generational steps:

{{AA}, {ABAB}, {ABBABB}, {ABBBABBB}}

The branchial graphs are determined by the foliation of the multiway graph that one uses. But given a foliation, one can then assemble strings corresponding to generational steps using the procedure above.

There is always an alternative, however: instead of combining strings from a branchial graph to produce the state for a generational step, one can always in a sense just wait, and eventually the full multiway system will have done the necessary sequence of updates to produce the complete state for the generational step.

Whenever there are no possible overlaps in the application of rules, the generational multiway graph must always yield a single path of history. But there is also another feature of such rules: they are guaranteed to be causal invariant. There are, however, plenty of rules that are causal invariant even though they allow overlaps—in a sense because their right-hand sides also appropriately agree. And for such rules, the generational multiway graph may have multiple paths of history.

A simple example is the rule:

{A → AB, A → BA}

This rule is causal invariant, and starting from A yields the full multiway graph:

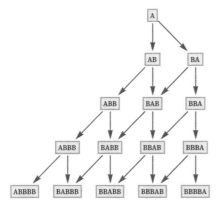

Its generational multiway graph is actually identical in this case—because all the rule ever does is to apply one transformation or the other to the single A that appears:

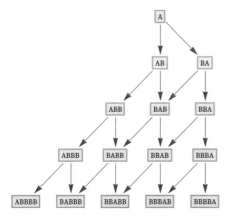

Starting from AA, however, the rule yields the full multiway graph

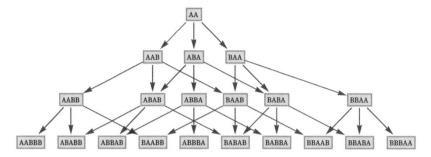

and the generational multiway graph:

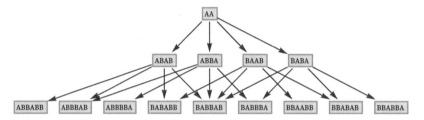

In an alternative rendering, these graphs after a few more steps become, respectively:

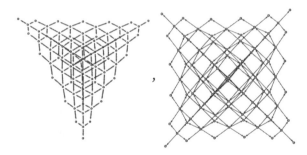

Note that in both cases, the number of states reached after t steps grows like t^2 (in the first case it is $\frac{1}{2} t(t+1)$; in the second case exactly t^2).

In the case of a rule like

{A → AB, A → BB}

the presence of many potential overlaps in where updates can be applied makes many of the possible states in the full multiway graph also appear in the generational multiway graph (in the limit about 64% of all possible states are generational results):

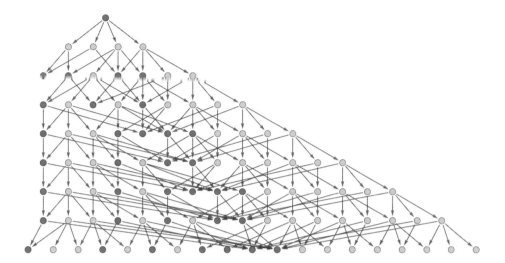

Generational multiway graphs share many features with full multiway graphs. For example, generational multiway graphs can also show causal invariance—and indeed unless strings grow too fast, any deviation from causal invariance must also appear in the generational multiway graph.

The basic construction of ordinary multiway graphs ensures that the number of states M_t after t steps can grow at most exponentially with t. In a generational multiway graph, there can be faster growth.

Consider for example the rule (whose full multiway graph grows in a Fibonacci sequence $\approx \phi^t$):

{A → AA, A → B}

Its full multiway graph grows in a Fibonacci sequence $\approx \phi^t$:

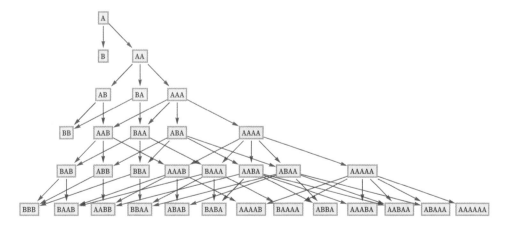

But its generational multiway graph grows much faster. After 3 generational steps it has the form

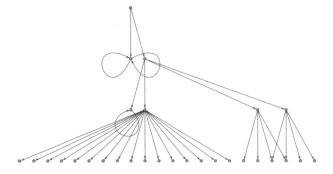

while after 4 steps (in a different rendering) it is:

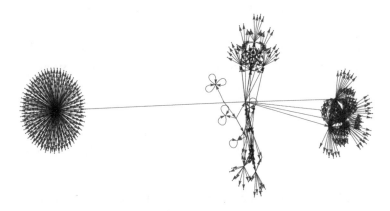

The number of states reached in successive steps is:

$\{1, 2, 5, 24, 455, 128\,702\}$

Although there is a distribution of lengths for the strings, say, at steps 4 and 5

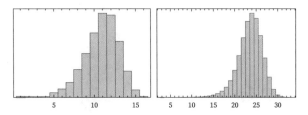

the fact that the maximum string length at generational step t is 2^{t-1}—combined with the lack of causal invariance for this rule—-allows for double exponential growth in the number of possible states with generational steps. In fact, with this particular rule, by step t almost all sequences of up to 2^{t-1} Bs and AAs have appeared (the missing fractions on steps 3, 4, 5 are 0.13, 0.078, 0.017) so at step t the total number of states approaches

$2^{2^{t-1}}$

6 | The Updating Process in Our Models

6.1 Updating Events and Causal Dependence

Consider the rule:

$$\{\{x, y\}, \{x, z\}\} \rightarrow \{\{x, y\}, \{x, w\}, \{y, w\}, \{z, w\}\}$$

When we discussed this rule previously, we showed the first few steps in its evolution as:

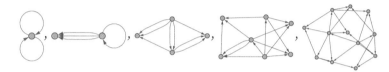

But to understand the updating process in our models in more detail, it is helpful to "look inside" these steps, and see the individual updating events of which they are comprised:

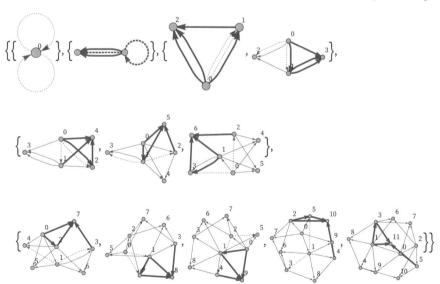

The $2_2 \rightarrow 4_2$ signature of the rule means that in each updating event, two relations are destroyed, and four new ones are created. In the pictures above, new relations from each event are shown in red; the ones that will disappear in the next event are shown dotted. The elements are numbers in the sequence they are created.

There are in general many possible sequences of updating events that are consistent with the rule. But in making the pictures above (and in much of our discussion in previous sections), we have used our "standard updating order", in which each step in the overall evolution in effect includes as many non-overlapping updates as will "fit". (In more detail, what is done is that in each overall step, relations are scanned from oldest to newest, in each case using them in an update event so long as this can be done without using any relation that has already been updated in this overall step.)

Our models—and the hypergraphs on which they operate—are in many ways more difficult to handle than the string-based systems we discussed in the previous section. But one way in which they are simpler is that they more directly expose causal relationships between events. To see if an event B depends on an event A, all we need do is to see whether elements that were involved in A are also involved in B.

Looking at the sequence of updates above, therefore, we can immediately construct a causal graph:

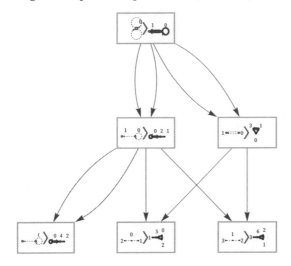

Another feature of our models is that every element can be thought of as having a unique "lineage", in that it was created by a particular updating event, which in turn was the result of some other updating event, and so on. When we introduced our models in section 2, we just said that any element created by applying a rule should be new and distinct from all others. If we were implementing the model, this might then make us imagine that the element would have a name based on some global counter, or a UUID.

But there is another, more deterministic (as well as more local and distributed) alternative: think of each new element as being a kind of encapsulation of its lineage (analogous to a chain of pointers, or to a hash like in blockchains [84] or Git). In the evolution above, for example, we could describe element 10 by just saying it was created as part of the relation {2,10} from the relations {{2,4},{2,5}} (as the second part of the output of an update that uses them)—but then we could say that these relations were in turn created from earlier relations, and so on recursively, all the way back to the initial state of the system:

{{2, 10}}

{{{2, 4}, {2, 5}} ▷ 2}

{{{{0, 1}, {0, 2}} ▷ 4, {{0, 2}, {0, 1}} ▷ 3} ▷ 2}

{{{{{0, 0}, {0, 1}} ▷ 1, {{0, 0}, {0, 1}} ▷ 2} ▷ 4, {{{0, 0}, {0, 1}} ▷ 3, {{0, 1}, {0, 1}} ▷ 1} ▷ 3} ▷ 2}

{{{{{{0, 0}, {0, 0}} ▷ 1, {{0, 0}, {0, 0}} ▷ 2} ▷ 1, {{{0, 0}, {0, 0}} ▷ 1, {{0, 0}, {0, 0}} ▷ 2} ▷ ?} ▷ 4,

{{{{0, 0}, {0, 0}} ▷ 1, {{0, 0}, {0, 0}} ▷ 2} ▷ 3, {{{0, 0}, {0, 0}} ▷ 3, {{0, 0}, {0, 0}} ▷ 4} ▷ 1} ▷ 3} ▷ 2}

The final expression here can also be written as:

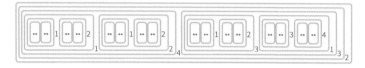

Roughly what this is doing is specifying an element (in this case the one we originally
labeled simply as 10) by giving a symbolic representation of the path in the causal graph that
led to its creation. And we can then use this to create a unique symbolic name for the
element. But while this may be structurally interesting, when it comes to actually using an
element as a node in a hypergraph, the name we choose to use for the element is irrelevant;
all that matters is what elements are the same, and what are different.

6.2 Multiway Systems for Our Models

Just like for the string substitution systems of section 5, we can construct multiway systems
[1:5.6] for our models, in which we include a separate path for every possible updating
event that can occur:

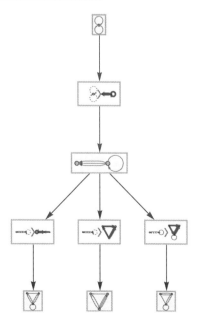

For string systems, it is straightforward to determine when states in the system should be merged: one just has see whether the strings corresponding to them are identical. For our systems, it is more complicated: we have to determine whether the hypergraphs associated with states are isomorphic [85], in the sense that they are structurally the same, independent of how their nodes might be labeled.

Continuing one more step with our rule, we see some cases of merging:

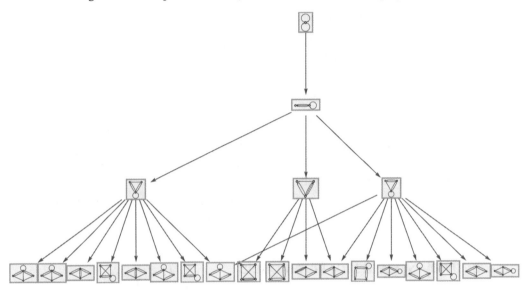

Here is an alternative rendering, now also showing the particular path obtained by following our "standard updating order":

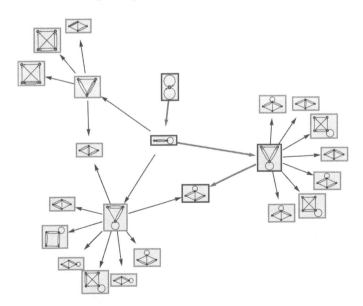

In general, each path in the multiway system corresponds to a possible sequence of updating events—here shown along with the causal relationships that exist between them:

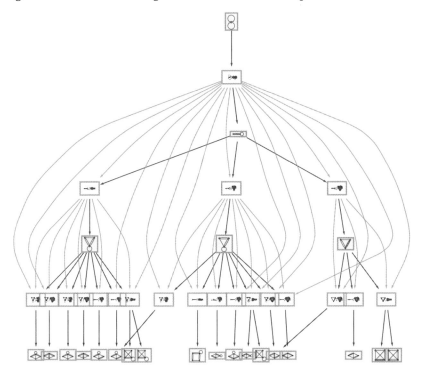

6.3 Causal Invariance

Like string substitution systems, our models can have the important feature of causal invariance [1:9.9]. In analogy with neighbor-independent string substitution systems, causal invariance is guaranteed if there is just a single relation on the left-hand side of a rule.

Consider for example the rule:

$$\{\{x, y\}\} \rightarrow \{\{x, y\}, \{y, z\}\}$$

Starting from a single self-loop, this gives the multiway system:

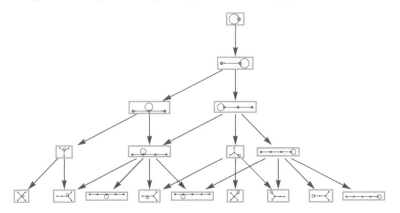

As implied by causal invariance, every pair of paths that diverge must reconverge. And looking at a few more steps, we can see that in fact with this particular rule, branches always recombine after just one step:

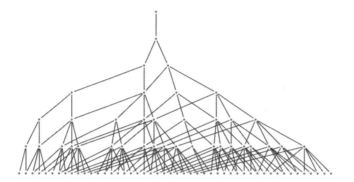

The different paths here lead to hypergraphs that look fairly different. But causal invariance implies that every time there is divergence, there must always eventually be reconvergence.

And for some rules, different paths give hypergraphs that do look very similar. An example is the rule

$$\{\{x, y\}\} \to \{\{y, z\}, \{z, x\}\}$$

where the hypergraphs produced on different paths differ only by the directions of their hyperedges:

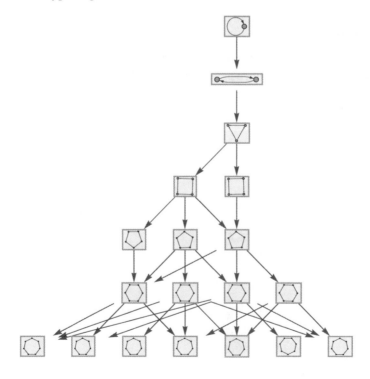

For rules that depend on more than one relation, causal invariance is not guaranteed, and in fact is fairly rare. Of the 4702 inequivalent $2_2 \to 3_2$ rules, perhaps 5% are causal invariant.

In some cases, the causal invariance is rather trivial. For example, the rule

$$\{\{x, y\}, \{x, y\}\} \to \{\{z, z\}, \{z, z\}, \{y, z\}\}$$

leads to a multiway graph that only allows one path of evolution:

A less trivial example is the rule

$$\{\{x, y\}, \{z, y\}\} \to \{\{x, w\}, \{y, w\}, \{z, w\}\}$$

which yields the multiway system:

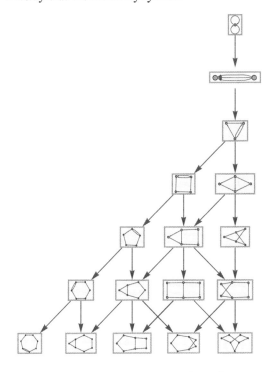

With our standard updating order, this rule eventually produces forms like

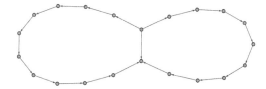

but the multiway system shows that other structures are also possible.

As another example, consider the rule

$$\{\{x, y\}, \{z, y\}\} \rightarrow \{\{x, z\}, \{y, z\}, \{w, z\}\}$$

which with our standard updating order gives:

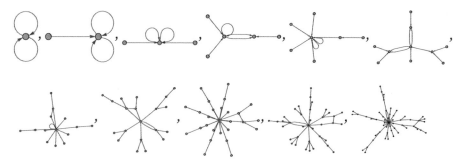

The multiway system for this rule branches rapidly

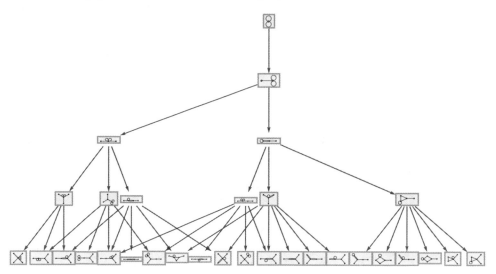

but every pair of branches still reconverges in one step.

The rule

$$\{\{x, y\}, \{x, z\}\} \rightarrow \{\{y, w\}, \{y, z\}, \{w, x\}\}$$

provides an example of causal invariance in which branches can take 3 steps to converge:

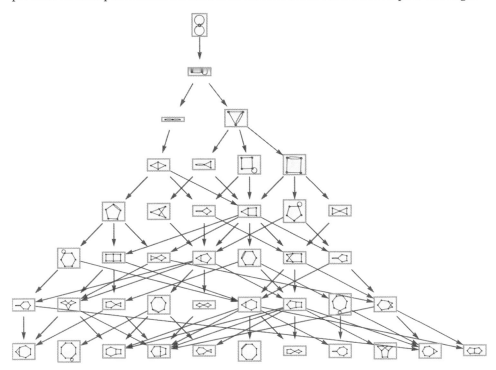

Among all possible rules, causal invariance is much more common for rules that generate disconnected hypergraphs. It is also perhaps slightly less common for rules with ternary relations instead of binary ones.

6.4 Testing for Causal Invariance

Testing for causal invariance in our models is similar in principle to the case of strings. Failure of causal invariance is again the result of branch pairs that do not resolve. And just like for strings, it is possible to test for total causal invariance by determining whether a certain finite set of core branch pairs resolve. (Again in analogy with strings, the finiteness of this set is a consequence of the finiteness of the hypergraphs involved in our rules.)

The core branch pairs that we need to test represent the minimal cases of overlap between left-hand sides of rules—or, in a sense, the minimal unifications of the hypergraphs that appear. For the two hypergraphs

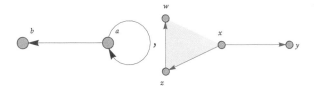

there are two possible unifications (where the purple edge shows the overlap):

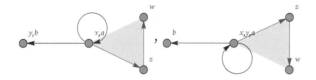

For a single rule with left-hand side

{{x, y}, {x, z}}

the core branch pairs arise from unifications associated with the possible self-overlaps of this small hypergraph. Representing two copies of the hypergraph as

the possible unifications are:

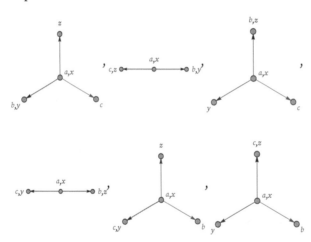

In the case of strings, all that matters is what symbols appear within the unification. In the case of hypergraphs, one also has to know how the unification in effect "attaches", and so one has to distinguish different labelings of the nodes.

Starting from the unifications, one applies the rule to find what branch pairs can be produced. These branch pairs form the core set of branch pairs for the rule—and determining whether the rule is causal invariant then becomes a matter of finding out whether these branch pairs resolve.

In the case of

$$\{\{x, y\}, \{x, z\}\} \rightarrow \{\{x, y\}, \{x, w\}, \{y, w\}, \{z, w\}\}$$

the application of the rule to the unifications above yields the following 58 core branch pairs:

Running the rule for one step yields resolutions for 6 of these branch pairs:

Running for another step resolves no additional branch pairs.

Will the rule turn out to be causal invariant in the end? As a comparison, consider the rule

$$\{\{x, y\}, \{x, z\}\} \rightarrow \{\{y, w\}, \{y, z\}, \{w, x\}\}$$

discussed in the previous subsection. This rule starts with 14 core branch pairs:

After one step, 6 of them resolve:

Then after another step the 8 remaining ones resolve, establishing that the rule is indeed causal invariant:

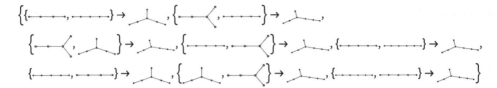

But in general there is no upper bound on the number of steps it can take for core branch pairs to resolve. Perhaps the fact that so many additional branch pairs are generated at each step in the rule $\{\{x,y\},\{x,z\}\}\to\{\{x,z\},\{x,w\},\{y,w\},\{z,w\}\}$ makes it seem unlikely that they will all resolve, but ultimately this is not clear.

And even if the rule does not show total causal invariance, it is still perfectly possible that it will be causal invariant for the particular set of states generated from a certain initial condition. However, determining this kind of partial causal invariance seems even more difficult than determining total causal invariance.

Note that if one looks at all 4702 $2_2 \to 3_2$ rules, the largest number of core branch pairs for any rule is 554; the largest number that resolve in 1 step is 132, and the largest number that remain unresolved is 430.

6.5 Causal Graphs for Causal Invariant Rules

An important consequence of causal invariance is that it establishes that a rule produces the same causal graph independent of the particular order in which update events occurred. And so this means, for example, that we can generate causal graphs just by looking at evolution with our standard updating order.

For rules that depend on only one relation, the causal graph is always just a tree

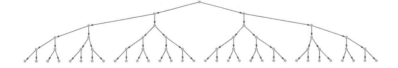

regardless of whether the structure generated is also a tree

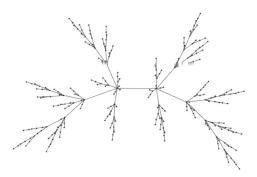

or has a more compact form:

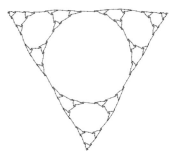

But as soon as a rule depends on more than one relation, the causal graph can immediately be more complicated. For example, consider even the rule:

$$\{\{x\}, \{x\}\} \rightarrow \{\{x\}, \{x\}, \{x\}\}$$

The multiway system for this rule shows that only one path is possible (immediately demonstrating causal invariance):

But the causal relationships between steps are not so straightforward

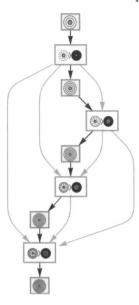

and after 15 steps the causal graph has the form

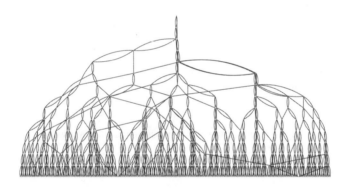

or in an alternative rendering:

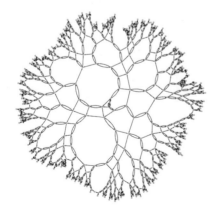

The fact that the multiway system is nontrivial does not mean that the causal graph for a particular rule evolution will be nontrivial. Consider for example a causal invariant rule that we discussed above:

$$\{\{x, y\}, \{z, y\}\} \rightarrow \{\{x, w\}, \{y, w\}, \{z, w\}\}$$

The multiway system for this rule, with causal connections shown, is:

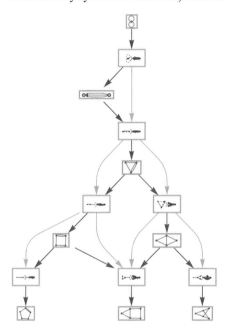

This yields the multiway causal graph:

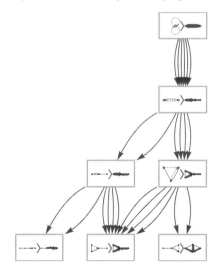

But the causal graph for any individual evolution is just:

For the causal invariant rule (also discussed above)

$\{\{x, y\}, \{z, y\}\} \rightarrow \{\{x, z\}, \{y, z\}, \{w, z\}\}$

the multiway system after 5 steps has the form:

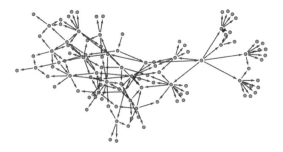

After 20 steps of evolution with our standard updating order gives:

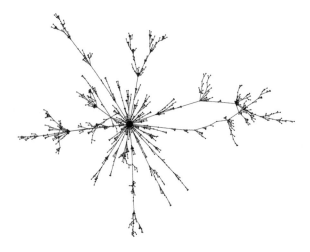

The causal graph for this rule after 10 steps is

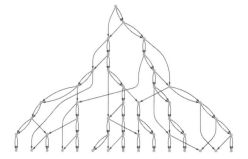

and after 20 steps, in a different rendering, it becomes:

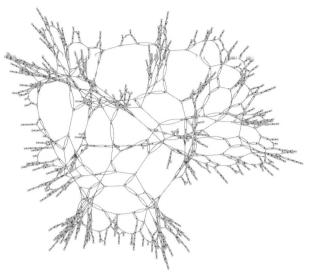

As another example, consider the rule (also discussed above):

$$\{\{x, y\}, \{x, z\}\} \rightarrow \{\{y, w\}, \{y, z\}, \{w, x\}\}$$

The multiway system for this rule (with events included) has the form:

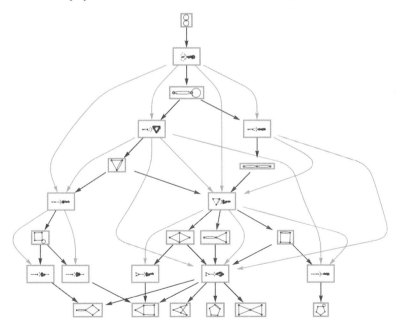

After 20 steps, the causal graph is:

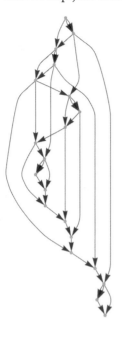

After 100 steps it is:

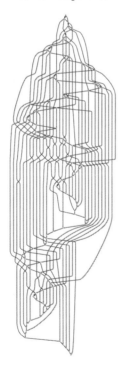

After 500 steps, in an alternative rendering, a grid-like structure emerges (the directed edges point outward from the center):

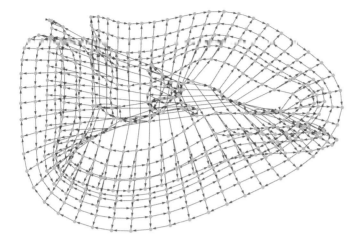

After 5000 steps, rendering the graph in 3D with surface reconstruction reveals an elaborate effective geometry:

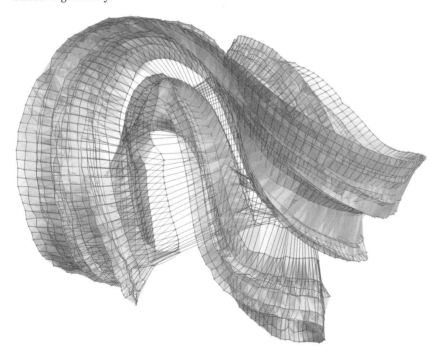

6.6 The Role of Causal Graphs

Even if we do not know that a rule is causal invariant, we can still construct a causal graph for it based on a particular updating order—and often different updating orders will give at least similar causal graphs.

Thus, for example, for the rule

$$\{\{x, y\}, \{x, z\}\} \rightarrow \{\{x, y\}, \{x, w\}, \{y, w\}, \{z, w\}\}$$

applying our standard updating order for 5 steps gives the causal graph:

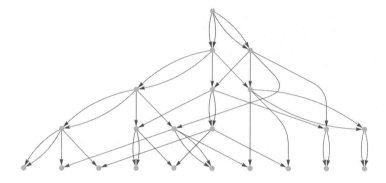

Continuing for 10 steps, we get:

This can also be rendered as:

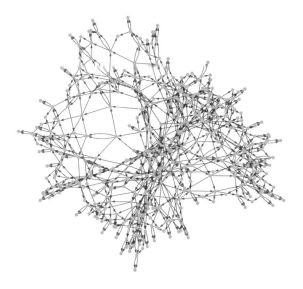

After 15 steps, there are 10,346 nodes:

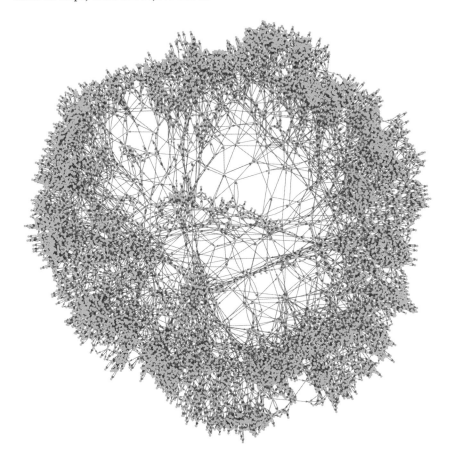

In effect the successive steps in the evolution of the system correspond to successive slices through this causal graph. In the case of causal invariant rules, any possible updating order must correspond to a possible causal foliation of the graph. But here we can at least say that the foliation obtained by looking at successive layers starting from the root corresponds to successive steps of evolution with our standard updating order.

For any system whose evolution continues infinitely, the causal graph will ultimately be infinite. But by slicing the graph as we have above, we are effectively showing the events that contribute to forming the state of the system after 15 steps of evolution (in this case, with our standard updating order):

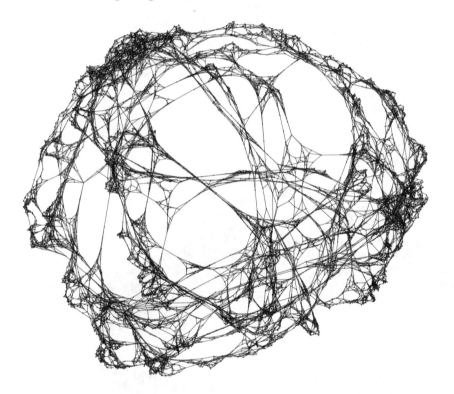

(Note that with this particular rule, the vast majority of relations that appear at step 15 were added specifically at that step, so in a sense most of the state at step 15 is associated just with the slice of the causal graph at layer 15.)

6.7 Typical Causal Graphs

As we discussed in 5.12, causal graphs for string substitution systems tend to have fairly simple structures. Causal graphs for our models tend to be considerably more complicated, and even among $2_2 \rightarrow 3_2$ rules considerable diversity is observed. A typical random sample of different forms is:

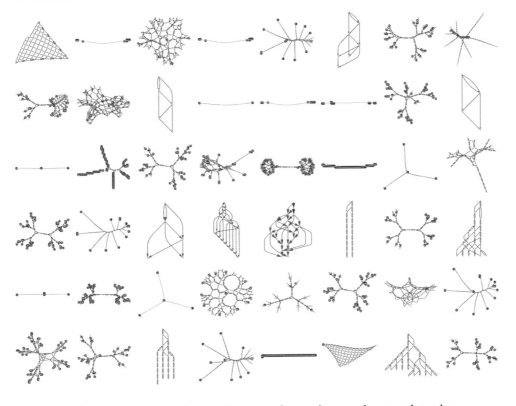

Even rules whose states seem quite simple can produce quite complex causal graphs:

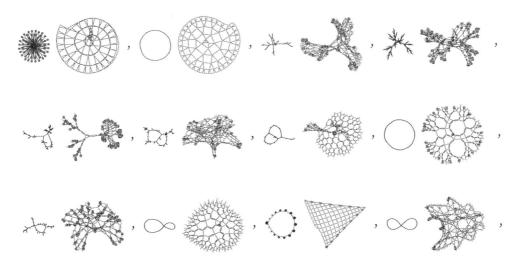

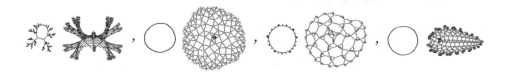

As a first example, consider the rule:

$$\{\{x, x\}, \{x, y\}\} \rightarrow \{\{y, y\}, \{z, y\}, \{x, z\}\}$$

At each step, the self-loop just adds a relation, and effectively moves around the growing loop:

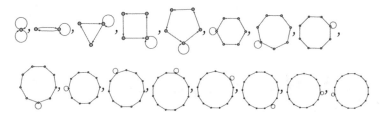

The causal graph captures the causal connections created by the self-loop encountering the same relations again after it goes all the way around:

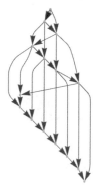

The structure gets progressively more complicated:

Re-rendering this gives

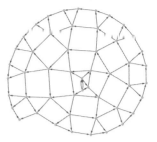

or after 500 steps:

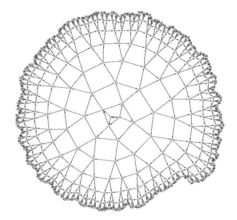

As another example, consider the rule:

$$\{\{x, y\}, \{x, z\}\} \rightarrow \{\{y, w\}, \{y, x\}, \{w, x\}\}$$

Here are the first 25 steps in its evolution (using our standard updating order):

After a few steps all that happens is that there is a small structure that successively moves around the loop creating new "hairs". The causal graph (here shown after 25 steps) captures this process:

An alternative rendering shows that a grid structure emerges:

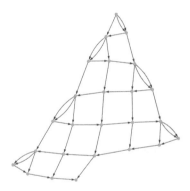

Here are the corresponding results after 100 steps:

 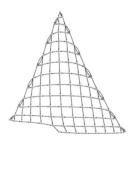

As a somewhat different example, consider the rule:

$$\{\{x, y\}, \{y, z\}\} \rightarrow \{\{x, w\}, \{x, y\}, \{w, z\}\}$$

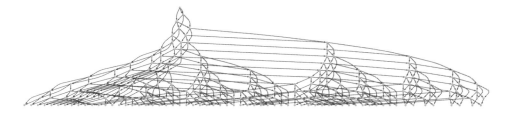

After the same number of steps, one can effectively see the separate trees in the causal graph:

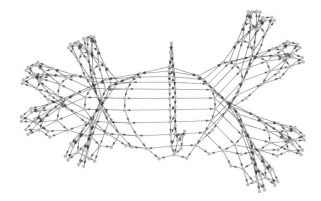

Re-rendering the causal graph, it has a structure that is quite similar to the actual state of the system:

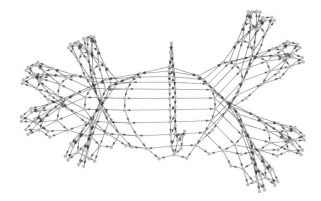

Continuing for a few more steps, a definite tree structure emerges:

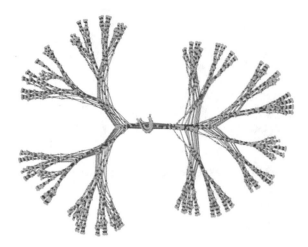

It is not uncommon for a causal graph to "look like" the actual hypergraph generated by one of our models. For example, rules that produce globular structures tend to produce similar "globular" causal graphs (here shown for three $2_2 \to 4_2$ rules from section 3):

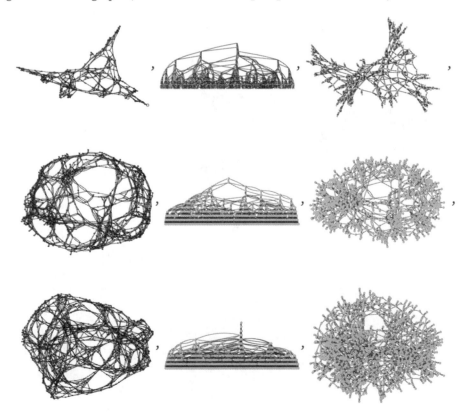

Rules that exhibit slow growth often yield either grid-like or "hyperbolic" causal graphs (here shown for some $2_3 \rightarrow 3_3$ rules from section 3):

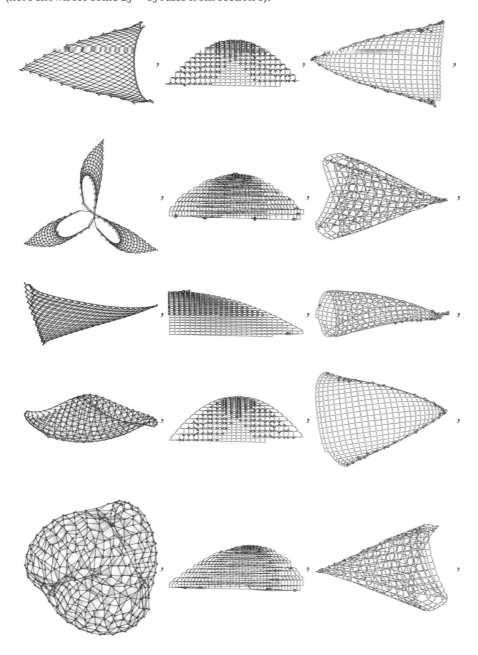

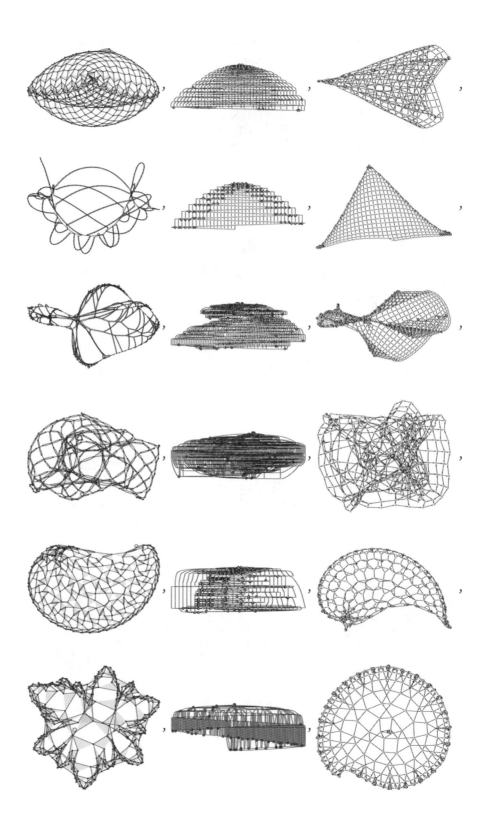

A typical source of grid-like causal graphs [1:p489] is rules where in a sense only one thing ever happens at a time, or, in effect, the rules operate like a mobile automaton [1:3.3] or a Turing machine, with a single active element. As an example, consider the rule (see 3.10):

$$\{\{x, y, y\}, \{z, x, u\}\} \rightarrow \{\{y, v, y\}, \{y, z, v\}, \{u, v, v\}\}$$

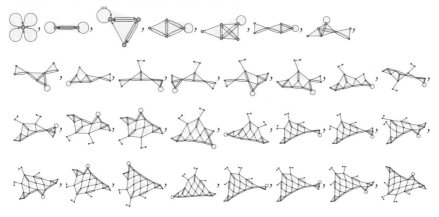

Updates can only occur at the position of the self-loop, which progressively "moves around", "knitting" a grid pattern. The causal graph captures the fact that "only one thing happens at a time":

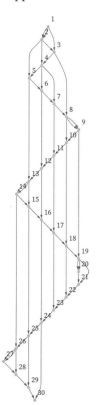

But what is notable is that if we ask about the overall causal relationships between events, we realize that even events that happened many steps apart in the evolution as shown here are actually directly causally connected, because in a sense "nothing else happened in between". Re-rendering the causal graph illustrates this, and shows how a grid is built up:

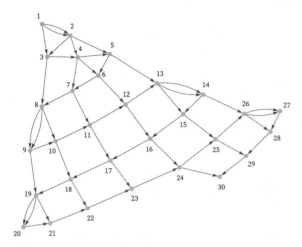

Sometimes the actual growth process can be more complicated, as in the case of the rule

$$\{\{x, y, y\}, \{z, y, u\}\} \rightarrow \{\{v, z, v\}, \{v, u, u\}, \{u, v, x\}\}$$

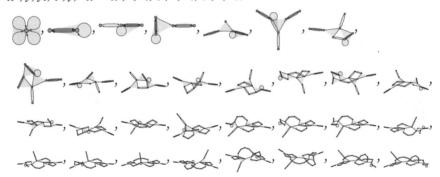

After 200 steps this yields:

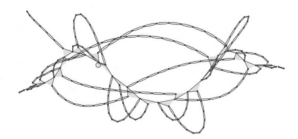

And after 1000 steps it gives:

But despite this elaborate structure, the causal graph is very simple:

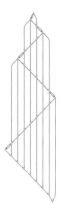

After 200 steps, the grid structure is clear:

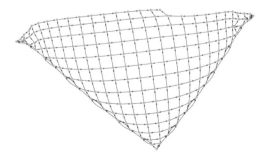

Sometimes the causal graph can locally be like a grid, while having a more complicated overall topological structure. Consider for example the rule:

$$\{\{x, y, y\}, \{z, x, u\}\} \rightarrow \{\{y, z, y\}, \{z, u, u\}, \{y, u, v\}\}$$

After 200 steps this gives:

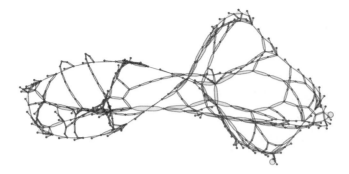

The corresponding causal graph is:

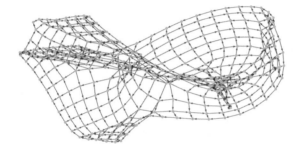

After 1000 steps with surface reconstruction this gives:

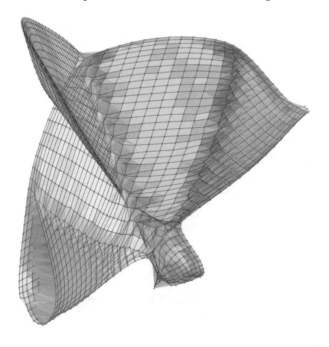

Rules (such as those with signature $2_2 \to 2_2$) that cannot exhibit growth inevitably terminate or repeat, thus leading to causal graphs that are either finite or repetitive—but may still have fairly complex structure. Consider for example the rule (compare 3.15):

$$\{\{x, y\}, \{y, z\}\} \to \{\{z, x\}, \{z, y\}\}$$

Evolution from a chain of 9 relations leads to a 31-step transient, then a 9-step cycle:

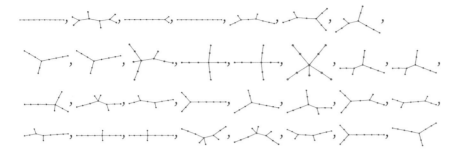

The first 30 layers in the causal graph are:

In an alternative rendering, the graph is:

After 50 more steps, the repetitive structure becomes clear:

Sometimes the structure of the causal graph may be very much a reflection of the updating order used. Consider for example the rather trivial "identity" rule:

$$\{\{x, y\}, \{y, z\}\} \rightarrow \{\{x, y\}, \{y, z\}\}$$

Starting with a chain of 3 relations, this shows update events according to our standard updating order (note that the same relation can be both created and destroyed at a particular step):

The corresponding causal graph is:

For a chain of length of 21 the causal graph consists largely of independent regions—except for the connection created by updates fitting differently at different steps:

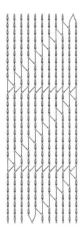

Re-rendering this gives a seemingly elaborate structure:

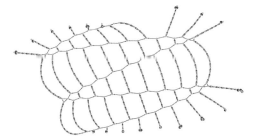

After 100 steps, though, its repetitive character becomes clear:

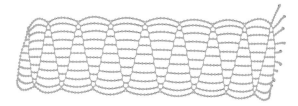

Note that if the initial condition is a ring rather than a chain, one gets

together with the tube-like structure:

6.8 Large-Scale Structure of Causal Graphs

In section 5 we used the cone volume C_t to probe the large-scale structure of causal graphs generated by string substitution systems. Now we use C_t to probe the large-scale structure of causal graphs generated by our models.

Consider for example the rule

$$\{\{x, y\}, \{x, z\}\} \rightarrow \{\{x, y\}, \{x, w\}, \{y, w\}, \{z, w\}\}$$

We found in section 4 that after a few steps, the volumes V_r of balls in the hypergraphs generated by this rule grow roughly like $r^{2.6}$, suggesting that in the limit the hypergraphs behave like a finite-dimensional space, with dimension ≈ 2.6.

The pictures below show the log differences in V_r and C_t for this rule after 15 steps of evolution:

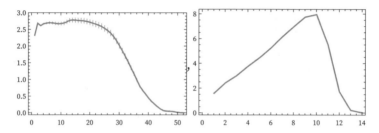

The linear increase in this plot implies exponential growth in C_t and indeed we find that for this rule:

$$C_t \sim 2.2^t$$

This exponential growth—compared with the polynomial growth of V_r—implies that expansion according to this rule is in a sense sufficiently rapid that there is increasing causal disconnection between different parts of the system.

The other three $2_2 \rightarrow 4_2$ globular-hypergraph-generating rules shown in the previous subsection show similar exponential growth in C_t, at least over the number of steps of evolution tested.

A rule such as

$$\{\{x, y, y\}, \{x, z, u\}\} \rightarrow \{\{u, v, v\}, \{v, z, y\}, \{x, y, v\}\}$$

whose hypergraph and causal graph (after 500 steps) are respectively

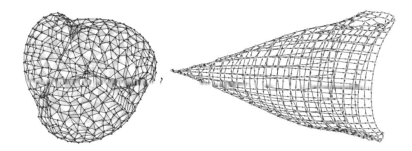

gives the following for the log differences of V_r and C_t after 10,000 steps:

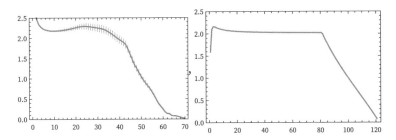

This implies that for this rule the hypergraphs it generates and its causal graph both effectively limit to finite-dimensional spaces, with the hypergraphs having dimension perhaps slightly over 2, and the causal graph having dimension 2.

Consider now the rule:

$$\{\{x, y, x\}, \{x, z, u\}\} \rightarrow \{\{u, v, u\}, \{v, u, z\}, \{x, y, v\}\}$$

The hypergraph and causal graph (after 1500 steps) for this rule are respectively:

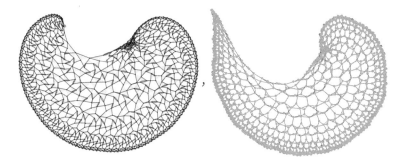

The log differences of V_r and C_t after 10,000 steps are then:

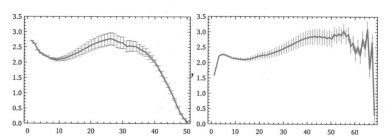

Both suggest limiting spaces with dimension 2, but with a certain amount of (negative) curvature.

6.9 Foliations of Causal Graphs

At least in a causal invariant system, the structure of the causal graph is always the same, and it defines the causal relationships that exist between updating events. But in relating the causal graph to actual underlying evolution histories for the system, we need to specify how we want to foliate the causal graph—or, in effect, how we want to define "steps" in the evolution of the system.

As an example, consider the rule:

$$\{\{x, y\}, \{z, y\}\} \rightarrow \{\{x, z\}, \{y, z\}, \{w, z\}\}$$

(This rule is probably not causal invariant, but this fact will not affect our discussion here.) The most obvious foliation for the causal graph basically follows our standard updating order:

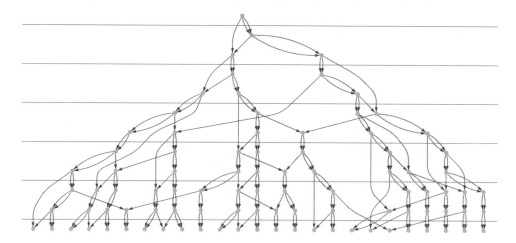

But this is not the only foliation we can use. In fact, we can divide the graph into slices in any way, so long as the slices respect the causal relationships defined by the graph, in the sense that within a slice the causal relationships allow the events to occur in any order, and between successive slices events must occur in the order of the slices. And with these criteria, for example, another possible foliation is

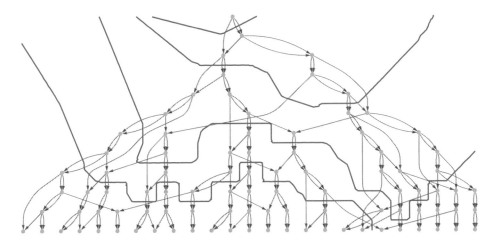

With the first foliation shown above, the hypergraphs from what we consider to be the first "few steps" in the evolution of the underlying rule are:

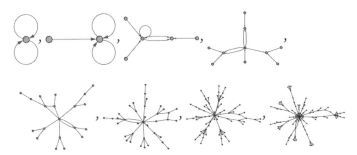

But the second foliation in effect has a different (and coarser) definition of "steps", and with this foliation the first few steps would be:

When we discussed foliations in the context of string substitution systems, there were a number of simplifying features in our discussion. First, the underlying system fundamentally involved a linear string of elements. And second, the main causal graph we actually considered was a simple grid.

With a rule like

$$\{\{x, y, y\}, \{y, z\}\} \rightarrow \{\{x, y\}, \{y, z, z\}\}$$

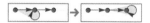

we can also get a simple grid causal graph (and this rule happens to be causal invariant). With the obvious foliation

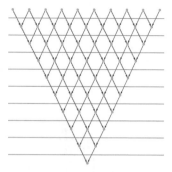

the steps in the evolution of the underlying system from a particular initial condition are:

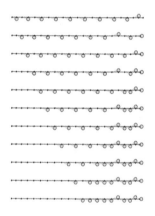

But given the grid structure of the causal graph, we can use the same diagonal slice method for generating foliations that we did in 5.14. And for example with the foliation

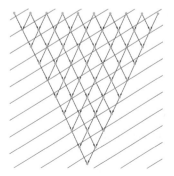

there are more steps involved in the evolution of the system:

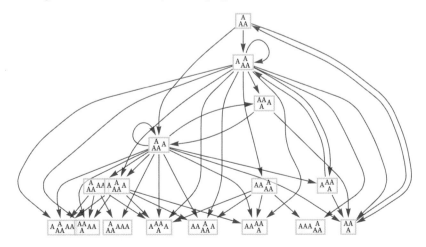

But when the causal graph does not have such a simple structure, the definition of foliations can be much more complicated. When the causal graph at least in some statistical sense limits to a sufficiently uniform structure, it should be possible to set up foliations that are analogous to the diagonal slices. And even in other cases, it will often be possible to set up foliations that can be described, for example, by the kind of lapse functions we discussed in 5.14.

But there is one issue that can make it impossible to set up any reasonable "progressive" foliation of a causal graph at all, and that is the issue of loops. This issue is actually already present even in the case of string substitution systems (and even causal invariant ones). Consider for example the rule:

{AA → A, A → AA}

Starting from AA the multiway causal graph for this rule is:

But note here the presence of several loops. And looking at the states graph in this case

one can see where these loops come from: they are reflections of the fact that in the evolution of the system, there are states that can repeat—and where in a sense a state can return to its past.

Whenever this happens, there is no way to make a progressive foliation in which events in future slices systematically depend only on events in earlier slices. (In the continuum limit, the analog is failure of strong hyperbolicity [86]; loops are the analog of closed timelike curves (e.g. [75])) (Self-loops also cause trouble for progressive foliations by forcing events to happen repeatedly within a slice, rather than only affecting later slices.)

The phenomenon of loops is quite common in string substitution systems, and already happens with the trivial rule A → A. It also happens for example with a rule like:

{AB → BAB, BA → A}

Starting with ABA, this gives the causal graph

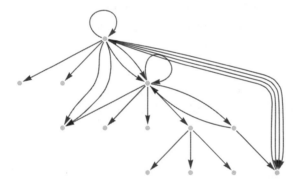

and has a states graph:

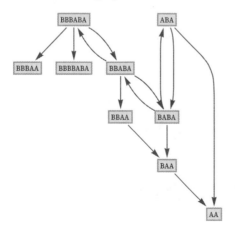

Loops can also happen in our models. Consider for example the very simple rule:

$\{\{\{x\}, \{x\}\} \to \{\{x\}\}, \{\{x\}\} \to \{\{x\}, \{x\}\}\}$

The multiway graph for this rule is:

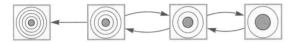

This contains loops, as does the corresponding causal graph:

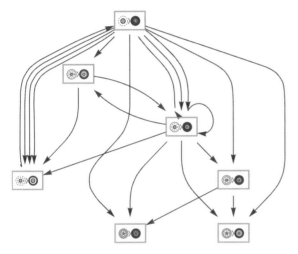

(Note that the issue discussed in 6.1 of when we consider states "identical" as opposed to "equivalent" can again arise here. There are similar issues when we consider finite-size systems where the whole state inevitably repeats—and where in principle we can define a cyclic analog of our foliations.)

6.10 Causal Disconnection

In 2.9 we discussed the fact that some rules—even though the rules themselves are connected—can lead to hypergraphs that are disconnected. And—unless one is dealing with rules with disconnected left-hand sides—any hypergraphs that are disconnected must also be causally disconnected.

As a simple example of what can happen, consider the rule:

$\{\{x, y\}\} \to \{\{y, z\}, \{y, z\}\}$

The evolution of this rule quickly leads to disconnected hypergraphs:

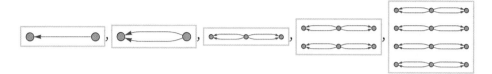

The corresponding causal graph is a tree:

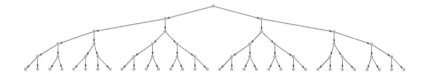

In this particular case, the different branches happen to correspond to isomorphic hypergraphs, so that in our usual way of creating a multiway graph, this rule leads to a connected multiway graph, which even shows causal invariance:

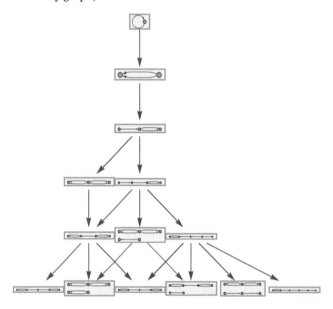

(Note that causal invariance is in a sense easier to achieve with disconnected hypergraphs, because there is no possibility of overlap, or of ambiguity in updates.)

In the case of an extremely simple rule like

$$\{\{x\}\} \rightarrow \{\{y\}, \{z\}\}$$

the evolution is immediately disconnected

the causal graph is a tree

but the multiway graph consists of a simple "counting" sequence of states:

In other rules, the disconnected pieces are not isomorphic, and the multiway graph can split. An example where this occurs is the rule:

$$\{\{x, y\}, \{x, z\}\} \rightarrow \{\{x, x\}, \{y, u\}, \{u, v\}\}$$

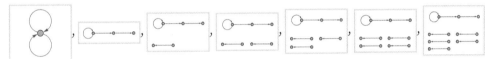

The multiway graph in this case is a tree:

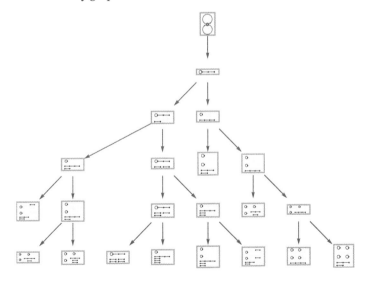

The multiway causal graph, however, does not have an exponential tree structure, but instead effectively just has one branch for each disconnected component in the hypergraph:

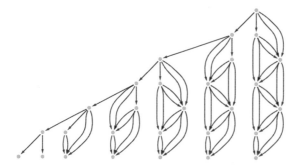

As a result, for this rule the ordinary causal graph has a simple, sequential form:

As a related example, consider the rule:

$$\{\{x, y\}, \{y, z\}\} \rightarrow \{\{u, v\}, \{v, x\}, \{x, y\}\}$$

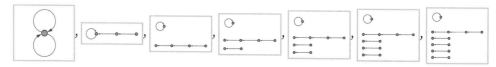

In this case, the multiway graph has the two-branch form

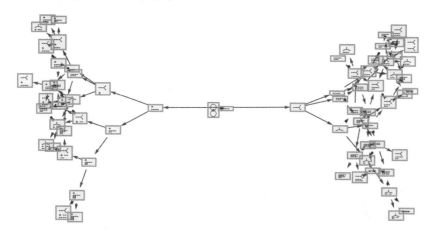

and the multiway causal graph has the similarly two-branch form

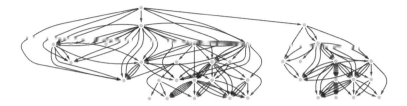

though the ordinary causal graph is still just:

Sometimes there can be multiple branches in both the multiway graph and the ordinary causal graph. An example occurs in the rule

$$\{\{x, y\}, \{x, z\}\} \rightarrow \{\{y, y\}, \{z, u\}, \{z, v\}\}$$

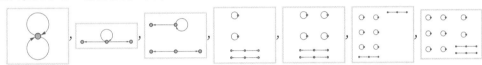

where the multiway graph is

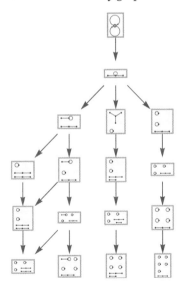

the multiway causal graph is

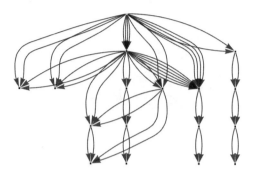

and the ordinary causal graph is:

Is it possible to have both an infinitely branching multiway graph, and an infinitely branching ordinary causal graph? One of the issues is that in general it can be undecidable whether this is ultimately infinite branching. Consider for example the rule:

$$\{\{x, x\}, \{x, y\}\} \rightarrow \{\{y, y\}, \{y, y\}, \{x, z\}\}\}$$

The ordinary causal graph for this rule has the form

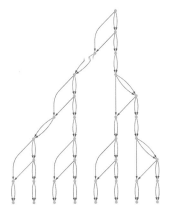

or in a different rendering after more steps:

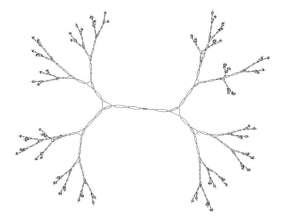

The multiway causal graph in this case is:

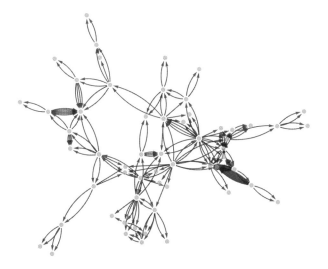

But now the multiway graph is:

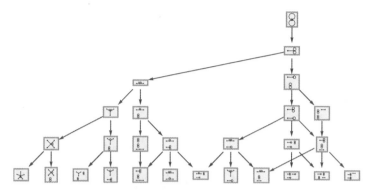

Continuing for more steps yields:

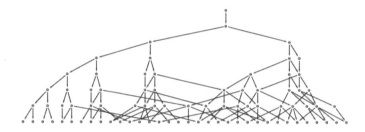

But while it is fairly clear that this multiway graph does not show causal invariance, it is not clear whether it will branch forever or not.

As a similar example, consider the rule:

$$\{\{x, y\}, \{y, z\}\} \rightarrow \{\{x, x\}, \{x, y\}, \{w, y\}\}$$

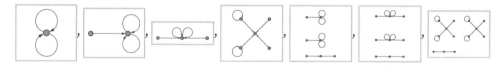

This yields the same ordinary causal graph as the previous rule

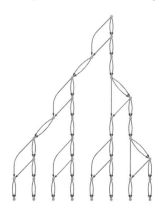

but now its multiway graph has a form that appears slightly more likely to branch forever:

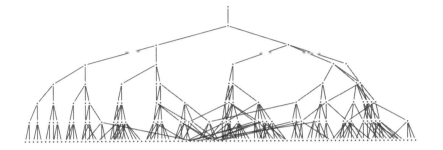

All the examples we have seen so far involve explicit disconnection of hypergraphs. However, it is also possible to have causal disconnection even without explicit disconnection of hypergraphs. As a very simple example, consider the rule:

$\{\{x, x\}\} \rightarrow \{\{x, x\}, \{x, x\}\}$

The causal graph in this case is

although the multiway graph is just:

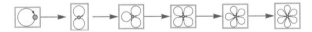

For the rule

$\{\{x, y\}\} \rightarrow \{\{x, x\}, \{x, z\}\}$

the causal graph is again a tree

but now the multiway graph is:

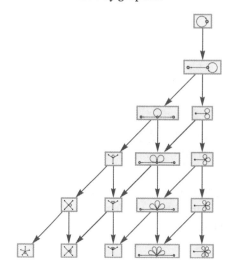

The rule

$$\{\{x, y\}\} \to \{\{x, y\}, \{y, z\}\}$$

gives exactly the same causal graph, but now its hypergraph is a tree:

Like some of the rules shown above, its multiway graph is somewhat complex:

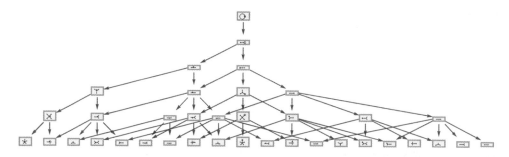

It is actually fairly common to have causal graphs that look like the corresponding hyper-graphs in the case of rules where effectively only one update happens at a time. An example occurs in the case of the rule (see 3.10):

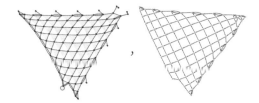

So far, we have only considered fairly minimal initial conditions. But as soon as it is possible to have multiple independent events occur in the initial conditions, it is also possible to get completely disconnected causal graphs. (Note that if an "initial creation event" to create the initial conditions was added, then the causal graphs would again be connected.) As an example of disconnected causal graphs, consider the rule

$$\{\{x\}\} \rightarrow \{\{x\}, \{x\}\}$$

with an initial condition consisting of connected unary relations:

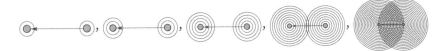

This rule yields a disconnected causal graph:

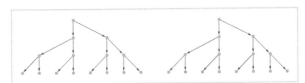

The multiway graph in this case is connected, and shows causal invariance:

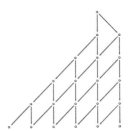

Sometimes the relationship between disconnection in the hypergraph and the existence of disconnected causal graphs can be somewhat complex. This shows results for the rule above with initial conditions consisting of increasing numbers of self-loops:

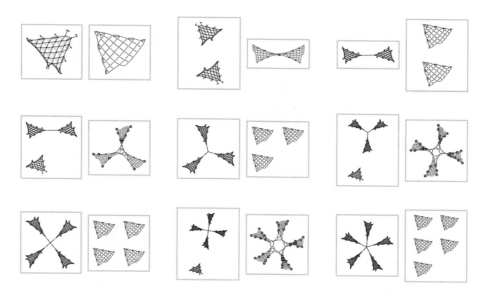

Even with rather simple rules, the forms of branching in causal graphs can be quite complex—even when the actual hypergraphs remain simple. Here are a few examples:

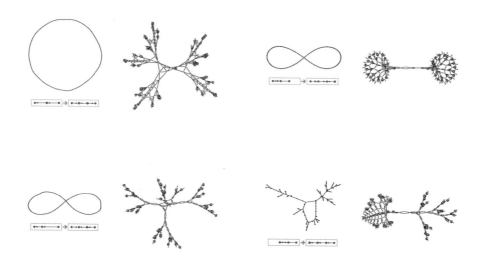

6.11 Global Symmetries and Conservation Laws

Given the rule (stated here using numbers rather than our usual letters)

$\{\{1, 2, 3\}, \{3, 4, 5\}\} \rightarrow \{\{6, 7, 1\}, \{6, 3, 8\}, \{5, 7, 8\}\}$

if we reverse the elements in each relation we get:

$\{\{3, 2, 1\}, \{5, 4, 3\}\} \rightarrow \{\{1, 7, 6\}, \{8, 3, 6\}, \{8, 7, 5\}\}$

But the canonical version of this rule is:

$\{\{1, 2, 3\}, \{3, 4, 5\}\} \rightarrow \{\{6, 7, 1\}, \{6, 3, 8\}, \{5, 7, 8\}\}$

In graphical form, the rule and its transform are:

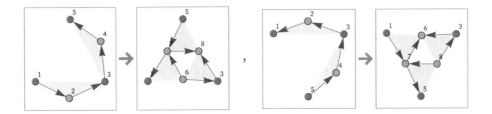

Most rules would not be left invariant under a reversal of each relation. For example, the rule

$\{\{1, 2, 3\}, \{2, 4, 5\}\} \rightarrow \{\{5, 6, 4\}, \{6, 5, 3\}, \{7, 8, 5\}\}$

yields after reversal of each relation

$\{\{3, 2, 1\}, \{5, 4, 2\}\} \rightarrow \{\{4, 6, 5\}, \{3, 5, 6\}, \{5, 8, 7\}\}$

but the canonical form of this is

$\{\{1, 2, 3\}, \{4, 3, 5\}\} \rightarrow \{\{4, 1, 6\}, \{2, 6, 1\}, \{1, 7, 8\}\}$

which is not the same as the original rule.

If a rule is invariant under a symmetry operation such as reversing each relation, it implies that the rule commutes with the symmetry operation. So given a rule R and a symmetry operation Θ, this means that for any state S, $R\,(\Theta\,S)$ must be the same as $\Theta\,(R\,S)$.

With the symmetric rule above, evolving from a particular initial state gives:

But now reversing the relations in the initial state gives essentially the same evolution, but with states whose relations have been reversed:

For the nonsymmetric rule above, evolution from a particular initial state gives:

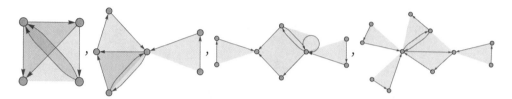

But if one now reverses the relations in the initial state, the evolution is completely different:

For rules with binary relations, the only symmetry operation that can operate on relations is reversal, corresponding to the permutation {2,1}. Of the 73 distinct $1_2 \to 2_2$ rules, 11 have this symmetry. Of the 4702 $2_2 \to 3_2$ rules, 92 have the symmetry. Of the 40,405 $2_2 \to 4_2$ rules, 363 have the symmetry. Those with the most complex behavior are:

$\{\{1, 2\}, \{2, 3\}\} \to \{\{1, 2\}, \{1, 4\}, \{2, 3\}, \{4, 3\}\}$

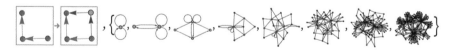

$\{\{1, 2\}, \{2, 3\}\} \to \{\{1, 4\}, \{1, 3\}, \{4, 5\}, \{5, 3\}\}$

For rules with ternary relations, there are six distinct symmetry classes corresponding to the six subgroups of the symmetric group S_3: no invariance, invariance under transposition of two elements (3 cases of S_2) ({1,3,2}, {3,2,1} or {2,1,3} only), invariance under cyclic rotation (A_3) ({2,3,1} and {3,1,2}), or invariance under any permutation (full S_3). Here are the numbers of rules of various signatures with these different symmetries:

	$1_3 \to 1_3$	$1_3 \to 2_3$	$1_3 \to 3_3$	$2_3 \to 1_3$	$2_3 \to 2_3$	$2_3 \to 3_3$	$3_3 \to 1_3$
none	114	8520	627072	7662	759444	79170508	559602
S_2 (each of 3)	20	282	3475	248	4413	63028	2933
A_3	2	4	40	4	8	131	40
S_3	2	3	25	3	5	41	21

Examples of rules with full S_3 symmetry include (compare 7.2):

$\{\{1, 2, 3\}, \{2, 3, 1\}\} \to \{\{2, 2, 4\}, \{4, 3, 3\}, \{1, 4, 1\}\}$

$\{\{1, 2, 3\}, \{2, 3, 1\}\} \to \{\{4, 4, 2\}, \{4, 1, 4\}, \{3, 4, 4\}\}$

An example of a rule with only cyclic (A_3) symmetry is:

$\{\{1, 2, 3\}, \{2, 3, 1\}\} \to \{\{1, 1, 4\}, \{4, 2, 2\}, \{3, 4, 3\}\}$

The existence of symmetry in a rule has implications for its multiway graph, effectively breaking its state transition graph into pieces corresponding to different cosets (compare [1:p963]). For example, starting from all 102 distinct 2-element ternary hypergraphs, the first completely symmetric rule above gives multiway system:

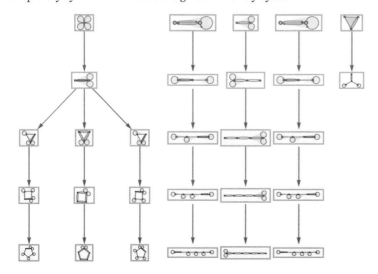

A somewhat simpler example of a completely symmetric rule is:

$$\{\{1, 2, 3\}, \{2, 3, 1\}\} \rightarrow \{\{1, 2, 3\}, \{2, 3, 1\}, \{3, 1, 2\}\}$$

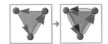

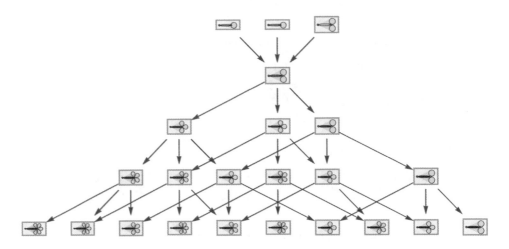

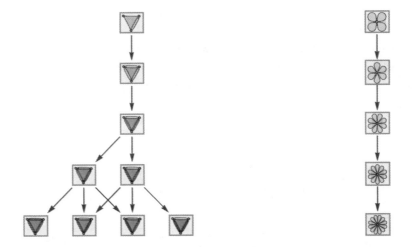

This rule has a simple conservation law: it generates new relations but not new elements. And as a result its multiway graph breaks into multiple separate components.

In general one can imagine many different kinds of conservation laws, some associated with identifiable symmetries, and some not. To get a sense of what can happen, let us consider the simpler case of string substitution systems.

The rule (which has reversal symmetry)

{BA → AB, AB → BA}

gives a multiway graph which consists of separate components distinguished by their total numbers of As and Bs:

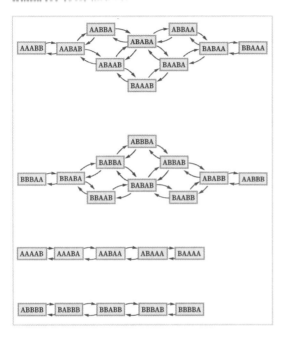

The rule

{AA → BB, BB → AA}

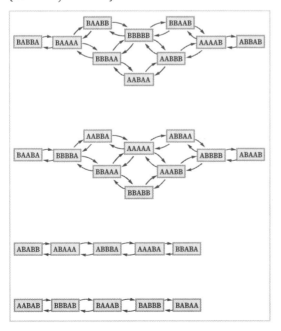

gives the same basic structure, but now what distinguishes the components is the difference in the number of ABs vs. BAs that occur in each string. In both these examples, the number of distinct components increases linearly with the length of the strings.

The rule

{AA → BB, AB → BA}

already gives exactly two components, one with an even number of Bs, and one with an odd number:

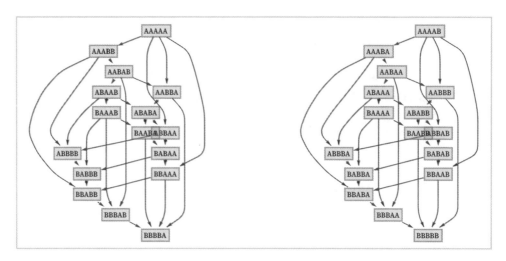

The rule

{AB → AA, BB → BA}

also gives two components, but now these just correspond to strings that start with A or start with B.

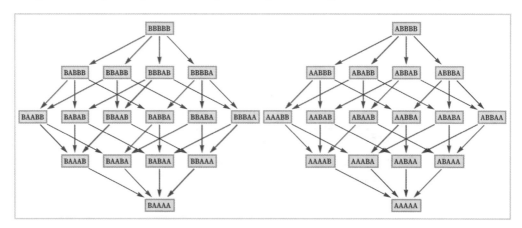

6.12 Local Symmetries

In the previous subsection, we considered symmetries associated with global transformations made on all relations in a system. Here we will consider symmetries associated with local transformations on relations involved in particular rule applications.

Every time one does an update with a given rule, say

$\{\{x, y\}, \{z, y\}\} \to \{\{x, x\}, \{y, y\}, \{z, w\}\}$

one needs to match the "variables" that appear on the left-hand side with actual elements in the hypergraph. But in general there may be multiple ways to do this. For example, with the hypergraph

$\{\{1, 2\}, \{3, 2\}\}$

one could either match

$\{x \to 1, y \to 2, z \to 3\}$

or:

$\{z \to 1, y \to 2, x \to 3\}$

The possible permutations of matches correspond to the automorphism group of the hypergraph that represents the left-hand side of the rule.

For 2_2 hypergraphs of which $\{\{x,y\},\{y,z\}\}$ is an example, there are only two possible automorphism groups: the trivial group (i.e. no invariances), and the group S_2 (i.e. permutations $\{2,3\}$, $\{1,3\}$ or $\{1,2\}$).

Here are automorphism groups for binary and ternary hypergraphs with various signatures. In each case the group order is included, as are a couple of sample hypergraphs:

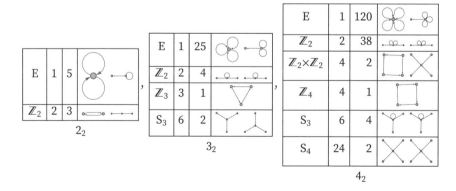

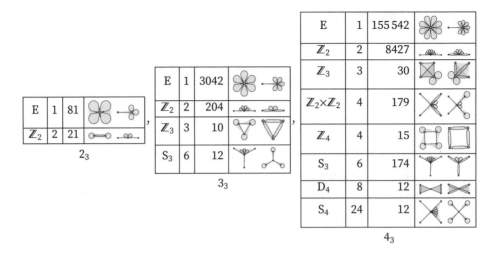

E	1	81
Z_2	2	21

2_3

E	1	3042
Z_2	2	204
Z_3	3	10
S_3	6	12

3_3

E	1	155 542
Z_2	2	8427
Z_3	3	30
$Z_2 \times Z_2$	4	179
Z_4	4	15
S_3	6	174
D_4	8	12
S_4	24	12

4_3

If the right-hand side of a rule has at least as high a symmetry as the left-hand side, then any possible permutation of matches of elements will lead to the same result—which means that the same update will occur, and the only consequence will be a potential change in path weightings in the multiway graph.

But if the right-hand side of the rule has lower symmetry than the left-hand side (i.e. its automorphism group is a proper subgroup), then different permutations of matches can lead to different outcomes, on different branches of the multiway system. It may still nevertheless be the case that some permutations will lead to identical outcomes—and this will happen whenever the canonical form of the rule is the same after a permutation of the elements on the left-hand side (cf. [87]).

Thus for example the rule

$\{\{x, y\}, \{z, y\}\} \rightarrow \{\{x, x\}, \{y, y\}, \{z, w\}\}$

is invariant under any of the permutations

$\{\{1, 2, 3\}, \{2, 1, 3\}, \{3, 1, 2\}, \{3, 2, 1\}\}$

of the elements corresponding to $\{x, y, z\}$. Note that the permutations that appear here do not form a group. To compose multiple such transformations one must take account of relabeling on the right-hand side as well as the left-hand side.

For the 3138 $2_2 \rightarrow 3_2$ rules that involve 3 elements on the left, the following lists the 10 of 64 subsets of the 6 possible permutations that occur:

In a sense, we can characterize the local symmetry of a rule by determining what permutations of inputs it leaves invariant. But we can do this not only for a single update, but for a sequence of multiple updates. In effect, all we have to do is to form a power of the rule, and then apply the same procedure as above.

There are several ways to define a notion of powers (or in general, products) of rules. As one example, we can consider situations in which a rule is applied repeatedly to an overlapping set of elements—so that in effect the successive rule applications are causally connected.

In this case—much as we did for testing total causal invariance—we need to work out the unifications of the possible initial conditions. Then we effectively just need to trace the multiway evolution from each of these unified initial conditions.

Consider for example the rule:

$$\{\{x, y\}\} \to \{\{x, y\}, \{y, z\}\}$$

The "square" of this rule is:

And its cube is:

The multiway graph for the original rule after 4 updates is:

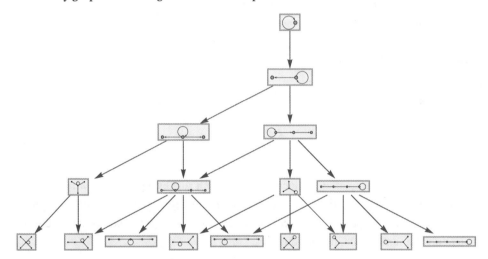

The "square" of the rule generates the same states in only 2 updates:

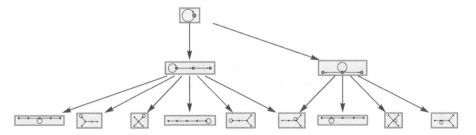

We can use the same approach to find the "square" of a rule like:

$$\{\{x, y\}, \{x, z\}\} \to \{\{x, y\}, \{x, w\}, \{y, w\}, \{z, w\}\}$$

The result is:

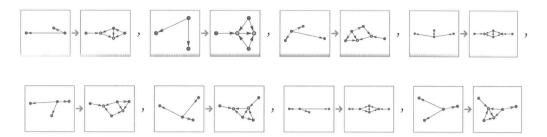

Using this for actual evolution gives the result:

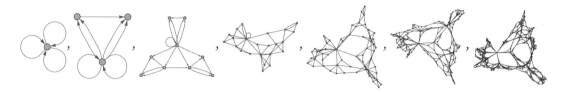

And now that we can compute the power of a rule, we have a way to compute the effective symmetry for multiple updates according to a rule. In general, after t updates we will end up with a collection of permutations of variables that leave the effective "power rule" invariant.

But if we now consider increasingly large values of t, we can ask whether the collections of permutations we get somehow converge to a definite limit. In direct analogy to the way that our hypergraphs can limit to manifolds, we may wonder whether these collections of permutations could limit to a Lie group (cf. [88]).

As a simple example, say that the permutations are of length n, but of the $n!$ possibilities, we only have the n cyclic permutations, say for $n = 4$:

$\{\{1, 2, 3, 4\}, \{2, 3, 4, 1\}, \{3, 4, 1, 2\}, \{4, 1, 2, 3\}\}$

As $n \to \infty$ we can consider this to limit to the Lie group U(1), corresponding to rotations by any angle θ on a circle.

It is not so clear [89][90] how to deal in more generality with collections of permutations, although one could imagine an analog of a manifold reconstruction procedure. To get an idea of how this might work, consider the inverse problem of approximating a Lie group by permutations. (Note that things would be much more straightforward if we could build up matrix representations, but this is not the setup we have.)

In some cases, there are definite known finite subgroups of Lie groups—such as the icosahedral group A_5 as a subset of the 3D rotation group SO(3). In such cases one can then explicitly consider the permutation representation of the finite group. It is also possible to imagine just taking a lattice (or perhaps some more general structure of the kind that might be used in symbolic dynamics [91][92]) and applying random elements of a particular Lie group to it, then in each case recording the transformation of lattice points that this yields. Typically these transformations will not be permutations, but it may be possible to approximate them as such. By inverting this kind of procedure, one can imagine potentially being able to go from a collection of permutations to an approximating Lie group.

6.13 Branchial Graphs and Multiway Causal Graphs

Consider the rule:

$$\{\{x, y\}, \{x, z\}\} \rightarrow \{\{x, y\}, \{x, w\}, \{y, w\}, \{z, w\}\}$$

If we pick a foliation for the first few steps in the multiway graph for this rule

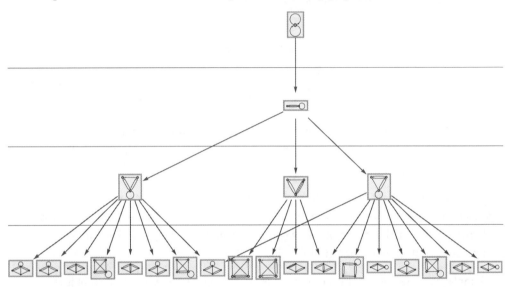

then just as in 5.15 for string substitution systems, we can generate branchial graphs that represent the connections defined by branch pairs between the states at each slice in the foliation:

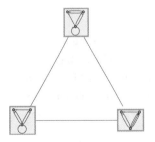

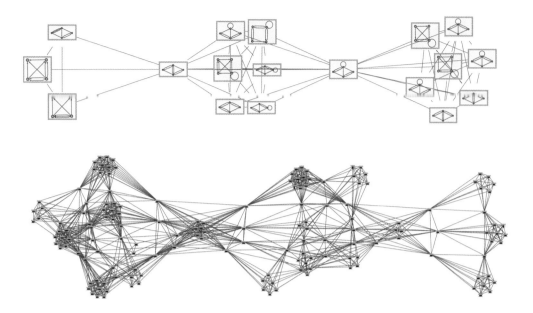

Branchial graphs provide one form of summary of the multiway evolution. Another summary is provided by the multiway causal graph, which includes causal connections between parts of hypergraphs both within a branch of the multiway system, and across different branches:

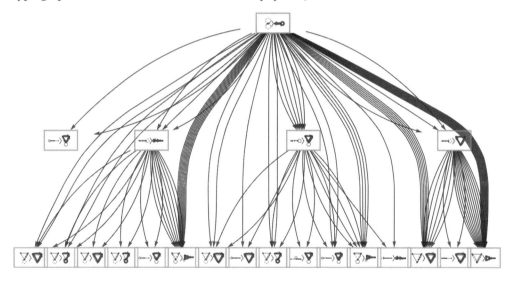

The multiway causal graph is in many respects the richest summary of the behavior of our models, and it will be important in our discussion of possible connections to physics.

In a case like the rule shown, the structure of branchial and multiway causal graphs is quite complex. As a simpler example, consider the causal invariant rule:

$$\{\{x, y\}\} \rightarrow \{\{x, y\}, \{y, z\}\}$$

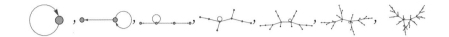

With this rule, the multiway graph has the form:

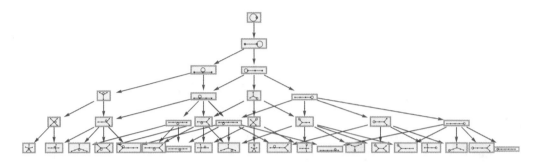

After more steps, and with a different rendering, the multiway graph is:

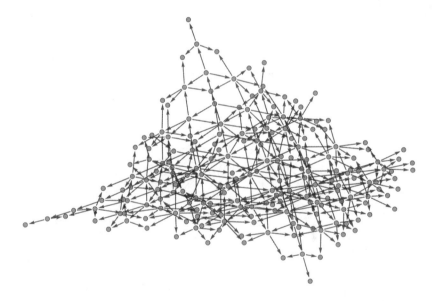

(In this case, the size of the multiway graph as measured by Σ_t increases slightly faster than 2^t.)

The branchial graphs with the standard layered foliation in this case are:

The volumes B_t in the branchial graph grow on successive steps like:

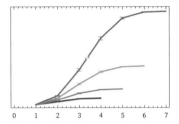

The multiway causal graph in this case is

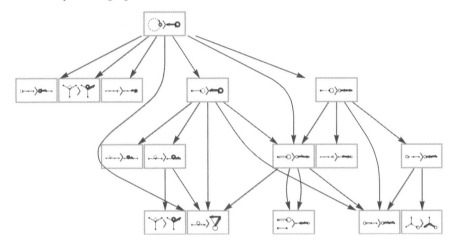

or with more steps and a different layout:

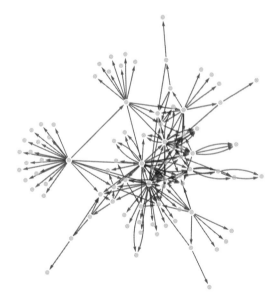

Note that in this case the ordinary multiway graph is simply:

As a slightly more complicated example, consider the causal invariant $2_2 \rightarrow 3_2$ rule:

$\{\{x, y\}, \{x, z\}\} \rightarrow \{\{y, w\}, \{y, z\}, \{w, x\}\}$

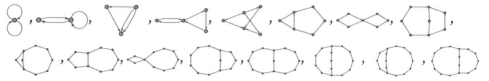

The multiway system in this case has the form:

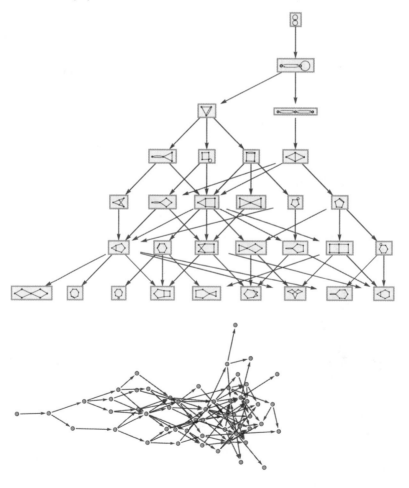

The sequence of branchial graphs in this case are:

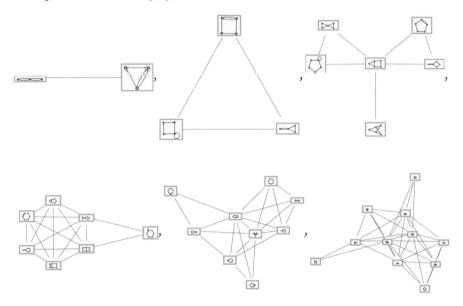

The causal graph for this rule is:

The multiway causal graph has many repeated edges:

Here it is in a different rendering:

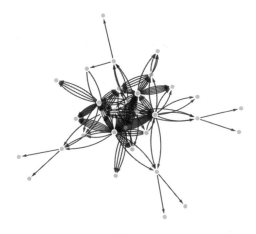

Note that in our models, even when the hypergraphs are disconnected, the branchial graphs can still be connected, as in the case of the rule:

$$\{\{x, y\}\} \to \{\{y, z\}, \{z, w\}\}$$

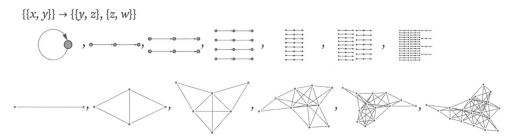

7 | Equivalence and Computation in Our Models

7.1 Correspondence with Other Systems

Our goal with the models introduced here is to have systems that are intrinsically as structureless as possible, and are therefore in a sense as flexible and general as possible. And one way to see how successful we have been is to look at what is involved in reproducing other systems using our models.

As a first example, consider the case of string substitution systems (e.g [1:3.5]). An obvious way to represent a string is to use a sequence of relations to set up what amounts to a linked list. The "payload" at each node of the linked list is an element of the string. If one has two kinds of string elements A and B, these can for example be represented respectively by 3-ary and 4-ary relations. Thus, for example, the string ABBAB could be (where the Bs can be identified from the "inner self-loops" in their 4-ary relations):

{{0, A1, 1}, {1, B2, B2, 2}, {2, B3, B3, 3}, {3, A4, 4}, {4, B5, B5, 5}}

Note that the labels of the elements and the order of relations are not significant, so equivalent forms are

{{1, 7, 2}, {2, 9, 9, 3}, {3, 10, 10, 4}, {4, 8, 5}, {5, 11, 11, 6}}

or, with our standard canonicalization:

{{1, 2, 2, 3}, {3, 4, 4, 5}, {6, 7, 7, 8}, {5, 9, 6}, {10, 11, 1}}

A rule like

{A → BA, B → A}

can then be translated to

{{{0, A1, 1}} → {{0, B1, B1, −2}, {−2, A2, 1}}, {{0, B1, B1, 1}} → {{0, A1, 1}}} or:

$\{\{\{x, y, z\}\} \to \{\{x, u, u, v\}, \{v, w, z\}\}, \{\{x, y, y, z\}\} \to \{\{x, u, z\}\}\}$

Starting with A, the original rule gives:

{A, BA, ABA, BAABA, ABABAABA, BAABAABABAABA, ABABAABABAABAABABAABA}

In terms of our translation, this is now:

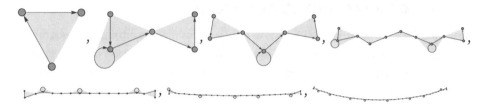

The causal graph for the rule in effect shows the dependence of the string elements

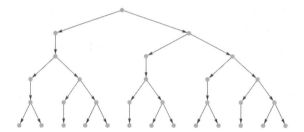

corresponding to the evolution graph (see 5.1):

We can also take our translation of the string substitution system, and use it in a multiway system:

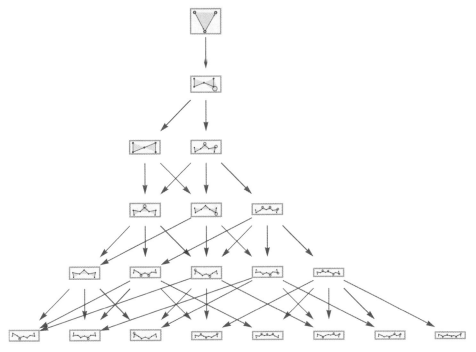

The result is a direct translation of what we could get with the underlying string system:

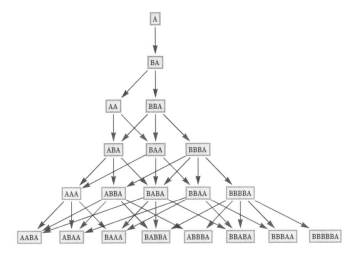

Having seen how our models can reproduce string substitution systems, we consider next the slightly more complex case of reproducing Turing machines [93].

As an example, consider the simplest universal Turing machine [1:p709][94][95] [96], which has the 2-state 3-color rule:

Given a tape with the Turing machine head at a certain position

a possible encoding uses different-arity hyperedges to represent different values on the tape, and different states for the head, then attaches the head to a certain position on the tape, and uses special (in this case 6-ary) hyperedges to provide "extensible end caps" to the tape:

With this setup, the rule can be encoded as:

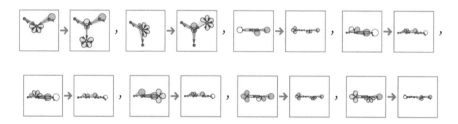

Starting from a representation of a blank tape, the first few steps of evolution are (note that the tape is extended as needed)

which corresponds to the first few steps of the Turing machine evolution:

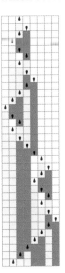

The causal graph for our model directly reflects the motion of the Turing machine head, as well as the causal connections generated by symbols "remembered" on the tape between head traversals:

Re-rendering this causal graph, we see that it begins to form a grid:

It is notable that even though in the underlying Turing machine only one action happens at each step, the causal graph still connects many events in parallel (cf. [1:p489]). After 1000 steps the graph has become a closer approximation to a flat 2D manifold, with the specific Turing machine evolution reflected in the detailed "knitting" of connections on its surface:

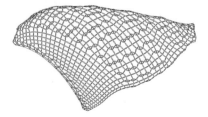

The rule we have set up allows only one thread of history, so the multiway system is trivial:

But with our model the underlying setup is general enough that it can handle not only ordinary deterministic Turing machines in which each possible case leads to a specific outcome, but also non-deterministic ones (as used in formulating NP problems) (e.g. [97]), in which there are multiple outcomes for some cases:

For a non-deterministic Turing machine, there can be multiple paths in the multiway system:

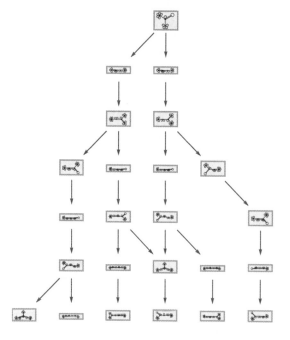

Continuing this, we see that the non-deterministic Turing machine shows a fairly complex pattern of branching and merging in the multiway system (this particular example is not causal invariant):

After a few more steps, and using a different rendering, the multiway system has the form:

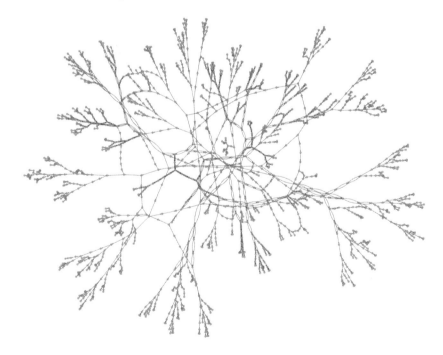

(Note that in actually using a non-deterministic Turing machine, say to solve an NP-complete problem, one needs to check the results on each branch of the multiway system—with different search strategies corresponding to using different foliations in exploring the multiway system.)

As a final example, consider using our models to reproduce cellular automata. Our models are in a sense intended to be as flexible as possible, while cellular automata have a simple but rigid structure. In particular, a cellular automaton consists of a rigid array of cells, with specific, discrete values that are updated in parallel at each step. In our models, on the other hand, there is no intrinsic geometry, no built-in notion of "values", and different updating events are treated as independent and "asynchronous", subject only to the partial ordering imposed by causal relations.

In reproducing a Turing machine using our models, we already needed a definite tape that encodes values, but we only had to deal with one action happening at a time, so there was no issue of synchronization. For a cellular automaton, however, we have to arrange for synchronization of updates across all cells. But as we will see, even though our models ultimately work quite differently, there is no fundamental problem in doing this with the models.

For example, given the rule 30 cellular automaton

we encode a state like

in the form

where the 6-ary self-loops represent black cells. Note that there is a quite complex structure that in effect maintains the cellular automaton array, complete with "extensible end caps" that allow it to grow.

Given this structure, the rule corresponding to the rule 30 cellular automaton becomes

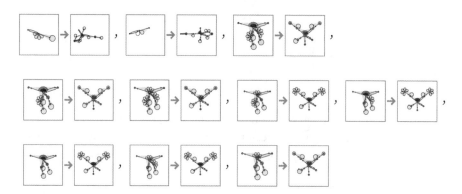

where the first two transformations relate to the end caps, and the remaining 8 actually implement the various cases of the cellular automata rule. Applying the rule for our model for a few steps to an initial condition consisting of a single black cell, we get:

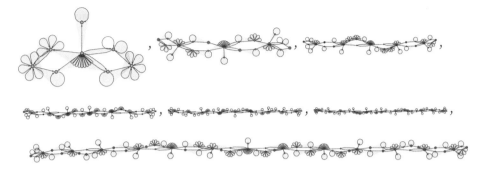

Each of these steps has information on certain cells in the cellular automaton at a certain step in the cellular automaton evolution. "Decoding" each of the steps in our model shown above, we get the following, in which the "front" of cellular automaton cells whose values are present at that step in our model are highlighted:

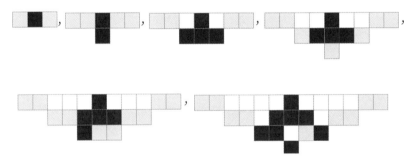

The particular foliation we have used to determine the steps in the evolution of our model corresponds to a particular foliation of the evolution of the cellular automaton:

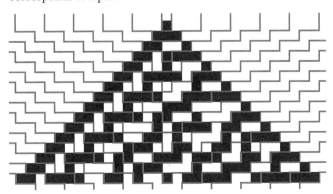

The final "spacetime" cellular automaton pattern is the same, but the foliation defines a specific order for building it up. We can visualize the way the data flows in the computation by looking at the causal graph (with events forming cells with different colors indicated):

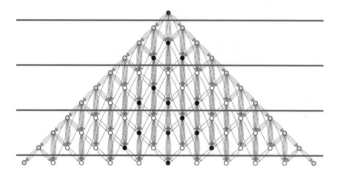

Here is the foliation of the causal graph that corresponds to each step in a traditional synchronized parallel cellular automaton updating:

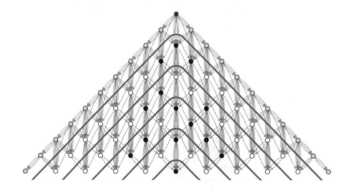

7.2 Alternative Formulations

We have formulated our models in terms of the rewriting of collections of relations between elements. And in this formulation, we might represent a state in one of our models as a list of (here 3-ary) relations

$$\{\{1, 2, 2\}, \{3, 1, 4\}, \{3, 5, 1\}, \{6, 5, 4\}, \{2, 7, 6\}, \{8, 7, 4\}\}$$

and the rule for the model as:

$$\{\{x, y, z\}, \{z, u, v\}\} \to \{\{w, z, v\}, \{z, x, w\}, \{w, y, u\}\}$$

where x, y, … are taken to be pattern or quantified variables, suggesting notations like [98]

$$\{\{x\_, y\_, z\_\}, \{z\_, u\_, v\_\}\} \to \{\{w, z, v\}, \{z, x, w\}, \{w, y, u\}\}$$

or [99]

$$\forall_{\{x,y,z,u,v\}} (\{\{x, y, z\}, \{z, u, v\}\} \to \{\{w, z, v\}, \{z, x, w\}, \{w, y, u\}\})$$

An alternative to these kinds of symbolic representations is to think—as we have often done here—in terms of transformations of directed hypergraphs. The state of one of our models might then be represented by a directed hypergraph such as

while the rule would be:

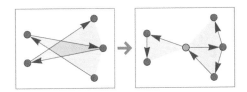

But in an effort to understand the generality of our models—as well as to see how best to enumerate instances of them—it is worthwhile to consider alternative formulations.

One possibility to consider is ordinary graphs. If we are dealing only with binary relations, then our models are immediately equivalent to transformations of directed graphs.

But if we have general k-ary relations in our models, there is no immediate equivalence to ordinary graphs. In principle we can represent a k-ary hyperedge (at least for $k > 0$) by a sequence of ordinary graph edges:

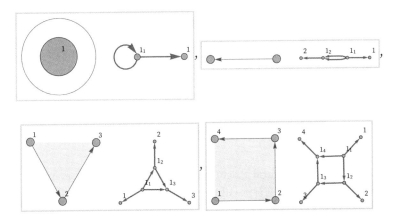

For the hypergraph above, this then yields:

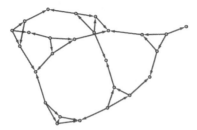

The rule above can be stated in terms of ordinary directed graphs as:

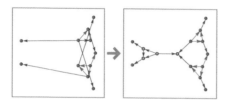

In terms of hypergraphs, the result of 5 and 10 steps of evolution according to this rule is

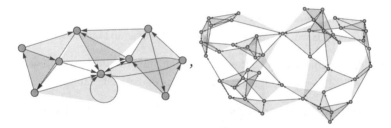

and the corresponding result in terms of ordinary directed graphs is:

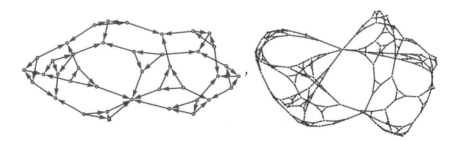

In thinking about ordinary graphs, it is natural also to consider the undirected case. And indeed—as was done extensively in [1:c9]—it is possible to study many of the same things we do here with our models also in the context of undirected graphs. However, transformations of undirected graphs lack some of the flexibility and generality that exist in our models based on directed hypergraphs.

It is straightforward to convert from a system described in terms of undirected graphs to one described using our models: just represent each edge in the undirected graph as a pair of directed binary hyperedges, as in:

Transformations of undirected graphs work the same—though with paired edges. So, for example, the rule

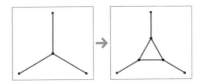

which yields

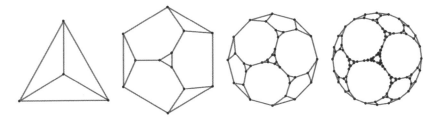

becomes

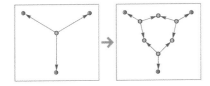

which yields:

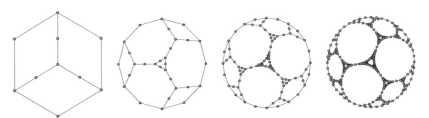

In dealing with undirected graphs—as in [1:c9]—it is natural to make the further simplification that all graphs are trivalent (or "cubic"). In the context of ordinary graphs, nothing is lost by this assumption: any higher-valence node can always be represented directly as a combination of trivalent nodes. But the point about restricting to trivalent graphs is that it makes the set of possible rules better defined—because without this restriction, one can easily end up having to specify an infinite family of rules to cover graphs of arbitrary valence that are generated. (In our models based on transformations for arbitrary relations, no analogous issue comes up.)

It is particularly easy to get intricate nested structures from rules based on undirected trivalent graphs; it is considerably more difficult to get more complex behavior:

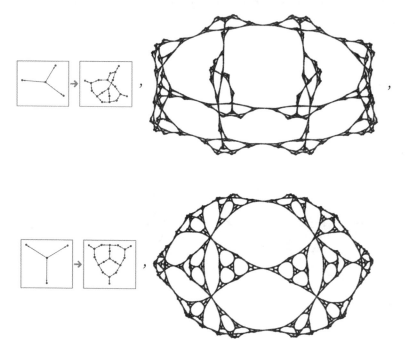

Another issue in models based on undirected graphs has to do with the fact that the objects that appear in their transformation rules do not have exactly the same character as the objects on which they act. In our hypergraph-based models, both sides of a transformation are collections of relations (that can be represented by hypergraphs)—just like what appears in the states on which these transformations act. But in models based on undirected graphs, what appears in a transformation is not an ordinary graph: instead it is a subgraph with "dangling connections" (or "half-edges") that must be matched up with part of the graph on which the transformation acts.

Given this setup, it is then unclear, for example, whether or not the rule above—stated in terms of undirected graphs—should be considered to match the graph:

(In a sense, the issue is that while our models are based on applying rules to collections of complete hyperedges, models based on undirected graphs effectively apply rules to collections of nodes, requiring "dangling connections" to be treated separately.)

Another apparent problem with undirected trivalent graphs is that if the right-hand side of a transformation has lower symmetry than the left-hand side, as in

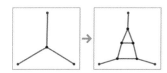

then it can seem "undefined" how the right-hand side should be inserted into the final graph. Having seen our models here, however, it is now clear that this is just one of many examples where multiple different updates can be applied, as represented by multiway systems.

A further issue with systems based on undirected trivalent graphs has to do with the enumeration of possible states and possible rules. If a graph is represented by pairs of vertices corresponding to edges, as in

$\{\{1, 2\}, \{1, 3\}, \{1, 4\}, \{2, 3\}, \{2, 4\}, \{3, 4\}\}$

the fact that the graph is trivalent in a sense corresponds to a global constraint that each vertex must appear exactly three times. The alternate "vertex-based" representation

$\{1 \to \{2, 3, 4\}, 2 \to \{1, 3, 4\}, 3 \to \{1, 2, 4\}, 4 \to \{1, 2, 3\}\}$

does not overcome this issue. In our models based on collections of relations, however, there are no such global constraints, and enumeration of possible states—and rules—is straightforward. (In our models, as in trivalent undirected graphs, there is, however, still the issue of canonicalization.)

In the end, though, it is still perfectly possible to enumerate distinct trivalent undirected graphs (here dropping cases with self-loops and multiple edges)

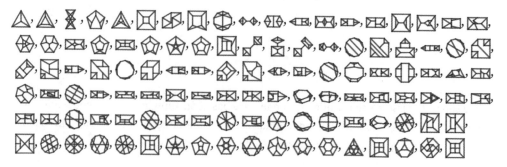

as well as rules for transforming them, and indeed to build up a rich analysis of their behavior [1:9.12]. Notions such as causal invariance are also immediately applicable, and for example one finds that the simplest subgraphs that do not overlap themselves, and so guarantee causal invariance, are [1:p515][87]:

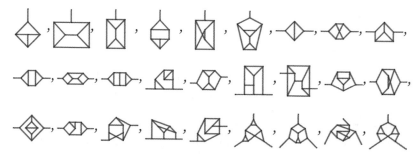

Directed graphs define an ordering for every edge. But it is also possible to have ordered graphs in which the individual edges are undirected, but an order is defined for the edges at any given vertex [87]. Trivalent such ordered graphs can be represented by collections of ordered triples, where each triple corresponds to a vertex, and each number in each triple specifies the destination in the whole list of a particular edge:

{{2, 1, 6}, {5, 4, 3}}

For visualization purposes one can "name" each element of each triple by a color

{<|■ → 2, □ → 1, ■ → 6|>, <|■ → 5, □ → 4, ■ → 3|>}

and then the ordered graph can be rendered as:

In the context of our models, an ordered trivalent graph can immediately be represented as a hypergraph with ternary hyperedges corresponding to the trivalent nodes, and binary hyperedges corresponding to the edges that connect these nodes:

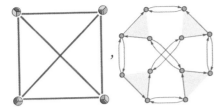

To give rules for ordered trivalent graphs, one must specify how to transform subgraphs with "dangling connections". Given the rule (where letters represent dangling connections)

$$\{\{4, a, b\}, \{1, c, d\}\} \to \{\{4, 8, a\}, \{1, 11, b\}, \{10, 2, c\}, \{7, 5, d\}\}$$

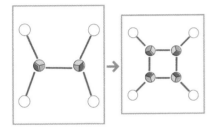

the evolution of the system is:

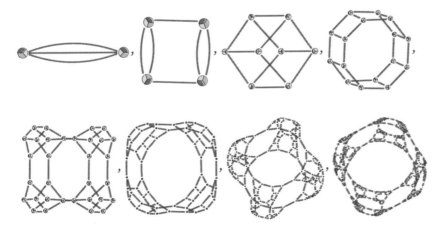

The corresponding rule for hypergraphs would be

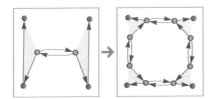

and the corresponding evolution is:

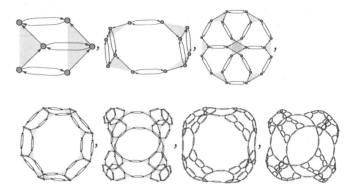

The rule just shown is example of a rule with 2 → 4 internal nodes and 4 dangling connections—which is the smallest class that supports growth from minimal initial conditions. There are altogether 264 rules of this type, with rules of the following forms (up to vertex orderings) [87]:

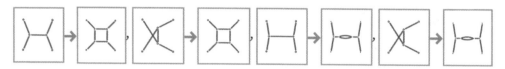

These rules produce the following distinct outcomes:

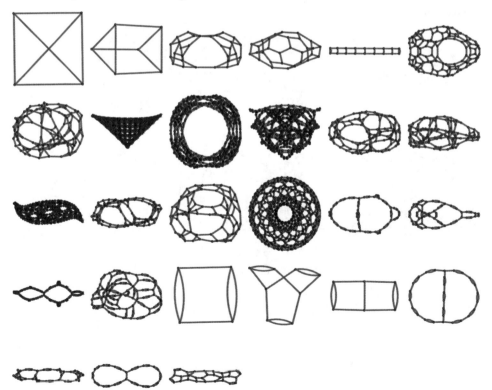

Even though there is a direct translation between ordered trivalent graphs and our models, what is considered a simple rule (for example for purposes of enumeration) is different in the two cases. And while it is more difficult to find valid rules with ordered trivalent graphs, it is notable that even some of the very simplest such rules generate structures with limiting manifold features that we see only after exploring thousands of rules in our models.

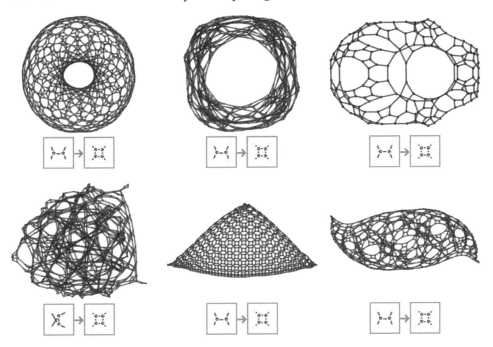

Our models are based on directed (or ordered) hypergraphs. And although the notion is not as natural as for ordinary graphs, one can also consider undirected (or unordered) hypergraphs, in which all elements in a hyperedge are in effect unordered and equivalent. (In general one can also imagine considering any specific set of permutations of elements to be equivalent.)

For unordered hypergraphs one can still use a representation like

{{1, 2, 3}, {1, 2, 4}, {3, 4, 5}}

but now there are no arrows needed within each hyperedge:

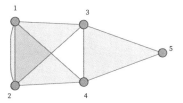

There are considerably fewer unordered hypergraphs with a given signature than ordered ones:

	ordered	unordered
1_2	2	2
2_2	8	4
3_2	32	11
4_2	167	30
5_2	928	95
6_2	5924	328
7_2	40 211	1211

	ordered	unordered
8_2	293 370	4779
9_2	2 255 406	19 902
10_2	18 201 706	86 682
1_3	5	3
2_3	102	15
3_3	3268	107
4_3	164 391	1098

	ordered	unordered
1_4	15	5
2_4	2032	51
3_4	678 358	1048
1_5	52	7
2_5	57 109	164
1_6	203	11
2_6	2 089 513	499

There is a translation between unordered hypergraphs and ordered ones, or specifically between unordered hypergraphs and directed graphs. Essentially one creates an incidence graph in which each node and each hyperedge in the unordered hypergraph becomes a node in the directed graph—so that the unordered hypergraph above becomes:

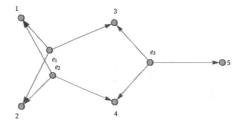

But despite this equivalence, just as in the case of ordered graphs, the sequence of rules will be different in an enumeration based on unordered hypergraphs from one based on ordered hypergraphs.

There are many fewer rules with a given signature for unordered hypergraphs than for ordered ones:

	unordered	ordered
$1_2 \rightarrow 1_2$	5	11
$1_2 \rightarrow 2_2$	19	73
$1_2 \rightarrow 3_2$	71	506
$1_2 \rightarrow 4_2$	296	3740
$1_2 \rightarrow 5_2$	1266	28 959
$2_2 \rightarrow 1_2$	16	64
$2_2 \rightarrow 2_2$	76	562
$2_2 \rightarrow 3_2$	348	4702
$2_2 \rightarrow 4_2$	1657	40 405
$2_2 \rightarrow 5_2$	7992	353 462

	unordered	ordered
$3_2 \rightarrow 1_2$	59	416
$3_2 \rightarrow 2_2$	347	4688
$3_2 \rightarrow 3_2$	1900	48 554
$4_2 \rightarrow 1_2$	235	3011
$4_2 \rightarrow 2_2$	1697	42 955
$5_2 \rightarrow 1_2$	998	23 211
$1_3 \rightarrow 1_3$	22	178
$1_3 \rightarrow 2_3$	257	9373
$2_3 \rightarrow 1_3$	223	8413
$1_4 \rightarrow 1_4$	84	3915

Here is an example of a $2_3 \to 3_3$ rule for unordered hypergraphs:

$$\{\{x, y, z\}, \{u, v, z\}\} \to \{\{x, x, w\}, \{u, v, x\}, \{y, z, y\}\}$$

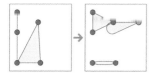

Starting from an unordered double ternary self-loop, this evolves as:

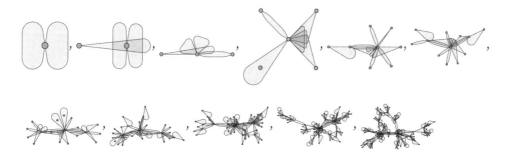

In general the behavior seen for unordered rules with a given signature is considerably simpler than for ordered rules with the same signature. For example, here is typical behavior seen with a random set of unordered $2_3 \to 3_3$ rules:

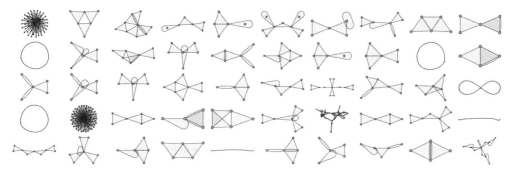

In ordered $2_3 \to 3_3$ rules, globular structures are quite common; in the unordered case they are not. Once one reaches $2_3 \to 4_3$ rules, however, globular structures become common even for unordered hypergraph rules:

$$\{\{x, y, z\}, \{u, y, v\}\} \to \{\{x, w, w\}, \{x, s, z\}, \{z, s, u\}, \{y, v, w\}\}$$

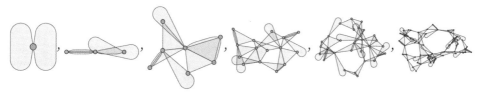

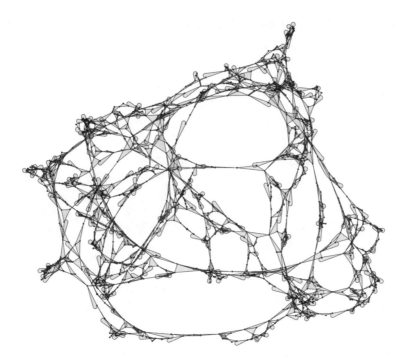

It is worth noting that the concept of unordered hypergraphs can also be applied for binary hyperedges, in which case it corresponds to undirected ordinary graphs. We discussed above the specific case of trivalent undirected graphs, but one can also consider enumerating rules that allow any valence.

An example is

$$\{\{x, y\}, \{x, z\}\} \to \{\{x, w\}, \{y, z\}, \{y, w\}, \{z, w\}\}$$

which evolves from an undirected double self-loop according to:

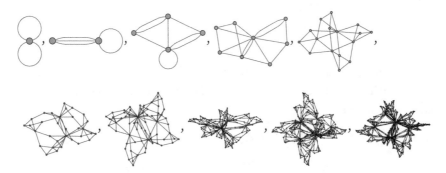

This rule is similar, but not identical, to a rule we have often used as an example:

$$\{\{x, y\}, \{x, z\}\} \to \{\{x, y\}, \{x, w\}, \{y, w\}, \{z, w\}\}$$

Interpreting this rule as referring to undirected graphs, it evolves according to:

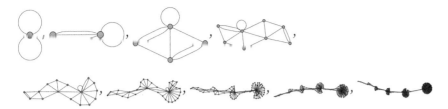

In general, rules for undirected graphs of a given signature yield significantly simpler behavior than rules of the same signature for directed graphs. And, for example, even among all the 7992 distinct $2_2 \to 5_2$ rules for undirected graphs, no globular structures are seen.

Hypergraphs provide a convenient approach to representing our models. But there are other approaches that focus more on the symbolic structure of the models. For example, we can think of a rule such as

$$\{\{x, y, z\}, \{z, u, v\}\} \to \{\{w, z, v\}, \{z, x, w\}, \{w, y, u\}\}$$

as defining a transformation for expressions involving a ternary operator f together with a commutative and associative (n-ary) operator ∘:

$$f[x, y, z] \circ f[z, u, v] \to f[w, z, v] \circ f[z, x, w] \circ f[w, y, u]$$

In this formulation, the ∘ operator can effectively be arbitrarily nested. But in the usual setup of our models, f cannot be nested. One could certainly imagine a generalization in which one considers (much as in [98]) transformations on symbolic expressions with arbitrary structures, represented by pattern rules like

$$f[g[x\_, y\_], z\_] \circ f[h[g[z\_, x\_], x\_]] \to \ldots$$

or even:

$$f[g[x\_, y\_], z\_] \circ f[h\_[g[z\_, x\_], h\_[x\_]]] \to \ldots$$

And much as in the previous subsection, it is always possible to represent such transformations in our models, for example by having fixed subhypergraphs that act as "markers" to distinguish different functional heads or different "types". (Similar methods can be used to have literals in addition to pattern variables in the transformations, as well as "named slots" [100].)

Our models can be thought of as abstract rewriting (or reduction) systems that operate on hypergraphs, or general collections of relations. Frameworks such as lambda calculus [101][102] and combinatory logic [103][104] have some similarities, but focus on defining reductions for tree structures, rather than general graphs or hypergraphs.

One can ask how our models relate to traditional mathematical systems, for example from universal algebra [105][106]. One major difference is that our models focus on transformations, whereas traditional axiomatic systems tend to focus on equalities. However, it is always possible to define two-way rules or pairs of rules $X \rightarrow Y$, $Y \rightarrow X$ which in effect represent equalities, and on which a variety of methods from logic and mathematics can be used.

The general case of our models seems to be somewhat out of the scope of traditional mathematical systems. However, particularly if one considers the simpler case of string substitution systems, it is possible to see a variety of connections [1:p938]. For example, two-way string rewrites can be thought of as defining the relations for a semigroup (or, more specifically, a monoid). If one adds inverse elements, then one has a group.

One thinks of the strings as corresponding to words in the group. Then the multiway evolution of the system corresponds to starting with particular words and repeatedly applying relations to them—to produce other words which for the purposes of the group are considered equivalent.

This is in a sense a dual operation to what happens in constructing the Cayley graph of a group, where one repeatedly adds generators to words, always reducing by using the relations in the group (see 4.17).

For example, consider the multiway system defined by the rule:

{AB → BA, BA → AB}

The first part of the multiway (states) graph associated with this rule is:

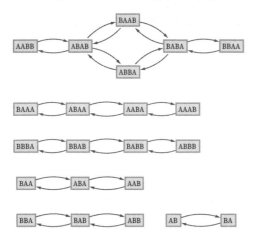

Ignoring inverse elements (which in this case just make double edges) the first part of the infinite Cayley graph for the group with relations AB↔BA has the form:

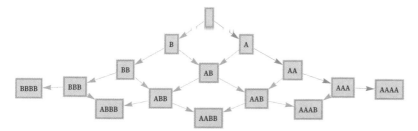

One can think of the Cayley graph as being created by starting with a tree, corresponding to the Cayley graph for a free group, then identifying nodes that are related by relations. The edges in the multiway graph (which correspond to updating events) thus have a correspondence to cycles in the Cayley graph.

As one further example, consider the (finite) group S_3 which can be thought of as being specified by the relations:

{ ↔ AA, AA ↔ BB, BB ↔ ABABAB}

The Cayley graph in this case is simply:

The multiway graph in this case begins:

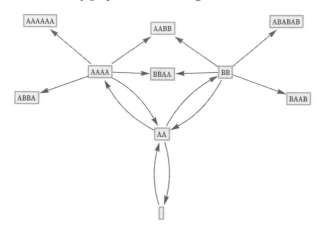

Continuing for a few more steps gives:

On successive steps, the volumes Σ_t in these multiway graphs grow like:

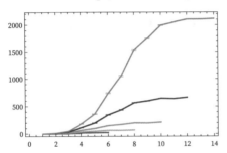

There does not appear to be any direct correspondence to quantities such as growth rates of Cayley graphs (cf. [22]).

7.3 Computational Capabilities of Our Models

An important way to characterize our models is in terms of their computational capabilities. We can always think of the evolution of one of our models as corresponding to a computation: the system starts from an initial state, then follows its rules, in effect carrying out a computation to generate a sequence of results.

The Principle of Computational Equivalence [1:c12] suggests that when the behavior of our models is not obviously simple it will typically correspond to a computation of effectively maximal sophistication. And an important piece of evidence for this is that our models are capable of universal computation.

We saw above that our models can emulate a variety of other kinds of systems. Among these are Turing machines and cellular automata. And in fact we already saw above how our models can emulate what is known to be the simplest universal Turing machine [1:p709][94][95] [96]. We also showed how our models can emulate the rule 30 cellular automaton, and we can use the same construction to emulate the rule 110 cellular automaton, which is known to be computation universal [1:11.8].

So what this means is that we can set up one of our models and then "program" it, by giving appropriate initial conditions, to make it do any computation, or emulate any other computational system. We have seen that our models can produce all sorts of behavior; what this shows is that at least in principle our models can produce any behavior that any computational system can produce.

But showing that we can set up one of our models to emulate a universal Turing machine is one thing; it is something different to ask what computations a random one of our models typically performs. To establish this for certain is difficult, but experience with the Principle of Computational Equivalence [1:c12] in a wide range of other kinds of systems with simple underlying rules strongly suggests that not only is sophisticated computation possible to achieve in our models, it is also ubiquitous, and will occur basically whenever the behavior we see is not obviously simple.

This notion has many consequences, but a particularly important one is computational irreducibility [1:12.6]. Given the simplicity of the underlying rules for our models, we might imagine that it would always be possible—by using some appropriately sophisticated mathematical or computational technique—to predict what the model would do after any number of steps. But in fact what the Principle of Computational Equivalence implies is that more or less whenever it is not obviously straightforward to do, making this prediction will actually take an irreducible amount of computational work—and that in effect we will not be able to compute what the system will do much more efficiently than by just following the steps of the actual evolution of the system itself.

Much of what we have done in studying our models here has been based on just explicitly running the models and seeing what they do. Computational irreducibility implies that this is not just something that is convenient in practice; instead it is something that cannot theoretically be avoided, at least in general.

Having said this, however, it is an inevitable feature of computational irreducibility that there is always an endless sequence of "pockets" of computational reducibility: specific features or questions that are amenable to computation or prediction without irreducible amounts of computational work.

But another consequence of computational irreducibility is the appearance of undecidability [107][108]. If we want to know what will happen in one of our models after a certain number of steps, then in the worst case we can just run the model for that many steps and see what it does. But if we want to know if the model will ever do some particular thing—even after an arbitrarily long time—then there can be no way to determine that with any guaranteed finite amount of effort, and therefore we must consider the question formally undecidable.

Will a particular rule ever terminate when running from a particular initial state? Will the hypergraphs it generates ever become disconnected? Will some branch pair generated in a multiway system ever resolve?

These are all questions that are in general undecidable in our models. And what the Principle of Computational Equivalence implies is that not only is this the case in principle; it is something ubiquitous, that can be expected to be encountered in studying any of our models that do not show obviously simple behavior.

It is worth pointing out that undecidability and computational irreducibility apply both to specific paths of evolution in our models, and to multiway systems. Multiway systems correspond to what are traditionally called non-deterministic computations [109]. And just as a single path of evolution in one of our models can reproduce the behavior of any ordinary deterministic Turing machine, so also the multiway evolution of our models can reproduce any non-deterministic Turing machine.

The fact that our models show computation universality means that if some system—like our universe—can be represented using computation of the kind done, for example, by a Turing machine, then it is inevitable that in principle our models will be able to reproduce it. But the important issue is not whether some behavior can in principle be programmed, but whether we can find a model that faithfully and efficiently reflects what the system we are modeling does. Put another way: we do not want to have to set up some elaborate program in the initial conditions for the model we use; we want there to be a direct way to get the initial conditions for the model from the system we are modeling.

There is another important point, particularly relevant, for example, in the effort to use our models in a search for a fundamental theory of physics. The presence of computation universality implies that any given model can in principle encode any other. But in practice this encoding can be arbitrarily complicated, and if one is going to make an enumeration of possible models, different choices of encoding can in effect produce arbitrarily large changes in the enumeration.

One can think of different classes of models as corresponding to different languages for describing systems. It is always in principle possible to translate between them, but the translation may be arbitrarily difficult, and if one wants a description that is going to be useful in practice, one needs to have a suitable language for it.

8 | Potential Relation to Physics

8.1 Introduction

Having explored our models and some of their behavior, we are now in a position to discuss their potential for application to physics. We shall see that the models generically show remarkable correspondence with a surprisingly wide range of known features of physics, inspiring the hope that perhaps a specific model can be found that precisely reproduces all details of physics. It should be emphasized at the outset that there is much left to explore in the potential correspondence between our models and physics, and what will be said here is merely an indication—and sometimes a speculative one—of how this might turn out.

(See also Notes & Further References.)

8.2 Basic Concepts

The basic concept of applying our models to physics is to imagine that the complete structure and content of the universe is represented by an evolving hypergraph. There is no intrinsic notion of space; space and its apparent continuum character are merely an emergent large-scale feature of the hypergraph. There is also no intrinsic notion of matter: everything in the universe just corresponds to features of the hypergraph.

There is also no intrinsic notion of time. The rule specifies possible updates in the hypergraph, and the passage of time essentially corresponds to these update events occurring. There are, however, many choices for the sequences in which the events can occur, and the idea is that all possible branches in some sense do occur.

But the concept is then that there is a crucial simplifying feature: the phenomenon of causal invariance. Causal invariance is a property (or perhaps effective property) of certain underlying rules that implies that when it comes to causal relationships between events, all possible branches give the same ultimate results.

As we will discuss, this equivalence seems to yield several core known features of physics, notably Lorentz invariance in special relativity, general covariance in general relativity, as well as local gauge invariance, and the perception of objective reality in quantum mechanics.

Our models ultimately just consist of rules about elements and relations. But we have seen that even with very simple such rules, highly complex structures can be produced. In particular, it is possible for the models to generate hypergraphs that can be considered to approximate flat or curved d-dimensional space. The dimension is not intrinsic to the model; it must emerge from the behavior of the model, and can be variable.

The evolving hypergraphs in our models must represent not just space, but also everything in it. At a bulk level, energy and momentum potentially correspond to certain specific measures of the local density of evolution in the hypergraph. Particles potentially correspond to evolution-stable local features of the hypergraph.

The multiway branching of possible updating events is potentially closely related to quantum mechanics, and much as large-scale limits of our hypergraphs may correspond to physical space, so large-scale limits of relations between branches may correspond to Hilbert spaces of states in quantum mechanics.

In the case of physical space, one can view different choices of updating orders as corresponding to different reference frames—with causal invariance implying equivalence between them. In multiway space, one can view different updating orders as different sequences of applications of quantum operators—with causal invariance implying equivalence between them that lead different observers to experience the same reality.

In attempting to apply our models to fundamental physics, it is notable how many features that are effectively implicitly assumed in the traditional formalism of physics can now potentially be explicitly derived.

It is inevitable that our models will show computational irreducibility, in the sense that irreducible amounts of computational work will in general be needed to determine the outcome of their behavior. But a surprising discovery is that many important features of physics seem to emerge quite generically in our models, and can be analyzed without explicitly running particular models.

It is to be expected, however, that specific aspects of our universe—such as the dimensionality of space and the masses and charges of particles—will require tracing the detailed behavior of models with particular rules.

It is already clear that modern mathematical methods can provide significant insight into certain aspects of the behavior of our models. One complication in the application of these methods is that in attempting to make correspondence between our models and physics, many levels of limits effectively have to be taken, and the mathematical definitions of these limits are likely to be subtle and complex.

In traditional approaches to physics, it is common to study some aspect of the physical world, but ignore or idealize away other parts. In our models, there are inevitably close connections between essentially all aspects of physics, making this kind of factored approach—as well as idealized partial models—much more difficult.

Even if the general structure of our models provides an effective framework for representing our physical universe at the lowest level, there does not seem to be any way to know within a wide margin just how simple or complex the specific rule—or class of equivalent rules—for our particular universe might be. But assuming a certain degree of simplicity, it is likely that fitting even a modest number of details of our universe will completely determine the rule.

The result of this would almost certainly be a large number of specific predictions about the universe that could be made even without irreducibly large amounts of computation. But even absent the determination of a specific rule, it seems increasingly likely that experimentally accessible predictions will be possible just from general features of our models.

8.3 Potential Basic Translations

As a guide to the potential application of our models to physics, we list here some current expectations about possible translations between features of physics and features of our models. This should be considered a rough summary, with every item requiring significant explanation and qualification. In addition, it should be noted that in an effort to clarify presentation, many highly abstract concepts have been indicated here by more mechanistic analogies.

Basic Physics Concepts

space: general limiting structure of basic hypergraph

time: index of causal foliations of hypergraph rewriting

matter (in bulk): local fluctuations of features of basic hypergraph

energy: flux of edges in the multiway causal graph through spacelike (or branchlike) hypersurfaces

momentum: flux of edges in the multiway causal graph through timelike hypersurfaces

(rest) mass: numbers of nodes in the hypergraph being reused in updating events

motion: possible because of causal invariance; associated with change of causal foliations

particles: locally stable configurations in the hypergraph

charge, spin, etc.: associated with local configurations of hyperedges

quantum indeterminacy: different foliations (of branchlike hypersurfaces) in the multiway graph

quantum effects: associated with locally unresolved branching in the multiway graph

quantum states: (instantaneously) nodes in the branchial graph

quantum entanglement: shared ancestry in the multiway graph / distance in branchial graph

quantum amplitudes: path counting and branchial directions in the multiway graph

quantum action density (Lagrangian): total flux (divergence) of multiway causal graph edges

Physical Theories & Principles

special relativity: global consequence of causal invariance in hypergraph rewriting

general relativity / general covariance: effect of causal invariance in the causal graph

locality / causality: consequence of locality of hypergraph rewriting and causal invariance

rotational invariance: limiting homogeneity of the hypergraph

Lorentz invariance: consequence of causal invariance in the causal graph

time dilation: effect of different foliations of the causal graph

relativistic mass increase: effect of different foliations of the causal graph

local gauge invariance: consequence of causal invariance in the multiway graph

lack of quantum cosmological constant: space is effectively created by quantum fluctuations

cosmological homogeneity: early universe can have higher effective spatial dimension

expansion of universe: growth of hypergraph

conservation of energy: equilibrium in the causal graph

conservation of momentum: balance of different hyperedges during rewritings

principle of equivalence: gravitational and inertial mass both arise from features of the hypergraph

discrete conservation laws: features of the ways local hypergraph structures can combine

microscopic reversibility: limiting equilibrium of hypergraph rewriting processes

quantum mechanics: consequence of branching in the multiway system

observer in quantum mechanics: branchlike hypersurface foliation

quantum objective reality: equivalence of quantum observation frames in the multiway graph

quantum measurements: updating events with choice of outcomes, that can be frozen by a foliation

quantum eigenstates: branches in multiway system

quantum linear superposition: additivity of path counts in the multiway graph

uncertainty principle: non-commutation of update events in the multiway graph

wave-particle duality: relation between spacelike and branchlike projections of the multiway causal graph

operator-state correspondence: states in the multiway graph are generated by events (operators)

path integral: turning of paths in the multiway graph is proportional to causal edge density

violation of Bell's inequalities, etc.: existence of causal connections in the multiway graph

quantum numbers: associated with discrete local properties of the hypergraph

quantization of charge, etc.: consequence of the discrete hypergraph structure

black holes / singularities: causal disconnection in the causal graph

dark matter: (possibly) relic oligons / dimension changes in of space

virtual particles: local structures continually generated in the spatial and multiway graphs

black hole radiation / information: causal disconnection of branch pairs

holographic principle: correspondence between spatial and branchial structure

Physical Quantities & Constructs

dimension of space: growth rate exponent in hypergraph / causal cones

curvature of space: polynomial part of growth rate in hypergraph / causal cones

local gauge group: limiting automorphisms of local hypergraph configurations

speed of light (c): measure of edges in spatial graph vs. causal graph

light cones: causal cones in the causal graph

unit of energy: count of edges in the causal graph

momentum space: limiting structure of causal graph in terms of edges

gravitational constant: proportionality between node counts and spatial volume

quantum parameter ($\hbar$): measure of edges in the branchial graph (maximum speed of measurement)

elementary unit of entanglement: branching of single branch pair

electric/gauge charges: counts of local hyperedge configurations

spectrum of particles: spectrum of locally stable configurations in the hypergraph

Idealizations, etc. Used in Physics

inertial frame: parallel foliation of causal graph

rest frame of universe: geodesically layered foliation of causal graph

flat space: uniform hypergraph (typically not maintained by rules)

Minkowski space: effectively uniform causal graph

cosmological constant: uniform curvature in the hypergraph

de Sitter space: cyclically connected hypergraph

closed timelike curves: loops in the causal graph (only possible in some rules)

point particle: a persistent structure in the hypergraph involving comparatively few nodes

purely empty space: not possible in our models (space is maintained by rule evolution)

vacuum: statistically uniform regions of the spatial hypergraph

vacuum energy: causal connections attributed purely to establishing the structure of space

isolated quantum system: disconnected part of the branchial/multiway graph

collapse of the wave function: degenerate foliation that infinitely retards branchlike entanglement

non-interacting observer in quantum mechanics: "parallel" foliation of multiway graph

free field theory: e.g. pure branching in the multiway system

quantum computation: following multiple branches in multiway system (limited by causal invariance)

string field theory: (potentially) continuous analog of the multiway causal graph for string substitutions

8.4 The Structure of Space

In our models, the structure of spacetime is defined by the structure of the evolving hypergraph. Causal foliations of the evolution can be used to define spacelike hypersurfaces. The instantaneous structure of space (on a particular spacelike hypersurface) corresponds to a particular state of the hypergraph.

A position in space is defined by a node in the hypergraph. A geometrical distance between positions can be defined as the number of hyperedges on the shortest path in the hypergraph between them. Although the underlying rules for hypergraph rewriting in our models depend on the ordering of elements in hyperedges, this is ignored in computing geometrical distance. (The geometrical distance discussed here is basically just a proxy for a true physical distance measured from dynamic information transmission between positions.) A shortest path on the hypergraph between two positions defines a geodesic between them, and can be considered to define a straight line.

The only information available to define the structure of space is the connectivity of the hypergraph; there is no predefined embedding or topological information. The continuum character of space assumed in traditional physics must emerge as a large-scale limit of the hypergraph (somewhat analogously to the way the continuum character of fluids emerges as a large-scale limit of discrete molecular dynamics (e.g. [1:p378][110]). Although our models follow definite rules, they can intrinsically generate effective randomness (much like the rule 30 cellular automaton, or the computation of the digits of π). This effective randomness makes large-scale behavior typically approximate statistical averages of small-scale dynamics.

In our models, space has no intrinsic dimension defined; its effective dimension must emerge from the large-scale structure of the hypergraph. Around every node at position X consider a geodesic ball consisting of all nodes that are a hypergraph distance not more than r away. Let $V_r(X)$ be the total number of nodes in this ball. Then the hypergraph can be considered to approximate d-dimensional space if

$$V_r(X) \sim r^d$$

for a suitable range of values of r. Here we encounter the first of many limits that must be taken. We want to consider the limit of a large hypergraph (say as generated by a large number of steps of evolution), and we want r to be large compared to 1, but small compared to the overall diameter of the hypergraph.

As a simple example, consider the hypergraph created by the rule

$$\{\{x, y\}, \{x, z\}\} \to \{\{x, y\}, \{x, w\}, \{y, w\}, \{z, w\}\}$$

Starting from a minimal initial condition of two self-loops, the first few steps of evolution with our standard updating order are:

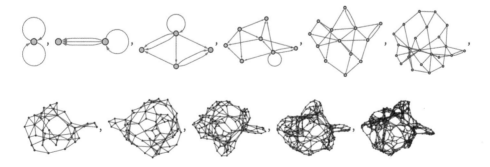

The hypergraph obtained after 12 steps has 1651 nodes and can be rendered as:

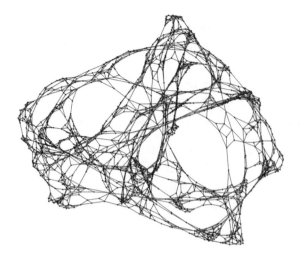

This plots the effective "dimension exponent" of r in V_r as a function of r, averaged over all nodes in the hypergraph, for a succession of steps in the evolution:

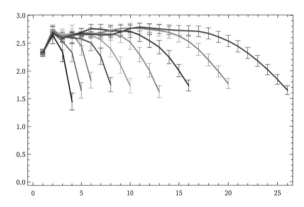

A constant limiting value d indicates approximation to a "flat" d-dimensional space. For integer d, this corresponds to ordinary d-dimensional Euclidean space, but in our models d often does not end up being integer valued, nor does it need to be constant at different positions, or through the course of evolution. It is also important to note that only some rules give $V_r \sim r^d$; exponential or more complex behavior is common.

Even when to leading order $V_r \sim r^d$, there are corrections. For small r (measured, say, relative to the diameter of the hypergraph) one can consider a power series expansion in r. By comparison to ordinary manifolds one can then write (e.g. [24][1:p1050])

$$V_r \sim r^d \left(1 - \frac{r^2}{6(d+2)} R + O(r^4)\right)$$

where R can be identified as the (Ricci) scalar curvature [25][26] of the limiting space. The value of this curvature is again purely determined by the (limiting) structure of the hypergraph. (Note that particularly if one goes beyond a pure power series, there is the potential for subtle interplay between change in dimension and what one might attribute to curvature.)

It is also possible to identify other limiting features of the hypergraph. For example, consider a small stretch of geodesic (where by "small" we mean still large compared to individual connections in the hypergraph, but small compared to the scale on which statistical features of the hypergraph change). Now create a tube of radius r by including every node with distance up to r from any node on the geodesic. The growth rate of the number of nodes in this tube can then be approximated as [44]

$$\tilde{V}_r \sim r^d (1 + \frac{r^2}{6} R_{ij} \delta x^i \delta x^j + O(r^4))$$

where now $R_{ij} \delta x^i \delta x^j$ is the projection of the Ricci tensor along the direction of the geodesic. (The Ricci tensor measures the change in cross-sectional area for a bundle of geodesics, associated with their respective convergence and divergence for positive and negative curvature.)

In a suitable limit, the nodes in the hypergraph correspond to points in a space. A tangent bundle at each point can be defined in terms of the equivalence class of geodesics through that point, or in our case the equivalence class of sequences of hyperedges that pass through the corresponding node in the hypergraph.

One can set up what in the limit can be viewed as a rank-p tensor field on the hypergraph by associating values with p hyperedges at each node. When these values correspond to intrinsic features of the hypergraph (such as V_r), their limits give intrinsic properties of the space associated with the hypergraph. And for example the Riemann tensor can be seen as emerging from essentially measuring areas of "rectangles" defined by loops in the hypergraph, though in this case multiple limits need to be taken.

8.5 Time and Spacetime

In our models, the passage of time basically corresponds to the progressive updating of the hypergraph. Time is therefore fundamentally computational: its passage reflects the performance of a computation—and typically one that is computationally irreducible. It is notable that in a sense the progression of time is necessary even to maintain the structure of space. And this effectively forces the entropic arrow of time (reflected in the effective randomization associated with irreducible computation) to be aligned with the cosmological arrow of time (defined by the overall evolution of the structure of space).

At the outset, time in our models has a very different character from space. The phenomenon of causal invariance, however, implies a link which leads to relativistic invariance. To see this, we can begin much as in the traditional development of special relativity [111] by considering what constitutes a physically realizable observer. In our model, everything is represented by the evolving hypergraph, including all of the internal state of any observer. One consequence of this is that the only way an observer can "sense" anything about the universe is by some updating event happening within the observer.

And indeed in the end all that any observer can ultimately be sensitive to is the causal relationships between different updating events that occur. From a particular evolution history of a hypergraph, we can construct a causal graph whose nodes correspond to updating events, and whose directed edges represent the causal relations between these events—in the sense that there is an edge between events A and B if the input to B involves output from A. For the evolution shown above, the beginning of the causal graph is:

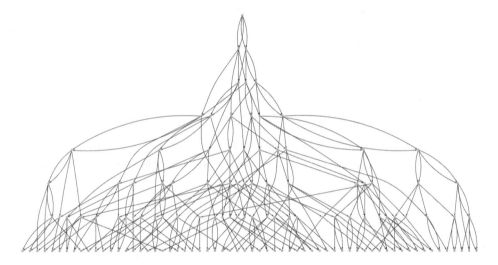

We can think of this causal graph as representing the evolution of our system in spacetime. The analog of a light cone is then the set of nodes that can be reached from a given node in the graph. Every edge in the graph represents a timelike relationship between events, and can be thought of as corresponding to a timelike direction in spacetime. Nodes that cannot be reached from each other by following edges of the graph can be thought of as spacelike separated. Just as for space with the "spatial hypergraphs" we discussed above, there is nothing in the abstract that defines the geometry of spacetime associated with the causal graph; everything must emerge from the pattern of connections in the graph, which in turn are generated by the operation of the underlying rules for our models.

In its original construction, a causal graph is in a sense a causal summary of a particular evolution history for a given rule, with a particular sequence of updating events. But when the underlying rule has the property of causal invariance, this has the important consequence that in the appropriate limit the causal graph obtained always has the same form, independent of the particular sequence of updating events. In other words, when there is causal invariance, the system in a sense always has a unique causal history.

The interpretation of this causal history in terms of a spacetime history, however, depends on what amount to definitions made by an observer. In particular, to define what can be interpreted as a time coordinate, one must set up a foliation of the causal graph, with successive slices corresponding to successive steps in time.

There are many such foliations that can be set up. The only fundamental constraint is that events in a given slice cannot be directly connected by an edge in the causal graph—or, in other words, they must be spacelike separated. The possible foliations thus correspond to possible sequences of spacelike hypersurfaces, analogous to those in standard discussions of spacetime.

(Note that the causal graph ultimately just defines a partial order on the set of events, and one could in principle imagine having arbitrarily complex foliations set up to imply any given total order of events. But such foliations are not realistic for macroscopic observers with bounded computational resources, and in our analysis of observable continuum limits we can ignore them.)

When one reaches a particular spacelike hypersurface, it represents a particular set of events having occurred, and thus a particular state of the underlying system having been reached, represented by a particular hypergraph. Different sequences of spacelike hypersurfaces thus correspond to different sequences of "instantaneous states" having been reached—corresponding to different evolution histories. But the crucial point is that causal invariance implies that even though the sequences of instantaneous states are different, the causal graphs representing the causal relationships between events that occur in them are always the same. And this is the essence of how the phenomena of relativistic invariance—and general covariance—are achieved.

8.6 Motion and Special Relativity

In the traditional formalism of physics, the principles of special relativity are in a sense introduced as axioms, and then their consequences are derived. In our models, what amount to these principles can in effect emerge directly from the models themselves, without having to be introduced from outside.

To see how this works, consider the phenomenon of motion. In standard physics, one thinks of different states of uniform motion as corresponding to different inertial reference frames (e.g. [111][112]). These different reference frames in turn correspond to different choices of sequences of spacelike hypersurfaces, or, in our setup, different foliations of the causal graph.

As a simple example, consider the string substitution system BA→AB, starting from ...BABABA... The causal graph for the evolution of this system can be drawn as a grid:

A simple foliation is just to form successive layers:

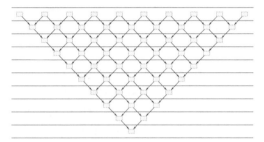

With this foliation, the sequence of states in the underlying string substitution system is:

```
B A B A B A B A B A B A B A B A B A B A
A B A B A B A B A B A B A B A B A B A B
A A B A B A B A B A B A B A B A B A B B
A A A B A B A B A B A B A B A B A B B B
A A A A B A B A B A B A B A B A B B B B
A A A A A B A B A B A B A B A B B B B B
A A A A A A B A B A B A B A B B B B B B
A A A A A A A B A B A B A B B B B B B B
A A A A A A A A B A B A B B B B B B B B
A A A A A A A A A B A B B B B B B B B B
A A A A A A A A A A B B B B B B B B B B
```

In drawing our foliation of the causal graph, we can think of time as being vertical, and space horizontal. Now imagine we want to represent uniform motion. We can do this by making our foliation use slices with a slope proportional to velocity:

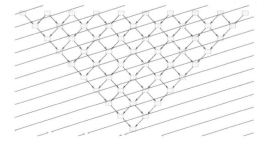

But imagine we want to show time vertically, while not destroying the partial order in our causal network. The unique way to do it (if we want to preserve straight lines) is to transform a point $\{t, x\}$ to $\{t - \beta x, x - \beta t\} / \sqrt{1 - \beta^2}$:

But this is precisely the usual Lorentz transformation of special relativity. And time dilation is then, for example, associated with the fact that to reach what corresponds to an event at slice t in the original foliation, one now has to go through a sequence of events that is longer by a factor of $\gamma = 1 / \sqrt{1 - \beta^2}$.

Normally one would argue for these results on the basis of principles supplied by special relativity. But the crucial point here is that in our models the results can be derived purely from the behavior of the models, without introducing additional principles.

Imagine simply using the transformed causal graph to determine the order of updating events in the underlying substitution system:

```
B A B A B A B A B A B A B A B A B A B A
A B B A B A B A B A B A B A B A B A B A
A B A B A B B A B A B A B A B A B A B A
A A B B A B A B B A B A B A B A B A B A
A A B A B B A B A B A B B A B A B A B A
A A B A B A B A B B A B A B A B B A B A
A A A B A B B A B A B B A B A B A B B A
A A A B A B A B B A B A B A B A B B A B
A A A A B B A B A B A B B A B A B A B B
A A A A B A B A B B A B A B B A B A B B
A A A A B A B A B A B B A B A B A B B B
A A A A A B A B B A B A B A B B A B B B
A A A A A B A B A B B A B A B A B B B B
A A A A A A B A B A B A B B A B B B B B
A A A A A A B A B A B B A B A B B B B B
A A A A A A A B B A B A B B A B B B B B
A A A A A A A B A B B A B A B B B B B B
A A A A A A A B A B A B A B B B B B B B
A A A A A A A A B B A B A B B B B B B B
A A A A A A A A B A B A B B B B B B B B
A A A A A A A A A B B A B B B B B B B B
A A A A A A A A A B A B B B B B B B B B
A A A A A A A A A A B B B B B B B B B B
```

If we look vertically down the picture we see a different sequence of states of the system. But the crucial point is that the final outcome of the evolution is exactly the same as it was with the original foliation. In some sense the "physics" is the same, independent of the reference frame. And this is the essence of relativistic invariance (and here we immediately see some of its consequences, like time dilation).

But in the context of the string substitution system, we can now see its origin of the invariance. It is the fact that the underlying rule we have used is causal invariant, so that regardless of the specific order in which updating events occur, the same causal graph is obtained, with the same final output.

In our actual models based on infinitely evolving hypergraphs, the details are considerably more complicated. But the principles are exactly the same: if the underlying rule has causal invariance, its limiting behavior will show relativistic invariance, and (so long as it has limiting geometry corresponding to flat d-dimensional space) all the usual phenomena of special relativity.

(Note that the concept of a finite speed of light, leading effectively to locality in the causal graph, is related to the fact that the underlying rules involve rewriting hypergraphs only of bounded size.)

8.7 The Vacuum Einstein Equations

In discussing the structure of space, we considered how the volumes of geodesic balls grow with radius. In discussing spacetime, we want to consider the analogous question of how the volumes of light cones [1:p1052]) grow with time. But to do this, we have to say what we mean by time, since—as we saw in the previous subsection—different foliations can lead to different identifications.

Any particular foliation—with its sequence of spacelike hypersurfaces—provides at every point a timelike vector that defines a time direction in spacetime. So if we start at any point in the causal graph, we can look at the forward light cone from this point, and follow the connections in the causal graph until we have gone a proper time t in the time direction we have defined. Then we can ask how how many nodes we have reached in the causal graph.

The result will depend on the underlying rule for the system. But if in the limit it is going to correspond to flat $(d + 1)$-dimensional spacetime, at any spacetime position X it must grow like:

$$C_t(X) \sim t^{d+1}$$

If we include the possibility of curvature, we get to first order

$$C_t(X) \sim t^{d+1}(1 - \frac{1}{6} \delta t^\mu \, \delta t^\nu \, R_{\mu\nu} (X) + ...)$$

where $R_{\mu\nu}$ is the spacetime Ricci tensor, and $\delta t^\mu \, \delta t^\nu \, R_{\mu\nu}$ is effectively its projection along the infinitesimal timelike vector δt^μ.

For any particular underlying rule, $C_t(X)$ will take on a definite form. But in making connections with traditional continuum spacetime, we are interested in its limiting behavior.

Assume, to begin, that we have scaled t to be measured relative to the size of the whole causal graph. Then for small t we can expand $C_t(X)$ to get the expression involving curvature above. But now imagine scaling up t. Eventually it is inevitable that the curvature term has the potential to affect the overall t dependence, and potentially change the effective exponent of t. But if the overall continuum limit is going to correspond to a $(d + 1)$-dimensional spacetime, this cannot happen. And what this means is that at least a suitably averaged version of the curvature term must not in fact grow [1:9.15].

The details are slightly complicated [113], but suffice it to say here that the constraint on $R_{\mu\nu}$ is obtained by averaging over directions, then averaging over positions with a weighting determined by the volume element $\sqrt{g}$ associated with the metric $g_{\mu\nu}$ defined by our choice of hypersurfaces. The requirement that this average not grow when t is scaled up can then be expressed as the vanishing of the variation of $\int R \sqrt{g}$, which is precisely the usual Einstein–Hilbert action—thereby leading to the conclusion that $R_{\mu\nu}$ must satisfy exactly the usual vacuum Einstein equations [114][115][75][116]:

$$R_{\mu\nu} - \frac{1}{2} R\, g_{\mu\nu} = 0$$

A full derivation of this is given in [113]. Causal invariance plays a crucial role, ensuring for example that timelike directions t^i associated with different foliations give invariant results. Much like in the derivation of continuum fluid behavior from microscopic molecular dynamics (e.g. [110]), one also needs to take a variety of fairly subtle limits, and one needs sufficient intrinsic generation of effective randomness [1:7.5] to justify the use of certain statistical averages.

But there is a fairly simple interpretation of the result above. Imagine all the geodesics that start at a particular point in the causal graph. The further we go, the more possible geodesic paths there will be in the graph. To achieve a power law corresponding to a definite dimension, the geodesics must in a sense just "stream outwards", evenly distributed in direction.

But the Ricci tensor specifically measures the rate at which bundles of geodesics change their cross-sectional area. And as soon as this change is nonzero, it will inevitably change the local density of geodesics and eventually grow to disrupt the power law. And so the only way a fixed limiting dimension can be achieved is for the Ricci curvature to vanish, just as it does according to the vacuum Einstein equations. (Note that higher-order terms, involving for example the Weyl tensor and other components of the Riemann tensor, yield changes in the shape of bundles of geodesics, but not in their cross-sectional area, and are therefore not constrained by the requirement of fixed limiting dimension.)

8.8 Matter, Energy and Gravitation

In our models, not only space, but also everything "in space", must be represented by features of our evolving hypergraphs. There is no notion of "empty space", with "matter" in it. Instead, space itself is a dynamic construct created and maintained by ongoing updating events in the hypergraph. And what we call "matter"—as well as things like energy—must just correspond to features of the evolving hypergraph that somehow deviate from the background activity that we call "space".

Anything we directly observe must ultimately have a signature in the causal graph. And a potential hypothesis about energy and momentum is that they may simply correspond to excess "fluxes" of causal edges in time and space. Consider a simple causal graph in which we have marked spacelike and timelike hypersurfaces:

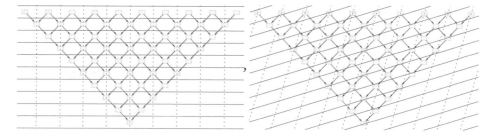

The basic idea is that the number of causal edges that cross spacelike hypersurfaces would correspond to energy, and the number that cross timelike hypersurfaces would correspond to momentum (in the spatial direction defined by a given hypersurface). Inevitably the results one gets would depend on the hypersurfaces one chooses, and so would differ from one observer to another.

And one important feature of this identification of energy and momentum is that it would explain why they follow the same relativistic transformations as time and space. In effect space and time are probing distances between nodes in the causal graph (as measured relative to a particular foliation), while momentum and energy are probing a directly dual property: the density of edges.

There is additional subtlety here, though, because causal edges are needed just to maintain the structure of spacetime—and whatever we measure as energy and momentum must just be some excess in the density of causal edges over the "background" corresponding to space. But even to know what we mean by density we have to have some notion of volume, but this is also itself defined in terms of edges in the causal graph.

But as a rough idealized picture, we might imagine that we have a causal graph that maintains the same overall structure, but adds some extra connections:

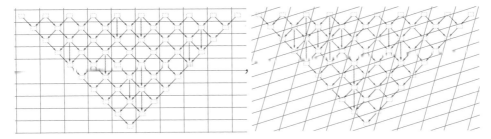

In our actual models, the causal graphs one gets are considerably more complicated. But one can still identify some features from the simple idealization. The basic concept is that energy and momentum add "extra causal connections" that are not "necessary" to define the basic structure of spacetime. In a sense the core thing that defines the structure of spacetime is the way that "elementary light cones" are knitted together.

Consider a causal graph like:

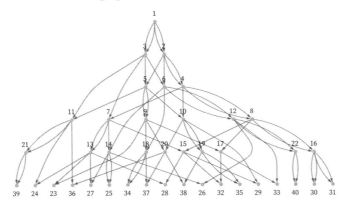

One can think of a set of edges like the ones indicated as in effect "outlining" the causal graph. But then there are other edges that add "extra connections". The edges that "outline the graph" in effect maximally connect spatially separated regions—or in a sense transmit causal information at a maximum speed. The other edges one can think of as having slower speeds—so they are typically drawn closer to vertical in a rendering like the one above.

But now let us return to our simple grid idealization of the causal graph—with additional vertical edges added. Now do foliations like the ones we used above to represent inertial frames, parametrized by a velocity ratio β relative to the maximum speed (taken to be 1). Define $E(\beta)$ to be the density of causal edge crossing of the spacelike hypersurfaces, and $p(\beta)$ the corresponding quantity for timelike hypersurfaces. Then for speed 1 edges, we have (up to an overall multiplier) (cf. [111][112]):

$$E(\beta) = p(\beta) = \frac{1-\beta}{\sqrt{1-\beta^2}}$$

But in general for edges with speed α we have

$$E(\beta) = \frac{1 - \alpha\beta}{\sqrt{1 - \beta^2}}, \quad p(\beta) = \frac{\alpha - \beta}{\sqrt{1 - \beta^2}}$$

which means that for any β

$$E(\beta)^2 - p(\beta)^2 = 1 - \alpha^2$$

thus showing that our crossing densities transform like energy and momentum for a particle with mass $\sqrt{1 - \alpha^2}$. In other words, we can potentially identify edges that are not maximum speed in the causal graph as corresponding to "matter" with nonzero rest mass. Perhaps not surprisingly, this whole setup is quite analogous to thinking about world lines of massive particles in elementary treatments of relativity.

But in our context, all of this must emerge from underlying features of the evolving hypergraph. Causal connections that transfer information at maximum speed can be thought of as arising from updating events that involve maximally separate nodes, and that are somehow always entraining "fresh" nodes. But causal connections that transfer information more slowly are associated with sequences of updating events that in effect reuse nodes. So in other words, rest mass can be thought of as being associated with local collections of nodes in the hypergraph that allow repeated updating events to occur without the involvement of other nodes.

Given this setup, it is possible to derive other features of energy, momentum and mass by methods similar to those used in typical discussions of relativity. It is first helpful to include units in the quantities we have introduced. If an elementary light cone has timeline extent T then we can consider its spacelike extent to be $c\,T$, where c is the speed of light. Within the light cone let us say that there are effectively μ causal edges oriented in the timelike direction. With the inertial frame foliations used above, the contribution of these causal edges to energy and momentum will be (the factor c in the energy case comes from the spacelike extent of the light cone):

$$E(\beta) = c \frac{\mu}{\sqrt{1 - \beta^2}} = c\,\mu\,(1 + \frac{\beta^2}{2} + O(\beta^4))$$

$$p(\beta) = \mu \frac{\beta}{\sqrt{1 - \beta^2}} = \mu\,\beta\,(1 + O(\beta^2))$$

But if we define the mass m as $\frac{\mu}{c}$ and substitute $\beta = \frac{v}{c}$, we get the standard formulas of special relativity [111][112], or to first order

$$E = m\,c^2 + \frac{1}{2}\,m\,v^2$$

$$p = m\,v$$

establishing in our model the relation $E = m\,c^2$ between energy and rest mass.

We should note that with our identification for energy and momentum, the conservation of energy becomes essentially the statement that the overall density of events in the causal network does not change as we progress through successive spacelike surfaces. And, as we will discuss later, if in effect the whole hypergraph is in some kind of dynamic equilibrium, then we can reasonably expect that this will be the case. Expansion (or, more specifically, non-uniform expansion) will lead to effective violations of energy conservation, much as it does for an expanding universe in the traditional formalism of general relativity [117][75].

In the previous subsection, we discussed the overall structure of spacetime, and we used the growth rate of the spacetime volume $C_t(X)$ as a way to assess this. But now let us ask about specific values of $C_t(X)$, complete with their "constant" multipliers. We can think of these multipliers as probing the local density of the causal graph. But deviations in this are what we have now identified as being associated with matter.

To compute $C_t(X)$ we ultimately need to be able to precisely count events in the causal graph. If the causal graph is somehow "uniform", then it cannot contain what can be considered to be "matter". In the setup we have defined, the presence of matter is effectively associated with "fluxes" of causal edges that reflect the non-uniform "arrangement" of nodes in the causal graph. To represent this, take $\rho(X)$ to be the "local density" of nodes in the causal graph. We can make a series expansion to probe deviations from uniformity in $\rho(X)$. And formally we can write

$$\rho(X) = \rho_0 \left(1 + \sigma \, \delta t^\mu \, \delta t^\nu \, T_{\mu\nu} \, ... \right)$$

where the t^μ are timelike vectors used in the definition of C_t and now $T_{\mu\nu}$ is effectively a tensor that represents "fluxes of edges" in the causal graph. But these fluxes are what we have identified as energy and momentum, and when we think about how causal edges traverse spacelike and timelike hypersurfaces, $T_{\mu\nu}$ turns out to correspond exactly to the standard energy-momentum tensor of general relativity.

So now we can combine our formula for the effect of local density with our formula for the effect of curvature from the previous section to get:

$$C_t(X) = \rho_0(1 + \sigma \, \delta t^i \, \delta t^j \, T_{ij} + ...) \, t^{d+1}(1 - \frac{1}{6} \delta t^i \, \delta t^j \, R_{ij} + ...)$$

But if we apply the same argument as in the previous subsection, then to maintain limiting fixed dimension we get the condition

$$R_{\mu\nu} - \frac{1}{2} R \, g_{\mu\nu} = \sigma' \, T_{\mu\nu}$$

which has exactly the form of Einstein's equations in the presence of matter [114][115][75][116].

Just as we interpreted the curvature part of these equations in the previous subsection in terms of the change in area of geodesic bundles, we can interpret the "matter" part in terms of the change of geodesics associated with additional local connections. As an example,

423

consider starting with a 2D hexagonal grid. Now imagine adding edges at each node. Doing this creates additional connections and additional geodesics, eventually producing something like the hyperbolic space examples in 4.2. So what the equation says is that any such effect, which would lead to negative curvature, must be compensated by positive curvature in the "background" spacetime—just as general relativity suggests.

8.9 Elementary Particles

Elementary particles are entities that—at least for some period—preserve their identity through space and time. In the context of our models, one can imagine that particles would correspond to structures in the hypergraph that are locally stable under the application of rules.

As an idealized example, consider rules that operate on an ordinary graph, and have the property of preserving planarity. Such rules can never remove non-planarity from a graph. But it is a basic result of graph theory [37][118] that any non-planarity can always be attributed to one of the two specific subgraphs:

If one inserts such subgraphs into an otherwise planar graph, they behave very much as "particle-like" structures. They can move around, but unless they meet and annihilate, they are preserved:

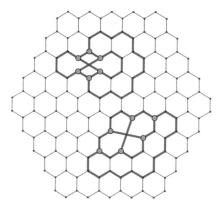

There are presumably analogs of this in hypergraph-rewriting rules of the kind that appear in our models. Given a particular set of rules, the expectation would be that a certain set of local sub-hypergraphs would be preserved by the rules. Existing results in graph theory do not go very far in elucidating the details.

However, there are analogs in other systems that provide some insight. Cellular automata provide a particularly good example. Consider the rule 110 cellular automaton [1:p32]. Starting from a random initial condition, the picture below shows how the system evolves to a collection of localized structures:

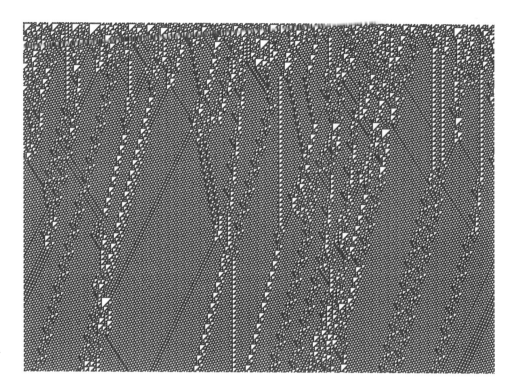

The form of these structures is hard to determine directly from the rule. (They are a little like hard-to-predict solutions to a Diophantine equation.) But by explicit computation one can determine for example that rule 110 supports the following types of localized structures [1:p292][119]

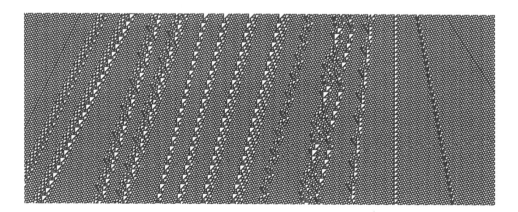

as well as the growing structure:

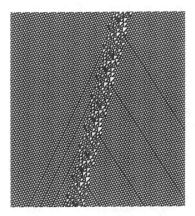

There is a complex web of possible interactions between localized structures, that can at least in some cases be interpreted in terms of conservation laws:

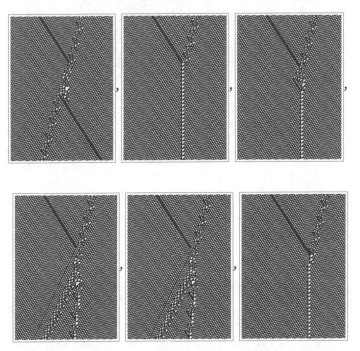

As in cellular automata, it is likely that not every one of our models will yield localized structures, although there is reason to think that some form of conserved structure will be more common in hypergraph rewriting than in cellular automata. But as in cellular automata, one can expect that with a given underlying rule, there will be a discrete set of possible localized structures, with hard-to-predict sizes and properties.

The particular set of localized structures will probably be quite specific to particular rules. But as we will discuss in the next subsection, there will often be symmetries that cause collections of similar structures to exist—or in fact force certain structures to exist.

In the previous subsection, we discussed the interpretation of energy and momentum in terms of additional edges in a causal graph. For particles, the expectation would be that there is a certain "core" structure that defines the core properties of a particle (like spin, charge, etc.), but that this structure is spread across a region of the hypergraph that maintains the "activity" associated with energy and momentum.

It is worth noting that even in an example like non-planarity, it is perfectly possible for topological-like features to effectively be spread out across many nodes, while still maintaining their discrete character.

In the previous subsection, we discussed the potential origin of rest mass in terms of "reuse" of nodes in the hypergraph. Once again, this seems to fit in well with our notion of the nature of particles—and to make it perfectly possible to imagine both "massive" and "massless" particles, associated with different kinds of structures in the evolving hypergraph.

In a system like the rule 110 cellular automaton, there is a clear "background structure" on which it is possible to identify localized structures. In some very simple cases, similar things happen in our models. For example, consider the rule:

$$\{\{x, y\}, \{y, z, u, v\}\} \rightarrow \{\{x, y, z, u\}, \{u, v\}\}$$

The evolution of this rule yields behavior like

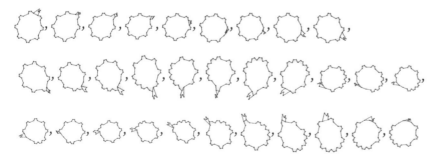

in which there is a circular "background", with a localized "particle-like" deformation. The causal graph (here generated for a larger case) also shows evidence of a particle-like structure on a simple grid-like background:

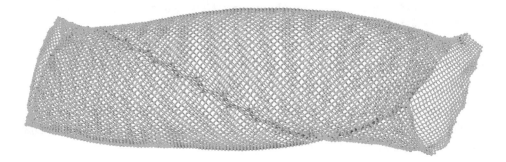

But in most of our models the "background" tends to be much more complicated, and so such direct methods for identifying particles cannot be used. But as an alternative, one can consider exploring the effect of perturbations, as in 4.14. In effect, one starts the system with a perturbation, then sees whether the perturbation somehow decomposes into quantized elements that one can identify as "particles". (The process is quite analogous to producing particles in a high-energy collision.)

Such quantized effects are at best rare in class 3 cellular automata, but they are a defining feature of class 4 cellular automata, and there is reason to believe that they will be at least fairly common in our models.

The defining feature of a localized "particle-like" structure is that it is capable of long-range propagation in the system. But the presence of even short-lived instances of particle-like structures will also potentially be identifiable—though with a certain margin of error—from detailed properties of the hypergraph in small regions. And in the "background" evolution of our models, one can expect that short-lived instances of particle-like structures will continually be being created and destroyed.

The process that in a sense "creates the structure of space" in our models can thus also be thought of as producing a "vacuum" full of particle-like activity. And particularly when this is combined with the phenomenon (to be discussed in a later subsection) that pairs of particle-like structures can be produced and subsequently merged in the multiway system, there is some definite similarity with the ubiquitous virtual particles that appear in traditional treatments of quantum field theory.

8.10 Reversibility and Irreversibility

One feature of the traditional formalism for fundamental physics is that it is reversible, in the sense that it implies that individual states of closed systems can be uniquely evolved both forward and backward in time. (Time reversal violation in things like K^o particle decays show that the rule for going forward and backward in time can be slightly different. In addition, the cosmological expansion of the universe defines an overall arrow of time.)

One can certainly set up manifestly reversible rewriting rules (like A→B, B→A) in models like ours. And indeed the example of cellular automata [1:9.2] tends to suggest that most kinds of behavior seen in irreversible rules can also be seen—though perhaps more rarely— in reversible rules.

But it is important to realize that even when the underlying rules for a system are not reversible, the system can still evolve to a situation where there is effective reversibility. One way for this to happen is for the evolution of the system to lead to a particular set of "attractor" states, on which the evolution is reversible. Another possibility is that there is no such well-defined attractor, but that the system nevertheless evolves to some kind of "equilibrium" in which measurable effects show effective reversibility.

In our models, there is an additional complication: the fact that different possible updating orders lead to following different branches of the multiway system. In most kinds of systems, irreversible rules tend to be associated with the phenomenon of multiple initial states merging to produce a single final state in which the information about the initial state is lost. But when there is a branch in a multiway system, this is reversed: information is effectively created by the branch, and lost if one goes backwards.

When there is causal invariance, however, yet something different happens. Because now in a sense every branching will eventually merge. And what this means is that in the multiway system there is a kind of reversibility: any information created by a branching will always be destroyed again when the branches merge—even though temporarily the "information content" may change.

It is important to note that this kind of microscopic reversibility is quite unrelated to the more macroscopic irreversibility implied by the Second Law of thermodynamics. As discussed in [1:9.3] the Second Law seems to first and foremost be a consequence of computational irreducibility. Even when the underlying rules for a system are reversible, the actual evolution of the system can so "encrypt" the initial conditions that no computationally feasible measurement process will succeed in reconstructing them. (The idea of considering computational feasibility clarifies past uncertainty about what might count as a reasonable "coarse graining procedure".)

In any nontrivial example of one of our models, computational irreducibility is essentially inevitable. And this means that the model will tend to intrinsically generate effective randomness, or in other words, the computation it does will obscure whatever simplicity might have existed in its initial conditions.

There can still be large-scale features—or particle-like structures—that persist. But the presence of computational irreducibility implies that even at a level as low as the basic structure of space we can expect our models to show the kind of irreversibility associated with the Second Law. And in a sense we can view this as the reason that things like a robust structure for space can exist: because of computational irreducibility, our models show a kind of equilibrium in which the details are effectively random, and the only features that are computationally feasible to measure are the statistical regularities.

8.11 Cosmology, Expansion & Singularities

In our models the evolving hypergraph represents the whole universe, and the expansion of the universe is potentially a consequence of the growth of the hypergraph. In the minimal case of a model involving a single transformation rule, the growth of the hypergraph must be monotonic, although the rate can vary depending on the local structure of the hypergraph. If there are multiple transformation rules, there can be both increase and decrease in hypergraph size. (Even with a single rule, there is also still the possibility—discussed below—of effective size decrease as a result of pieces of the hypergraph becoming disconnected.)

In the case of uniform growth, measurable quantities such as length and energy would essentially all continually scale as the universe evolves. The core structure of particles—embodied for example in topological-like features of the hypergraph—could potentially persist even as the number of nodes "within them" increases. Since the rate of increase in size in the hypergraph would undoubtedly greatly exceed the measurable growth rate of the universe, uniform growth implies a kind of progressive refinement in which the length scale of the discrete structure of the hypergraph becomes ever more distant from any given measured length scale—so that in effect the universe is becoming an ever closer approximation to continuous.

In traditional cosmology, one thinks of the universe as effectively having exactly three dimensions of space (cf. [120]). In our models, dimension is in effect a dynamical variable. Possibly some of what is normally attributed to curvature in space can instead be reformulated as dimension change. But even beyond this, there is the potential for new phenomena associated, for example, with local change of dimension. In general, a change of dimension—like curvature—affects the density of geodesics. Changes of dimension generated by an underlying rule may potentially lead to effects that for example mimic the presence of mass, or positive or negative energy density. (There could also be dimension-change "waves", perhaps with some rather unusual features.)

In our models, the universe starts from some initial configuration. It could be something like a single self-loop hypergraph. Or in the multiway system it could be multiple initial hypergraphs. (Note that we can always "put the initial conditions into the rule" by adding a rule that says "from nothing, create the initial conditions".)

An obvious question is whether any traces of the initial conditions might persist, perhaps even through the whole evolution of the system. The effective randomness associated with computational irreducibility in the evolution will inevitably tend to "encrypt" most features of the initial conditions [1:9.3] to the point where they are unrecognizable. But it is still conceivable that, for example, some global symmetry breaking associated with the first few hypergraph updating events could survive—and the remote possibility exists that this could be visible today in the large-scale structure of the universe, say as a pattern of density fluctuations in the cosmic microwave background.

Our models have potentially important implications for the early universe. If, for example, the effective dimension of the universe was initially much higher than 3 (as is basically inevitable if the initial conditions are small), there will have been a much higher level of causal contact between different parts of the universe than we have deduced by extrapolating the 3D expansion of the universe today [1:p1055]. (In effect this happens because the volume of the past light cone will grow like t^d—or perhaps exponentially with t—and not just like t^3.)

As we discussed in 2.9, it is perfectly possible in our models for parts of the hypergraph to become disconnected as a result of the operation of the rule. But assuming that the rule is local (in the sense that its left-hand side is a connected hypergraph), pieces of the hypergraph that become disconnected can never interact again. Even independent of outright disconnection of the spatial graph, it is also possible for the causal graph to "tear" into disconnected parts that can never interact again (see 6.10):

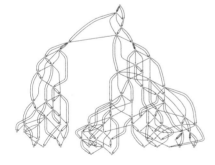

A disconnection in the causal graph corresponds to an event horizon in our system—that cannot be crossed by any timelike curve. (And indeed our causal graphs—consisting as they do of "elementary light cones knitted together"—are like microscopic analogs of the causal diagrams often used in studying general relativity. Note that in our models, as in ordinary general relativity, there are two kinds of event horizons: "cosmic"—like the one above—in which effectively two distinct subuniverses are created, and "black hole", in which there is a region of the causal graph with incoming, but not outgoing, edges.)

We can also ask about other extreme phenomena in spacetime. Closed timelike curves correspond to loops in the causal graph, and with some rules they can occur. But they do not represent any real form of "time travel"; they just correspond to the presence of states that are precisely repeated as a result of the evolution of the system. (Note that in our models, time effectively corresponds to the progression of computation, and has a very different underlying character from something like space.)

Wormholes and effective faster-than-light travel are not specifically excluded by the structure of our models, especially insofar as there can potentially be deviations in the effective local dimensionality of space. But insofar as the conditions to get general relativity as a limiting effective theory are satisfied, these will occur only in the circumstances where they do in that theory.

8.12 Basic Concepts of Quantum Mechanics

Quantum mechanics is a key known feature of physics, and also, it seems, a natural and inevitable feature of our models. In classical physics—or in a system like a cellular automaton—one basically has rules that specify a unique path of history for the evolution of a system. But our models are not set up to define any such unique path of history. Instead, the models just give possible rewrites that can be performed on hypergraphs—but they do not say when or where these rewrites should be applied. So this means that—like the formalism of quantum mechanics—our models in a sense allow many different paths of history.

There is, however, ultimately nothing non-deterministic about our models. Although they allow many different sequences of updating events—each of which can be viewed as a different path of history—the models still completely determine the overall set of possible sequences of updating events. And indeed at a global level, everything about the model can be captured in a multiway graph [1:5.6]—like the one below—with nodes in the graph corresponding to states of the system (here, for simplicity, a string substitution system), and every possible path through the graph corresponding to a possible history.

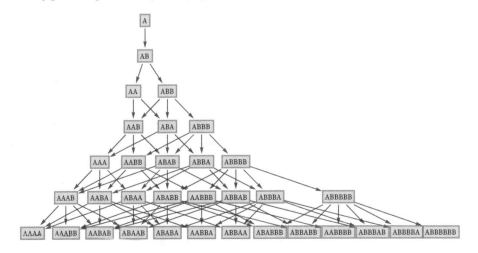

In the standard formalism of quantum mechanics, one usually just imagines that all one can determine are probabilities for different histories or different outcomes. But this has made it something of a mystery why we have the impression that a definite objective reality seems to exist. One possible explanation would be that at some level a branch of reality exists for every possible behavior, and that we just experience the branch that our thread of consciousness has happened to follow.

But our models immediately suggest another, more complete, and arguably much more scientifically satisfying, possibility. In essence, they suggest that there is ultimately a global objective reality, defined by the multiway system, and it is merely the locality of our experience that causes us to describe things in terms of probabilities, and all the various detailed features of the standard formalism of quantum mechanics.

We will proceed in two stages. First, we will discuss the notion of an observer in the context of multiway systems, and the relation of this to questions about objective reality. And having done this, we will be in a position to discuss ideas like quantum measurement, and the role that causal invariance turns out to play in allowing observers to experience definite, seemingly classical results.

So how might we represent a quantum observer in our models? The first key point is that the observer—being part of the universe—must themselves be a multiway system. And in addition, everything the observer does—and experiences—must correspond to events that occur in the model.

This latter point also came up when we discussed spacetime—and we concluded there that it meant we only needed to consider the graph of causal relationships between events. To characterize any given observer, we then just had to say how the observer would sample this causal graph. A typical example in studying spacetime is to consider an observer in an inertial reference frame—which corresponds to a particular foliation of the causal graph. But in general to characterize what any observer will experience in the course of time, we need some sequence of spacelike hypersurfaces that form a foliation which respects the causal relationships—and thus the ordering relations between events—defined by the causal graph.

But now we can see an analog of this in the quantum mechanical case. However, instead of considering foliations of the causal graph, what we need to consider now are foliations of the multiway graph:

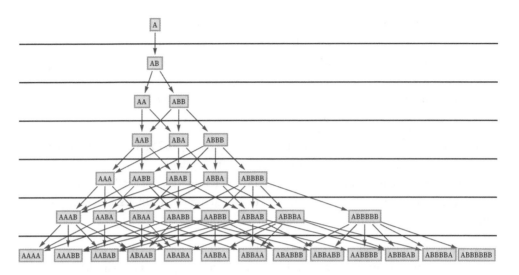

In the course of time, the observer progresses through such a foliation, in effect at each step observing some collection of states, with certain relationships between them. A different observer, however, might want to sample the states differently, and might effectively define a different foliation.

One can potentially think of a different foliation as being a different "quantum observation frame" or "quantum frame", analogous to the different reference frames one considers in studying spacetime. In the case of something like an inertial frame, one is effectively defining how an observer will sample different parts of space over the course of time. In a quantum observation frame one might have a more elaborate specification, involving sampling particular states of relevance to some measurement or another. But the key point is that a quantum observer can in principle use any quantum observation frame that corresponds to a foliation that respects the relationships between states defined by the multiway graph (and thus has a meaningful notion of time).

In both the spacetime case and the quantum case, the slices in the foliation are indexed by time. But while in the spacetime case, where each slice corresponds to a spacelike hypersurface that spans ordinary space, in the quantum case, each slice corresponds to what we can call a branchlike hypersurface that spans not ordinary space, but instead the space of states, or the space of branches in the multiway system. But even without knowing the details of this space, we can already come to some conclusions.

In particular, we can ask what observers with different quantum observation frames—and thus different choices of branchlike hypersurfaces—will conclude about relationships between states. And the point is that so long as the foliations that are used respect the orderings defined by the multiway graph, all observers must inevitably come to the same conclusions about the structure of the multiway graph—and therefore, for example, the relationships between states. Different observers may sample the multiway graph differently, and experience different histories, but they are always ultimately sampling the same graph.

One feature of traditional quantum formalism is its concept of making measurements that effectively reduce collections of states—as exist in a multiway system—to what is basically a single state analogous to what would be seen in a classical single path of evolution. From the point of view of quantum observation frames, one can think of such a measurement as being achieved by sculpting the quantum observation frame to effectively pick out a single state in the multiway system·

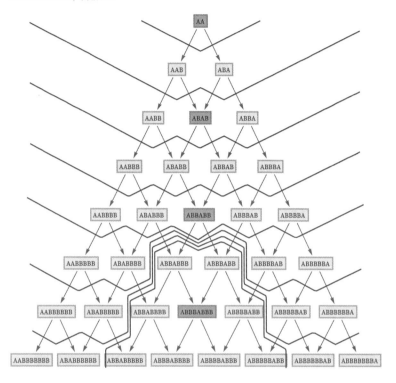

We will discuss this in more detail below. But the basic idea is as follows. Imagine that our universe is based on a simple string substitution system such as {A→AB}. If we start from a state AA, as in the picture above, the multiway evolution from this state immediately leads to multiple outcomes, associated with different updating events. But let us say that we just wanted some kind of "classical" summary of the evolution, ignoring all these different branches.

One thing we might do is not trace individual updates, but instead just look at "generational states" (5.21) in which all updates that can consistently be applied together have been applied. And with the particular rule shown here, we then get the unique sequence of states highlighted above. And as we will discuss below, we can indeed consider these generational states as corresponding to definite ("classical-like") states of the system, that can consistently be thought of as potential results of measurements.

But now let us imagine how this might work in something closer to a complete experiment. We are running the multiway system shown above. Multiple states are being generated. But at some moment we as observers notice that actually several states that have been produced (say ABBA and AABB) can be combined together to form a consistent generational state (ABBABB). But even though these states ultimately had a common ancestor, they now seem to be on different "branches of history".

But now causal invariance makes a crucial contribution. Because it implies that all such different branches must eventually converge. And indeed after a couple of steps, the fully assembled generational state ABBABB appears in the multiway system. To us as observers this is in a sense the state we were looking for (it is the "result of our measurement"), and as far as possible, we want to use it as our description of the system.

And by setting up an appropriate quantum observation frame, that is exactly what we can do. For example, as illustrated in the picture above, we can make the foliation we choose effectively freeze the generational state, so that in the description we use of the system, the state stays the same in successive slices.

The structure of the multiway system puts constraints on what foliations we can consistently set up. In the case shown here, it does allow us to freeze this particular state forever, but to do this consistently, it effectively forces us to freeze more and more states over time. And as we will see later, this kind of spreading of effects in the multiway graph is closely related to decoherence in the standard formalism of quantum mechanics.

In what we just discussed, causal invariance is what guarantees that states the observer notices can consistently be assembled to form a generational ("classical-like") state that will always actually converge in the multiway system to form that state. But it is worth pointing out that (as discussed in [121]) strict causal invariance is not ultimately needed for a picture like this to work.

Recall that the observer themselves is also a multiway system. So "within their consciousness" there will usually be many "simultaneous" states. Looked at formally from the outside, the observer can be seen to involve many distinct states. But one could imagine that the internal experience of the observer would be in effect to conflate these states.

Causal invariance ensures that branches in the multiway system will actually merge—just as a result of the evolution of the multiway system. But if the observer "experientially" conflates states, this in effect represents an additional way in which different branches in the multiway system will at least appear to merge [121]. Formally, one can think of this—in analogy to the operation of automated theorem-proving systems—as like the observer "adding lemmas" that assert the equivalence of branches, thereby allowing the system to be "completed" to the point where relevant branches converge. (For a given system, there is still the question of whether only a sufficiently bounded number of lemmas is needed to achieve the convergence one wants.)

Independent of whether there is strict causal invariance or not, there is also the question of what kinds of quantum observation frames are possible. In the end—just like in the space-time case—such frames reflect the description one is choosing to make of the world. And setting up different "coordinates", one is effectively changing one's description, and picking out different aspects of a system. And ultimately the restrictions on frames are computational ones. Something like an inertial frame in spacetime is simple to describe, and its coordinates are simple to compute. But a frame that tries to pick out some very particular aspect of a quantum system may run into issues of computational irreducibility. And as a result, much as happens in connection with the Second Law of thermodynamics [1:9.3], there can still for example be elaborate correlations that exist between different parts of a quantum system, but no realistic measurement—defined by a computationally feasible quantum observation frame—will succeed in picking them out.

8.13 Quantum Formalism

To continue understanding how our models might relate to quantum mechanics, it is useful to describe a little more of the potential correspondence with standard quantum formalism. We consider—quite directly—each state in the multiway system as some quantum basis state |S>.

An important feature of quantum states is the phenomenon of entanglement—which is effectively a phenomenon of connection or correlation between states. In our setup (as we will see more formally soon), entanglement is basically a reflection of common ancestry of states in the multiway graph. ("Interference" can then be seen as a reflection of merging—and therefore common successors—in the multiway graph.)

Consider the following multiway graph for a string substitution system:

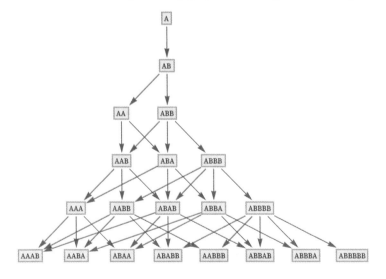

Each pair of states generated by a branching in this graph are considered to be entangled. And when the graph is viewed as defining a rewrite system, these pairs of states can also be said to form a branch pair.

Given a particular foliation of the multiway graph, we can now capture the entanglement of states in each slice of the foliation by forming a branchial graph in which we connect the states in each branch pair. For the string substitution system above, the sequence of branchial graphs is then:

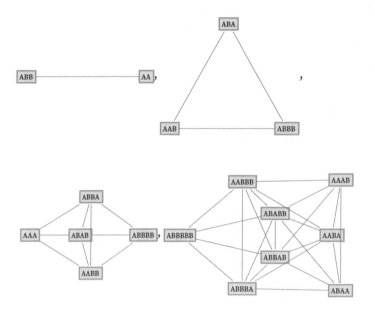

In physical terms, the nodes of the branchial graph are quantum states, and the graph itself forms a kind of map of entanglements between states. In general terms, we expect states that are closer on the branchial graph to be more correlated, and have more entanglement, than ones further away.

As we discussed in 5.17, the geometry of branchial space is not expected to be like the geometry of ordinary space. For example, it will not typically correspond to a finite-dimensional manifold. We can still think of it as a space of some kind that is reached in the limit of a sufficiently large multiway system, with a sufficiently large number of states. And in particular we can imagine—for any given foliation—defining coordinates of some kind on it, that we will denote $\overset{\leftrightarrow}{b}$. So this means that within a foliation, any state that appears in the multiway system can be assigned a position $(t, \overset{\leftrightarrow}{b})$ in "multiway space".

In the standard formalism of quantum mechanics, states are thought of as vectors in a Hilbert space, and now these vectors can be made explicit as corresponding to positions in multiway space.

But now there is an additional issue. The multiway system should represent not just all possible states, but also all possible paths leading to states. And this means that we must assign to states a weight that reflects the number of possible paths that can lead to them:

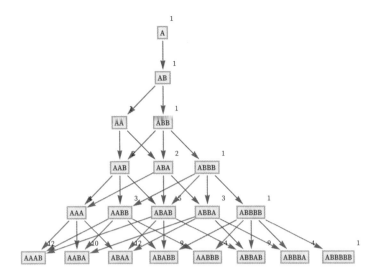

In effect, therefore, each branchlike hypersurface can be thought of as exposing some linear combination of basic states, each one with a certain weight:

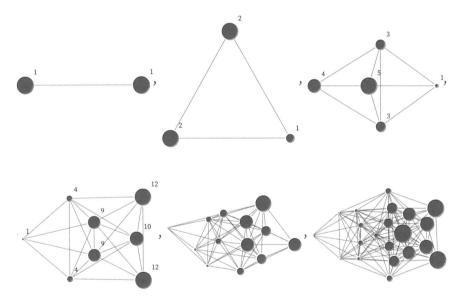

Let us say that we want to track what happens to some part of this branchlike hypersurface. Each state undergoes updating events that are represented by edges in the multiway graph. And in general the paths followed in the multiway graph can be thought of as geodesics in multiway space. And to determine what happens to some part of the branchlike hypersurface, we must then follow a bundle of geodesics.

A notable feature of the multiway graph is the presence of branching and merging, and this will cause our bundle of geodesics to diverge and converge. Often in standard quantum formalism we are interested in the projection of one quantum state on another < | >. In our setup, the only truly meaningful computation is of the propagation of a geodesic bundle. But as an approximation to this that should be satisfactory in an appropriate limit, we can use distance between states in multiway space, and computing this in terms of the vectors $\xi_i = (t_i, b_i^2)$ the expected Hilbert space norm [122][123] appears: $(\xi_1 - \xi_2)^2 = \xi_1^2 + \xi_2^2 - 2\,\xi_1.\xi_2$.

Time evolution in our system is effectively the propagation of geodesics through the multiway graph. And to work out a transition amplitude <i | S | f> between initial and final states we need to see what happens to a bundle of geodesics that correspond to the initial state as they propagate through the multiway graph. And in particular we want to know the measure (or essentially cross-sectional area) of the geodesic bundle when it intersects the branchlike hypersurface defined by a certain quantum observation frame to detect the final state.

To analyze this, consider a single path in the multiway system, corresponding to a single geodesic. The critical observation is that this path is effectively "turned" in multiway space every time a branching event occurs, essentially just like in the simple example below:

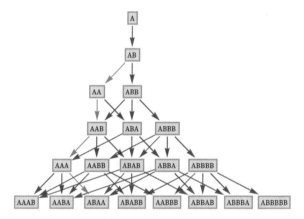

If we think of the turns as being through an angle θ, the way the trajectory projects onto the final branchlike hypersurface can then be represented by $e^{i\theta}$. But to work out the angle θ for a given path, we need to know how much branching there will be in the region of the multiway graph through which it passes.

But now recall that in discussing spacetime we identified the flux of edges through spacelike hypersurfaces in the causal graph as potentially corresponding to energy. The spacetime causal graph, however, is just a projection of the full multiway causal graph, in which branchlike directions have been reduced out. (In a causal invariant system, it does not matter what "direction" this projection is done in; the reduced causal graph is always the same.) But now suppose that in the full multiway causal graph, the flux of edges across spacelike hypersurfaces can still be considered to correspond to energy.

Now note that every node in the multiway causal graph represents some event in the multiway graph. But events are what produce branching—and "turns"—of paths in the multiway graph. So what this suggests is that the amount of turning of a path in the multiway graph should be proportional to energy, multiplied by the number of steps, or effectively the time. In standard quantum formalism, energy is identified with the Hamiltonian H, so what this says is that in our models, we can expect transition amplitudes to have the basic form e^{iHt}—in agreement with the result from quantum mechanics.

To think about this in more detail, we need not just a single energy quantity—corresponding to an overall rate of events—but rather we want a local measure of event rate as a function of location in multiway space. In addition, if we want to compute in a relativistically invariant way, we do not just want the flux of causal edges through spacelike hypersurfaces in some specific foliation. But now we can make a potential identification with standard quantum formalism: we suppose that the Lagrangian density $\mathcal{L}$ corresponds to the total flux in all directions (or, in other words, the divergence) of causal edges at each point in multiway space.

But now consider a path in the multiway system going through multiway space. To know how much "turning" to expect in the path, we need in effect to integrate the Lagrangian density along the path (together with the appropriate volume element). And this will give us something of the form e^{iS}, where S is the action. But this is exactly what we see in the standard path integral formulation of quantum mechanics [124].

There are many additional details (see [121]). But the correspondence between our models and the results of standard quantum formalism is notable.

It is worth pointing out that in our models, something like the Lagrangian is ultimately not something that is just inserted from the outside; instead it must emerge from actual rules operating on hypergraphs. In the standard formalism of quantum field theory, the Lagrangian is stated in terms of quantum field operators. And the implication is therefore that the structure of the Lagrangian must somehow emerge as a kind of limit of the underlying discrete system, perhaps a bit like how fluid mechanics can emerge from discrete underlying molecular dynamics (or cellular automata) [110].

One notable feature of standard quantum formalism is the appearance of complex numbers for amplitudes. Here the core concept is the turning of a path in multiway space; the complex numbers arise only as a convenient way to represent the path and understand its projections. But there is an additional way complex numbers can arise. Imagine that we want to put a metric on the full $(t, \vec{x}, \vec{b})$ space of the multiway causal graph. The normal convention for $(t, \vec{x})$ space is to have real-number coordinates and a norm based on $t^2 - x^2$—but an alternative is use $i\,t$ for time. In extending to $(t, \vec{x}, \vec{b})$ space, one might imagine that a natural norm which allows the contributions of t, x and b components to be appropriately distinguished would be $t^2 - x^2 + i\,b^2$.

8.14 Quantum Measurement

Above we gave a brief summary of how quantum measurement can work in the context of our models. Here we give some more detail.

In a sense the key to quantum measurement is reconciling our notion that "definite things happen in the universe" with the formalism of quantum mechanics—or the branching structure of a multiway system.

But if definite things are going to happen, what might they be?

Here we will again consider the example of a string substitution system, although the core of what we say also applies to the full hypergraph case. Consider the rule

{A → AB, B → A}

We could imagine a simple "classical" procedure for evolving according to this rule, in which we just do all updates we can (say, based on a left-to-right scan) at each step:

But in fact we know that there are many other possibilities, that can be represented by the multiway system:

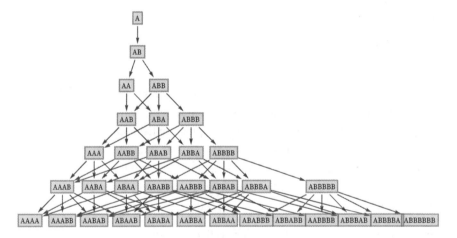

Most of the states that appear in the multiway system are, however, "unfinished", in the sense that there are additional "independent" updates that can consistently be done on them. For example, with the rule {A→BA} there are 4 separate updates that can be applied to AAAA:

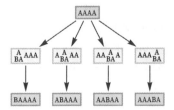

But none of these depend on the others, so they can in effect all be done together, giving the result BABABABA.

Put another way, all of these updates involve "spacelike separated" parts of the string, so they are all causally independent, and can all consistently be carried out at the same time. As discussed in 5.21, doing all updates across a state together can be thought of as evolving a system in "generational steps" to produce "generational states".

In some multiway cases, there may be a single sequence of generational states:

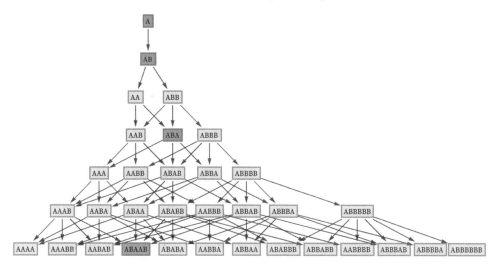

In other cases, there can be several branches of generational states:

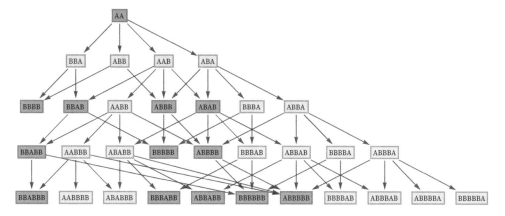

The presence of multiple branches is a consequence of having a mixture of spacelike and branchlike separated events that can be applied to a single state. For example, with the rule {A→AB,A→BB} the first and second updates here are spacelike separated, but the first and third are branchlike separated:

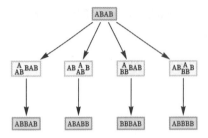

A view of quantum measurement is that it is an attempt to describe multiway systems using generational states. Sometimes there may be a unique "classical path"; sometimes there may be several outcomes for measurements, corresponding to several generational states.

But now let us consider the actual process of doing an experiment on a multiway system—or a quantum system. Our basic goal is—as much as possible—to describe the multiway system in terms of a limited number of generational states, without having to track all the different branches in the multiway system.

At some point in the evolution of a string substitution system we might see a large number of different strings. But we can view them all as part of a single generational state if they in effect yield only spacelike separated events. In other words, if the strings can be assembled without "branchlike ambiguity" they can be thought of as forming a consistent generational state.

In the standard formalism of quantum mechanics, we can think of the states in the multiway system as being quantum states. The construct we form by "assembling" these states can be thought of as a superposition of the states. Causal invariance then implies that through the evolution of the multiway system any such superposition will then actually become a single quantum state. In some sense the observer "did nothing": they just notionally identified a collection of states. It was the actual evolution of the system that produced the specific combined state.

In describing a quantum system—or a multiway system—one must in effect define coordinates, and in particular one must specify what foliation one is going to use to represent the progress of time. And this freedom to pick a "quantum observation frame" is critical in being able to maintain a view in which one imagines "definite things to happen" in the system.

With a foliation like the following, at any given time there is a mixture of different states, and no attempt has been made to find a way to "summarize" what the system is doing:

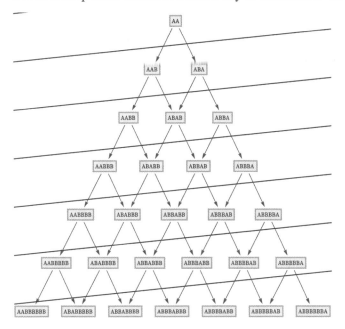

Consider, however, a foliation like the following:

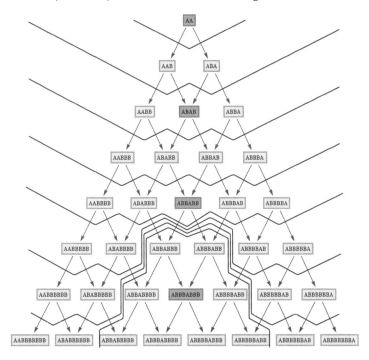

In this picture, generational states have been highlighted, and a foliation has been selected that essentially "freezes time" around a particular generational state. In effect, the observer is choosing a quantum observation frame in which there is a definite classical outcome for the behavior of the system.

"Freezing time" around a particular state is something an observer can choose to do in their description of the system. But the crucial point is that the actual dynamics of the evolution of the multiway system cause this choice to have implications.

In particular, in the case shown, the region of the multiway system in which "time is frozen" progressively expands. The choice the observer has made to freeze a particular state is causing more and more states to have to be considered as similarly frozen. In the physics of quantum measurement, one is used to the idea that for a quantum measurement to be considered to have a definite result, it must involve more and more quantum degrees of freedom. What we see here is effectively a manifestation of this phenomenon.

In freezing time in something like the foliation in the picture above what we are effectively doing is creating a coordinate singularity in defining our quantum observation frame. And there is an analogy to this in general relativity and the physics of spacetime. Just as we freeze time in our quantum frame, so also we can freeze time in a relativistic reference frame. For example, as an object approaches the event horizon of a black hole, its time as described by a typical coordinate system set up by an observer far from the black hole will become frozen—and just like in our quantum case, we will consider the state to stay fixed.

But there is a complicated issue here. To what extent is the singularity—and the freezing of time—a feature of our description, and to what extent is it something that "really happens"? This depends in a sense on the relationship one has to the system. In traditional thinking about quantum measurement, one is most interested in the "impressions" of observers who are in effect embedded in the system. And for them, the coordinate system they chose in effect defines their reality.

But one can also imagine being somehow "outside the system". For example, one might try to set up a quantum experiment (or a quantum computer) in which the construction of the system somehow makes it natural to maintain a "frozen time" foliation. The picture below shows a toy example in which the multiway system by its very construction has a terminal state for which time does not advance:

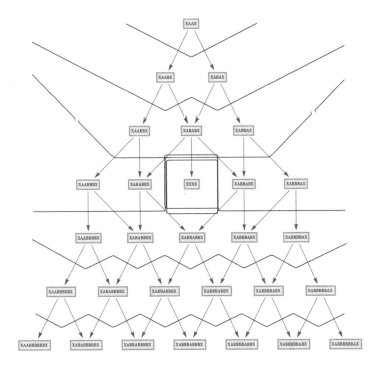

But now the question arises of what can be achieved in the multiway system corresponding to the actual physical universe. And here we can expect that one will not be able to set up truly isolated states, and that instead there will be continual inevitable entanglement. What one might have imagined could be maintained as a separate state will always become entangled with other states.

The picture below shows a slightly more realistic multiway system, with an attempt to construct a foliation that freezes time:

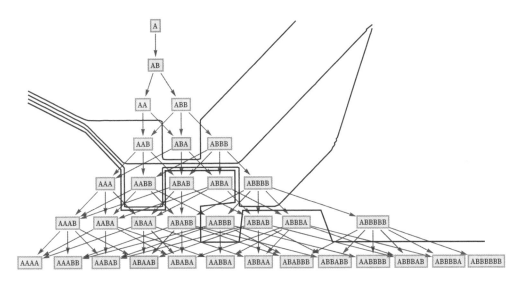

And what we see here is that in a sense the structure of the multiway graph limits the extent to which we can freeze time. In effect, the multiway system forces decoherence— or entanglement—-just by its very structure.

We should note that it is not necessarily the case that there is just a single possible sequence of generational states, corresponding in a sense to a single possible "classical path". Here is an example where there are four generational states that occur at a particular generational step. And now we can for example construct a foliation that—at least for a while—"freezes time" for all of these generational states:

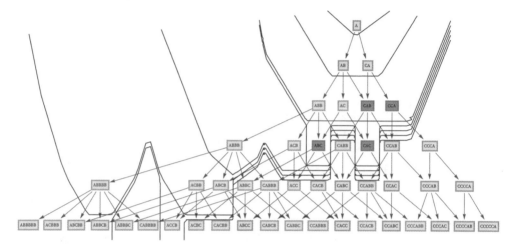

It is worth pointing out that if we try to freeze time for something that is not a proper generational state, there will be an immediate issue. A proper generational state contains the results of all spacelike separated events at a particular point in the evolution of a system. So when we freeze time for it, we are basically allowing other branchlike separated events to occur, but not other spacelike separated ones. However, if we tried to freeze time for a state that did not include all spacelike separated events, there would quickly be a mismatch with the progress of time for the excluded events—or in effect the singularity of quantum observation frame would "spill over" into a singularity in the causal graph, leading to a singularity in spacetime.

In other words, the fact that the states that appear in quantum measurement are generational states is not just a convenience but a necessity. Or, put another way, in doing a quantum measurement we are effectively setting up a singularity in branchial space, and only if the states we measure are in effect "complete in spacetime" will this singularity be kept only in branchial space; otherwise it will also become a singularity in physical spacetime.

In general, when we talk about quantum measurement, we are talking about how an observer manages to construct a description of a system that in effect allows the observer to "make a conclusion" about what has happened in the system. And what we have seen is that appropriate "time-freezing foliations" allow us to do this. And while there may be some restrictions, it is usually in principle possible to construct such foliations in a multiway system, and to have them last as long as we want.

But in practice, as the pictures above begin to suggest, after a while the foliations we have to construct can get increasingly complicated. In effect, what we are having to do in constructing the foliation is to "reverse engineer" the actual evolution of the multiway system, so that with our elaborate description we are still managing to maintain time as frozen for a particular state, carefully avoiding complicated entanglements that have built up with other states.

But there is a problem here. Because in effect we are asking the observer to "outcompute" the system itself. Yet we can expect that the evolution of the multiway system, say for one of our models, will usually correspond to an irreducible computation. And so we will be asking the observer to do a more and more elaborate computation to maintain the description they are using. And as soon as the computation required exceeds the capability of the observer, the observer will no longer be able to maintain the description, and so decoherence will be inevitable.

It is worthwhile to compare this situation with what happens in thermodynamic processes, and in particular with apparent entropy increase. In a reversible system, it is always in principle possible to recognize, say, that the initial conditions for the systems were simple (and "low entropy"). But in practice the actual configurations of the system usually become complicated enough that this is increasingly difficult to do. In traditional statistical mechanics one talks of "coarse-grained" measurements as a way to characterize what an observer can actually analyze about a system.

In computational terms we talk about the computational capabilities of the observer, and how computational irreducibility in the evolution of the system will eventually overwhelm the computational capabilities of the observer, making apparent entropy increase inevitable [1:9.3].

In the quantum case, we now see how something directly analogous happens. The analog of coarse graining is the effort to create a foliation with a particular apparent outcome. But eventually this becomes infeasible, and—just like in the thermodynamic case—we in effect see "thermalization", which we can now attribute to the effects of computational irreducibility.

8.15 Operators in Quantum Mechanics

In standard quantum formalism, there are states, and there are operators (e.g. [125]). In our models, updating events are what correspond to operators. In the standard evolution of the multiway system, all applicable operators are in effect "automatically applied" to every state to generate the actual evolution of the system. But to understand the correspondence with standard quantum formalism, we can imagine just applying particular operators by doing only particular updating events.

Consider the string substitution system:

{AB → ABA, BA → BAB}

In this system we effectively have two operators O_1 and O_2, corresponding to these two possible updating rules. We can think about building up an operator algebra by considering the relations between different sequences of applications of these operators.

In particular, we can study the commutator:

$$[O_1, O_2] = O_1 \, O_2 - O_2 \, O_1$$

In terms of the underlying rules, this commutator corresponds to:

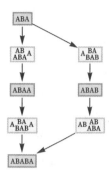

At the first step, the results of applying O_1 and O_2 to the initial state are different, and we can say that the states generated form a branch pair. But then at the second step, the branch pair resolves, and the branches merge to the same state. In effect, we can represent this by saying that O_1 and O_2 commute, or that:

$$[O_1, O_2] = O_1 \, O_2 - O_2 \, O_1 = 0$$

In general, there is a close relationship between causal invariance—and its implication for the resolution of all branch pairs—and the commuting of operators. And given our discussion above this should not be considered surprising: as we discussed, when there is causal invariance, it means that all branches can resolve to a single ("classical") state, just like in standard quantum formalism the commuting of operators is associated with seemingly classical behavior.

But there is a key point here: even if causal invariance implies that branch pairs (and similarly commutators) will eventually resolve, they may take time to do so. And it is this delay in resolution that is the core of what leads to what we normally think of as quantum effects.

Once a branch pair has resolved, there are no longer multiple branches, and a single state has emerged. But before the branch pair has resolved, there are multiple states, and therefore what one might think of as "quantum indeterminacy".

In the case where a branch pair has not yet resolved, the corresponding commutator will be nonzero—and in a sense the value of the commutator measures the branchlike distance between the states reached by applying the two different updates (corresponding to the two different operators).

In our model for spacetime, if a single event in the causal graph is connected in the causal graph to two different events we can ask what the spacelike separation of these events might be, and we might suppose that this spatial distance is determined by the speed of light c (say multiplied by the elementary time corresponding to traversal of the causal edge).

In thinking now about the multiway system, we can ask what the branchlike separation of states in a branch pair might be. This will now be a distance on a branchial graph—or effectively a distance in state space—and we can suppose that this distance is determined by $\hbar$. And depending on our conventions for measuring branchial distance, we might introduce an i, yielding a setup very much aligned with traditional quantum formalism.

Another interpretation of the non-commuting of operators is connected to the entanglement of quantum states. And here we now have a very direct picture of entanglement: two states are entangled if they are part of the same unresolved branch pair, and thus have a common ancestor.

The multiway graph gives a full map of all entanglements. But at any particular time (corresponding to a particular slice of a foliation defined by a quantum observation frame), the branchial graph gives a snapshot that captures the "instantaneous" configuration of entanglements. States closer on the branchial graph are more entangled; those further apart are less entangled.

It is important to note that distance on the branchial graph is not necessarily correlated with distance on the spatial graph. If we look at events, we can use the multiway causal graph to give a complete map of all connections, involving both branchlike and spacelike (as well as timelike) separations. Ultimately, the underlying rule determines what connections will exist in the multiway causal graph. But just as in the standard formalism of quantum mechanics, it is perfectly possible for there to be entanglement of spacelike-separated events.

8.16 Wave-Particle Duality, Uncertainty Relations, etc.

Wave-particle duality was an early but important concept in standard quantum mechanics, and turns out to be a core feature of our models, independent even of the details of particles. The key idea is to look at the correspondence between spacelike and branchlike projections of the multiway causal graph.

Let us consider some piece of "matter", ultimately represented as features of our hypergraphs. A complete description of what the matter does must include what happens on every branch of the multiway graph. But we can get a picture of this by looking at the multiway causal graph—which in effect has the most complete representation of all meaningful spatial and branchial features of our models.

Fundamentally what we will see is a bundle of geodesics that represent the matter, propagating through the multiway causal graph. Looked at in terms of spacelike coordinates, the bundle will seem to be following a definite path—characteristic of particle-like behavior. But inevitably the bundle will also be extended in the branchlike direction—and this is what leads to wave-like behavior.

Recall that we identified energy in spacetime as corresponding to the flux of causal edges through spacelike hypersurfaces. But as mentioned above, whenever causal edges are present, they correspond to events, which are associated with branching in the multiway graph and the multiway causal graph. And so when we look at geodesics in the bundle, the rate at which they turn in multiway space will be proportional to the rate at which events happen, or in other words, to energy—yielding the standard $E \propto \omega$ proportionality between particle energy and wave frequency.

Another fundamental phenomenon in quantum mechanics is the uncertainty principle. To understand this principle in our framework, we must think operationally about the process of, for example, first measuring position, then measuring momentum. It is best to think in terms of the multiway causal graph. If we want to measure position to a certain precision Δx we effectively need to set up our detector (or arrange our quantum observation frame) so that there are $O(1/\Delta x)$ elements laid out in a spacelike array. But once we have made our position measurement, we must reconfigure our detector (or rearrange our quantum observation frame) to measure momentum instead.

But now recall that we identified momentum as corresponding to the flux of causal edges across timelike hypersurfaces. So to do our momentum measurement we effectively need to have the elements of our detector (or the pieces of our quantum observation frame) laid out on a timelike hypersurface. But inevitably it will take at least $O(1/\Delta x)$ updating events to rearrange the elements we need. But each of these updating events will typically generate a branch in the multiway system (and thus the multiway causal graph). And the result of this will be to produce an $O(1/\Delta x)$ spread in the multiway causal graph, which then leads to an $O(1/\Delta x)$ uncertainty in the measurement of momentum.

(Another ultimately equivalent approach is to consider different foliations, and to note for example that with a finer foliation in time, one is less able to determine the "true direction" of causal edges in the multiway graph, and thus to determine how many of them will cross a spacelike hypersurface.)

To make our discussion of the uncertainty principle more precise, we should consider operators—represented by sequences of updating events. In the $(t, \vec{x}, \hat{b})$ space of the multiway causal graph, the operators corresponding to position and momentum must generate events that correspond to moving at different angles; as a result the operators do not commute.

And with this setup we can see why position and momentum, as well as energy and time, form canonically conjugate pairs for which uncertainty relations hold: it is because these quantities are associated with features of the multiway causal graph that probe distinct (and effectively orthogonal) directions in multiway causal space.

8.17 Correspondence between Relativity and Quantum Mechanics

One of the surprising consequences of the potential application of our models to physics is their implications around deep relationships between relativity and quantum mechanics. These are particularly evident in thinking about the multiway causal graph. As a toy model, consider the graph:

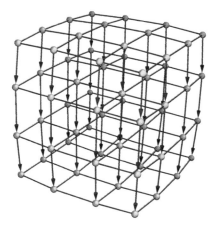

Timelike edges go down, but then in each slice there are spacelike and branchlike edges. A more realistic example of the very beginning of such a graph is:

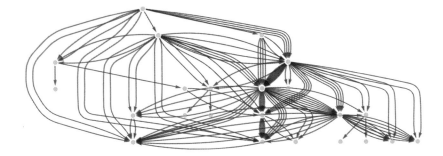

The multiway causal graph in a sense captures in one graph both relativity and quantum mechanics. Time is involved in both of them, and in our models it is an essentially computational concept, involving progressive application of the underlying rules of the system. But then relativity is associated with the structure formed by spacelike and timelike edges, while quantum mechanics is primarily associated with the structure formed by branchlike and timelike edges.

The spacelike direction corresponds to ordinary physical space; the branchlike direction is effectively the space of quantum states. Distance in the spacelike direction is ordinary spacetime distance. Distance in the branchlike direction reflects the level of quantum entanglement between states. When we form foliations in time, spacelike hypersurfaces represent in a sense the instantaneous configuration of space, while branchlike hypersurfaces represent the instantaneous entanglements between quantum states.

It should be emphasized that (unlike in the idealization of our first picture above) the detailed structure of the spacelike+timelike component of the multiway causal graph will in practice be very different from that of the branchlike+timelike one. The spacelike+timelike component is expected to limit to something like a finite-dimensional manifold, reflecting the characteristics of physical spacetime. The branchlike+timelike one potentially limits to an infinite dimensional space (that is perhaps a projective Hilbert space), reflecting the characteristics of the space of quantum states. But despite these substantial geometrical differences, one can expect many structural aspects and consequences to be basically the same.

We are used to the idea of motion in space. In the context of our models—and of the multiway causal graph—motion in space in effect corresponds to progressively sampling more spacelike edges in the graph. But now we can see a quantum analog: we can also have motion in the branchlike direction, in which, in effect, we progressively sample more branchlike edges, reaching more quantum states. Velocity in space is thus the analog of the rate at which additional states are sampled (and thus entangled).

In relativity there is a fairly well-developed notion of an idealized observer. The observer is typically represented by some some causal foliation of spacetime—like an inertial reference frame that moves without forces acting on it. One can also define an observer in quantum mechanics, and in the context of our models it makes sense—as we have done above—to parametrize the observer in terms of a quantum observation frame that consists not of a sequence of spacelike hypersurfaces, but instead of a series of branchlike ones.

A quantum observation frame in a sense defines a plan for how an observer will sample possible quantum states—and the analog of an inertial frame in spacetime is presumably a quantum observation frame that corresponds to a fixed plan that cannot be affected by anything outside. And in general, the analog in quantum mechanics of a world line in relativity is presumably a measurement plan.

In special relativity a key idea is to think about comparing the perceptions of observers in different inertial frames. But in the context of our models we can now do the exact same thing for quantum observers. And the analog of relativistic invariance then becomes a statement of perception or measurement invariance: that in the end different quantum observers (despite the branching of states) in a sense perceive the same things to happen, or, in other words, that there is at some level an objective reality even in quantum mechanics.

Our analogy between relativity and quantum mechanics suggests asking about quantum analogs of standard relativistic phenomena. One example is relativistic time dilation, in which, in effect, sampling spacelike edges faster reduces the rate of traversing timelike edges. The analog in quantum mechanics is presumably the quantum Zeno effect [126][127], in which more rapid measurement—corresponding to faster sampling of branchlike edges—slows the time evolution of a quantum system.

A key concept in relativity is the light cone, which characterizes the maximum rate at which causal effects spread in spacelike directions. In our models, spacetime causal edges in effect define elementary light cones, which are then knitted together by the structure of the (spacetime) causal graph. But now in our models there is a direct analog for quantum mechanics, visible in the full multiway causal graph.

In the multiway causal graph, every event effectively has a cone of causal influence. Some of that influence may be in spacelike directions (corresponding to ordinary relativistic light cone effects), but some of it may be in branchlike directions. And indeed, whenever there are branches in the multiway graph, these correspond to branchlike edges in the multiway causal graph.

So what this means is that in addition to a light cone of effects in spacetime, there is also what we may call an entanglement cone, which defines the region affected in branchial space by some event. In the light cone case, the spacelike extent of the light cone is set by the speed of light (c). In the entanglement cone case (as we will discuss below) the branchlike extent of the entanglement cone is essentially set by $\hbar$.

As we have mentioned, the definition of time is shared between spacelike and branchlike components of the multiway causal graph. Another shared concept appears to be energy (or in general, energy-momentum, or action). Time is effectively defined by displacement in the timelike direction; energy appears to be defined by the flux of causal edges in the timelike direction. In the relativistic setting, energy can be thought of as flux of causal edges through spacelike hypersurfaces; in the quantum mechanical setting, it can be thought of as a flux of causal edges through branchlike hypersurfaces.

An important feature of the spacetime causal graph is that it can potentially describe curved space, and reproduce general relativity. And here again we can now see that in our models there are analogs in quantum mechanics. One issue, though, is that whereas ordinary space is—at least on a large scale—finite-dimensional, comparatively flat, and well modeled by a simple Lorentzian manifold, branchial space is much more complicated, probably in the limit infinite–dimensional, and not at all flat.

At a mathematical level, we are in quantum mechanics used to forming commutators of operators, and in many cases finding that they do not commute, with their "deviation" being measured by $\hbar$. In general relativity, one can also form commutators, and indeed the Riemann tensor for measuring curvature is precisely the result of computing the commutator of two covariant derivatives. And perhaps even more analogously the Ricci scalar curvature gives the angle deficit for transport around a loop in spacetime.

In our context, therefore, the non-flatness of space is directly analogous to a core phenomenon of quantum mechanics: the non-commuting of operators.

In the general relativity case, we are used to thinking about the propagation of bundles of geodesics in spacetime, and the fact that the Ricci scalar curvature determines the local cross-section of the bundle. Now we can also consider the more general propagation of bundles of geodesics in the multiway causal graph. But when we look along branchlike directions, the limiting space we see tends to be highly connected, and effectively of high negative curvature. And what this means is that a bundle of geodesics can be expected to spread out rapidly in branchlike directions.

But this has an immediate interpretation in quantum mechanics: it is the phenomenon of decoherence, whereby quantum effects get spread (and entangled) across large numbers of quantum degrees of freedom.

In relativity, the speed of light c sets a maximum speed for the propagation of effects in space. In quantum mechanics, our entanglement cones in essence also set a maximum speed for the propagation of effects in branchial space. In special relativity, there is then a maximum speed defined for any observer—or, in other words, a maximum speed for motion. In quantum mechanics, we can now expect that there will also be a maximum speed for entanglement, or for measurement: it is not possible to set up a quantum observation frame that achieves a higher speed while still respecting the causal relations in the multiway causal graph. We will call this maximum speed ζ, and in 8.20 we will discuss its possible magnitude.

One may ask to what extent the correspondences between relativity and quantum mechanics that we have been discussing rely on our models. In principle, for example, one could imagine a kind of "multicausal continuum" that is a mathematical structure (conceivably related to twistor spaces [128]) corresponding to a continuum limit of our multiway causal graph. But while there are challenges in understanding the limits associated with our models, this seems likely to be even more difficult to construct and handle—and has the great disadvantage that it cannot be connected to explicit models that are readily amenable, for example, to enumeration.

8.18 Event Horizons and Singularities in Spacetime and Quantum Mechanics

Having discussed the general correspondence between relativity and quantum mechanics suggested by our models, we can now consider the extreme situation of event horizons and singularities.

As we discussed above, an event horizon in spacetime corresponds in our models to disconnection in the causal graph: after some slice in our foliation in time, there is no longer causal connection between different parts of the system. As a result, even if the system is locally causal invariant, branch pairs whose products go on different sides of the disconnection can never resolve. The only way to make a foliation in which this does not happen is then effectively to freeze time before the disconnection occurs.

When there is a true disconnection in the causal graph, there is no choice about this. But it is also perfectly possible just to imagine setting up a coordinate system that freezes time in a particular region of space—although it will typically take more and more effort (and energy) to consistently maintain such a coordinate singularity as other parts of the system evolve.

But now there is an interesting correspondence with quantum measurement. As we discussed in 8.14, in the context of our models, one can view a quantum measurement (or a "collapse of the wave function") as being associated with a foliation that freezes time for the state that is the outcome of the measurement. In essence, therefore, quantum measurement corresponds to having a coordinate singularity in a particular region of branchial space.

What about an event horizon? As we saw above, one way in which an event horizon can occur is if some branch of the multiway system simply terminates, so that in a sense time stops for it. Another possibility is that—at least temporarily—there can be a disconnected piece in the branchial graph. Consider for example the (causal invariant) string substitution system:

{A → BB, BBB → AA}

The multiway system for this rule is

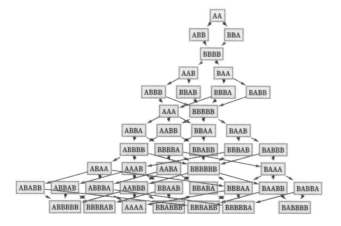

and the branchial graph shows temporary disconnections

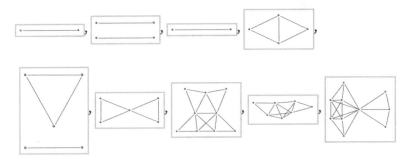

although the "spacetime" causal graph stays connected:

One can think of these temporary disconnections in the branchial graphs as corresponding to isolated regions of branchial space where entanglement at least temporarily cannot occur—and where some pure quantum state (such as qubits) can be maintained, at least for some period of time.

In some sense, one can potentially view such disconnections as being like black holes in branchial space. But the continued generation of branch pairs (in a potential analog to Hawking radiation [129]) causes the "black hole" to dissipate.

A different situation can occur when there is also disconnection in the causal graph—leading in our models to disconnection in the spatial hypergraph—and thus a spacetime event horizon. As a simple example, consider the string substitution system (starting from AA):

{AA → AAAB}

The causal graph in this case is

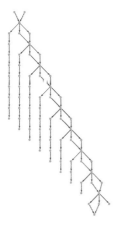

and the sequence of branchial graphs (with the standard foliation) is:

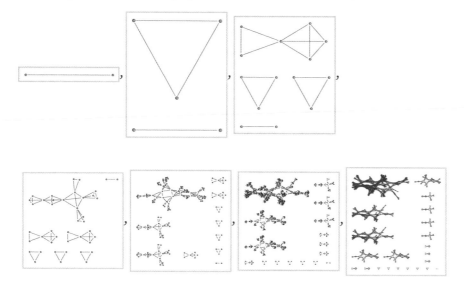

What has happened here is that there are event horizons both in physical space and in branchial space.

We can expect similar phenomena in our full models, and extrapolating this to a physical black hole what this represents is the presence of both a causal event horizon (associated with motion in space, propagation of light, etc.) and an entanglement event horizon (associated with quantum entanglement). The causal event horizon will be localized in physical space (say at the Schwarzschild radius [130]); the entanglement event horizon can be considered instead to be localized in branchial space.

It should be noted that these horizons are in a sense linked through the multiway causal graph, which in the example above initially has the form

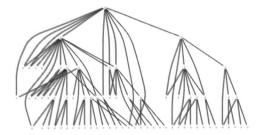

and after more steps builds up the structure:

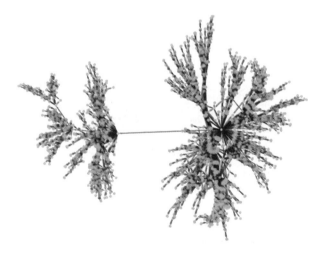

In this graph, there are both spacelike and branchlike connections, and here both of them exhibit disconnection, and therefore event horizons. And even though the geometrical structure of branchial space is very different from physical space, there are potentially further correspondences to be made between them. For example, while the speed of light c governs the maximum spacelike speed, the maximum entanglement rate ζ that we introduced above governs the maximum "branchlike speed", or entanglement rate.

When a disconnection occurs in the spacetime causal graph (and thus the spatial hypergraph), we can think of this as implying that geodesics in spacetime would have to exceed c in order not to be trapped. When a disconnection occurs in the branchial graph, we can think of geodesics having to "exceed speed ζ" in order not to be trapped.

It is worth pointing out that the analog of a true singularity—and not just an event horizon—can occur in our models if there are paths in the multiway system that simply terminate, as for B, BB, etc. in:

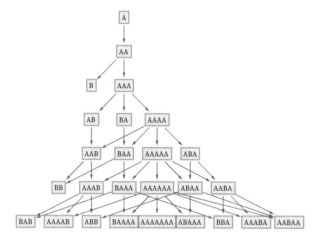

When this happens, there are many geodesics that in effect converge to a single point, like in spacetime singularities in general relativity. Here, however, we see that this can happen not only in physical space, but also in the multiway system, or, in other words, in branchial space. (In our systems, it is probably the case that singularities must be enclosed in event horizons, in the analog of the cosmic censorship hypothesis.)

Many results from general relativity can presumably be translated to our models, and can apply both to physical space and branchial space (see [121]). In the case of a black hole, our models suggest that not only may a causal event horizon form in physical space; also an entanglement horizon may form in branchial space. One may then imagine that quantum information is trapped inside the entanglement horizon, even without crossing the causal event horizon—with implications perhaps similar to recent discussions of resolutions to the black hole quantum information problem [131][132][133].

There is a simple physical picture that emerges from this setup. As we have discussed, quantum measurement can be thought of as a choice of coordinates that "freeze time" for some region in branchial space. For an observer close to the entanglement horizon, it will not be possible to do this. Much like an observer at a causal event horizon will be stretched in physical space, so also an observer at an entanglement horizon will be stretched in branchial space. And the result is that in a sense the observer will not be able to "form a classical thought": they will not success-fully be able to do a measurement that definitively picks the branch of the multiway system in which something fell into the black hole, or the one in which it did not.

8.19 Local Gauge Invariance

An important phenomenon discussed especially in the context of quantum field theories is local gauge invariance (e.g. [134]). In our models this phenomenon can potentially arise as a result of local symmetries associated with underlying rules (see 6.12). The basic idea is that these symmetries allow different local configurations of rule applications—that can be thought of as different local "gauge" coordinate systems.

But the collection of all such possible configurations appears in the multiway graph (and the multiway causal graph)—so that a local choice of gauge can then be represented by a particular foliation in the multiway graph. But causal invariance then implies the equivalence of foliations—and establishes local gauge invariance.

As a very simple example, consider the rule:

Starting from a square, this rule can be applied in two different ways:

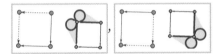

There is similar freedom if one applies the rule twice to a larger region:

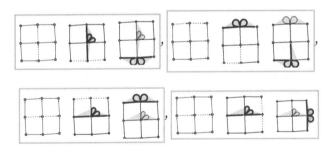

In both cases one can think of the freedom to apply the rule in different ways as being like a symmetry, for example characterized by the list of possible permutations of input elements.

But now imagine taking the limit of a large number of steps. Then one can expect to apply the resulting aggregate rule in a large number of ways. And much as we expect the limit of our spatial hypergraphs to be able to be represented—at least in certain cases—as a continuous manifold, we can expect something similar here. In particular, we can think of ourselves as winding up with a very large number of permutations corresponding to equivalent rule applications, which in the limit can potentially correspond to a Lie group.

Each different possible choice of how to apply the rule corresponds to a different event that is represented in the multiway graph, and the multiway causal graph:

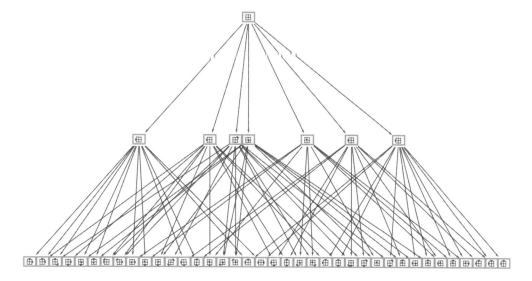

But the important point is that local choices of how the rule is repeatedly applied must always correspond to purely branchlike connections in the multiway causal graph.

The picture is analogous to the one in traditional mathematical physics. The spatial hypergraph can be thought of as a base space for a fiber bundle, then the different choices of which branchlike paths to follow correspond to different choices of coordinate systems (or gauges) in the fibers of the fiber bundle (cf. [135][136]). The connection between fibers is defined by the foliation that is chosen.

There is an analog when one sets up foliations in the spacetime causal graph—in which case, as we have argued, causal invariance leads to general covariance and general relativity. But here we are dealing with branchlike paths, and instead of getting general relativity, we potentially get gauge theories.

In traditional physics, local gauge invariance already occurs in classical theories (such as electromagnetism), and it is notable that for us it appears to arise from considering multiway systems. Yet although multiway systems appear to be deeply connected to quantum mechanics, the aggregate symmetry phenomenon that leads to gauge theories in effect makes slightly different use of the structure of the multiway causal graph.

But much as in other cases, we can think about geodesics—now in the multiway causal graph—and can study the properties of the effective space that emerges, with local phenomena (including things like commutators) potentially reflecting features of the Lie algebra.

In traditional physics an important consequence of local gauge invariance is its implication of the existence of fields, and gauge bosons such as the photon and gluon. In our models the mathematical derivations that lead to this implication should be similar. But by looking at the evolution of our models, it is possible to get a more explicit sense of how this works. Consider a particular sequence of updates with the rule shown above:

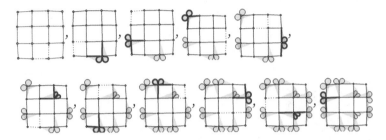

At the beginning, symmetry effectively allows many equivalent updates to be made. But once a particular update has been made, this has consequences for which of the possible updates—each independently equivalent on their own—can be made subsequently. These "consequences" are captured in the causal relationships encoded in the multiway causal graph—which have not only branchlike but also spacelike extent, corresponding in essence to the propagation of effects in what can be described as a gauge field.

8.20 Units and Scales

Most of our discussion so far has focused on how the structure of our models might correspond to the structure of our physical universe. But to make direct contact between our models and known physics, we need to fill in actual units and scales for the constructs in our models. In this section we give some indication of how this might work.

In our models, there is a fundamental unit of time (that we will call $\bar{T}$) that represents the interval of time corresponding to a single updating event. This interval of time in a sense defines the scale for everything in our models.

Given $\bar{T}$, there is an elementary length $\bar{L}$, determined by the speed of light c according to:

$$\bar{L} = c\,\bar{T}$$

The elementary length defines the spatial separation of neighboring elements in the spatial hypergraph.

Another fundamental scale is the elementary energy $\bar{E}$: the contribution of a single causal edge to the energy of a system. The energy scale ultimately has both relativistic and quantum consequences. In general relativity, it relates to how much curvature a single causal edge can produce, and in quantum mechanics, it relates to how much change in angle in an edge in the multiway graph a single causal edge can produce.

The speed of light c determines the elementary length in ordinary space, specifying in effect how far one can go in a single event, or in a single elementary time. To fill in scales for our models, we also need to know the elementary length in branchial space—or in effect how far in state space one can go in a single event, or a single elementary time (or, in effect, how far apart in branchial space two members of a branch pair are). And it is an obvious supposition that somehow the scale for this must be related to $\hbar$.

An important point about scales is that there is no reason to think that elementary quantities measured with respect to our current system of units need be constant in the history of the universe. For example, if the universe effectively just splits every spatial graph edge in two, the number of elementary lengths in what we call 1 meter will double, and so the elementary length measured in meters will halve.

Given the structure of our models, there are two key relationships that determine scales. The first—corresponding to the Einstein equations—relates energy density to spacetime curvature, or, more specifically, gives the contribution of a single causal edge (with one elementary unit of energy) to the change of V_r and the corresponding Ricci curvature:

$$\frac{G}{c^4} \frac{\bar{E}}{\bar{L}^d} \approx \frac{1}{\bar{L}^2}$$

(Here we have dropped numerical factors, and G is the gravitational constant, which, we may note, is defined with its standard units only when the dimension of space $d = 3$.)

The second key relationship that determines scales comes from quantum mechanics. The most obvious assumption might be that quantum mechanics would imply that the elementary energy should be related to the elementary time by $\bar{E} \approx \hbar/\bar{T}$. And if this were the case, then our various elementary quantities would be equal to their corresponding Planck units [137], as obtained with $G = c = \hbar = 1$ (yielding elementary length $\approx 10^{-35}$ m, elementary time $\approx 10^{-43}$ s, etc.)

But the setup of our models suggests something different—and instead suggests a relationship that in effect also depends on the size of the multiway graph. In our models, when we make a measurement in a quantum system, we are at a complete quantum observation frame—or in effect aggregating across all the states in the multiway graph that exist in the current slice of the foliation that we have defined with our quantum frame.

There are many individual causal edges in the multiway causal graph, each associated with a certain elementary energy $\bar{E}$. But when we measure an energy, it will be the aggregate of contributions from all the individual causal edges that we have combined in our quantum frame.

A single causal edge, associated with a single event which takes a single elementary time, has the effect of displacing a geodesic in the multiway graph by a certain unit distance in branchial space. (The result is a change of angle of the geodesic—with the formation of a single branch pair perhaps being considered to involve angle $\frac{\pi}{2}$.)

Standard quantum mechanics in effect defines $\hbar$ through $E = \hbar\,\omega$. But in this relationship E is a measured energy, not the energy associated with a single causal edge. And to convert between these we need to know in effect the number of states in the branchial graph associated with our quantum frame, or the number of nodes in our current slice through the multiway system. We will call this number Ξ.

And finally now we can give a relation between elementary energy and elementary time:

$$\bar{E}\,\Xi \approx \frac{\hbar}{\bar{T}}$$

In effect, $\hbar$ sets a scale for measured energies, but $\hbar/\Xi$ sets a scale for energies of individual causal edges in the multiway causal graph.

This is now sufficient to determine our elementary units. The elementary length is given in dimension $d = 3$ by

$$\bar{L} \approx \left(\frac{G\,\hbar}{c^3\,\Xi}\right)^{1/(d-1)} \approx \frac{l_P}{\sqrt{\Xi}} \approx \frac{10^{-35}\ \text{m}}{\sqrt{\Xi}}$$

$$\bar{T} \approx \frac{t_P}{\sqrt{\Xi}} \approx \frac{10^{-43}\ \text{s}}{\sqrt{\Xi}}$$

$$\bar{E} \approx \frac{E_P}{\sqrt{\Xi}} \approx \frac{10^9\ \text{J}}{\sqrt{\Xi}} \approx \frac{10^{19}\ \text{GeV}}{\sqrt{\Xi}}$$

where l_P, t_P, E_P are the Planck length, time and energy.

To go further, however, we must estimate Ξ. Ultimately, Ξ is determined by the actual evolution of the multiway system for a particular rule, together with whatever foliation and other features define the way we describe our experience of the universe. As a simple model, we might then characterize what we observe as being "generational states" in the evolution of a multiway system, as we discussed in 5.21.

But now we can use what we have seen in studying actual multiway systems, and assume that in one generational step of at least a causal invariant rule each generational state generates on average some number κ of new states, where κ is related to the number of new elements produced by a single updating event. In a generation of evolution, therefore, the total number of states in the multiway system will be multiplied by a factor κ.

But to relate this to observed quantities, we must ask what time an observer would perceive has elapsed in one generational step of evolution. From our discussion above, we expect that the typical time an observer will be able to coherently maintain the impression of a definite "classical-like" state will be roughly the elementary time $\bar{T}$ multiplied by the number of nodes in the branchlike hypersurface. The number of nodes will change as the multiway graph grows. But in the current universe we have defined it to be Ξ.

Thus we have the relation

$$\Xi \approx K^{\frac{t_H}{\Xi T}}$$

where t_H is the current age of the universe, and for this estimate we have ignored the change of generation time at different points in the evolution of the multiway system.

Substituting our previous result for $\bar{T}$ we then get:

$$\Xi \approx K^{\frac{t_H}{t_p} \frac{1}{\sqrt{\Xi}}} \approx K^{\frac{10^{61}}{\sqrt{\Xi}}}$$

There is a rough upper limit on κ from the signature for the underlying rule, or effectively the ratio in the size of the hypergraphs between the right and left-hand sides of a rule. (For most of the rules we have discussed here, for example, $\kappa \lesssim 2$.) The lower limit on κ is related to the "efficiency" of causal invariance in the underlying rule, or, in effect, how long it takes branch pairs to resolve relative to how fast new ones are created. But inevitably $\kappa > 1$.

Given the transcendental equation

$$\Xi = K^{\frac{\sigma}{\sqrt{\Xi}}}$$

we can solve for Ξ to get

$$\Xi = e^{2\,W(\frac{1}{2}\sigma\log(\kappa))}$$

where W is the product log function [138] that solves $w\,e^w = z$. But for large $\sigma \log(\kappa)$ (and we imagine that $\sigma \approx 10^{61}$), we have the asymptotic result [30]:

$$\Xi \approx \frac{(\sigma\log(\kappa))^2}{4\log^2(\frac{1}{2}\sigma\log(\kappa))}$$

Plotting the actual estimate for Ξ as a function of κ we get the almost identical result:

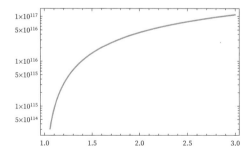

If $\kappa = 1$, then we would have $\Xi = 1$, and for κ extremely close to 1, $\Xi \approx 1 + \sigma\,(\kappa - 1) + \ldots$ But even for $\kappa = 1.01$ we already have $\Xi \approx 10^{112}$, while for $\kappa = 1.1$ we have $\Xi \approx 10^{115}$, for $\kappa = 2$ we have $\Xi \approx 4 \times 10^{116}$ and for $\kappa = 10$ we have $\Xi \approx 5 \times 10^{117}$.

To get an accurate value for κ we would have to know the underlying rule and the statistics of the multiway system it generates. But particularly at the level of the estimates we are giving, our results are quite insensitive to the value of κ, and we will assume simply:

$$\Xi \approx 10^{116}$$

In other words, for the universe today, we are assuming that the number of distinct instantaneous complete quantum states of the universe being represented by the multiway system (and thus appearing in the branchial graph) is about 10^{116}.

But now we can estimate other quantities:

elementary length $\bar{L}$	$\overset{?}{\approx} 10^{-93}$ m	10^{-35} m $\Xi^{-\frac{1}{2}}$
elementary time $\bar{T}$	$\overset{?}{\approx} 10^{-101}$ s	10^{-43} s $\Xi^{-\frac{1}{2}}$
elementary energy $\bar{E}$	$\overset{?}{\approx} 10^{-30}$ eV	10^{28} eV $\Xi^{-\frac{1}{2}}$
elementary lengths across current universe	$\overset{?}{\approx} 10^{120}$	10^{62} $\Xi^{\frac{1}{2}}$
elements in spatial hypergraph	$\overset{?}{\approx} 10^{358}$	10^{184} $\Xi^{\frac{3}{2}}$
elements in branchial graph Ξ	$\overset{?}{\approx} 10^{116}$	Ξ
overall updates of universe so far	$\overset{?}{\approx} 10^{119}$	10^{61} $\Xi^{\frac{1}{2}}$
individual updating events in universe so far	$\overset{?}{\approx} 10^{477}$	10^{245} Ξ^{2}

The fact that our estimate for the elementary length $\bar{L}$ is considerably smaller than the Planck length indicates that our models suggest that space may be more closely approximated by a continuum than one might expect.

The fact that the elementary energy $\bar{E}$ is much smaller than the surprisingly macroscopic Planck energy ($\approx 10^{19}$ GeV ≈ 2 GJ, or roughly the energy of a lightning bolt) is a reflection of the fact the Planck energy is related to measurable energy, not the individual energy associated with an updating event in the multiway causal graph.

Given the estimates above, we can use the rest mass of the electron to make some additional very rough estimates—subject to many assumptions—about the possible structure of the electron:

number of elements in an electron	$\overset{?}{\approx} 10^{35}$	10^{-23} $\Xi^{\frac{1}{2}}$
radius of an electron	$\overset{?}{\approx} 10^{-81}$ m	10^{-42} m $\Xi^{-\frac{1}{3}}$
number of elementary lengths across an electron	$\overset{?}{\approx} 10^{12}$	10^{-8} $\Xi^{\frac{1}{6}}$

In quantum electrodynamics and other current physics, electrons are assumed to have zero intrinsic size. Experiments suggest that any intrinsic size must be less than about 10^{-22} m [139][140]—nearly 10^{60} times our estimate.

Even despite the comparatively large number of elements suggested to be within an electron, it is notable that the total number of elements in the spatial hypergraph is estimated to be more than 10^{200} times the number of elements in all known particles of matter in the universe—suggesting that in a sense most of the "computational effort" in the universe is expended on the creation of space rather than on the dynamics of matter as we know it.

The structure of our models implies that not only length and time but also energy and mass must ultimately be quantized. Our estimates indicate that the mass of the electron is $> 10^{36}$ times the quantized unit of mass—far too large to expect to see "numerological relations" between particle masses.

But with our model of particles as localized structures in the spatial hypergraph, there seems no reason to think that structures much smaller than the electron might not exist— corresponding to particles with masses much smaller than the electron.

Such "oligon" particles involving comparatively few hypergraph elements could have masses that are fairly small multiples of 10^{-30} eV. One can expect that their cross-sections for interaction will be extremely small, causing them to drop out of thermal equilibrium extremely early in the history of the universe (e.g. [141][142]), and potentially leading to large numbers of cold, relic oligons in the current universe—making it possible that oligons could play a role in dark matter. (Relic oligons would behave as a more-or-less-perfect ideal gas; current data indicates only that particles constituting dark matter probably have masses $\gtrsim 10^{-22}$ eV [143].)

As we discussed in the previous subsection, the structure of our models—and specifically the multiway causal graph—indicates that just as the speed of light c determines the maximum spacelike speed (or the maximum rate at which an observer can sample new parts of the spatial hypergraph), there should also be a maximum branchlike speed that we call ζ that determines the maximum rate at which an observer can sample new parts of the branchial graph, or, in effect, the maximum speed at which an observer can become entangled with new "quantum degrees of freedom" or new "quantum information".

Based on our estimates above, we can now give an estimate for the maximum entanglement speed. We could quote it in terms of the rate of sampling quantum states (or branches in the multiway system)

$$\frac{1}{\bar{T}} \approx \Xi \frac{\bar{E}}{\hbar} \approx 10^{102}/ \text{second}$$

but in connecting to observable features of the universe, it seems better to quote it in terms of the energy associated with edges in the causal graph, in which case the result based on our estimates is:

$$\zeta \approx \frac{\bar{E}}{\bar{T}} \approx 10^{62} \text{ GeV/ second} \approx 10^{52} \ W \approx 10^5 \text{ solar masses / second}$$

This seems large compared to typical astrophysical processes, but one could imagine it being relevant for example in mergers of galactic black holes.

8.21 Specific Models of the Universe

If we pick a particular one of our models, with a particular set of underlying rules and initial conditions, we might think we could just run it to find out everything about the universe it generates. But any model that is plausibly similar to our universe will inevitably show computational irreducibility. And this means that we cannot in general expect to shortcut the computational work necessary to find out what it does.

In other words, if the actual universe follows our model and takes a certain number of computational steps to get to a certain point, we will not be in a position to reproduce in much less than this number of steps. And in practice, particularly with the numbers in the previous subsection, it will therefore be monumentally infeasible for us to find out much about our universe by pure, explicit simulation.

So how, then, can we expect to compare one of our models with the actual universe? A major surprise of this section is how many known features of fundamental physics seem in a sense to be generic to many of our models. It seems, for example, that both general relativity and quantum mechanics arise with great generality in models of our type—and do not depend on the specifics of underlying rules.

One may suspect, however, that there are still plenty of aspects of our universe that are specific to particular underlying rules. A few examples are the effective dimension of space, the local gauge group, and the specific masses and couplings of particles. The extent to which finding these for a particular rule will run into computational irreducibility is not clear.

It is, however, to be expected that parameters like the ones just mentioned will put strong constraints on the underlying rule, and that if the rule is simple, they will likely determine it uniquely.

Of all the detailed things one can predict from a rule, it is inevitable that most will involve computational irreducibility. But it could well be that those features that we have identified and measured as part of the development of physics are ones that correspond to computationally reducible aspects of our universe. Yet if the ultimate rule is in fact simple, it is likely that just these aspects will be sufficient to determine it.

In section 7 we discussed some of the many different representations that can be used for our models. And in different representations, there will inevitably be a different ranking of simplicity among models. In setting up a particular representation for a model, we are in effect defining a language—presumably suitable for interpretation by both humans and our current computer systems. Then the question of whether the rule for the universe is simple in this language is in effect just the question of how suitable the language is for describing physics.

Of course, there is no guarantee that there exists a language in which, with our current concepts, there is a simple way to describe the rule for our physical universe. The results of this section are encouraging, but not definitive. For they at least suggest that in the representation we are using, known features of our universe generically emerge: we do not have to define some thin and complicated subset to achieve this.

8.22 Multiway Systems in the Space of All Possible Rules

We have discussed the possibility that our physical universe might be described as following a model of the type we have introduced here, with a particular rule. And to find such a rule would be a great achievement, and might perhaps be considered a final answer to the core question of fundamental physics.

But if such a rule is found, one might then go on and ask why—out of the infinite number of possibilities—it is this particular rule, or, for example, a simple rule at all. And here the paradigm we have developed makes a potential additional suggestion: perhaps there is not just one rule being used after all, but instead in a sense all possible rules are simultaneously used.

In the multiway systems we have discussed so far, there is a single underlying rule, but separate branches for all possible sequences of updating events. But one can imagine a rule-space multiway system, that includes branches not only for every sequence of updating events, but also for every possible rule used to do the updating. Somewhat like with updating events, there will be many states reached to which many of the possible rules cannot apply. (For example, a rule that involves only ternary edges cannot apply to a state with only binary edges.) And like with updating events, branches with different sequences of rules applied may reach equivalent states, and thus merge.

Operationally, it is not so difficult to see how to set up a rule-space multiway system. All it really involves is listing not just one or a few possible rules that can be used for each updating event, but in a sense listing all possible rules. In principle there are an infinite number of such rules, but any rule that involves rewriting a hypergraph that is larger than the hypergraph that represents the whole universe can never apply, so at least at any given point in the evolution of the system, the number of rules to consider is finite. But like with the many other kinds of limits we have discussed, we can still imagine taking the limit of all infinitely many possible rules.

As a toy example of a rule-space multiway system, consider all inequivalent 2 → 2 rules on strings of As and Bs:

{AA → AA, AA → AB, AA → BB, AB → AA, AB → AB, AB → BA}

We can immediately construct the rule-space multiway graph for these rules (here starting from all possible length-4 sequences of As and Bs):

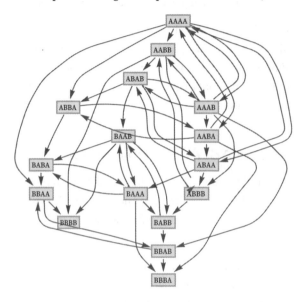

Different branches of the rule-space multiway system use different rules:

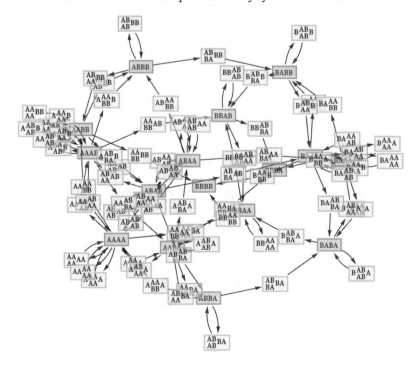

One can include causal connections:

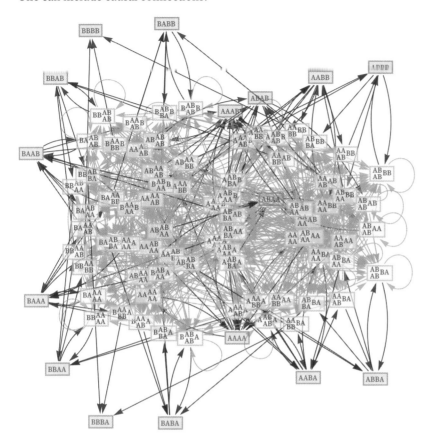

But even removing multiedges, the full rule-space multiway causal graph is complicated:

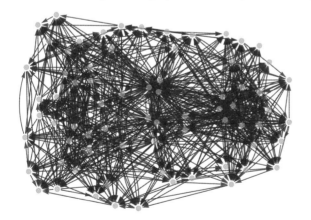

The "branchial graph" of the rule-space multiway system, though, is fairly simple, at least after one step (though it is now really more of a "rule-space graph"):

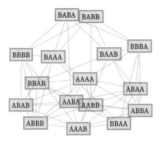

At least in this toy example, we already see something important: the rule-space multiway system is causal invariant: given branching even associated with using different rules, there is always corresponding merging—so the graph of causal relationships between updating events, even with different rules, is always the same.

Scaling up to unbounded evolutions and unbounded collections of rules involves many issues. But it seems likely that causal invariance will survive. And ultimately one may anticipate that across all possible rules it will emerge as a consequence of the Principle of Computational Equivalence [1:c12]. Because this principle implies that in the space of all possible rules, all but those with simple behavior are equivalent in their computational capabilities. And that means that across all the different possible sequences of rules that can be applied in the rule-space multiway system there is fundamental equivalence—with the result that one can expect causal invariance.

But now consider the role of the observer, who is inevitably embedded in the system, as part of the same rule-space multiway graph as everything else. Just as we did for ordinary multiway graphs above, we can imagine foliating the rule-space multiway graph, with the role of space or branchial space now being taken by rule space. And one can think of exploring rule space as effectively corresponding to sampling different possible descriptions of how the universe works, based on different underlying rules.

But if each event in the rule-space multiway graph is just a single update, based on a particular (finite) rule, there is immediately a consequence. Just like with light cones in ordinary space, or entanglement cones in branchial space, there will be a new kind of cone that defines a limit on how fast it is possible to "travel" in rule space.

For an observer, traveling in rule space involves ascribing different rules to the universe, or in effect changing one's "reference frame" for interpreting how the universe operates. (An "inertial frame" in rule space would probably correspond to continuing to use a particular rule.) But from the Principle of Computational Equivalence [1:c12] (and specifically from the idea of computation universality (e.g. [1:c11])) it is always possible to set up a computation that will translate between interpretations. But in a sense the further one goes in rule space, the more difficult the translation may become—and the more computation it will require.

But now remember that the observer is also embedded in the same system, so the fundamental rate at which it can do computation is defined by the structure of the system. And this is where what one might call the "translation cone" comes from: to go a certain "distance" in rule space, the observer must do a certain irreducible amount of computational work, which takes a certain amount of time.

The maximum rate of translation is effectively a ratio of "rule distance" to "translation effort" (measured in units of computational time). In a sense it probes something that has been difficult to quantify: just how "far apart" are different description languages, that involve different computational primitives? One can get some ideas by thinking about program size [144][145][146], or running time, but in the end new measures that take account of things, like the construction of sequences of abstractions, seem to be needed [147].

For our current discussion, however, the main point is the existence of a kind of "rule-space relativity". Depending on how an observer chooses to describe our universe, they may consider a different rule—or rather a different branch in the rule-space multiway system—to account for what they see. But if they change their "description frame", causal invariance (based on the Principle of Computational Equivalence) implies that they will still find a rule (or a branch in the rule-space multiway system) that accounts for what they see, but it will be a different one.

In the previous section, we discussed equivalences between our models and other formulations. The fact that we base our models on hypergraph rewriting (or any of its many equivalent descriptions) is in a sense like a choice of coordinate system in rule space—and there are presumably infinitely many others we could use.

But the fact that there are many different possible parametrizations does not mean that there are not definite things that can be said. It is just that there is potentially a higher level of abstraction that can be reached. And indeed, in our models, not only have we abstracted away notions of space, time, matter and measurement; now in the rule-space multiway system we are in a sense also abstracting away the very notion of abstraction itself (see also [2]).

9 | Notes & Further References

Structure of Models & Methodology

The class of models studied here represent a simplification and generalization of the trivalent graph models introduced in [1:c9] and [87] (see also [148]).

The methodology of computational exploration used here has been developed particularly in [5][31][1]. Some exposition of the methodology has been given in [149].

The class of models studied here can be viewed as generalizing or being related to a great many kinds of abstract systems. One class is graph rewriting systems, also known as graph transformation systems or graph grammars (e.g. [150]). The models here are generalizations of both the double-pushout and single-pushout approaches. Note that the unlabeled graphs and hypergraphs studied here are different from the typical cases usually considered in graph rewriting systems and their applications.

Multiway systems as used here were explicitly introduced and studied in [1:p204] (see also [1:p938]). Versions of them have been invented many times, most often for strings, under names such as semi-Thue systems [151], string rewriting systems [152], term rewriting systems [65], production systems [153], associative calculi [154] and canonical systems [153][155].

Connections to Physics Theories

An outline of applying models of a type very similar to those considered here was given in [1:c9]. Some additional exposition was given in [156][157][158]. The discussion here contains many new ideas and developments, explored in [159].

For a survey of ultimate models of physics, see [1:p1024]. The possibility of discreteness in space has been considered since antiquity [160][161][162][163]. Other approaches that have aspects potentially similar to what is discussed here include: causal dynamical triangulation [164][165][166], causal set theory [167][168][169], loop quantum gravity [170][171], pregeometry [172][173][174], quantum holography [175][176][177], quantum relativity [178], Regge calculus [179], spin networks [180][181][182][183][184], tensor networks [185], superrelativity [186], topochronology [187], topos theory [188], twistor theory [128]. Other discrete and computational approaches to fundamental physics include: [189][190][191][192][193][194][195][196].

The precise relationships among these approaches and references and the current work are not known. In some cases it is expected that conceptual motivations may be aligned; in others specific mathematical structures may have direct relevance. The latter may also be the case for such areas as conformal field theory [197], higher-order category theory [198], non-commutative geometry [199], string theory [200].

Appendix: Implementation

Tools Created for This Project

A variety of new functions have been added to the Wolfram Function Repository to directly implement, visualize and analyze the models defined here [201].

Basic Direct Symbolic Transformation

The class of models defined here can be implemented very directly just using symbolic transformation rules of the kind on which the Wolfram Language [98] is based.

It is convenient to represent relations as Wolfram Language lists, such as {1,2}. One way to represent collections is to introduce a symbolic operator σ that is defined to be flat (associative) and orderless (commutative):

In[•]:= SetAttributes[σ, {Flat, Orderless}]

Thus we have, for example:

In[•]:= $\sigma[\sigma[a, b], \sigma[c]]$

Out[•]= $\sigma[a, b, c]$

We can then write a rule such as

$\{\{x, y\}\} \rightarrow \{\{x, y\}, \{y, z\}\}$
more explicitly as:

In[•]:= $\sigma[\{x\_, y\_\}] :\rightarrow \text{Module}[\{z\}, \sigma[\{x, y\}, \{y, z\}]]$

This rule can then be applied using standard Wolfram Language pattern matching:

In[•]:= $\sigma[\{a, b\}] \text{ /. } \sigma[\{x\_, y\_\}] :\rightarrow \text{Module}[\{z\}, \sigma[\{x, y\}, \{y, z\}]]$

Out[•]= $\sigma[\{a, b\}, \{b, z\$393804\}]$

The Module causes a globally unique new symbol to be created for the new node z every time it is used:

In[•]:= $\sigma[\{a, b\}] \text{ /. } \sigma[\{x\_, y\_\}] :\rightarrow \text{Module}[\{z\}, \sigma[\{x, y\}, \{y, z\}]]$

Out[•]= $\sigma[\{a, b\}, \{b, z\$393808\}]$

But in applying the rule to a collection with more than one relation, there is immediately an issue with the updating process. By default, the Wolfram Language performs only a single update in each collection:

In[•]:= σ[{a, b}, {c, d}] /. σ[{x_, y_}] :→ Module[{z}, σ[{x, y}, {y, z}]]

Out[•]= σ[{a, b}, {b, z$393812}, {c, d}]

As discussed in the main text, there are many possible updating orders one can use. A convenient way to get a whole "generation" of update events is to define an inert form of collection σ1 then repeatedly replace collections σ until a fixed point is reached:

In[•]:= σ[{a, b}, {c, d}] //. σ[{x_, y_}] :→ Module[{z}, σ1[{x, y}, {y, z}]]

Out[•]= σ[σ1[{a, b}, {b, z$393816}], σ1[{c, d}, {d, z$393817}]]

By replacing σ1 with σ at the end, one gets the result for a complete generation update:

In[•]:= σ[{a, b}, {c, d}] //. σ[{x_, y_}] :→ Module[{z}, σ1[{x, y}, {y, z}]] /. σ1 → σ

Out[•]= σ[{a, b}, {b, z$393821}, {c, d}, {d, z$393822}]

NestList applies this whole process repeatedly, here for 4 steps:

In[•]:= evol = NestList[# //. σ[{x_, y_}] :→ Module[{z}, σ1[{x, y}, {y, z}]] /. σ1 → σ &, σ[{1, 1}], 4]

Out[•]= {σ[{1, 1}], σ[{1, 1}, {1, z$393826}], σ[{1, 1}, {1, z$393826}, {1, z$393827}, {z$393826, z$393828}],
σ[{1, 1}, {1, z$393826}, {1, z$393827}, {1, z$393829}, {z$393826, z$393828}, {z$393826, z$393830},
{z$393827, z$393831}, {z$393828, z$393832}], σ[{1, 1}, {1, z$393826}, {1, z$393827},
{1, z$393829}, {1, z$393833}, {z$393826, z$393828}, {z$393826, z$393830}, {z$393826, z$393834},
{z$393827, z$393831}, {z$393827, z$393835}, {z$393828, z$393832}, {z$393828, z$393837},
{z$393829, z$393836}, {z$393830, z$393838}, {z$393831, z$393839}, {z$393832, z$393840}]}

Replacing σ by a Graph operator, one can render the results as graphs:

In[•]:= evol /. σ → (Graph[DirectedEdge @@@ {###}] &)

Out[•]=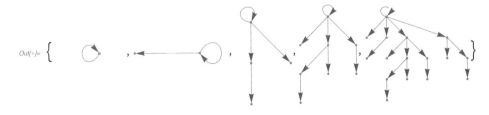

IndexGraph creates a graph in which nodes are renamed sequentially:

In[ ]:= evol /. σ → (IndexGraph[DirectedEdge @@@ {╫╫}, VertexLabels → Automatic] &)

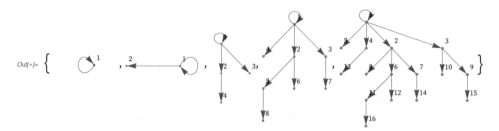

Here is the result with a different graph layout:

In[ ]:= evol /.
σ → (IndexGraph[DirectedEdge @@@ {╫╫}, GraphLayout → "SpringElectricalEmbedding"] &)

Exactly the same approach works for rules that involve multiple relations. For example, consider the rule:

$$\{\{x, y\}, \{x, z\}\} \to \{\{x, z\}, \{x, w\}, \{y, w\}, \{z, w\}\}$$

This can be run for 2 steps using:

In[ ]:= NestList[♯ //.
σ[{x_, y_}, {x_, z_}] :> Module[{w}, σ1[{x, z}, {x, w}, {y, w}, {z, w}]] /.
σ1 → σ &, σ[{1, 1}, {1, 1}], 2]

Out[ ]:= {σ[{1, 1}, {1, 1}], σ[{1, 1}, {1, w$393851}, {1, w$393851}, {1, w$393851}],
σ[{1, w$393851}, {1, w$393851}, {1, w$393852}, {1, w$393852}, {1, w$393853},
{w$393851, w$393852}, {w$393851, w$393853}, {w$393851, w$393853}]]}

Here is the result after 10 steps, rendered as a graph:

In[●]:= Nest[♯ //.

σ[{x_, y_}, {x_, z_}] :→ Module[{w}, σ1[{x, z}, {x, w}, {y, w}, {z, w}]] /.

σ1 → σ &, σ[{1, 1}, {1, 1}], 10] /. σ → (Graph[DirectedEdge @@@ {♯♯♯}] &)

Out[●]=

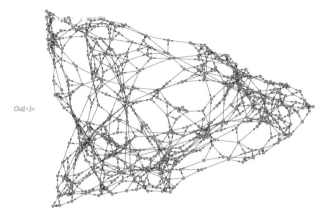

Alternative Syntactic Representation

As an alternative to introducing an explicit head such as σ, one can use a system-defined matchfix operator such as AngleBracket (entered as :<:, :>:) that does not have a built-in meaning. With the definition

In[●]:= SetAttributes[AngleBracket, {Flat, Orderless}]

one immediately has for example

In[●]:= ⟨a, ⟨b, c⟩⟩

Out[●]= ⟨a, b, c⟩

and one can set up rules such as

In[●]:= ⟨{x_, y_}, {x_, z_}⟩ :→ Module[{w}, ⟨{x, z}, {x, w}, {y, w}, {z, w}⟩]

Pattern Sequences

Instead of having an explicit "collection operator" that is defined to be flat and orderless, one can just use lists to represent collections, but then apply rules that are defined using OrderlessPatternSequence:

In[●]:= {{0, 0}, {0, 0}, {0, 0}} /. {OrderlessPatternSequence[{x_, y_}, {x_, z_}, rest___]} :→

Module[{w}, {{x, z}, {x, w}, {y, w}, {z, w}, rest}]

Out[●]= {{0, 0}, {0, w$37227}, {0, w$37227}, {0, w$37227}, {0, 0}}

Note that even though the pattern appears twice, /. applies the rule only once:

In[ ]:= {{0, 0}, {0, 0}, {0, 0}, {0, 0}} /. {OrderlessPatternSequence[{x_, y_}, {x_, z_}, rest___]} :→
Module[{w}, {{x, z}, {x, w}, {y, w}, {z, w}, rest}]

Out[ ]= {{0, 0}, {0, w$48054}, {0, w$48054}, {0, w$48054}, {0, 0}, {0, 0}}

Subset Replacement

Yet another alternative is to use the function SubsetReplace (built into the Wolfram Language as of Version 12.1). SubsetReplace replaces subsets of elements in a list, regardless of where they occur:

In[ ]:= SubsetReplace[{a, b, b, a, c, a, d, b}, {a, b} → x]

Out[ ]= {x, x, c, x, d}

Unlike ReplaceAll (/.) it keeps scanning for possible replacements even after it has done one:

In[ ]:= SubsetReplace[{a, a, a, a, a}, {a, a} → x]

Out[ ]= {x, x, a}

One can find out what replacements SubsetReplace would perform using SubsetCases:

In[ ]:= SubsetCases[{a, b, c, d, e}, {_, _}]

Out[ ]= {{a, b}, {c, d}}

This uses SubsetReplace to apply a rule for one of our models; note that the rule is applied twice to this state (Splice is used to make the sequence of lists be spliced into the collection):

In[ ]:= SubsetReplace[{{0, 0}, {0, 0}, {0, 0}, {0, 0}},
{{x_, y_}, {x_, z_}} :→ Splice[Module[{w}, {{x, z}, {x, w}, {y, w}, {z, w}}]]]

Out[ ]= {{0, 0}, {0, w$55383}, {0, w$55383}, {0, w$55383}, {0, 0}, {0, w$55384}, {0, w$55384}, {0, w$55384}}

This gives the result of 10 applications of SubsetReplace:

In[ ]:= Nest[SubsetReplace[{{x_, y_}, {x_, z_}} :→ Splice[Module[{w}, {{x, z}, {x, w}, {y, w}, {z, w}}]]],
{{1, 2}, {1, 3}}, 10] // Short

Out[ ]= {{1, w$55543}, {1, w$55637}, {w$55490, w$55637}, ≪705≫, {w$55401, w$55452}, {2, w$55394}}

This turns each list in the collection into a directed edge, and renders the result as a graph:

In[∘]:= Graph[DirectedEdge @@@ %]

Out[∘]=

IndexGraph can then for example be used to relabel all elements in the graph to be sequential integers.

Note that SubsetReplace does not typically apply rules in exactly our "standard updating order".

Parallelization

Our models do not intrinsically define updating order (see section 6), and thus allow for asynchronous implementation with immediate parallelization, subject only to the local partial ordering defined by the graph of causal relationships (or, equivalently, of data flows). However, as soon as a particular sequence of foliations—or a particular updating order—is defined, its implementation may require global coordination across the system.

Appendix: Graph Types

A visual summary of the relationships between graph types is given in [202].

Single-Evolution-History Graphs

Graphs obtained from particular evolution histories, with particular sequences of updating events. For rules with causal invariance, the ultimate causal graph is independent of the sequence of updating events.

Spatial Graph

Hypergraph whose nodes and hyperedges represent the elements and relations in our models. Update events locally rewrite this hypergraph. In the large-scale limit, the hypergraph can show features of continuous space. The hypergraph potentially represents the "instantaneous" configuration of the universe on a spacelike hypersurface. Graph distances in the hypergraph potentially approximate distances in physical space.

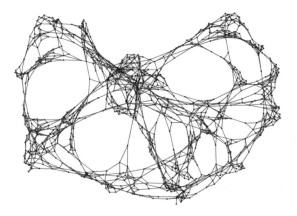

Causal Graph ("Spacetime Causal Graph")

Graph with nodes representing updating events and edges representing their causal relationships. In causal invariant systems, the same ultimate causal graph is obtained regardless of the particular sequence of updating events. The causal graph potentially represents the causal history of the universe. Causal foliations correspond to sequences of spacelike hypersurfaces. The effect of an update event is represented by a causal cone, which potentially corresponds to a physical light cone. The translation from time units in the causal graph to lengths in the spatial graph is potentially given by the speed of light c.

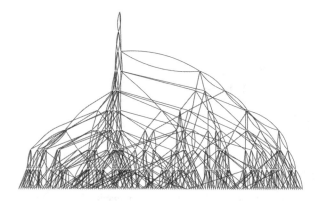

Multiway-Evolution-Related Graphs

Graphs obtained from all possible evolution histories, following every possible sequence of updating events. For rules with causal invariance, different paths in the multiway system lead to the same causal graph.

Multiway States Graph (Multiway Graph)

Graph representing all possible branches of evolution for the system. Each node represents a possible complete state of the system at a particular step. Each connection corresponds to the evolution of one state to another as a result of an updating event. The multiway graph potentially represents all possible paths of evolution in quantum mechanics. In a causal invariant system, every branching in the multiway system must ultimately reconverge.

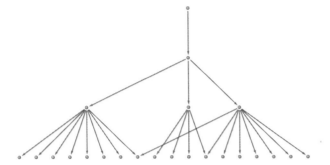

Multiway States+Causal Graph

Graph representing both all possible branches of evolution for states, and all causal relationships between updating events. Each node representing a state connects to other states via nodes representing updating events. The updating events are connected to indicate their causal relationships. The multiway states+causal graph in effect gives complete, causally annotated information on the multiway evolution.

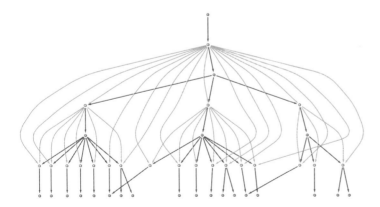

Multiway Causal Graph

Graph representing causal connections among all possible updating events that can occur in all possible paths of evolution for the system. Each node represents a possible updating event in the system. Each edge represents the causal relationship between two possible updating events. In a causal invariant system, the part of the multiway causal graph corresponding to a particular path of evolution has the same structure for all possible paths of evolution. The multiway causal graph provides the ultimate description of potentially observable behavior of our models. Its edges represent both spacelike and branchlike relationships, and can potentially represent causal relations both in spacetime and through quantum entanglement.

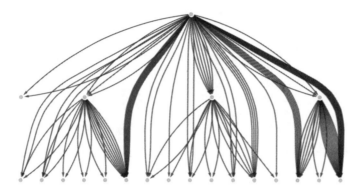

Branchial Graph

Graph representing the common ancestry of states in the multiway system. Each node represents a state of the system, and two nodes are joined if they are obtained on different branches of evolution from the same state. To define a branchial graph requires specifying a foliation of the multiway graph. The branchial graph potentially represents entanglement in the "branchial space" of quantum states.

Acknowledgements

I have been developing the ideas here for many years [203]. I worked particularly actively on them in 1995–1998, 2001 and 2004–2005 [148][1]. But they might have languished forever had it not been for Jonathan Gorard and Max Piskunov, who encouraged me to actively work on them again, and who over the past several months have explored them with me, providing extensive help, input and new ideas. For important additional recent help I thank Jeremy Davis, Sushma Kini and Ed Pegg, as well as Roger Dooley, Jesse Friedman, Andrea Gerlach, Charles Pooh, Chris Perardi, Toni Schindler and Jessica Wong. For recent input I thank Elise Cawley, Roger Germundsson, Chip Hurst, Rob Knapp, José Martin-Garcia, Nigel Goldenfeld, Isabella Retter, Oliver Ruebenkoenig, Matthew Szudzik, Michael Trott, Catherine Wolfram and Christopher Wolfram. For important help and input in earlier years, I thank David Hillman, Todd Rowland, Matthew Szudzik and Oyvind Tafjord. I have discussed the background to these ideas for a long time, with a great many people, including: Jan Ambjørn, John Baez, Tommaso Bolognesi, Greg Chaitin, David Deutsch, Richard Feynman, David Finkelstein, Ed Fredkin, Gerard 't Hooft, John Milnor, John Moussouris, Roger Penrose, David Reiss, Rudy Rucker, Dana Scott, Bill Thurston, Hector Zenil, as well as many others, notably including students at our Wolfram Summer Schools over the past 17 years. My explorations would never have been possible without the Wolfram Language, and I thank everyone at Wolfram Research for their consistent dedication to its development over the past 33 years, as well as our users for their support.

Tools, Data & Source Materials

Extensive tools, data and source material related to this document and the project it describes are available at wolframphysics.org.

This document is available in complete computable form as a Wolfram Notebook, including Wolfram Language input for all results shown. The notebook can be run directly in the Wolfram Cloud or downloaded for local use.

Specialized Wolfram Language functions developed for this project are available in the Wolfram Function Repository [204] for immediate use in the Wolfram Language. A tutorial of their use is given in [205].

The Registry of Notable Universes [8] contains results on specific examples of our models, including all those explicitly used in this document.

An archive of approximately 1000 working notebooks associated with this project from 1994 to the present is available at wolframphysics.org. In addition, there is an archive of approximately 500 hours of recorded streams of working sessions (starting in fall 2019) associated with this project.

References

[1] S. Wolfram (2002), *A New Kind of Science*, Wolfram Media, wolframscience.com/nks/.

[2] S. Wolfram (2020), "Finally We May Have a Path to the Fundamental Theory of Physics... and It's Beautiful", Stephen Wolfram Writings, writings.stephenwolfram.com/2020/04/finally-we-may-have-a-path-to-the-fundamental-theory-of-physics-and-its-beautiful.

[3] M. P. Szudzik (2017), "The Rosenberg–Strong Pairing Function". arXiv:1706.04129.

[4] E. Pegg, Jr. (2019), TupleIndex, Wolfram Function Repository. resources.wolframcloud.com/FunctionRepository/resources/TupleIndex.

[5] S. Wolfram (1983), "Statistical Mechanics of Cellular Automata", *Rev Mod Phys* 55, 601–44. doi:10.1103/RevModPhys.55.601.

[6] Wolfram Research (2002), CellularAutomaton, Wolfram Language function, reference.wolfram.com/language/ref/CellularAutomaton (updated 2017).

[7] Wolfram Research (2007), TuringMachine, Wolfram Language function, reference.wolfram.com/language/ref/TuringMachine.html.

[8] Wolfram Physics Project (2020), "Registry of Notable Universes", wolframphysics.org/universes/.

[9] M. Piskunov (2020), ConnectedWolframModelQ, Wolfram Function Repository, resources.wolframcloud.com/FunctionRepository/resources/ConnectedWolframModelQ.

[10] Wolfram Research (2007), BellB, Wolfram Language function, reference.wolfram.com/language/ref/BellB.html.

[11] OEIS Foundation, *The On-Line Encyclopedia of Integer Sequences*, oeis.org.

[12] E. Pegg, Jr. (2020), "Ordered Hypergraph Canonicalization", Technical Document, wolframcloud.com/obj/wolframphysics/Documents/OrderedHypergraphCanonicalization.nb.

[13] Wolfram Research (2017), FeatureSpacePlot, Wolfram Language function, reference.wolfram.com/language/ref/FeatureSpacePlot.html (updated 2018).

[14] Wolfram Research (2015), ImageIdentify, Wolfram Language function, reference.wolfram.com/language/ref/ImageIdentify.html.

[15] J. McLoone (2019), NonConvexHullMesh, Wolfram Function Repository, resources.wolframcloud.com/FunctionRepository/resources/NonConvexHullMesh.

[16] O. Zariski (1995), *Algebraic Surfaces*, Springer.

[17] W. P. Thurston (1997), "Orbifolds", in *The Geometry and Topology of Three–Manifolds*, Princeton U Press, 297–355.

[18] E. Kasner and F. Supnick (1943), "The Apollonian Packing of Circles", *Proc Natl Acad Sci USA* 29, 378–84. doi:10.1073/pnas.29.11.378.

[19] J. Stillwell (1996), *Sources of Hyperbolic Geometry*, American Mathematical Society.

[20] H. S. M. Coxeter (1942), *Non-Euclidean Geometry*, U of Toronto Press.

[21] G. H. Hardy and E. M. Wright (1938), *An Introduction to the Theory of Numbers*, Clarendon Press.

[22] C. Druțu and M. Kapovich (2018), *Geometric Group Theory*, Colloquium.

[20] B. Mandelbrot (1977), *Fractals: Form, Chance, and Dimension*, W. H. Freeman.

[24] A. Gray (1974), "The Volume of a Small Geodesic Ball of a Riemannian Manifold", *Michigan Math J* 20, 329–44. doi:10.1307/mmj/1029001150.

[25] G. Ricci-Curbastro (1904), "Direzioni e invarianti principali in una varietà qualunque" ["Principal Directions and Invariants in Any Manifold"], *Atti Ist Ven* 63, 1233–39. JFM 35.0145.01.

[26] A. Gray, E. Abbena and S. Salamon (2006), *Modern Differential Geometry of Curves and Surfaces with Mathematica*, 3rd ed., Chapman and Hall.

[27] Y. Olliver (2013), "A Visual Introduction to Riemann Curvatures and Some Discrete Generalizations", *CRM Proc & Lect Note* 56, 197–220. doi:10.1090/crmp/056/08.

[28] Wolfram Research (2020), MeshConnectivityGraph, Wolfram Language function, reference.wolfram.com/language/ref/MeshConnectivityGraph.html.

[29] G. H. Hardy (1912), "Properties of Logarithmico-Exponential Functions", *P Lond Math Soc* s2-10, 54–90. doi:10.1112/plms/s2-10.1.54.

[30] Wolfram Research (2020), Asymptotic, Wolfram Language function, reference.wolfram.com/language/ref/Asymptotic.html.

[31] S. Wolfram (1984), "Universality and Complexity in Cellular Automata", *Physica D* 10, 1–35. doi:10.1016/0167-2789(84)90245-8.

[32] Wolfram Research, Graph Measures & Metrics, Wolfram Language guide, reference.wolfram.com/language/guide/GraphMeasures.html.

[33] M. Newman (2010), *Networks*, Oxford U Press.

[34] Wolfram Research (2010), KirchoffMatrix, Wolfram Language function, reference.wolfram.com/language/ref/KirchhoffMatrix.html (updated 2015).

[35] M. Reuter, F. E. Wolter and N. Peinecke (2006), "Laplace–Beltrami Spectra as 'Shape-DNA' of Surfaces and Solids", *Comput Aided Design* 38, 342–66. doi:10.1016/j.cad.2005.10.011.

[36] Wolfram Research (2016), PlanarGraph, Wolfram Language function, reference.wolfram.com/language/ref/PlanarGraph.html.

[37] C. Kuratowski (1930), "Sur le problème des courbes gauches en topologie", *Fund Math* 15, 271–83. doi:10.4064/fm-15-1-271-283. Translated as "On the Problem of Skew Curves in Topology" (1983), J. Jaworowski (trans.), *Graph Theory, Lect Notes Math* 1018, 1–13. doi:10.1007/BFb0071605.

[38] N. Robertson and P. D. Seymour (1983), "Graph Minors. I. Excluding a Forest", *J Comb Theory B* 35, 39–61. doi:10.1016/0095-8956(83)90079-5.

[39] S. Wolfram (1985), "Origins of Randomness in Physical Systems", *Phys Rev Lett* 55, 449–52. doi:10.1103/PhysRevLett.55.449.

[40] L. Lovász (2012), *Large Networks and Graph Limits*, American Mathematical Society.

[41] Wolfram Research (2010), GraphDifference, Wolfram Language function, reference.wolfram.com/language/ref/GraphDifference.html (updated 2015).

[42] R. Forman (2003), "Bochner's Method for Cell Complexes and Combinatorial Ricci Curvature", *Discrete Comput Geom* 29, 323–74. doi:10.1007/s00454-002-0743-x.

[43] J. Jost (2011), *Riemann Geometry and Geometric Analysis*, Springer.

[44] A. Gray (2004), *Tubes*, 2nd ed., Springer.

[45] H. Poincaré (1895), "Analysis situs", *J Éc Polytech* 2, 1–121.

[46] J. Lauri and R. Scapellato (2003), *Topics in Graph Automorphisms and Reconstruction*, Cambridge U Press.

[47] B. D. McKay and C. E. Praeger (1994), "Vertex-Transitive Graphs Which Are Not Cayley Graphs, I", *J Austral Math Soc Ser A* 56, 53–63. doi:10.1017/S144678870003473X.

[48] A. Eskin, D. Fisher and K. Whyte (2007), "Quasi-Isometries and Rigidity of Solvable Groups", *Pure Appl Math Q* 3, 927–47. arXiv:math/0511647.

[49] B. C. Hall (2013), *Quantum Theory for Mathematicians*, Springer.

[50] R. I. Grigorchuk (1985), "Degrees of Growth of Finitely Generated Groups, and the Theory of Invariant Means", *Math USSR Izv* 25, 259–300. doi:10.1070/IM1985v025n02ABEH001281.

[51] S. Wolfram (2004), "String Substitution Systems", draft document, wolframcloud.com/obj/wolframphysics/WorkingMaterial/2004/FeaturedItems/StringSubstitutionSystems.nb.

[52] E. L. Post (1947), "Recursive Unsolvability of a Problem of Thue", *J Symbolic Logic* 12, 1–11. doi:10.2307/2267170.

[53] A. A. Markov (1947), "Невозможность некоторых алгоритмов в теории ассоциативных систем" ["Impossibility of Certain Algorithms in the Theory of Associative Systems"], *Dokl Akad Nauk SSSR* 55, 587–90.

[54] H. Grassmann (1861), *Lehrbuch der Arithmetik für höhere Lehranstalten* ["Textbook of Arithmetic for Institutions of Higher Learning"], Verlag von T. C. F. Enslin.

[55] A. Church and J. B. Rosser (1936), "Some Properties of Conversion", *T Am Math Soc* 39, 472–82. doi:10.1090/S0002-9947-1936-1501858-0.

[56] M. H. A. Newman (1942), "On Theories with a Combinatorial Definition of 'Equivalence'", *Ann Math* 43, 223–43. doi:10.2307/1968867.

[57] J. Milnor (1968), "A Note on Curvature and Fundamental Group", *J Differential Geom* 2, 1–7. doi:10.4310/jdg/1214501132.

[58] M. Gromov (1981), "Groups of Polynomial Growth and Expanding Maps", *Publ Math-Paris* 53, 53–78. doi:10.1007/BF02698687.

[59] S. Wolfram, (2019), StringOverlaps, Wolfram Function Repository, resources.wolframcloud.com/FunctionRepository/resources/StringOverlaps.

[60] B. Buchberger (1987), "History and Basic Features of the Critical-Pair/Completion Procedure", *J Symb Comput* 3, 3–38. doi:10.1016/S0747-7171(87)80020-2.

[61] D. E. Knuth and P. Bendix (1983), "Simple Word Problems in Universal Algebras", in *Automation of Reasoning*, J. H. Siekmann and G. Wrightson (eds.), Springer, 342–76.

[62] B. Buchberger (1976), "A Theoretical Basis for the Reduction of Polynomials to Canonical Forms", *ACM SIGSAM Bulletin* 10, 19–29. doi:10.1145/1088216.1088219.

[63] Terese (2003), *Term Rewriting Systems*, M. Bezem, et al. (eds.), Cambridge U Press.

[64] F. Baader and T. Nipkow (1998), *Term Rewriting and All That*, Cambridge U Press.

[65] N. Dershowitz and J. P. Jouannaud (1990), "Rewrite Systems", in *Handbook of Theoretical Computer Science, Vol. B: Formal Models and Semantics*, J. v. Leeuwen (ed.), Elsevier, 243–320.

[66] J. Gorard (2020), CausalInvariantQ, Wolfram Function Repository, resources.wolframcloud.com/FunctionRepository/resources/CausalInvariantQ.

[67] S. Wolfram (2019), StringOverlapsQ, Wolfram Function Repository, resources.wolframcloud.com/FunctionRepository/resources/StringOverlapsQ.

[68] Wolfram Research (2006), UnforgeableWordConstant, MathematicalConstant entity, Wolfram Language Knowledgebase, Entity["MathematicalConstant","UnforgeableWordConstant"].

[69] G. Birkhoff (1940), *Lattice Theory*, American Mathematical Society.

[70] Wolfram Research (2014), BreadthFirstScan, Wolfram Language function, reference.wolfram.com/language/ref/BreadthFirstScan.html (updated 2015).

[71] Wolfram Research (2010), DepthFirstScan, Wolfram Language function, reference.wolfram.com/language/ref/DepthFirstScan.html (updated 2015).

[72] H. Minkowski (1908), "Die Grundgleichungen für die elektromagnetischen Vorgänge in bewegten Körpern" ["The Fundamental Equations for Electromagnetic Processes in Moving Bodies"], *Nachr Ges Wiss Göttingen, Math-Phys Kl*, 53–111.

[73] H. Minkowski (1909), "Raum und Zeit", *Phys Z* 10, 104–11. Translated as "Time and Space" (1918), in *The Monist, Vol. 28*, E. H. Carus (trans.), Open Court Publishing, 288–302.

[74] R. Arnowitt, S. Deser and C. W. Misner (1959), "Dynamical Structure and Definition of Energy in General Relativity", *Phys Rev* 116, 1322–30. doi:10.1103/PhysRev.116.1322.

[75] C. W. Misner, K. S. Thorne and J. A. Wheeler (1973), *Gravitation*, W. H. Freeman.

[76] Wolfram Research (2012), GlobalClusteringCoefficient, Wolfram Language function, reference.wolfram.com/language/ref/GlobalClusteringCoefficient.html (updated 2015).

[77] Wolfram Research (2012), LocalClusteringCoefficient, Wolfram Language function, reference.wolfram.com/language/ref/LocalClusteringCoefficient.html (updated 2015).

[78] H. S. M. Coxeter (1964), *Projective Geometry*, Blaisdell Publishing.

[79] G. E. Moorhouse (2007), "Incidence Geometry", course notes for a graduate course, Fall 2007. ericmoorhouse.org/handouts/Incidence_Geometry.pdf.

[80] U. Brehm, M. Greferath and S. E. Schmidt (1995), "Projective Geometry on Modular Lattices", in *Handbook of Incidence Geometry*, F. Buekenhout (ed.), Elsevier, 1115–42.

[81] J. v. Neumann (1936), "Continuous Geometry", *P Natl Acad Sci* 22, 92–100. doi:10.1073/pnas.22.2.92.

[82] Wolfram Research (2018), FindEquationalProof, Wolfram Language function, reference.wolfram.com/language/ref/FindEquationalProof.html (updated 2020).

[83] Y. Matiyasevič (1967), "Простые примеры неразрешимых канонических исчислений" ["Simple Examples of Undecidable Associative Calculi"], *Dokl Akad Nauk SSSR* 173, 1264–66.

[84] S. Nakamoto (2008), *Bitcoin: A Peer-to-Peer Electronic Cash System*, bitcoin.org/bitcoin.pdf.

[85] J. Gorard (2019), IsomorphicHypergraphQ, Wolfram Function Repository, resources.wolframcloud.com/FunctionRepository/resources/IsomorphicHypergraphQ.

[86] J. Frauendiener and H. Friedrich (eds.) (2002), *The Conformal Structure of Space-Times*, Springer.

[87] S. Wolfram (2004), "Network Substitution Systems", draft document, wolframcloud.com/obj/wolframphysics/WorkingMaterial/2004/FeaturedItems/NetworkSubstitutionSystems.nb.

[88] D. J. Binder and S. Rychkov (2019), "Deligne Categories in Lattice Models and Quantum Field Theory, or Making Sense of $O(N)$ Symmetry with Non-integer N". arXiv:1911.07895.

[89] A. M. Turing (1938), "Finite Approximations to Lie Groups", *Ann Math* 39, 105–11. doi:10.2307/1968716.

[90] A. Thom (2018), "Finitary Approximations of Groups and Their Applications", in *Proceedings of the International Congress of Mathematicians, Vol. III*, B. Sirakov, P. N. d. Souza and M. Viana (eds.), World Scientific, 1779–1800.

[91] J. G. Sinaǐ (1968), "Построение марковских разбиений" ["Construction of Markov Partitionings"], *Funkcional Anal i Priložen* 2, 70–80. MR 0250352.

[92] D. Lind and B. Marcus (1995), *An Introduction to Symbolic Dynamics and Coding*, Cambridge U Press.

[93] M. Piskunov (2019), "Confluent Set Substitution Systems", Wolfram Summer School, community.wolfram.com/groups/-/m/t/1729148.

[94] S. Wolfram (2007), "The Prize Is Won; The Simplest Universal Turing Machine Is Proved", Stephen Wolfram Writings, writings.stephenwolfram.com/2007/10/the-prize-is-won-the-simplest-universal-turing-machine-is-proved/.

[95] Wolfram Research (2007), "The Wolfram 2,3 Turing Machine Research Prize", turingprize.org.

[96] A. Smith (2007), "Universality of Wolfram's 2,3 Turing Machine", wolframscience.com/prizes/tm23/TM23Proof.pdf.

[97] S. A. Cook (1971), "The Complexity of Theorem-Proving Procedures", *ACM S Theory Comput* STOC71, 151–58. doi:10.1145/800157.805047.

[98] Wolfram Research, the Wolfram Language, wolfram.com/language/.

[99] Wolfram Research (2003), ForAll, Wolfram Language function, reference.wolfram.com/language/ref/ForAll.html.

[100] Wolfram Research (2014), Association, Wolfram Language function, reference.wolfram.com/language/ref/Association.html, (updated 2016).

[101] A. Church (1936), "An Unsolvable Problem of Elementary Number Theory", *Am J Math* 58, 345–63. doi:10.2307/2371045.

[102] H. P. Barendregt (1981), *The Lambda Calculus. Its Syntax and Semantics*, North-Holland.

[103] M. Schönfinkel (1924), "Über die Bausteine der mathematischen Logik" ["On the Building Blocks of Mathematical Logic"], *Math Ann* 92, 305–16. doi:10.1007/BF01448013.

[104] H. B. Curry (1930), "Grundlagen der kombinatorischen Logik" ["Foundations of Combinatory Logic"], *Am J Math* 52, 509–36. doi:10.2307/2370619.

[105] A. N. Whitehead (1898), *A Treatise on Universal Algebra*, Cambridge U Press.

[106] S. N. Burris and H. P Sankappanavar (1981), *A Course in Universal Algebra*, Springer. Revised online edition (2012), math.uwaterloo.ca/~snburris/htdocs/ualg.html.

[107] K. Gödel (1930), "Über formal unentscheidbare Sätze der 'Principia Mathematica' und verwandter Systeme I", *Monatsh Math* 38, 173–98. Translated as *On Formally Undecidable Propositions of Principia Mathematica and Related Systems* (1992), B. Meltzer (trans.), Dover.

[108] M. Davis (ed.) (1965), *The Undecidable: Basic Papers on Undecidable Propositions, Unsolvable Problems and Computable Functions*, Raven Press.

[109] M. Rabin and D. S. Scott (1959), "Finite Automata and Their Decision Problems", *IBM J Res Dev* 3, 114–25. doi:10.1147/rd.32.0114.

[110] S. Wolfram (1986), "Cellular Automaton Fluids 1: Basic Theory", *J Stat Phys* 45, 471–526. doi:10.1007/BF01021083.

[111] A. Einstein (1916), "Die Grundlage der allgemeinen Relativitätstheorie", *Ann Phys–Leipzig* 354, 769–822. doi:10.1002/andp.19163540702. Translated as *Relativity: The Special and the General Theory* (2010), Martino Fine Books.

[112] W. Rindler (1991), *Introduction to Special Relativity*, 2nd ed., Oxford U Press.

[113] J. Gorard (2020), "Some Relativistic and Gravitational Properties of the Wolfram Model", wolframcloud.com/obj/wolframphysics/Documents/some-relativistic-and-gravitational-properties-of-the-wolfram-model.pdf.

[114] A. Einstein (1915), "Die Feldgleichungen der Gravitation", *Sitzber K Preuss Aka* 48, 844–47. Translated as "The Field Equations of Gravitation", in *The Collected Papers of Albert Einstein, Vol. 6: The Berlin Years: Writings, 1914–1917* (1997), A. Engel (trans.), Princeton U Press, 117–20.

[115] D. Hilbert (1915), "Die Grundlagen der Physik. (Erste Mitteilung)", *Nachr Ges Wiss Göttingen, Math-Phys Kl*, 395–407. Translated as "The Foundations of Physics (First Communication)", in *The Genesis of General Relativity* (2007), M. Janssen, et al. (eds.), Springer, 1925–38.

[116] Y. Choquet-Bruhat (2009), *General Relativity and the Einstein Equations*, Oxford U Press.

[117] G. Lemaître (1927), "Un Univers homogène de masse constante et de rayon croissant, rendant compte de la vitesse radiale des nébuleuses extra-galactiques", *Ann Soc Sci Brux* A47, 49–59. Translated as "A Homogenous Universe of Constant Mass and Increasing Radius Accounting for the Radial Velocity of Extra-Galactic Nebulae" (1931), *Mon Not R Astron Soc* 91, 483–90. doi:10.1093/mnras/91.5.483.

[118] B. Bollobás (1979), *Graph Theory*, Springer.

[119] S. Wolfram (2017), "Persistent Structures in Rule 110", Wolfram Data Repository, datarepository.wolframcloud.com/resources/Persistent-Structures-in-Rule110.

[120] Y. Gershtein and A. Pomarol (2018–2019), "Extra Dimensions", in *2019 Review of Particle Physics*, M. Tanabashi, et al. (Particle Data Group), *Phys Rev D* 98, 030001.

[121] J. Gorard (2020), "Some Quantum Mechanical Properties of the Wolfram Model", wolframcloud.com/obj/wolframphysics/Documents/some-quantum-mechanical-properties-of-the-wolfram-model.pdf.

[122] J. v. Neumann (1927), "Mathematische Begründung der Quantenmechanik" ["Mathematical Foundations of Quantum Mechanics"], *Nachr Ges Wiss Göttingen, Math-Phys Kl*, 1–57. JFM 53.0848.03.

[123] D. Hilbert, J. v. Neumann and L. Nordheim (1928), "Über die Grundlagen der Quanten-mechanik" ["About the Foundations of Quantum Mechanics"], *Math Ann* 98, 1–30. doi:10.1007/BF01451579.

[124] R. Feynman and A. R. Hibbs (1965), *Quantum Mechanics and Path Integrals*, McGraw-Hill.

[125] P. A. M. Dirac (1930), *The Principles of Quantum Mechanics*, Oxford U Press.

[126] A. Degasperis, L. Fonda and G. C. Ghirardi (1974), "Does the Lifetime of an Unstable System Depend on the Measuring Apparatus?", *Nuovo Ciment A* 21, 471–84. doi:10.1007/BF02731351.

[127] E. C. G. Sudarshan and B. Misra (1977), "The Zeno's Paradox in Quantum Theory", *J Math Phys* 18, 756–63. doi:10.1063/1.523304.

[128] M. Atiyah, M. Dunajski and L. J. Mason (2017), "Twistor Theory at Fifty: From Contour Integrals to Twistor Strings", *P R Soc A* 473, 20170530. doi:10.1098/rspa.2017.0530.

[129] S. W. Hawking (1974), "Black Hole Explosions?", *Nature* 248, 30–31. doi:10.1038/248030a0.

[130] K. Schwarzschild (1916), "Über das Gravitationsfeld einer Kugel aus inkompressibler Flüssigkeit nach der Einsteinschen Theorie" ["About the Gravitational Field of a Sphere of Incompressible Liquid According to Einstein's Theory"], *Sitzber K Preuss Akad Wiss, Phys-Math Kl*, 424–34.

[131] J. M. Maldacena (2003), "Eternal Black Holes in AdS", *J High Energy Phys* 0304, 21. arXiv:hep-th/0106112.

[132] L. Susskind, L. Thorlacius and J. Uglum (1993), "The Stretched Horizon and Black Hole Complementarity", *Phys Rev D* 48, 3743–61. arXiv:hep-th/9306069.

[133] A. Almheiri, et al. (2019), "The Page Curve of Hawking Radiation from Semiclassical Geometry", *J High Energy Phys* 149, 1–23. arXiv:1908.10996.

[134] J. C. Taylor (ed.) (2001), *Gauge Theories in the Twentieth Century*, Imperial College Press.

[135] N. Steenrod (1951), *The Topology of Fibre Bundles*, Princeton U Press.

[136] A. Marsh (2016), "Gauge Theories and Fiber Bundles: Definitions, Pictures, and Results". arXiv:1607.03089v2.

[137] M. Planck (1900), "Über irreversible Strahlungsvorgänge" ["On Irreversible Radiation Processes"], *Sitzber K Preuss Aka* 5, 440–80. doi:10.1002/andp.19003060105.

[138] Wolfram Research (1996), ProductLog, Wolfram Language function, reference.wolfram.com/language/ref/ProductLog.html.

[139] H. Dehmelt (1988), "A Single Atomic Particle Forever Floating at Rest in Free Space: New Value for Electron Radius", *Phys Scripta* T22, 102–10. doi:10.1088/0031-8949/1988/T22/016.

[140] D. Bourilkov (2000), "Search for TeV Strings and New Phenomena in Bhabha Scattering at LEP2", *Phys Rev D* 62, 076005. arXiv:hep-ph/0002172.

[141] S. Wolfram (1979), "Abundances of New Stable Particles Produced in the Early Universe", *Phys Lett B* 82, 65–68. doi:10.1016/0370-2693(79)90426-X.

[142] E. W. Kolb and M. S. Turner (1990), *The Early Universe*, in *Frontiers in Physics, Vol. 69*, Addison-Wesley.

[143] L. Baudis and S. Profumo (2018–2019), "Dark Matter", in *2019 Review of Particle Physics*, M. Tanabashi, et al. (Particle Data Group), *Phys Rev D* 98, 030001.

[144] G. Chaitin (1966), "On the Length of Programs for Computing Finite Binary Sequences", *J ACM* 13, 547–69. doi:10.1145/321356.321363.

[145] A. N. Kolmogorov (1968), "Three Approaches to the Quantitative Definition of Information", *Int J Comput Math* 2, 157–68. doi:10.1080/00207166808803030.

[146] R. J. Solomonoff (1960), *A Preliminary Report on a General Theory of Inductive Inference*, revision of Report V-131, Zator and Air Force Office of Scientific Research.

[147] S. Wolfram (2018), "Logic, Explainability and the Future of Understanding", Stephen Wolfram Writings, writings.stephenwolfram.com/2018/11/logic-explainability-and-the-future-of-understanding/.

[148] S. Wolfram, et al. (1994–2020), "Archives of the Wolfram Physics Project: Working Materials", wolframphysics.org/archives/index.

[149] S. Wolfram (2011), "The Role of Live Experiments at the Wolfram Science Summer School", Wolfram Summer School, wolfram.com/broadcast/video.php?v=929.

[150] G. Rozenberg (ed.) (1997–1999), *Handbook of Graph Grammars and Computing by Graph Transformation, Vols. 1–3*, World Scientific.

[151] A. Thue (1914), "Probleme über Veränderungen von Zeichenreihen nach gegebenen Regeln" ["Problems about the Changes of Symbol Series According to Fixed Rules"], *Christiana Vid Selsk Skr I, Mat Nat Kl* 10, reprinted in *Selected Papers of Axel Thue* (1977), Universitetsforlaget, 493–524.

[152] R. V. Book and F. Otto (1993), *String-Rewriting Systems*, Springer.

[153] E. L. Post (1943), "Formal Reductions of the General Combinatorial Decision Problem", *Am J Math* 65, 197–215. doi:10.2307/2371809.

[154] A. A. Markov (1951), "теория алгоритмов", *Trudy Mat Inst. Steklov* 38, 176–89. Translated as "Theory of Algorithms" (1960), E. Hewitt (trans.), *Amer Math Soc Transl* 15, 1–14.

[155] J. R. Büchi (1964), "Regular Canonical Systems", *Arch math Logik* 6, 91–111. doi:10.1007/BF01969548.

[156] O. Tafjord (2004), "NKS and the Nature of Space and Time", presented at NKS 2004, Boston, MA. wolframscience.com/conference/2004/presentations/material/oyvindtafjord.nb.

[157] I. Retter [Thiesen] (2011), "Networks as Manifolds", Wolfram Summer School, education.wolfram.com/summer/assets/alumni/2011/IsabellaThiesen.pdf.

[158] S. Wolfram (2013), "What Is Spacetime, Really?", Stephen Wolfram Writings, writings.stephenwolfram.com/2015/12/what-is-spacetime-really/.

[159] S. Wolfram, J. Gorard, M. Piskunov, et al. (2019–2020), "Archives of the Wolfram Physics Project: Working Materials", wolframphysics.org/archives/index?i=2019.

[160] S. Berryman (2016), "Ancient Atomism", in *The Stanford Encyclopedia of Philosophy*, E. N. Zalta (ed.), Metaphysics Research Lab, Stanford University, plato.stanford.edu/entries/atomism-ancient/.

[161] R. Descartes (1644), *Principia Philosophiae*. Reprinted in *René Descartes: Principles of Philosophy* (1982), R. P. Miller (trans.), Springer.

[162] W. Thomson [Kelvin] (1887), "On the Division of Space with Minimum Partitional Area", *Philos Mag* 24, 503.

[163] A. Einstein (1917), Albert Einstein to Walter Dällenbach, after February 15, 1917, reprinted in *The Collected Papers of Albert Einstein, Vol. 8: The Berlin Years: Correspondence, 1914–1918* (1998), A. M. Hentschel (trans.), Princeton U Press, 285–87.

[164] R. Loll (2001), "Discrete Lorentzian Quantum Gravity", *Nucl Phys B* 94, 96–107. arXiv:hep-th/0011194.

[165] J. Ambjørn, M. Carfora and A. Marzuoli (1997), *The Geometry of Dynamical Triangulations*, Springer.

[166] J. Ambjørn, J. Jurkiewicz and R. Loll (2009), "Quantum Gravity, or the Art of Building Spacetime", in *Approaches to Quantum Gravity*, D. Oriti (ed.), Cambridge U Press, 341–59. arXiv:hep-th/0604212.

[167] L. Bombelli, J. Lee, D. Meyer and R. D. Sorkin (1987), "Space-time as a Causal Set", *Phys Rev Lett* 59, 521–24. doi:10.1103/PhysRevLett.59.521.

[168] F. Dowker (2006), "Causal Sets as Discrete Spacetime", *Contemp Phys* 47, 1–9. doi:10.1080/17445760500356833.

[169] F. Markopoulou (2000), "The Internal Description of a Causal Set: What the Universe Looks Like from the Inside", *Commun Math Phys* 211, 559–83. doi:10.1007/s002200050826.

[170] A. Ashtekar (1986), "New Variables for Classical and Quantum Gravity", *Phys Rev Lett* 57, 2244–47. doi:10.1103/PhysRevLett.57.2244.

[171] C. Rovelli (1998), "Loop Quantum Gravity", *Living Rev Relativ* 1, revised 2008. doi:10.12942/lrr-1998-1.

[172] J. A. Wheeler (1964), "Geometrodynamics and the Issue of Final State", in *Relativity, Groups and Topology*, C. DeWitt and B. DeWitt (eds.), Gordon & Breach, 317–520.

[173] J. A. Wheeler (1980), "Pregeometry: Motivations and Prospects", in *Quantum Theory and Gravitation*, A. R. Marlov (ed.), Academic Press, 1–11.

[174] D. Meschini, M. Lehto and J. Piilonen (2005), "Geometry, Pregeometry and Beyond", *Stud Hist Philos Mod Phys* 36, 435–64. doi:10.1016/j.shpsb.2005.01.002.

[175] J. D. Bekenstein (1981), "Universal Upper Bound on the Entropy-to-Energy Ratio for Bounded Systems", *Phys Rev D* 23, 287–98. doi:10.1103/PhysRevD.23.287.

[176] G. 't Hooft (1993), "Dimensional Reduction in Quantum Gravity", *Conf Proc* C930308, 284–96. arXiv:gr-qc/9310026.

[177] R. Bousso (2002), "The Holographic Principle", *Rev Mod Phys* 74, 825–74. arXiv:hep-th/0203101.

[178] D. R. Finkelstein (1996), *Quantum Relativity*, Springer.

[179] T. Regge (1961), "General Relativity without Coordinates", *Nuovo Cimento* 19, 558–71. doi:10.1007/BF02733251.

[180] R. Penrose (1971), "Angular Momentum: An Approach to Combinatorial Spacetime", in *Quantum Theory and Beyond*, T. Bastin (ed.), Cambridge U Press, 151–80.

[181] C. Rovelli and L. Smolin (1995), "Spin Networks and Quantum Gravity", *Phys Rev D* 52, 5743–59. doi:10.1103/PhysRevD.52.5743.

[182] J. C. Baez (2000), "An Introduction to Spin Foam Models of *BF* Theory and Quantum Gravity", in *Geometry and Quantum Physics, Lecture Notes in Physics, Vol. 543*, H. Gausterer, L. Pittner and H. Grosse (eds.), Springer, 25–93.

[183] J. C. Baez (1996), "Spin Networks in Gauge Theory", *Adv Math* 117, 253–72. doi:10.1006/aima.1996.0012.

[184] J. P. Moussouris (1983), "Quantum Models as Space-Time Based on Recoupling Theory", PhD diss., Oxford University.

[185] B. Swingle (2012), "Constructing Holographic Spacetimes Using Entanglement Renormalization". arXiv:1209.3304.

[186] P. Leifer (1997), "Superrelativity as an Element of a Final Theory", *Found Phys* 27, 261–85. doi:10.1007/BF02550454.

[187] D. Bohm (1962), "A Proposed Topological Formulation of Quantum Theory", in *The Scientist Speculates*, I. J. Good (ed.), Basic Books, 302–14.

[188] A. Döring and C. J. Isham (2008), "A Topos Foundation for Theories of Physics: I. Formal Languages for Physics", *J Math Phys* 49, 053515. doi:10.1063/1.2883740.

[189] G. 't Hooft (2016), *The Cellular Automaton Interpretation of Quantum Mechanics*, Springer.

[190] K. Svozil (1986), "Are Quantum Fields Cellular Automata?", *Phys Lett A* 119, 153–56. doi:10.1016/0375-9601(86)90436-6.

[191] E. Fredkin (2003), "An Introduction to Digital Philosophy", *Int J Theor Phys* 42, 189–247. doi:10.1023/A:1024443232206.

[192] K. Zuse (1967), "Rechnender Raum", *Elektron Datenverarb* 8, 336–44. Translated as "Calculating Space", MIT Project MAC (1970), AZT-70-164-GEMIT.

[193] J. G. Russo (1993), "Discrete Strings and Deterministic Cellular Strings", *Nucl Phys* B406, 104–44. arXiv:hep-th/9304003.

[194] L. H. Kauffman and H. P. Noyes (1996), "Discrete Physics and the Dirac Equation", *Phys Lett A* 218, 139–46. arXiv:hep-th/9603202.

[195] T. Bastin and C. W. Kilmister (1995), *Combinatorial Physics*, World Scientific.

[196] J. C. Amson and L. H. Kauffman (eds.) (2014), *Scientific Essays in Honor of H. Pierre Noyes on the Occasion of His 90th Birthday*, World Scientific.

[197] P. Ginsparg (1988), "Applied Conformal Field Theory", in *Fields, Strings and Critical Phenomena (Les Houches, Session XLIX, 1988)*, E. Brézin and J. Zinn-Justin (eds.), North-Holland, 1–168.

[198] J. Baez and J. Dolan (1998), "Categorification", in *Higher Category Theory*, E. Getzler and M. Kapranov (eds.), *Comtemp Math* 230, 1–36. arXiv:math/9802029.

[199] A. Connes (1994), *Noncommutative Geometry*, Academic Press.

[200] M. B. Green, J. H. Schwarz and E. Witten (1987), *Superstring Theory, Vol. 1*, Cambridge U Press.

[201] Wolfram Physics Project (2020), "Software Tools", wolframphysics.org/tools/.

[202] Wolfram Physics Project (2020), "Visual Summary", wolframphysics.org/visual-summary/.

[203] S. Wolfram (2020), "How We Got Here: The Backstory of the Wolfram Physics Project", Stephen Wolfram Writings, writings.stephenwolfram.com/2020/04/how-we-got-here-the-backstory-of-the-wolfram-physics-project/.

[204] Wolfram Research (2019), Wolfram Function Repository, resources.wolframcloud.com/FunctionRepository/.

[205] S. Wolfram (2020), "Hands-On Introduction to the Wolfram Physics Project", wolframcloud.com/obj/wolframphysics/Tools/hands-on-introduction-to-the-wolfram-physics-project.nb.

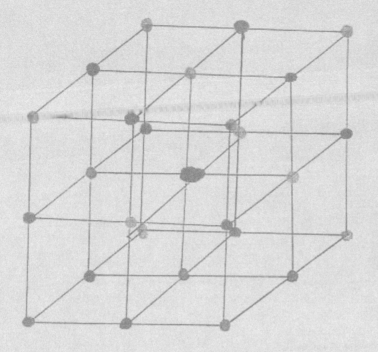

HISTORY

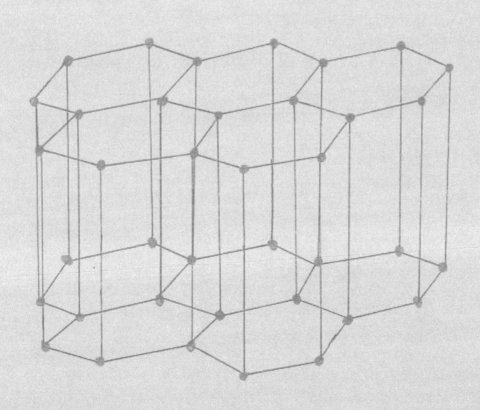

How We Got Here: The Backstory of the Wolfram Physics Project

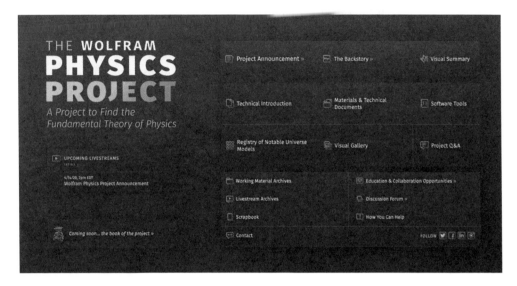

"Someday…"

I've been saying it for decades: "Someday I'm going to mount a serious effort to find the fundamental theory of physics." Well, I'm thrilled that today "someday" has come, and we're launching the Wolfram Physics Project. And getting ready to launch this project over the past few months might be the single most intellectually exciting time I've ever had. So many things I'd wondered about for so long getting solved. So many exciting moments of "Surely it can't be that simple?" And the dawning realization, "Oh my gosh, it's actually going to work!"

Physics was my first great intellectual passion. And I got started young, publishing my first paper when I was 15. I was lucky enough to be involved in physics in one of its golden ages, in the late 1970s. Not that I was trying to find a fundamental theory of physics back then. Like essentially all physicists, I spent my time on the hard work of figuring out the consequences of the theories we already had.

But doing that got me progressively more involved with computers. And then I realized: computation is its own paradigm. There's a whole way of thinking about the world using the idea of computation. And it's very powerful, and fundamental. Maybe even more fundamental than physics can ever be. And so it was that I left physics, and began to explore the computational universe: in a sense the universe of all possible universes.

That was forty years ago, and much has happened since then. My science led me to develop technology. The technology led me to more science. I did big science projects. I did big technology projects. And between the science and the technology, I felt like I was gradually building a tower that let me see and do more and more.

I never forgot physics, though. And as I studied the computational universe I couldn't help wondering whether maybe somewhere, out in this abstract computational world, might be our physical universe, just waiting to be discovered. Thirty years ago I had my first idea about how this might work. And over the decade that followed I figured out quite a bit—found some encouraging signs—and eventually started to tell the world about it.

I kept on thinking about really pushing it further. I'd talk about it when I could, sometimes in very public venues. But I was off doing other, very satisfying things. It so happened that technology I'd built became very widely used by physicists. But to most of the physics community I was basically an ex-physicist, who sometimes said strange and alien things about fundamental physics.

Meanwhile, two decades went by. I always hoped that one day I'd get to do my physics project. But I didn't know when, and my hopes were dimming. But then, a bit more than a year ago, I had a little idea that solved a nagging problem I'd had with my approach. And when I talked about it with two young physicists at our annual Summer School they were so enthusiastic. And I realized, "Yes, there are people who really want to see this problem solved." And after everything I've built and thought about, I have a responsibility to see if it can be done. Oh, and by the way, I really want to do it! It just seems like such a fun and fascinating thing. So why not just do it?

We got started in earnest late last fall. I started doing lots of new computer experiments. New ideas started flowing. And it was incredible. We started to figure out so much. My plan had been that we'd mostly just describe as clearly as possible what I basically already knew, then launch it as a project for other people to get involved. But it was just too easy and too fun to figure things out. We had a new paradigm and things just started tumbling out. In all my years of doing science and technology, I've never seen anything like it. It's been wonderful.

But the plan was always to share the fun, and now we're ready to do that. We're publishing everything we've done so far (including all the tools, archives, even working-session videos), and we're looking forward to seeing if this is the time in history when we finally get to figure out the fundamental theory for our universe. Oh, and I finally get to bring to closure something I've wanted to do for more than half my life, and that in some ways I've spent half a century preparing for.

Why Wasn't This Already Figured Out?

People have thought about what we'd now call the fundamental theory of physics through-out recorded history. From creation myths, to philosophy, to science, it's been a long story. And most of the time, it's actually seemed as if the answer was not far away, at least to the standards of explanation of the day. But it never quite got solved.

And if—as I believe—our project is finally on the right track, we kind of now know why. We just didn't have the modern paradigm of computation before, and so we didn't have the right way of thinking about things. Looking back, though, there were an awful lot of good ideas, that were very much in the right direction. And particularly in recent times, there was an awful lot of mathematical methodology developed that's very relevant and on target.

What does it matter what the fundamental theory of physics is? It'd certainly be an impres-sive achievement for science to figure it out. And my guess is that knowing it is eventually going to have some far-reaching long-term consequences for our general ways of thinking about things. Conceivably the theory will have near-term applications too. But in terms of what's done year after year in developing technology, doing science or even understanding theological questions, knowing the fundamental theory of physics isn't directly relevant; it's more like an ultimate "background question". And that's realistically pretty much how it's been treated throughout most of history.

Back in ancient Greek times, almost every serious Greek philosopher seems to have had a theory. The details were different. But there was a theme. That somehow everything in the universe consists of the same thing or things repeated over and over again. Maybe it was all water. Maybe it was four elements. Maybe Platonic solids. Maybe atoms. Maybe the world is assembled like sentences from a grammar. To us today these seem quite vague and almost allegorical. But there was an important idea: that everything we see in the world might actually be the result of something simple and formalizable underneath.

As the centuries went by, the idea of "natural laws" sharpened, sometimes with an almost computational feel. "God can only run the world by natural laws", or "The universe is the thoughts of God actualized". The 1600s brought the whole idea of describing the world using what amount to mathematical models. But while this had a huge effect on what could be studied and computed in physics, it didn't immediately change the thinking that much about what the universe might ultimately be made of. It was still just tiny corpuscles (AKA atoms), though now presumed to be bound by gravitational forces.

But what did begin to change was the whole idea that there should be any kind of "explicit explanation" for the universe that one could reason about: maybe there were just equations that were true about the universe, and that was all that could be said, a bit like Euclid's axioms for geometry. But around the same time, systematic experimental science began to rise—and there implicitly emerged the picture (charmingly resonant with modern debates about machine learning) that physics should consist of finding equations that would represent theories that could fit experimental data.

In the 1800s, as mathematical physics reached the point where it could deal with partial differential equations, and the notion of fields became popular, there started to be ideas about the universe being "all fields". First there was the ether (along with the rather good idea that atoms might be knotted vortices in the ether). Later people wondered if the electromagnetic field could underlie everything. When the electron was discovered people wondered if perhaps everything was in fact made of electrons. And so on. But a key theme was that to figure out things about the universe, you should either just do experiments, or you should take known equations and compute: you weren't expected to be able to reason about the universe.

That made special relativity in 1905 quite a shock: because, once again, one was figuring out physics by abstract reasoning. But somehow that just reinforced the "trust the mathematics" idea, and for example—in what I consider to be one of the most important wrong turns in the history of physics—there emerged the idea of a mathematical notion of "spacetime", in which (despite our strong intuitive sense to the contrary) space and time are treated as "the same kind of thing".

The introduction of general relativity in 1915—in addition to giving us the theory of gravity—brought with it the notion that "high-end" modern mathematics (in this case tensors and differential geometry) could inform physics. And that was an important piece of methodological input when quantum mechanics, and soon quantum field theory, were developed in the 1920s. Yes, it was difficult to "understand" the theory. But really the mathematics was the intellectual meat of what was going on, and should guide it. And that was what let one calculate things anyway. "Interpretation" was more philosophy than physics.

The question of what space "is" had been discussed by philosophers since antiquity. Euclid had implicitly made a pretty definitive statement with his very first common notion "a point is that which has no part": i.e. there is no discreteness to points, or, in other words, space is continuous. And by the time calculus arose in the late 1600s, it was pretty much taken for granted that space was continuous, and position was a continuous variable.

At different times, Descartes, Riemann and Einstein all had their doubts. But the force of the mathematical methodology provided by calculus was just too great. Still, in the 1930s there started to be problems with infinities in quantum calculations—and with quantization all the rage it started almost being assumed that space must be quantized too. But with the calculus-based thinking of the time nobody managed to make that work. (Graph theory was presumably too immature—and basically unknown—for the idea of space as a graph to arise.) Then in the 1940s the mathematical problems with infinities were avoided (by the idea of renormalization), and—with some important exceptions—the notion that space might be discrete basically disappeared from physics.

Meanwhile, mathematical methods based on calculus were doing great in advancing physics. Quantum electrodynamics (QED) and general relativity were both particularly successful, and it started to seem as if figuring out everything in physics was just a question of doing the math well enough.

But then there were the particles. The muon. The pion. The hyperons. For a while it had seemed that electrons, photons, protons and neutrons were what everything was made of. But by the 1950s particle accelerators were starting to discover many tens of new "elementary" particles. What were all these things?

Oh, and they were all tied up with the strong nuclear force that held nuclei together. And despite all its success in QED, quantum field theory and its "just-work-everything-out-step-by-step" mathematics just didn't seem to apply. So a different approach developed: S-matrix theory. It was mathematically elaborate (functions of many complex variables), in some ways elegant, but in a sense very formal. Instead of saying "this is how things are built up from something underneath" it basically just said "Here are some mathematical constraints. Whatever solutions they have are what will happen. Don't ask why."

And when it came to the particles, there were two approaches. One—roughly allied with quantum field theory—said that inside all these particles was something more fundamental, a new kind of particle called a quark. The other approach—allied with S-matrix theory—imagined something more "democratic" with different particles all just related by some kind of consistency condition.

Through the 1960s these two approaches duked it out. S-matrix theory was definitely ahead—notably spawning Regge theory and what later became string theory. There were quantum-field-theory ideas like what became QCD, but they didn't look promising. But by the early 1970s it began to be clear that quarks were something real, and in 1973 the phenomenon of asymptotic freedom was discovered, and quantum field theory was saved.

In 1974 came the surprise discovery of a new kind of quark, and physics entered a golden age of rapid progress, essentially powered by quantum field theory. (And, yes, I was involved in that, and it was a lot of fun.) Soon the Standard Model emerged, and everything seemed to be fitting together, and it seemed once again that it was just a matter of calculating, and everything could be figured out.

There were still mysteries: for example, why these particular particles, with these particular masses? But there was a methodology, and there was a sense that somehow this would all work out. An important piece of the story was the use of the theory of Lie groups (a piece of "high-end math" that made its way into physics in the 1950s). Which group was the one for the universe? The Standard Model involved three groups: $SU(3)$, $SU(2)$ and $U(1)$. But could these all be combined into a single, bigger group, perhaps $SU(5)$ or $SO(10)$—a single "grand unified" model? Around 1980 it all looked very promising.

But there was one key prediction: the proton should be unstable, decaying, albeit very slowly. But then the experiments started coming in: no proton decay. What was particle physics to do? There were new theories, with new particles. But no new particles showed up. Meanwhile, people kept computing more and more with the Standard Model. And everything kept on working. One decimal place, two, three, four.

It was difficult—but somehow routine—to do these calculations. And it seemed like particle physics had entered a phase like atomic physics and nuclear physics before it, where it was really just a question of calculating what one needed.

But there was a crack in all of this. And it was gravity. Yes, quantum field theory had worked well in particle physics. But when it was applied to gravity, it really didn't work at all. That wasn't important for computing things about the Standard Model. But it showed there was something else that had to be figured out in physics.

Meanwhile, the theory of gravity had steadily been developing, based on general relativity, which was unchanged since 1915. Until about the 1950s, there had been hopes of generalizing general relativity to make a "unified field theory" that could encompass "matter" as well as gravity. (And in fact, once again, there were good ideas here, about "everything being made of space".) But it hadn't worked out—though for example Einstein remarked that perhaps that was because it was being incorrectly assumed that space is continuous.

General relativity is a difficult mathematical theory, fraught with issues of what is real, and what is "just math". It didn't get nearly as much attention as quantum field theory, but by the 1960s it was becoming better understood, there were starting to be sensitive experimental tests, and it was pretty clear that things like black holes were real predictions of the theory. And the discovery of the cosmic microwave background heightened interest in cosmology in general, and in the early universe in particular.

In a way, particle physics had been propelled at the end of World War II by the success of the Manhattan Project. But a generation had passed, and by the end of the 1980s it no longer seemed compelling to spend billions of dollars to build the next particle accelerator. But right around then, there started to be more and more done in cosmology. More and more details about the early universe. More and more mystery about the dark matter that seems to exist around galaxies.

And somehow this progress in cosmology just emphasized the importance of figuring out how particle physics (and quantum field theory) could be brought together with general relativity. But what was to be done?

At the tail end of the 1970s-golden-age of particle physics there was another injection of "fancy math", this time around fiber bundles and algebraic topology. The original application (instanton solutions to the equations of QCD) didn't work out. But there began to develop a new kind of interchange between the front lines of pure mathematics and theoretical physics.

And as traditional particle physics plateaued, there was more and more emphasis on quantum gravity. First there was supergravity—a kind of extension of the quark model and group theory "let's just figure out more particles" tradition. But soon the focus turned to something new: string theory. Well, actually, it wasn't new at all. String theory had been developed, and rejected, as part of the S-matrix initiative in the 1960s. But now it was retooled, and directed at quantum gravity with enough vigor that by the end of the 1980s a large fraction of all particle physicists were working on it.

It didn't really connect to anything experimentally visible. And it also had all sorts of weird problems—like implying that the universe should really be 26-dimensional, or maybe 10-dimensional. But the physics community was committed to it, and the theory kept on getting patched, all the while becoming more complicated. But even though the physics wasn't terribly compelling, there were starting to be some spinoffs in math, that made elegant—and important—connections across different areas of high-end pure mathematics.

And in the mid-1990s the high-end math paid back to physics again, bringing M-theory—which seemed to miraculously weave together disparate directions in string theory. For a while there were claims that M theory would be "it"—the fundamental theory of physics. But gradually the hopes faded, with rather little to show.

There was another frontier, though. In the 1970s an initially rather rickety calculation had suggested that black holes—instead of being "completely black"—should emit particles as a result of quantum mechanics. For a while this was basically a curiosity, but slowly the calculations became more streamlined—and it began to look as if whole black holes in a sense had enough mathematical perfection that they could actually be studied a bit like little particles. And in the late 1990s from the mathematics of string theory there emerged the so-called AdS/CFT correspondence—an elaborate mathematical connection between a limiting case of general relativity and a limiting case of quantum field theory.

I don't think anyone would claim that AdS/CFT is itself anything like a fundamental theory of physics. But in the past 20 years it's steadily grown to become perhaps the central hope for fundamental physics, mathematically hinting at a variety of deep connections—which, as it happens, look like they may actually dovetail quite beautifully with what we've recently figured out.

The last time there was a widespread "we're almost there" feeling about the fundamental theory of physics was probably around 1980, with another blip in the mid-1990s. And since then the focus of physics has definitely turned elsewhere. But there have been some initiatives—many actually dating from the 1970s and before—that have still continued in various pockets of the physics and math communities. Twistor theory. Causal set theory. Loop quantum gravity. Spin networks. Non-commutative geometry. Quantum relativity. Typically these have seemed like increasingly disconnected—and sometimes almost quixotic—efforts. But one of the wonderful things that's come out of our project so far is that actually the core formalisms of a surprising number of these initiatives look to be directly and richly relevant.

But what about other approaches to finding a fundamental theory of physics? Realistically I think the landscape has been quite barren of late. There's a steady stream of people outside the physics community making proposals. But most of them are deeply handicapped by not connecting to quantum field theory and general relativity. Yes, these are mathematically sophisticated theories that pretty much take a physics PhD's worth of study to understand. But they're the best operational summaries we have right now of what's known in physics, and if one doesn't connect to them, one's basically throwing away everything that was achieved in 20th-century physics.

Is it surprising that a fundamental theory of physics hasn't been found yet? If—as I think— we're now finally on the right track, then no, not particularly. Because it requires ideas and paradigms that just hadn't been developed until quite recently. Of course, to find a fundamental theory of physics you have to go to the effort of trying to do it, and you have to believe it's possible. And here perhaps the biggest impediment has been the sheer size of physics as an enterprise. After its successes in the mid-20th century, physics became big—and being a physicist became a top aspiration. But with size came institutionalization and inertia.

About a hundred years ago it was a small collection of people who originally invented the two great theories (general relativity and quantum field theory) that have basically defined fundamental physics for the past century. I don't think it would have been a great surprise to any of them that to make further progress one would need new ideas and new directions. But to most modern physicists—perhaps six or seven academic generations removed from the founders of these fields, and embedded in a large structure with particular ways of doing things—the existing ideas and directions, and the kinds of things that can be done with them, just seem like the only way it can be. So if in the normal course of science, a fundamental theory of physics does not appear—as it did not—there ends up being almost a collective conclusion that to find it must be too hard, or even impossible. And not really what physics, or physicists, should be doing.

So who will do it? There's a pretty thin set of possibilities. It pretty much has to be someone who knows the methods and achievements of mainstream physics well, or, essentially, someone who has been a physicist. It also pretty much has to be someone who's not too deeply embedded in the current world of physics and its existing ideas, prejudices and "market forces". Oh, and it requires tools and resources. It doesn't hurt to have experience in doing and leading large projects. And it requires the confidence and resolve to try a big and difficult project that few people will believe in—as well, of course, as a deep interest in actually finding out the answer.

The project that we're now launching almost didn't happen. And if a few more years had gone by, it's pretty certain it wouldn't have. But things lined up in just such a way that a small window was opened. And I'm thrilled at the way it's turning out. But let me now tell a little more of the story of how it got here.

The Beginning of the Story

As a young kid growing up in England in the 1960s I viewed the space program as a kind of beacon of the future, and I intently followed it. But when I wanted to know how spacecraft and their instruments worked I realized I had to learn about physics—and soon I left space behind, and was deeply into physics.

I was probably 11 years old when I started reading my first college physics textbook, and when I was 12 I compiled a "Concise Directory of Physics" with 111 pages of carefully typed information and data about physics:

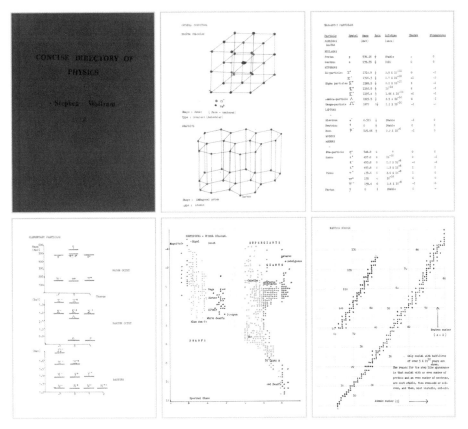

All this information collection had definite shades of "Wolfram|Alpha-ism". And the "visualiz-ations" presaged a lifelong interest in information presentation. But my Concise Directory also had something else: pages listing the "elementary particles". And soon these became my great obsession. The pions. The kaons. The muon. The cascade hyperons. To me they were the ultimate story in science, and I was soon learning all their quirks ("The K zero isn't its own antiparticle!" "The omega minus has strangeness -3!")

I spent the summer when I was 13 writing the 132-page, single-spaced, typed "The Physics of Sub-atomic Particles". At the time, I basically showed it to no one, and it's strange to look at it now—47 years later. It's basically an exposition of particle physics, told in a historical arc. Some of it is shockingly similar to what I just wrote in the previous section of this piece—except for the change of tense and the Americanization:

produce a rigorous proof of crossing symmetry from field theory.
There is currently a considerable amount of disagreement between the proponents of the so-called 'analytic S-matrix theory' and those of ordinary field theory. While some suggest the complete abandonment of field theory, because of such problems as renormalisation, others calculate, for example, the properties of the hydrogen atom,

It's charming to read my 13-year-old self's explanation of quantum field theory (not bad), or my authoritative description of a just-proposed theory of the muon that I'm guessing I found out about from *New Scientist*, and that turned out to be completely wrong.

By the next summer I was writing a 230-page treatise "Introduction to the Weak Interaction", featuring some of my most favorite elementary particles, and showing a pretty good grasp of quantum mechanics and field theory:

Pretty soon I had reached the edge of what was known in particle physics, but so far what I had done was basically exposition; I hadn't really tried to figure out new things. But by the summer of 1974 it was increasingly clear that something unexpected was going in physics. Several experiments were showing an unanticipated rise in the electron-positron annihilation cross-section—and then, rather dramatically, in November, the J/ψ particle was discovered. It was all a big surprise, and at first people had no idea what was going on. But 14-year-old me decided I was going to figure it out.

Those were days long before the web, and it wasn't easy to get the latest information. But from where I lived when I wasn't at school, it was about a 6-mile bicycle ride to the nearest university library, and I did it often. And pretty soon I had come up with a theory: maybe—contrary to what had long been believed—the electron is not in fact a point particle, but actually has internal structure.

By then, I had read many academic papers, and pretty soon I had written one of my own. It took two tries, but then, there it was, my first published paper, complete—I now notice—with some self-references to earlier work of mine, in true academic style:

It was a creative and decently written paper, but it was technically a bit weak (heck, I was only 15), and, at least at the time, its main idea did not pan out. But of course there's an irony to all this. Because—guess what—45 years later, in our current model for fundamental physics, the electron is once again not a point particle! Back in 1975, though, I thought maybe it had a radius of 10^{-18} meters; now I think it's more likely 10^{-81} meters. So at the very least 15-year-old me was wrong by 63 orders of magnitude!

Being a "teenage physicist" had its interesting features. At my boarding school (the older-than-the-discovery-of-America Eton), there was much amusement when mail came addressed to me as "Dr. S. Wolfram". Soon I started doing day trips to go to physics seminars in Oxford—and interacting with "real physicists" from the international physics community. I think I was viewed as an exotic phenomenon, usually referred to in a rather Wild-West way as "The Kid". (Years later, I was amused when one of my children, precocious in a completely different domain, earned the very same nickname.)

I really loved physics. And I wanted to do as much physics as I could. I had started using computers back in 1973—basically to do physics simulations. And by 1976 I'd realized something important about computers. The one thing I didn't like about physics was that it involved doing all sorts of—to me, tedious—mathematical calculations. But I realized that I could get computers to do those for me. And, needless to say, that's how, eventually, Mathematica, Wolfram|Alpha, etc. came to be.

I left high school when I was 16, worked doing physics at a government lab in England for about 6 months, and then went to Oxford. By this point, I was producing physics papers at a decent rate, and the papers were getting progressively better. (Or at least good enough that by age 17 I'd had my first run-in with academic thievery.)

Mostly I worked on particle physics—at that time by far the hottest area of physics. But I was also very interested in questions like the origin of the Second Law of thermodynamics, and particularly its relation to gravity. (If things always become more disordered, how come galaxies form, etc.?) And from this (as well as questions like "where's the antimatter in the universe?") I got interested in cosmology, and, inevitably, in connecting it to particle physics.

Nowadays everyone knows about that connection, but back then few people were interested in it.

Particle physics, though, was a completely different story. There were exciting discoveries practically every week, and the best and brightest were going into the field. QCD (the theory of quarks and gluons) was taking off, and I had a great time doing some of the "obvious" calculations. And of course, I had my secret weapon: computers. I've never really understood why other people weren't using them, but for me they were critical. They let me figure out all this stuff other people couldn't. And I think the process of writing programs made me a better physicist too. Looking at my papers from back then, the notation and structure got cleaner and cleaner—as might befit a future lifelong language designer.

After a bit more than a year in Oxford, and now with ten physics papers to my name, I "dropped out of college", and went to Caltech as a graduate student. It was a very productive time for me. At the peak I was writing a physics paper every couple of weeks, on quite a range of topics. (And it's nice to see that some of those papers still get referenced today, 40 years later.)

Caltech was at the time a world center for particle physics, with almost everyone who was someone coming through at one time or another. Most of them were much older than me, but I still got to know them—not just as names in the physics literature but as real people with their various quirks.

Murray Gell-Mann and Richard Feynman were the two biggest names in physics at Caltech at the time. I got on particularly well with Feynman, even if—in his rather competitive way— he would often lament that he was three times my age. (In the way these things come around, I'm now the same age as he was when I first met him...)

After a bit more than a year, I put together some of the papers I'd written, officially got my PhD, and took up a nice research faculty position at Caltech. I'd had the goal of "being a physicist" since I was about 10 years old, and now, at age 20, I was actually officially a physicist.

"So what now?" I wondered. There were lots of things I wanted to do in physics. But I felt limited by the computer tools I had. So—actually within a couple of weeks of getting my PhD—I resolved that I should spend the time just to build the tools I needed. And that's how I came to start developing my first big computer system and language.

I approached it a bit like a problem in natural science, trying to develop a theory, find principles, etc. But it was different from anything I'd done before: it wasn't constrained by the universe as the universe is. I just had to invent abstract structures that would fit together and be useful.

The system I built (that I called SMP, for "Symbolic Manipulation Program") had all sorts of ideas, some good, some not so good. One of the most abstract—and, arguably, obscure— ideas had to do with controlling how recursive evaluation works. I thought it was neat, and perhaps powerful. But I don't think anyone (including me) ever really understood how to use it, and in the end it was effectively relegated to a footnote.

But here's the irony: that footnote is now a front-and-center issue in our models of fundamental physics. And there's more. Around the time I was building SMP I was also thinking a lot about gauge theories in physics. So there I was thinking about recursion control and about gauge invariance. Two utterly unrelated things, or so I thought. Until just recently, when I realized that in some fundamental sense they're actually the same thing!

"You Can't Leave Physics"

It took a couple of years to build the first version of SMP. I continued to do particle physics, though I could already feel that the field was cooling, and my interests were beginning to run to more general, theoretical questions. SMP was my first large-scale "practical" project. And not only did it involve all sorts of software engineering, it also involved managing a team—and ultimately starting my first company.

Physicists I knew could already tell I was slipping away from physics. "You can't leave physics", they would say. "You're really good at this." I still liked physics, and I particularly liked its "let's just figure this out" attitude. But now I wasn't just applying that methodology in quantum field theory and cosmology; I was also using it in language design, in software development, in entrepreneurism, and in other things. And it was working great.

The process of starting my first company was fraught with ahead-of-my-time-in-the-interaction-between-companies-and-universities issues, that ultimately caused me to leave Caltech. And right in the middle of that, I decided I needed to take a break from my mainline "be a physicist" activities, and just spend some time doing "something fun".

I had been thinking for a long time about how it is that complex things manage to happen in nature. My two favorite examples were neural networks (yes, back in 1981, though I never figured out how to make them do anything very useful back then) and self-gravitating gases. And in my "just have fun" approach I decided to try to make the most minimal model I could, even if it didn't really have much to do with either of these examples, or officially with "physics".

It probably helped that I'd spent all that time developing SMP, and was basically used to just inventing abstract things from scratch. But in any case, what I came up with were very simple rules for arrays of 0s and 1s. I was pretty sure that—as such—they wouldn't do anything interesting. But it was basically trivial for me to just try running them on a computer. And so I did. And what I found was amazing, and gradually changed my whole outlook on science and really my whole worldview—and sowed the seeds that have now, I believe, brought us a path to the fundamental theory of physics.

What I was looking at were basically some of the very simplest programs one can imagine. And I assumed that programs that simple wouldn't be able to behave in anything other than simple ways. But here's what I actually saw in my first computer experiment (here rendered a bit more crisply than in my original printouts):

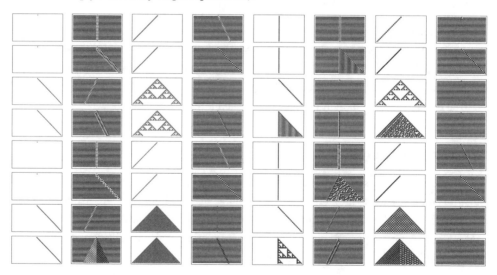

Yes, some of the behavior is simple. And some of it involves nice, recognizable fractal patterns. But then there are other things going on, like my all-time favorite—what I called "rule 30":

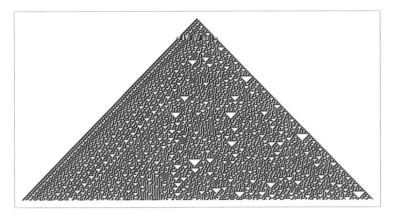

At first, I didn't understand what I was seeing, and I was convinced that somehow the simplicity of the underlying rules must ultimately force the behavior to be simple. I tried using all sorts of methods from physics, mathematics, computer science, statistics, cryptography and so on to "crack" these systems. But I always failed. And gradually I began to realize that something fundamental was going on—that somehow in just running their rules, simple as they were, these systems were intrinsically creating some kind of irreducible complexity.

I started writing papers about what I'd discovered, at first couched in very physics-oriented terms:

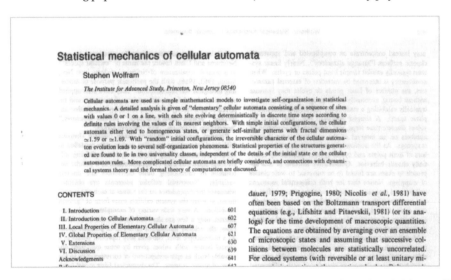

The papers were well received—in physics, in mathematics, and in other fields too, like biology. (Where perhaps it helped that—in a nod to historical antecedents—I called my models "cellular automata", though I meant abstract cells, not biological ones.)

Meanwhile, I had moved to the Institute for Advanced Study, in Princeton (where there were still people telling stories about their interactions with Kurt Gödel and "Johnny" von Neumann and his computer, and where, yes, my office was upstairs from where Einstein had once worked). I started building up a whole effort around studying "complexity" and how it could arise from simple rules. And gradually I started to realize that what I'd seen in that little computer experiment in 1981 was actually a first sign of something very big and very important.

Looking back, I see that experiment as my personal analog of turning a telescope to the sky and seeing the moons of Jupiter. But the challenge was really to understand the significance of what I'd seen—which in the end took me decades. But the first step was just to start thinking not in terms of the kinds of methods I'd used in physics, but instead fundamentally in terms of computation, treating computation not just as a methodology but a paradigm.

The summer of 1984 was when I think I finally began to seriously understand computation as a paradigm. Early that summer I'd finally recognized rule 30 for what it was: a powerful computational system. Then—in writing an article for *Scientific American* (nominally on "Computer Software in Science and Mathematics")—I came up with the term "computational irreducibility", and began to understand its significance.

That fall I wrote a short paper that outlined the correspondence with physics, and the fundamental implications (which now loom large in our current project) of computational irreducibility for physics:

VOLUME 54, NUMBER 8   PHYSICAL REVIEW LETTERS   25 FEBRUARY 1985

Undecidability and Intractability in Theoretical Physics

Stephen Wolfram

The Institute for Advanced Study, Princeton, New Jersey 08540
(Received 26 October 1984)

Physical processes are viewed as computations, and the difficulty of answering questions about them is characterized in terms of the difficulty of performing the corresponding computations. Cellular automata are used to provide explicit examples of various formally undecidable and computationally intractable problems. It is suggested that such problems are common in physical models, and some other potential examples are discussed.

PACS numbers: 02.90.+p, 01.70.+w, 05.90.+m

There is a close correspondence between physical processes and computations. On one hand, theoretical models describe physical processes by computations that transform initial data according to algorithms representing physical laws. And on the other hand, computers themselves are physical systems, obeying physical laws. This paper explores some fundamental consequences of this correspondence.[1]

The behavior of a physical system may always be calculated by simulating explicitly each step in its evolution. Much of theoretical physics has, however, been concerned with devising shorter methods of calculation that reproduce the outcome without tracing tine equations.[2] One expects in fact that universal computers are as powerful in their computational capabilities as any physically realizable system can be, so that they can simulate any physical system.[3] This is the case if in all physical systems there is a finite density of information, which can be transmitted only at a finite rate in a finite-dimensional space.[4] No physically implementable procedure could then short cut a computationally irreducible process.

Different physically realizable universal computers appear to require the same order of magnitude times and information storage capacities to solve particular classes of finite problems.[5] One computer may be

One of the nice things for me about the Institute for Advanced Study is that it was a small place, with not only physicists, but also lots of world-class mathematicians. (I had interacted a bit with Michael Atiyah and Roger Penrose about mathematics-for-physics when I was in Oxford, but at Caltech it was physics and nothing but.) Two top-of-the-line mathematicians, John Milnor and Bill Thurston, both got interested in my cellular automata. But try as they might, they could prove pretty much nothing; they basically hit a wall of computational irreducibility.

Yes, there is undecidability in mathematics, as we've known since Gödel's theorem. But the mathematics that mathematicians usually work on is basically set up not to run into it. But just being "plucked from the computational universe", my cellular automata don't get to avoid it. And ultimately our physics project will run into the same issues. But one of the wonderful things that's become clear in the last few months is that actually there's quite a layer of computational reducibility in our models of physics—which is critical for our ability to perceive the world coherently, but also makes math able to be useful.

But back to the story. In addition to my life doing basic science, I had a "hobby" of doing consulting for tech companies. One of those companies was a certain ultimately-poorly-named Thinking Machines Corporation, that made massively parallel computers that happened to be ideally suited to running cellular automata. And in an effort to find uses for their computers, I decided to see whether one could model fluid flow with cellular automata. The idea was to start not with the standard physics equations for fluid flow, but instead just to have lots of computational particles with very simple rules, and then see whether on a large scale fluid flow could emerge.

As it turned out, with my interest in the Second Law of thermodynamics, I'd actually tried something quite similar back in 1973, as one of the very first programs I ever wrote. But I hadn't seen anything interesting then, partly because of what one might think of as a piece of technical bad luck, but probably more importantly because I didn't yet grasp the paradigm that would allow me to understand what was going on. But in 1985 I did understand, and it was neat: from tiny computational rules that didn't immediately have physics in them was emerging a piece of physics that was normally described with the equations of physics. And, yes, now it looks like that's how all of physics may work—but we'll come to that.

By 1985 I was pretty clear on the notion that one could use the computational paradigm and the methods around it to explore a wide range of phenomena and questions. But for me the "killer app" was understanding the origins of complexity, and trying to build a general "theory of complexity". It wasn't physics, it wasn't mathematics, it wasn't computer science. It was something new. I called it "complex systems theory" (avoiding, at least for a while, a preexisting and completely different field of computer science called "complexity theory").

I was 25 years old but already pretty established in science, with "mainstream cred" from my early work in physics, and a lot of momentum from my work in complexity and in practical computing. I liked a lot doing complex systems research myself, but I thought that to really make progress more people needed to be involved. So I started organizing. I launched a journal (which is still thriving today). And then I talked to universities (and other places) to see where the best place to start a research center would be.

Eventually I picked the University of Illinois, and so in the fall of 1986 there I went, themed as a professor of physics, mathematics and computer science, and director of the Center for Complex Systems Research. It was a good setup, but I quickly realized it wasn't a good fit for me. Yes, I can organize things (and, yes, I've been a CEO now for more than half my life). But I do best when I'm organizing my own things, rather than being inside another organization. And, most important, I like actually doing things—like science—myself.

So rather quickly, I went to Plan B: instead of trying to get lots of other people to help push forward the science I wanted to see done, I'd set myself up to be as efficient as possible, and then I'd try to just do what I thought should be done myself. But the first thing I needed was good computational tools. And so it was that I started to build Mathematica, and what's now the Wolfram Language, and to start my company, Wolfram Research.

We launched the first version of Mathematica in June 1988, and I think it's fair to say that it was an instant hit. Physicists were particularly keen on it, and rather quickly it induced an interesting transition. Before Mathematica, if a typical physicist needed to compute something on a computer, they'd delegate it to someone else to actually do. But Mathematica for the first time made computing "high level" enough that physicists themselves could do their own computations. And it's been wonderful to see over the years immense amounts of physics research done with the tools we've built. (It's very nice to have been told many times that, apart from the internet, Mathematica is the largest methodological advance in the doing of physics in this generation.)

For a few years, the rapid development of Mathematica and our company entirely consumed me. But by 1991 it was clear that if I concentrated full-time on it, I could generate far more ideas than our company—at the size it then was—could possibly absorb. And so I decided it was time for me to execute the next step in my plan—and start actually using the tools we'd developed, to do the science I wanted to do. And so in 1991 I became a remote CEO (as I still am) and started work on my "science project".

Maybe It Could Apply to Physics

Pretty quickly I had a table of contents for a book I planned to write—that would work through the consequences of the computational paradigm for complexity and other things. Part of it was going to be exploration: going out into the computational universe and studying what programs do—and part of it was going to be applications: seeing how to apply what I'd learned to different areas of science, and beyond. I didn't know what I'd end up discovering, but I figured the process of writing the book would take a year or two.

My first question was just how general the phenomena I'd discovered in cellular automata actually were. Did they depend on things updating in parallel? Did they depend on having discrete cells? And so on. I started doing computer experiments. Often I'd think "this is finally a kind of system that isn't going to do anything interesting". And I kept on being wrong. I developed a mantra, "The computational animals are always smarter than you are". Even when you can give all sorts of arguments about why such-and-such a system can't do anything interesting, it'll find a way to surprise you, and do something you'd never predict.

What was going on? I realized it was something very general, and very fundamental to basically any system. I call it the Principle of Computational Equivalence, and it's now the guiding principle for a lot of my thinking. It explains computational irreducibility. It gives us a way to organize the computational universe. It tells us about the power of minds. It shows us how to think about the possibilities of artificial intelligence. It gives us perspectives on alien intelligence. It gives us a way to think about free will. And now it seems to give us a way to understand some ultimate questions about our perception of possible physical universes.

I think it was in 1990, right before I began the book project, that I started wondering about applying my ideas to fundamental physics. There'd been a whole "digital physics" movement (particularly involving my friend Ed Fredkin) around using cellular automata to model fundamental physics. But frankly it had put me off. I'd hear "I've discovered an electron in my cellular automaton", but it just sounded like nonsense to me. "For goodness' sake, learn what's already known in physics!", I would say. Of course I loved cellular automata, but— particularly with their rigid built-in notions of space and time—I didn't think they could ever be more than allegories or toy models for actual physics, and pushing them as more than that seemed damaging, and I didn't like it.

But, OK, so not cellular automata. But what underlying computational structure might actually work? I was pretty sure it had to be something that didn't have its own built-in notion of space. And immediately I started thinking about networks.

Things like cellular automata are very clean and easy to define, and program on a computer. Networks—at least in their most obvious form—aren't. My first foray into studying network-based systems was in 1992 and wound up as part of "Chapter 5: Two Dimensions and Beyond". And like every other kind of system I studied, I found that these network systems could generate complex behavior.

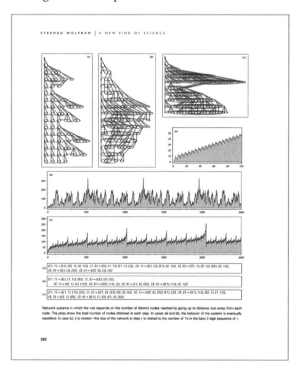

By 1993 I'd studied lots of kinds of abstract systems. And I was working down the table of contents of my planned book, and starting to ask questions like: "What can all this tell us about biology?" "What about human perception?" "Mathematics?" And it was quite exciting, because every time I'd look at a new area I'd realize "Yes, the things I've found in the computational universe really tell us new and interesting things here!"

So finally in 1994 I decided to try and tackle fundamental physics. I've got this whole shelf of drafts of what became my book, and I just pulled down the versions from 1994. It's already got "Chapter 9: Fundamental Physics", but the contents are still embryonic. It gradually grows through 1995 and 1996. And then in 1997, there it is: "Space as a Network", "Time and Causal Networks", etc.

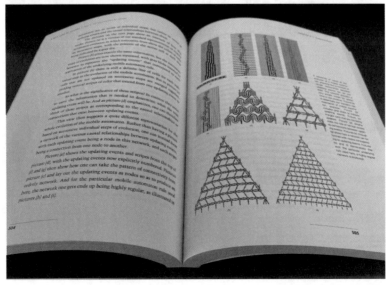

I'd figured out the story of how space could be made as the limit of a discrete network and how different possible updating sequences for graphs led to different threads of time. And I'd come up with the idea of causal invariance, and realized that it implied special relativity. I'd also begun to understand how curvature in space worked, but I didn't yet "have" general relativity

I've got all my notebooks from those times (and they're even now in our online archives). It's a little weird to pull them up now, and realize how tiny screens were back then. But for the most part everything still runs, and I can see how I started to do searches for "the rule" that could build something like our universe.

By then I was in year 6 of my "one-year" book project. At the beginning I'd called my book *A Science of Complexity*. But even by 1994 I'd realized that it was a bigger story than that—and I'd renamed the book *A New Kind of Science*. There was a whole intellectual edifice to discover, and I was determined to work through all the "obvious questions" so I could coherently describe it.

From a personal point of view it's certainly the hardest project I've ever done. I was still remote-CEOing my company, but every day from early in the evening until perhaps 6 am I'd work on science, painstakingly trying to figure out everything I could. On a good day, I'd write a whole page of the book. Sometimes I'd spend the whole day just computing one number that would end up in tiny print in the notes at the back.

When I first embarked on the book project I talked to people quite a bit about it. But they'd always be saying "What about this? What about that?" But no! I had a plan and if I was ever going to get the project done, I knew I had to stick to it, and not get distracted. And so I basically decided to become a hermit, focus intensely on doing the project, and not talk to anyone about it (except that I did have a sequence of research assistants, including some very talented individuals).

The years went by. I'd started the book not long after I turned 30. Now I was approaching 40. But, slowly, inexorably, I was working through the table of contents, and getting towards the end. It was 2001 when I returned to put the finishing touches on Chapter 9. By then I had a pretty good idea how general relativity could work in my model, but in 2001 I got it: a derivation of general relativity that was kind of an analog for the emergence of spacetime from networks of my derivation from 16 years earlier of the emergence of fluid flow from simple cellular automata.

And finally, in 2002, after ten and a half years of daily work, my book was finished. And what I had imagined might be a short "booklet" of perhaps 150 pages had become a 1280-page tome, with nearly a third of a million words of detailed notes at the back. I intended the book to be a presentation (as its title said) of a new kind of science, based on the computational paradigm, and informed by studying the computational universe of simple programs.

But I had wanted to include some "use cases", and physics was one of those, along with biology, mathematics and more. I thought what I had done in physics was a pretty interest-ing beginning, and gave great evidence that the computational paradigm would provide an important new way to think about fundamental physics. As I look back now, I realize that a whole 100 pages of *A New Kind of Science* are devoted to physics, but at the time I think I considered them mostly just a supporting argument for the value of the new kind of science I was developing.

"Please Don't Do That Project"

A New Kind of Science launched on May 14, 2002, and quickly climbed onto bestseller lists. I don't think there's a perfect way to deliver big ideas to the world, but all the trouble I'd taken trying to "package" what I'd figured out, and trying make my book as clear and accessible as possible, seemed to be paying off. And it was great: lots of people seemed to get the core ideas of the book. Looking back, though, it's remarkable how often media coverage of the book talked about physics, and the idea that the universe might be described by a simple program (complete with headlines like "Is the Universe a Computer?" and "The Cosmic Code").

But as someone who'd studied the history of science for a long time, I full well knew that if the new paradigm I was trying to introduce was as important as I believed, then inevitably it would run into detractors, and hostility. But what surprised me was that almost all the hostility came from just one field: physics. There were plenty of physicists who were very positive, but there were others for whom my book somehow seemed to have touched a nerve.

As an almost lifelong lover of physics, I didn't see a conflict. But maybe from the outside it was more obvious—as a cartoon in a review of my book in the *New York Times* (with a remarkably prescient headline) perhaps captured:

If social media had existed at the time, it would undoubtedly have been different. But as it was, it was a whole unchecked parade: from Nobel prizewinners with pitchforks, to a then-graduate-student launching their career by "proving" that my physics was "wrong". Why did they feel so strongly? I think they thought (and some of them told me as much) that if I was right, then what they'd done with their traditional mathematical methods, and all the wonderful things they'd built, would get thrown away.

I never saw it that way (and, ironically, I made my living building a tool used to support those traditional mathematical methods). But at the time—without social media—I didn't have a useful way to respond. (To be fair, it often wasn't clear there was much to say beyond "I don't share your convictions", or "Read what the book actually says… and don't forget the 300,000 words of notes at the back!".)

But there was unfortunately a casualty from all this: physics. As it now turns out (and I'm very happy about it), far from my ideas being in conflict with what's been done in physics, they are actually beautifully aligned. Yes, the foundations are different. But all those traditional mathematical methods now get extra power and extra relevance. But it's taken an additional 18 years for us to find that out. And it almost didn't happen at all.

It's been interesting to watch the general progression of the ideas I discussed in *A New Kind of Science*. What's been most dramatic (and I'm certainly not solely responsible) has been the quiet but rapid transition—after three centuries—of new models for things being based not on equations but instead on programs. It's happened across almost every area. With one notable exception: fundamental physics.

Perhaps it's partly because the tower of mathematical sophistication in models is highest there. Perhaps it's because of the particular stage of development of fundamental physics as a field, and the fact that, for the most part, it's in a "work out the existing models" phase rather than in a "new models" phase.

A few months after my book appeared, I did a big lecture tour of universities and the like. People would ask about all kinds of things. But pretty much everywhere, some people (quite often physicists) would ask about fundamental physics. But, somewhat to my disappointment, their questions tended to be more philosophical than technical. Somehow the notion of applying these ideas to fundamental physics was just a little too dangerous to discuss.

But I decided that whatever other people might think, I should see what it would take to make progress. So in 2004 I set about expanding what I'd figured out so far. I made my explorations more streamlined than before, and pretty soon I was beginning to write summaries of what was out there:

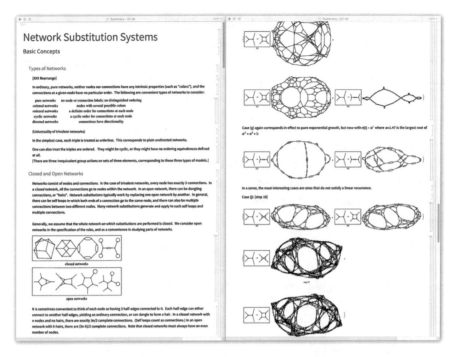

But there was something that bugged me. Somehow my model felt a bit fragile, a bit contrived. At least with the formalism I had, I couldn't just "write down any rule"; it was a bit like writing down numbers, but they had to be prime. And there was another, more technical, problem as well. For my derivations of special and general relativity to work, I needed a model that was causal invariant, and my searches were having a hard time finding nontrivial examples.

And right in the middle of trying to figure out what to do about this, something else happened: I started working on Wolfram|Alpha. In a sense Wolfram|Alpha was an outgrowth of *A New Kind of Science*. Before the book I had assumed that to build a serious computational knowledge engine (which is something I had, in one form or another, been interested in since I was a kid) one would first have to solve the general problem of AI. But one of the implications of my Principle of Computational Equivalence is that there is no bright line between "intelligence" and "mere computation". And that meant that with all our computational capabilities we should already be able to build a computational knowledge engine.

And so I decided to try it. Of course at the beginning we didn't know if it would work. (Is there too much data in the world? Is it too hard to make it computable? Is it too hard to understand natural language? Etc.) But it did work. And in 2009 we launched Wolfram|Alpha.

But I was still enthusiastic about my physics project. And in February 2010 I made it a major part of a talk I gave at TED, which the TED team initially titled "Computing a Theory of Everything" (confusingly, there also now seems to be a version of the same talk with the alternate title "Computing a Theory of All Knowledge"). And—as I was recently reminded—I told the audience that I was committed to seeing the project done, "to see if, within this decade, we can finally hold in our hands the rule for our universe".

OK, well, it's now April 2020. So we didn't make it "within the decade". Though, almost exactly 10 years later, we're now launching the Wolfram Physics Project and I think we're finally on a path to it.

So why didn't this happen sooner? Frankly, in retrospect, it should have. And if I'd known what I know now, I absolutely would have done it. Yes, our Wolfram Language technology has gotten better in the course of the decade, and that's made the project considerably easier. But looking back at what I had done even in 2004, I can now see that I was absolutely on the right track, and I could have done then almost everything I'm doing now.

Most of the projects I've ever done in my life—from my "Concise Directory of Physics" onward—I've done first and foremost because I was interested in them, and because I thought I would find them intellectually fulfilling. But particularly as I've gotten older, there's been another increasingly important factor: I find I get pleasure out of doing projects that I think other people will find useful—and will get their own fulfillment out of. And with the tools I've built—like Mathematica and Wolfram|Alpha and the Wolfram Language—as well as with *A New Kind of Science* and my other books and writings, that's worked well, and it's been a source of great satisfaction to me.

But with the physics project, there was a problem. Because after I effectively "tested the market" in 2002, it seemed as if my core "target customers" (i.e. physicists interested in fundamental physics) didn't want the project. And in fact a few of them came right out and said it: "Please don't do that project".

I personally thought the project would be really interesting. But it wasn't the only project I thought would be interesting. And basically I said "Nah, let me not put lots of effort into a project people basically don't want".

What did I do instead? The most important theme of the past decade for me has been the emergence of the Wolfram Language as a full-scale computational language, and my increasing realization of the significance of having such a language. I view it as being a key step in the development of the computational paradigm—and the crucial link between what computation makes possible, and the way we humans think about things.

It provides a way for us to express ourselves—and organize our thoughts—in computational terms. I view it in some ways as analogous to the creation of mathematical notation four centuries or so ago. And just as that launched the modern development of mathematical science and mathematical thinking, so now I believe that having a full-scale computational language will open up the development of all the "computational X" fields, and the full potential of computational thinking. And this is not something just limited to science. Through ideas like computational contracts I think it's going to inform a lot of how our world operates in the years to come, and how we want to shape (through ethics, etc.) what AIs do, and how we define the future of the human condition.

It's not yet nearly as obvious as it will become. But I think computational language is eventually going to be seen as a pivotal intellectual idea of our times. It also has the rare and interesting feature of being something that is both fundamental and creative. It's about "drilling down" to find the essence both of our thinking and of what computation makes possible. But it's also about the creative design of a language.

And for me personally it's in many ways the ideal project. It involves developing deep understanding across as many areas as possible. It involves the continual exercise of creativity. And it's also a big project, that benefits from organizational skills and resources. And I'm very happy indeed to have spent the past decade on it.

Sometimes I've thought about how it compares as a project to fundamental physics. At a practical level, building a computational language is like building a progressively taller tower—from which one can progressively see further, and occasionally reach major new kinds of applications and implications. Fundamental physics is much more of a one-shot project: you try an approach to fundamental physics and either it works, or it doesn't; there's not the same kind of feeling of progressively building something.

Computational language also began to feel to me like an ultimately more fundamental project—at least for us humans—than fundamental physics. Because it's about the generality of computation and the generality of our ways of thinking, not the specifics of the physical universe in which we "happen to exist". And as I thought about the distant future (complete with my "box of a trillion souls" image), the physical universe seemed less and less relevant to the essence of the human condition. As a kind of "disembodied digital soul", it doesn't matter what the underlying "machine code" of the universe is; you're operating just at the level of abstract computation. So maybe the fundamental theory of physics is ultimately just an "implementation note". (As I now realize from our recent discoveries, the actual situation is more nuanced, and much more philosophically fascinating.)

But even though my main focus has been computational language and its implications, I've been doing quite a few other things. Occasionally I've even written about physics. And I've kept thinking about the fundamental physics project. Is there a "positive" way, I wondered, to do the project, so as many people as possible will be pleased to see it done?

I wondered about offering a prize for finishing what I had started. I had a great experience with something like that in 2007, when Alex Smith won the prize I had set up for proving my conjecture that a particular Turing machine was universal, thereby establishing what the very simplest possible universal Turing machine is. And in fact last fall I put up some new prizes for longstanding questions about rule 30. But for fundamental physics, I didn't think a prize could work. For the Turing machine problem or the rule 30 problems it's realistic for someone to just "swoop in" and figure it out. For fundamental physics, there's a big a tower of ideas to learn just to get started.

From time to time I would talk to physicist friends of mine about the fundamental physics project. (I usually didn't even try with physicists I didn't know; they would just give me quizzical looks, and I could tell they were uncomfortably wondering if I had lost my marbles.) But even with my friends, when I started to describe the details of the project, I don't think over the course of 18 years I managed to keep anyone's attention for more than 15 minutes. And quite soon I would just ask "So, what's new in physics as far as you are concerned?", and off we would go talking about string theory or particle phenomenology or conformal field theory or whatever. (And sometimes they would say, surprised that I cared, "Wow, you still really know about this stuff!")

Finally, though, a few years ago I had an idea about the fundamental physics project: why not just do the project as an educational project? Say, more or less, "We're going to try to climb the Mount Everest of science. We don't know if we'll succeed, but you might enjoy seeing what we do in trying to make the climb." After all, when I talked to non-physicists—or kids--about the project, they were often very excited and very curious. And with all the effort put into STEM education, and into encouraging people to learn about science, I thought this would be a good opportunity. But whenever I really thought about doing the project (and I was still assuming that we'd just be "starting the climb"; I had no idea we'd be able to get as far as we have now), I came back to the "problem of the physicists" (or "phyzzies" as I nicknamed them). And I didn't have a solution.

And so it was that year after year, my project of trying to find the fundamental theory of physics languished.

Two Young Physicists and a Little Idea

Every year for the past 17 years—starting the year after *A New Kind of Science* was published—we've held an annual summer school. It always ends up with an outstanding group of students (mostly college, grad and postdoc). And for me (and also some of our R&D staff) it's become a once-a-year three-week opportunity to explore all sorts of new ideas. In the early years, the Summer School concentrated specifically on what was in my book (it was originally designed to solve the problem of people asking us for guidance on how to do the kind of science in the book). In more recent years, it's basically become about all aspects of the methodology that I and our company have developed.

But from the beginning until now, there've always been a few students each year who say they want to work on "Chapter 9". Many interesting projects have come out of that, though few really used the full network models I'd developed, basically because those were too technically difficult to use in projects that could get done in three weeks.

In 2014, though, a young student just graduating with a degree in physics from Moscow State University (and with various competitive coding achievements to his name) came to the Summer School, determined to work on network-based models of fundamental physics. As the beginning of his project description put it: "The ultimate goal is to figure out the fundamental theory of physics." His actual project was a nice study of the longtime behavior of networks with planarity-preserving rules. The next year, having now completed a master's degree in physics in Moscow, the same student—whose name is Max Piskunov—came to the Summer School a second time (something we rarely allow), to continue his work on network-based models of fundamental physics.

After the Summer School, he was very keen to continue working on these models, and asked me if I could be a PhD advisor for him. I said that unfortunately I wasn't in that business anymore, and that even more unfortunately I didn't know any currently active physicists who'd be suitable. As it turned out, he succeeded in finding a university where there were physicists who were now working on "network science"—though eventually they apparently told him "It's too risky for you to work on network models for physics; there isn't a well-defined criterion for success".

From time to time I would ask after Max, and was a little disappointed to hear that he was off doing a PhD on "traditional" cosmology-meets-particle-physics. But then, in 2018 Max showed up again as a visitor at our Summer School—still really wanting to work on network-based models of fundamental physics. I said I'd really like to work on them too, but just didn't see a way to do it. He said he at least wanted to try his hand at writing more streamlined code for them.

Over the next couple of months I would occasionally talk to Max on the phone, and every time I felt more and more like I really should actually try to do something on the project; I'd been putting it off far too long.

But then I had a little idea. I'd always been saying that I wanted models that are as minimal and structureless as possible. And then I'd say that networks were the best way I knew to get these, but that there were probably others. But even though I thought about lots of abstract structures through my work on the Wolfram Language, I never really came up with anything I was happy with. Until September 9, 2018.

I was asking myself: what lies at the heart of abstract representations, in computation, in mathematics, and so on? Well, I realized, I should know! Because in a sense that's what I've been trying to model all these years in the Wolfram Language, and in SMP before it. And, actually, for more than 40 years, everything I've done has basically been built on the same ultimate underlying answer: transformation rules for symbolic expressions.

It's what the Wolfram Language is based on (and it's what SMP was based on too). So why hadn't I ever thought of using it for models of fundamental physics? The main reason was that somehow I never fully internalized that there'd be something useful left if one "took all the content out of it". Most of the time we're defining transformation rules for symbolic expressions that are somehow useful and meaningful to us—and that for example contain functions that we think of as "representing something".

It's a little shocking that after all these years I could basically make the same mistake again: of implicitly assuming that the setup for a system would be "too simple for it to do anything interesting". I think I was very lucky all those years ago with cellular automata, that it was so easy to try an experiment that I did it, just "on a whim".

But in September 2018 I think I was feeling more motivated by the abstract aesthetics than anything else. I realized there might be an elegant way to represent things—even things that were at least vaguely similar to the network-based models I had studied back in the 1990s. My personal analytics record that it took about 8 minutes to write down the basics:

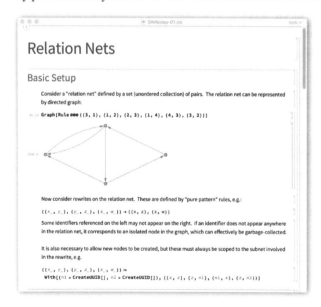

I wanted to do more systematic studies, but I expected it was going to be somewhat complicated, and I was in the middle of working on the final stages of design for Version 12 of the Wolfram Language. Meanwhile, Max took it upon himself to create some optimized low-level code. But in the fall of 2018 he was taking a break from graduate school, working at Lyft in Silicon Valley on machine vision for autonomous driving. Still, by January 2019 he had code running, and within a few minutes of trying it out, I was finding things like:

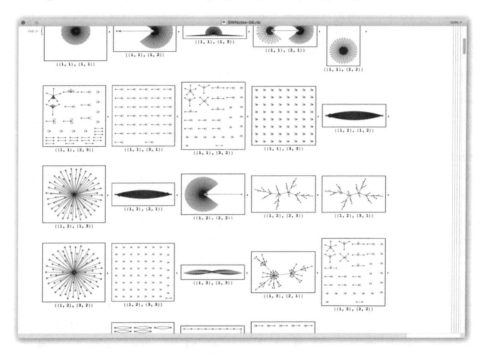

When one looks at the array of squares produced, say, by cellular automata, our human visual system is pretty good at giving us an impression of how much complexity is involved. But that works much less well for things like graphs and networks, where in particular there is inevitably much more arbitrariness in their rendering.

I wanted to do more systematic studies, but I expected it was going to be somewhat complicated, and I was in the middle of working on the final stages of design for Version 12 of the Wolfram Language. Meanwhile, Max took it upon himself to create some optimized low-level code. But in the fall of 2018 he was taking a break from graduate school, working at Lyft in Silicon Valley on machine learning for autonomous driving. Still, by January 2019 he had code running, and within a few minutes of trying it out, I was finding things like:

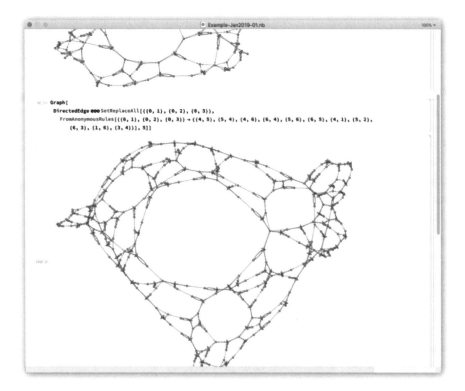

This was going to be interesting. But I was still in the middle of other things, and Max was going to come to the Summer School again—so I put it aside again for a few months.

Then on May 24 Murray Gell-Mann, the inventor of quarks, and a physicist I had known at Caltech, died. And as has become something of a tradition for me, I spent some days writing an obituary piece about him. And in doing that, I began thinking about all those things I had liked so much so long ago in particle physics. But what had happened to them in the past 40 years?

I started looking around on the web. Some things had definitely advanced. The mass of the lambda, that I had always known as 1115 MeV, was now measured as 1115.683 MeV. Calculations that I'd done to a first order of approximation had now been done to three orders. But in general I was shocked, and saddened. Things that had generated so much excitement and had been the pride of particle physics were now barely making it as stubs on Wikipedia. What had happened to this beautiful field? It felt like I was seeing what had once been a bustling and glorious city, now lying almost abandoned, and in some ways in ruins.

Of course, this is often the rhythm of science: some methodological advance sparks a golden age, and once everything easily accessible with that methodology has been done, one is faced with a long, hard slog that can last a century before there is some new methodological advance.

But going to the Summer School in June, I was again thinking about how to do my fundamental physics project.

Max was there. And so—as an instructor—was Jonathan Gorard. Jonathan had first come to the Summer School in 2017, just before his last year as an undergraduate in mathematics (+ theoretical physics, computer science and philosophy) at King's College London. He'd been publishing papers on various topics since he was 17, most recently on a new algorithm for graph isomorphism. He said that at the Summer School he wanted to work either on cosmology in the context of "Chapter 9", or on something related to the foundations of mathematics.

I suggested that he try his hand at what I considered something of an old chestnut: finding a good symbolic way to represent and analyze automated proofs, like the one I had done back in 2000 of the simplest axiom system for logic. And though I had no idea at the time, this turned out to be a remarkably fortuitous choice. But as it was, Jonathan threw himself into the project, and produced the seeds of what would become through his later work the Wolfram Language function FindEquationalProof.

Jonathan had come back to the Summer School in 2018 as an instructor, supervising projects on things like infinite lists and algebraic cryptography. And now he was back again as an instructor in 2019, having now also become a graduate student at Cambridge, with a nice fellowship, and nominally in a group doing general relativity.

It had been planned that Jonathan, Max and I would "talk about physics" at the Summer School. I was hopeful, but after so many years a bit pessimistic. I thought my little idea defined a new, immediate path about what one might do. But I still wasn't convinced there was a "good way to do the project".

But then we started discussing things. And I started feeling a stronger and stronger sense of responsibility. These ideas needed to be explored. Max and Jonathan were enthusiastic about them. What excuse did I have not to pursue the ideas, and see where they could go? Wouldn't it be terrible if we failed to find the fundamental theory of physics just because I somehow got put off working on it?

Of course, there were technical, physics issues too. One of the big ones—which had got me stuck back in 2004—was that I'd had difficulty finding examples of rules that both had nontrivial behavior, and showed the property of causal invariance needed to basically "generate a single thread of time". Why did I care so much about causal invariance? First, because it gave me derivations of both special and general relativity. But philosophically even more important to me, because it avoided something I considered highly undesirable: a view of quantum mechanics in which there is a giant tree of possible histories, with no way to choose between them.

Jonathan had said a few times early in the Summer School that he didn't see why I was so concerned about causal invariance. I kept on pushing back. Then one day we went on a long walk, and Jonathan explained an idea he had (which, knowing him, he may have just come up with right there). What if the underlying rules didn't need to have causal invariance, because us observers would implicitly add it just by the way we analyze things?

What was this idea really? It was an application of things Jonathan knew from working on automated theorem proving, mixing in ideas from general relativity, and applying them to the foundations of quantum mechanics. (Basically, his concept was that we observers, because we're branching just like the system we're observing, effectively define "lemmas" to help us made sense of what we observe, and these lead to effective rules that have causal invariance.)

At first I was skeptical. But the issue with not finding enough causal invariance had been a blocker 16 years earlier. And it felt like a big weight lifted if that issue could be removed. So by the end of the walk I was convinced that, yes, it was worth looking at rules even if they were not explicitly causal invariant, because they could still be "saved" by the "Jonathan Interpretation of Quantum Mechanics" as I called it (Jonathan prefers the more formal term "completion interpretation", referring to the process of creating lemmas, which is called "completion" in automated theorem proving). As it turns out, the jury is still out on whether causal invariance is intrinsic or "in the eye of the observer". But Jonathan's idea was crucial as far as I was concerned in clearing the way to exploring these models without first doing a giant search for causal invariance.

It took another month or so, but finally on August 10 I sent back to Jonathan and Max a picture we had taken, saying "The origin picture ... and .... *I'm finally ready to get to work*!"

Oh My Gosh, It's Actually Going to Work!

August 29, 2019, was a big birthday for me. Shockingly quickly I had gone from being "the youngest person in the room" to the oldest. But now I was turning 60. I did a "looking to the future" livestream that day, and a few days later I gave a speech at my birthday party. And both times I said that now, finally, I was going to make a serious effort on my project to find the fundamental theory of physics. And to myself I was saying "This is something I've been talking about doing for more than half my life; if I don't do it now, it's time to give up on the idea that I ever will."

"Maybe it'll work, maybe it won't", I was thinking to myself. "But this is sort of the last chance for me to find out, so let's give it a try." And so we started. My original plan was in a sense fairly modest. I wanted to take the things I'd already investigated, and "spruce them up" in the context of my new models—then get everything out there for other people to help in what I expected would be a long, hard grind towards a fundamental theory of physics.

The first step was to build tools. Nice, streamlined Wolfram Language tools. Max had already written some core simulation functions. But now it was a question of figuring out about visualizations, enumerations and various forms of analysis. How do you best display a hypergraph? What's the right way to enumerate rules? And so on.

But by the middle of October we had the basics, and by the end of October I'd pretty much cleared my calendar of everything but the "bare CEO essentials", and was ready to just "do physics" for a while. It felt a little like being back where I was in the 1970s. Except for one huge difference: now I had the whole technology tower I'd spent most of the intervening 40 years building. No scratch paper. No handwritten calculations. Just notebooks and Wolfram Language. A medium for thinking directly in computational terms.

And it was exhilarating. Everything went so fast. I was basically forming my thoughts directly in the language, typing as I went, then immediately having the computer show me the results. It felt as if the computer was providing about as direct an amplification of my cognitive abilities as I could imagine. And I even started to feel a bit better about the multi-decade delay in the project. Because I realized that even if my only goal from the beginning had been to just do this project, my best chance would pretty much have been to build the Wolfram Language first.

There was something that made me nervous, though. Back in 1991 when I started working on *A New Kind of Science*, I'd also had the experience of rapid discovery. But what had happened then was that I hadn't been able to stop—and I'd just dug in and gone on and on discovering things, for a decade. Intellectually it had been very rewarding, but personally it was extremely grueling. And I didn't want to go through anything like that again. So I resolved that instead of going on until we'd "answered all the obvious questions", we'd just figure out the minimum needed to coherently explain the ideas, then turn it over to the world to share the fun of taking it further.

Pretty soon we started outlining the website. There'd be lots of technical information and exposition. There'd be a Registry of Notable Universes for candidate models we'd identified. To lighten the load of what I thought might be a project with glacially slow progress to report, there'd be "universe swag". And on the front of the website I was planning to write, a little apologetically: "We're going to try to find a fundamental theory of physics. It may be the wrong approach, or the wrong century, but we're going to try anyway".

But meanwhile I was spending almost every waking hour doing that "trying". I was looking at thousands of rules, slowly building up intuition. And we were talking about how what I was seeing might relate to things in physics, like space and time and quantum mechanics and general relativity. And it got more and more interesting.

Things I'd thought vaguely about in the past we were now starting to see very explicitly in the rules I was running. We knew enough to know what to look for. But thinking abstractly about something is very different from seeing an actual example. And there were many surprises. So many "I never thought it might do *that*"s. But having seen examples one could then start to build up an abstract framework. Without the examples one wouldn't ever have had the imagination to come up with it. But once one saw it, it often seemed maddeningly "obvious".

Our first big target was to understand the nature of space. How could the mathematical structures that have been used to characterize space emerge from our simple rules? I thought I already knew the basic answer from what I did back in the 1990s. But now I had a more streamlined model, and more streamlined tools, and I wanted to tighten my understanding.

I generated thousands of screenfuls of visualizations:

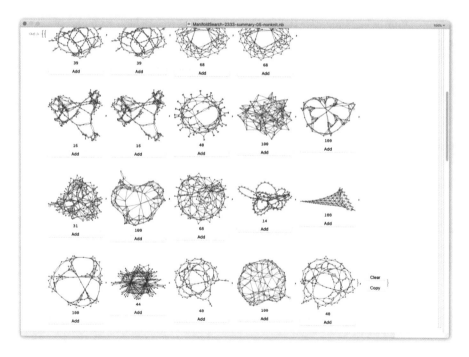

I think if I had lived a century earlier I would have been a zoologist. And what I was doing here was a kind of zoology: trying to catalog the strange forms and habits of these rules, and identify their families and phyla. It was a glimpse into an unseen part of the computational universe; a view of something there was no particular reason that us humans would have a way to understand. But I was pretty sure that at least some of these rules would connect with things we already knew. And so I started to hunt for examples.

Most of what I do on a daily basis I can do on just one computer. But now I needed to search millions of cases. Conveniently, there's pretty seamless support for parallel computation in the Wolfram Language. So soon I'd commandeered about 100 cores, and every computation I could immediately parallelize. (I was also set up to use external cloud services, but most of the time I was doing computations that with the 100X speedup were either taking only seconds, and were part of my "interactive thinking loop", or were easy enough to run overnight on my own machines, with the minor thrill of seeing in the morning what they'd produced.)

Back when I was studying things like cellular automata in the 1980s and 1990s I used to print out endless arrays of little thumbnails, then look through them, and type in the identifiers for ones I thought were worth another look. Now that was all a lot more streamlined, with images in notebooks, selectable with a simple click. But how could I automate actually looking through all these rules?

One of the things I've learned from decades of studying the computational universe is to take seriously my mantra "The computational animals are always smarter than you are". You think you've come up with a foolproof test for catching rules that have such-and-such a behavior. Well, some rule will turn out to have a way around it, doing something you never thought about. And what I've found is that in the end the best way to have a chance of catching the unexpected is to use the "broadest spectrum" tools one has, which typically means one's own eyes.

Pretty soon one begins to have a mental classification of the kinds of forms one's seeing. And if one verbalizes it, one ends up describing them in terms of objects we're used to ("ball of wool", "sea urchin", etc.) And in modern times that suggests a way to get some help: use machine learning that's been trained, like we have, to distinguish these different kinds of things. And so instead of just making simple arrays of pictures, I often made feature space plots, where forms that "seem similar" were grouped together.

And that meant that in just a glance I could typically see what unexpected outliers there might be. I looked through a particular collection of 79 million rules this way (with just a little additional filtering). First I found this—something that might seem more in line with my childhood interest in space, as in spacecraft, than with space in fundamental physics

And pretty soon things I also found things like these:

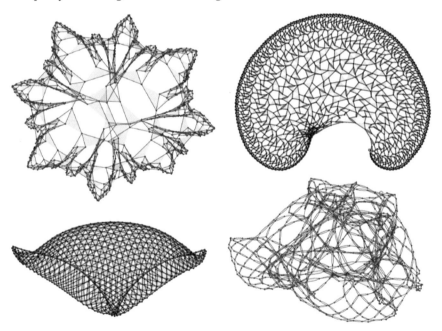

These are not things I could ever guess would be there. But having found them, they can be connected to existing mathematical ideas (in this case, about manifolds). But seeing these examples embedded in so many others that don't immediately connect to anything we know immediately makes one wonder whether perhaps our existing mathematical ideas can be generalized—and whether maybe this could be the key to understanding how space can emerge from our underlying rules.

Both in its early history, and in modern times, mathematics has been inspired by the natural world. Now we're seeing it inspired by the computational world. How does one generalize curvature to fractional dimensional space? What does it mean to have a space with smoothly varying dimension? And so on. They're elegant and interesting mathematical questions raised by looking at the computational world.

It could have been that everything in the computational world of our models would immediately run into computational irreducibility, and that mathematical ideas would be essentially powerless—as they were when I was studying cellular automata in the 1980s. But by November of last year, it was beginning to become clear that things were different now, and that there was a chance of a bridge between the mathematical traditions of existing theoretical physics and the kinds of things we needed to know about our models.

Once there's sophisticated mathematics, we can begin to rely on that. But to explore, we still have to use things like our eyes. And that makes visualization critical. But in our models, what's ultimately there are graphs, or hypergraphs. Nowadays we've got good automated tools in the Wolfram Language for coming up with "good" ways to lay out graphs. But it's always arbitrary. And it would be much better if we could just "intrinsically" understand the graph. But unfortunately I don't think we humans are really built for that. Or at least I'm not. (Though years ago, before computers could do automated graph layout, I once looked for a human "graph detangler" and found a young student who was spectacularly better than everyone else. Interestingly, she later became a distinguished knitwear designer.)

But to try to help in "understanding" graphs I did have one plan—that actually I'd already hatched when I was first thinking about these things in the early 1990s: use VR to really "get inside" and experience graphs. So now—with VR back in vogue—I decided to give it a try. We're still working on a fully interactive VR environment for manipulating graphs, but to start off I tried just using VR to explore static graphs. And, yes, it was somewhat useful. But there was a practical problem for me: rapid descent into motion sickness. An occupational hazard, I suppose. But not one I expected in studying fundamental physics.

Given a better understanding of space in our models, we started looking more carefully at things like my old derivation of the Einstein equations for gravity. Jonathan tightened up the formalism and the mathematics. And it began to become clear that it wasn't just a question of connecting our models to existing mathematical physics: our models were actually clarifying the existing mathematical physics. What had been pure, abstract mathematics relying on potentially arbitrary collections of "axiomatic" assumptions one could now see could arise from much more explicit structures. Oh, and one could check assumptions by just explicitly running things.

Doing something like deriving the Einstein equations from our models isn't at some level particularly easy. And inevitably it involves a chain of mathematical derivations. Pure mathematicians are often a little horrified by the way physicists tend to "hack through" subtle mathematical issues ("Do these limits really commute?" "Can one uniquely define that parameter?" Etc.). And this was in many ways an extreme example.

But of course we weren't adrift with no idea whether things were correct—because at least in many cases we could just go and run a model and measure things, and explicitly check what was going on. But I did feel a little bad. Here we were coming up with beautiful mathematical ideas and questions. But all I could do was barbarically hack through them—and I just kept thinking "These things deserve a mathematician who'll really appreciate them". Which hopefully in time they'll get.

As we went through November, we were starting to figure out more and more. And it seemed like every conversation we had, we were coming up with interesting things. I didn't know where it would all go. But as a committed preserver of data I thought it was time to start recording our conversations, as well as my own experiments and other work on the project. And altogether we've so far accumulated 431 hours of recordings.

We're going to make these recordings available online. And with Wolfram Language speech-to-text it's easy to process their audio, and to get word clouds that indicate some of the flow of the project:

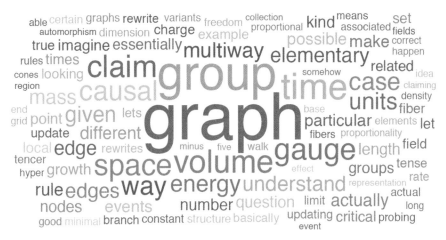

What Terrible Timing!

So there we were in the middle of February. Things had gone better than I'd ever imagined they could. And we were working intensely to get everything ready to present to the world. We set a date: March 16, 2020. We were planning announcements, technical documents, an 800ish-page book, an extensive website, livestreams, outreach. All the kinds of things needed to launch this as a project, and explain it to people.

But meanwhile—like so many other people—we were watching the developing coronavirus epidemic. I'd asked the data science and biology teams at our company to start curating data and making it available. I'd been looking at some epidemic modeling—some of it even done with cellular automata. I'd noted that the spreading of an epidemic in a human network was bizarrely similar to the growth of geodesic balls in hypergraphs.

What should we do? We kept going, steadily checking off items on our project-management tracking list. But as March 16 approached, it was clear there was now a pandemic. The US began to shut down. I did an AMA on my experience as a 29-year work-from-home CEO. Meetings about physics were now interspersed with meetings about shutting down offices. Numerous people at our company pointed out to me that Isaac Newton had come up with the core ideas for both calculus and his theory of gravity in 1665, when Cambridge University had been closed because of the plague.

I oscillated between thinking that in the midst of such a worldwide crisis it was almost disrespectful to be talking about something like a fundamental theory of physics, and thinking that perhaps people might like an intellectual distraction. But in the end we decided to wait. We'd get everything ready, but then pause.

And after all, I thought, after waiting more than thirty years to do this project, what's a few more weeks?

What Happens Now

If you're reading this, it means our project is finally released. And we begin the next stage in the long journey I've described here. I can't help echoing Isaac Newton's words from the 1686 preface to his *Principia*: "I heartily beg that what I have done here may be read with forbearance; and that my labors in a subject so difficult may be examined, not so much with a view to censure, as to remedy their defects."

But the world has changed since then, and now we can send out tweets and do livestreams. I'm thrilled about what we've been able to figure out, not least because I consider it so elegant and so intellectually satisfying. Sometimes back when I was doing particle physics, I'd think "That's a bit hacky, but if that's how our universe works, so be it". Now I feel a certain pride that we seem to live in a universe that works in such an elegant way.

Forty years ago I thought I'd spend my life as a physicist. Things didn't work out that way, and I'm very happy with what happened instead. But now after decades "in the wilderness" I'm back. Not just "doing physics", but trying to attack the very center of it. I'm quite certain that if I'd spent the past 40 years as a physicist nothing like this would have been possible. It's one of those cases where it's almost inevitable that making progress will need that strange combination of having inside knowledge yet "being an outsider".

Of course, we're not finished. I think we finally have a path to a fundamental theory of physics. But we're not there yet. And what I'm hoping now is that we can mount a project that will succeed in getting us there.

It's going to take physicists, mathematicians, computer scientists and others. It's going to take ideas and work, and perhaps quite a bit of time. I hope it will be a worldwide effort that can happen across a spectrum of academic and other environments. Most of it will be a decentralized effort.

I personally look forward to continuing to be deeply involved—and I'm hoping that we'll be able to set up a substantial centralized effort to apply the decades of experience we've had in doing highly challenging R&D projects to make progress as rapidly as possible on this project.

It's been a great privilege for me to be "in the right place at the right time" to discover what we've discovered. Physics did so much for me in my early years, and I'm thrilled to have the opportunity to "give something back" so many years later. I can't wait to see what will develop as we home in on a fundamental theory of physics. But at this stage in my life perhaps my greatest pleasure is to see others get excitement and fulfillment from things I put into the world. And to provide something for the next generation of 12-year-old physics wannabes.

So let's all go and try to find the fundamental theory of physics together! It's going to be great!

BACKGROUND

A New Kind of Science:
A 15-Year View

Preface ›

1 | The Foundations for a New Kind of Science ›

2 | The Crucial Experiment ›

3 | The World of Simple Programs ›

4 | Systems Based on Numbers ›

5 | Two Dimensions and Beyond ›

6 | Starting from Randomness ›

7 | Mechanisms in Programs and Nature ›

8 | Implications for Everyday Systems ›

9 | Fundamental Physics ›

10 | Processes of Perception and Analysis ›

11 | The Notion of Computation ›

12 | The Principle of Computational Equivalence ›

Notes ›

Index   Copyright Page   Colophon

It's now 15 years since I published my book *A New Kind of Science*—more than 25 since I started writing it, and more than 35 since I started working towards it. But with every passing year I feel I understand more about what the book is really about—and why it's important. I wrote the book, as its title suggests, to contribute to the progress of science. But as the years have gone by, I've realized that the core of what's in the book actually goes far beyond science—into many areas that will be increasingly important in defining our whole future.

So, viewed from a distance of 15 years, what is the book really about? At its core, it's about something profoundly abstract: the theory of all possible theories, or the universe of all possible universes. But for me one of the achievements of the book is the realization that one can explore such fundamental things concretely—by doing actual experiments in the computational universe of possible programs. And in the end the book is full of what might at first seem like quite alien pictures made just by running very simple such programs.

Back in 1980, when I made my living as a theoretical physicist, if you'd asked me what I thought simple programs would do, I expect I would have said "not much". I had been very interested in the kind of complexity one sees in nature, but I thought—like a typical reductionistic scientist—that the key to understanding it must lie in figuring out detailed features of the underlying component parts.

In retrospect I consider it incredibly lucky that all those years ago I happened to have the right interests and the right skills to actually try what is in a sense the most basic experiment in the computational universe: to systematically take a sequence of the simplest possible programs, and run them.

I could tell as soon as I did this that there were interesting things going on, but it took a couple more years before I began to really appreciate the force of what I'd seen. For me it all started with one picture:

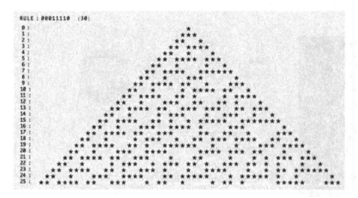

Or, in modern form:

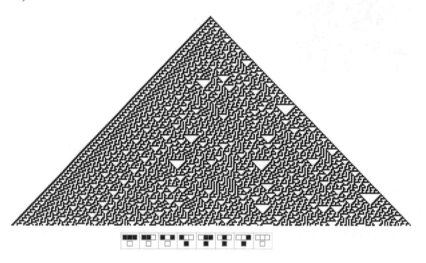

I call it rule 30. It's my all-time favorite discovery, and today I carry it around everywhere on my business cards. What is it? It's one of the simplest programs one can imagine. It operates on rows of black and white cells, starting from a single black cell, and then repeatedly applies the rules at the bottom. And the crucial point is that even though those rules are by any measure extremely simple, the pattern that emerges is not.

It's a crucial—and utterly unexpected—feature of the computational universe: that even among the very simplest programs, it's easy to get immensely complex behavior. It took me a solid decade to understand just how broad this phenomenon is. It doesn't just happen in programs ("cellular automata") like rule 30. It basically shows up whenever you start enumerating possible rules or possible programs whose behavior isn't obviously trivial.

Similar phenomena had actually been seen for centuries in things like the digits of pi and the distribution of primes—but they were basically just viewed as curiosities, and not as signs of something profoundly important. It's been nearly 35 years since I first saw what happens in rule 30, and with every passing year I feel I come to understand more clearly and deeply what its significance is.

Four centuries ago it was the discovery of the moons of Jupiter and their regularities that sowed the seeds for modern exact science, and for the modern scientific approach to thinking. Could my little rule 30 now be the seed for another such intellectual revolution, and a new way of thinking about everything?

In some ways I might personally prefer not to take responsibility for shepherding such ideas ("paradigm shifts" are hard and thankless work). And certainly for years I have just quietly used such ideas to develop technology and my own thinking. But as computation and AI become increasingly central to our world, I think it's important that the implications of what's out there in the computational universe be more widely understood.

Implications of the Computational Universe

Here's the way I see it today. From observing the moons of Jupiter we came away with the idea that—if looked at right—the universe is an ordered and regular place, that we can ultimately understand. But now, in exploring the computational universe, we quickly come upon things like rule 30 where even the simplest rules seem to lead to irreducibly complex behavior.

One of the big ideas of *A New Kind of Science* is what I call the Principle of Computational Equivalence. The first step is to think of every process—whether it's happening with black and white squares, or in physics, or inside our brains—as a computation that somehow transforms input to output. What the Principle of Computational Equivalence says is that above an extremely low threshold, all processes correspond to computations of equivalent sophistication.

It might not be true. It might be that something like rule 30 corresponds to a fundamentally simpler computation than the fluid dynamics of a hurricane, or the processes in my brain as I write this. But what the Principle of Computational Equivalence says is that in fact all these things are computationally equivalent.

It's a very important statement, with many deep implications. For one thing, it implies what I call computational irreducibility. If something like rule 30 is doing a computation just as sophisticated as our brains or our mathematics, then there's no way we can "outrun" it: to figure out what it will do, we have to do an irreducible amount of computation, effectively tracing each of its steps.

The mathematical tradition in exact science has emphasized the idea of predicting the behavior of systems by doing things like solving mathematical equations. But what computational irreducibility implies is that out in the computational universe that often won't work, and instead the only way forward is just to explicitly run a computation to simulate the behavior of the system.

A Shift in Looking at the World

One of the things I did in *A New Kind of Science* was to show how simple programs can serve as models for the essential features of all sorts of physical, biological and other systems. Back when the book appeared, some people were skeptical about this. And indeed at that time there was a 300-year unbroken tradition that serious models in science should be based on mathematical equations.

But in the past 15 years something remarkable has happened. For now, when new models are created—whether of animal patterns or web browsing behavior—they are overwhelmingly more often based on programs than on mathematical equations.

Year by year, it's been a slow, almost silent, process. But by this point, it's a dramatic shift. Three centuries ago pure philosophical reasoning was supplanted by mathematical equations. Now in these few short years, equations have been largely supplanted by programs. For now, it's mostly been something practical and pragmatic: the models work better, and are more useful.

But when it comes to understanding the foundations of what's going on, one's led not to things like mathematical theorems and calculus, but instead to ideas like the Principle of Computational Equivalence. Traditional mathematics-based ways of thinking have made concepts like force and momentum ubiquitous in the way we talk about the world. But now as we think in fundamentally computational terms we have to start talking in terms of concepts like undecidability and computational irreducibility.

Will some type of tumor always stop growing in some particular model? It might be undecidable. Is there a way to work out how a weather system will develop? It might be computationally irreducible.

These concepts are pretty important when it comes to understanding not only what can and cannot be modeled, but also what can and cannot be controlled in the world. Computational irreducibility in economics is going to limit what can be globally controlled. Computational irreducibility in biology is going to limit how generally effective therapies can be—and make highly personalized medicine a fundamental necessity.

And through ideas like the Principle of Computational Equivalence we can start to discuss just what it is that allows nature—seemingly so effortlessly—to generate so much that seems so complex to us. Or how even deterministic underlying rules can lead to computationally irreducible behavior that for all practical purposes can seem to show "free will".

Mining the Computational Universe

A central lesson of *A New Kind of Science* is that there's a lot of incredible richness out there in the computational universe. And one reason that's important is that it means that there's a lot of incredible stuff out there for us to "mine" and harness for our purposes.

Want to automatically make an interesting custom piece of art? Just start looking at simple programs and automatically pick out one you like—as in our WolframTones music site from a decade ago. Want to find an optimal algorithm for something? Just search enough programs out there, and you'll find one.

We've normally been used to creating things by building them up, step by step, with human effort—progressively creating architectural plans, or engineering drawings, or lines of code. But the discovery that there's so much richness so easily accessible in the computational universe suggests a different approach: don't try building anything; just define what you want, and then search for it in the computational universe.

Sometimes it's really easy to find. Like let's say you want to generate apparent randomness. Well, then just enumerate cellular automata (as I did in 1984), and very quickly you come upon rule 30—which turns out to be one of the very best known generators of apparent randomness (look down the center column of cell values, for examples). In other situations you might have to search 100,000 cases (as I did in finding the simplest axiom system for logic, or the simplest universal Turing machine), or you might have to search millions or even trillions of cases. But in the past 25 years, we've had incredible success in just discovering algorithms out there in the computational universe—and we rely on many of them in implementing the Wolfram Language.

At some level it's quite sobering. One finds some tiny program out in the computational universe. One can tell it does what one wants. But when one looks at what it's doing, one doesn't have any real idea how it works. Maybe one can analyze some part—and be struck by how "clever" it is. But there just isn't a way for us to understand the whole thing; it's not something familiar from our usual patterns of thinking.

Of course, we've often had similar experiences before—when we use things from nature. We may notice that some particular substance is a useful drug or a great chemical catalyst, but we may have no idea why. But in doing engineering and in most of our modern efforts to build technology, the great emphasis has instead been on constructing things whose design and operation we can readily understand.

In the past we might have thought that was enough. But what our explorations of the computational universe show is that it's not: selecting only things whose operation we can readily understand misses most of the immense power and richness that's out there in the computational universe.

A World of Discovered Technology

What will the world look like when more of what we have is mined from the computational universe? Today the environment we build for ourselves is dominated by things like simple shapes and repetitive processes. But the more we use what's out there in the computational universe, the less regular things will look. Sometimes they may look a bit "organic", or like what we see in nature (since after all, nature follows similar kinds of rules). But sometimes they may look quite random, until perhaps suddenly and incomprehensibly they achieve something we recognize.

For several millennia we as a civilization have been on a path to understand more about what happens in our world—whether by using science to decode nature, or by creating our own environment through technology. But to use more of the richness of the computational universe we must at least to some extent forsake this path.

In the past, we somehow counted on the idea that between our brains and the tools we could create we would always have fundamentally greater computational power than the things around us—and as a result we would always be able to "understand" them. But what the Principle of Computational Equivalence says is that this isn't true: out in the computational universe there are lots of things just as powerful as our brains or the tools we build. And as soon as we start using those things, we lose the "edge" we thought we had.

Today we still imagine we can identify discrete "bugs" in programs. But most of what's powerful out there in the computational universe is rife with computational irreducibility—so the only real way to see what it does is just to run it and watch what happens.

We ourselves, as biological systems, are a great example of computation happening at a molecular scale—and we are no doubt rife with computational irreducibility (which is, at some fundamental level, why medicine is hard). I suppose it's a tradeoff: we could limit our technology to consist only of things whose operation we understand. But then we would miss all that richness that's out there in the computational universe. And we wouldn't even be able to match the achievements of our own biology in the technology we create.

Machine Learning and the Neural Net Renaissance

There's a common pattern I've noticed with intellectual fields. They go for decades and perhaps centuries with only incremental growth, and then suddenly, usually as a result of a methodological advance, there's a burst of "hypergrowth" for perhaps 5 years, in which important new results arrive almost every week.

I was fortunate enough that my own very first field—particle physics—was in its period of hypergrowth right when I was involved in the late 1970s. And for myself, the 1990s felt like a kind of personal period of hypergrowth for what became *A New Kind of Science*—and indeed that's why I couldn't pull myself away from it for more than a decade.

But today, the obvious field in hypergrowth is machine learning, or, more specifically, neural nets. It's funny for me to see this. I actually worked on neural nets back in 1981, before I started on cellular automata, and several years before I found rule 30. But I never managed to get neural nets to do anything very interesting—and actually I found them too messy and complicated for the fundamental questions I was concerned with.

And so I "simplified them"—and wound up with cellular automata. (I was also inspired by things like the Ising model in statistical physics, etc.) At the outset, I thought I might have simplified too far, and that my little cellular automata would never do anything interesting. But then I found things like rule 30. And I've been trying to understand its implications ever since.

In building Mathematica and the Wolfram Language, I'd always kept track of neural nets, and occasionally we'd use them in some small way for some algorithm or another. But about 5 years ago I suddenly started hearing amazing things: that somehow the idea of training neural nets to do sophisticated things was actually working. At first I wasn't sure. But then we started building neural net capabilities in the Wolfram Language, and finally two years ago we released our ImageIdentify.com website—and now we've got our whole symbolic neural net system. And, yes, I'm impressed. There are lots of tasks that had traditionally been viewed as the unique domain of humans, but which now we can routinely do by computer.

But what's actually going on in a neural net? It's not really to do with the brain; that was just the inspiration (though in reality the brain probably works more or less the same way). A neural net is really a sequence of functions that operate on arrays of numbers, with each function typically taking quite a few inputs from around the array. It's not so different from a cellular automaton. Except that in a cellular automaton, one's usually dealing with, say, just 0s and 1s, not arbitrary numbers like 0.735. And instead of taking inputs from all over the place, in a cellular automaton each step takes inputs only from a very well-defined local region.

Now, to be fair, it's pretty common to study "convolutional neural nets", in which the patterns of inputs are very regular, just like in a cellular automaton. And it's becoming clear that having precise (say 32-bit) numbers isn't critical to the operation of neural nets; one can probably make do with just a few bits.

But a big feature of neural nets is that we know how to make them "learn". In particular, they have enough features from traditional mathematics (like involving continuous numbers) that techniques like calculus can be applied to provide strategies to make them incrementally change their parameters to "fit their behavior" to whatever training examples they're given.

It's far from obvious how much computational effort, or how many training examples, will be needed. But the breakthrough of about five years ago was the discovery that for many important practical problems, what's available with modern GPUs and modern web-collected training sets can be enough.

Pretty much nobody ends up explicitly setting or "engineering" the parameters in a neural net. Instead, what happens is that they're found automatically. But unlike with simple programs like cellular automata, where one's typically enumerating all possibilities, in current neural nets there's an incremental process, essentially based on calculus, that manages to progressively improve the net—a little like the way biological evolution progressively improves the "fitness" of an organism.

It's plenty remarkable what comes out from training a neural net in this way, and it's plenty difficult to understand how the neural net does what it does. But in some sense the neural net isn't venturing too far across the computational universe: it's always basically keeping the same basic computational structure, and just changing its behavior by changing parameters.

But to me the success of today's neural nets is a spectacular endorsement of the power of the computational universe, and another validation of the ideas of *A New Kind of Science*. Because it shows that out in the computational universe, away from the constraints of explicitly building systems whose detailed behavior one can foresee, there are immediately all sorts of rich and useful things to be found.

NKS Meets Modern Machine Learning

Is there a way to bring the full power of the computational universe—and the ideas of *A New Kind of Science*—to the kinds of things one does with neural nets? I suspect so. And in fact, as the details become clear, I wouldn't be surprised if exploration of the computational universe saw its own period of hypergrowth: a "mining boom" of perhaps unprecedented proportions.

In current work on neural nets, there's a definite tradeoff one sees. The more what's going on inside the neural net is like a simple mathematical function with essentially arithmetic parameters, the easier it is to use ideas from calculus to train the network. But the more what's going is like a discrete program, or like a computation whose whole structure can change, the more difficult it is to train the network.

It's worth remembering, though, that the networks we're routinely training now would have looked utterly impractical to train only a few years ago. It's effectively just all those quadrillions of GPU operations that we can throw at the problem that makes training feasible. And I won't be surprised if even quite pedestrian (say, local exhaustive search) techniques will fairly soon let one do significant training even in cases where no incremental numerical approach is possible. And perhaps even it will be possible to invent some major generalization of things like calculus that will operate in the full computational universe. (I have some suspicions, based on thinking about generalizing basic notions of geometry to cover things like cellular automaton rule spaces.)

What would this let one do? Likely it would let one find considerably simpler systems that could achieve particular computational goals. And maybe that would bring within reach some qualitatively new level of operations, perhaps beyond what we're used to being possible with things like brains.

There's a funny thing that's going on with modeling these days. As neural nets become more successful, one begins to wonder: why bother to simulate what's going on inside a system when one can just make a black-box model of its output using a neural net? Well, if we manage to get machine learning to reach deeper into the computational universe, we won't have as much of this tradeoff any more—because we'll be able to learn models of the mechanism as well as the output.

I'm pretty sure that bringing the full computational universe into the purview of machine learning will have spectacular consequences. But it's worth realizing that computational universality—and the Principle of Computational Equivalence—make it less a matter of principle. Because they imply that even neural nets of the kinds we have now are universal, and are capable of emulating anything any other system can do. (In fact, this universality result was essentially what launched the whole modern idea of neural nets, back in 1943.)

And as a practical matter, the fact that current neural net primitives are being built into hardware and so on will make them a desirable foundation for actual technology systems, though, even if they're far from optimal. But my guess is that there are tasks where for the foreseeable future access to the full computational universe will be necessary to make them even vaguely practical.

Finding AI

What will it take to make artificial intelligence? As a kid, I was very interested in figuring out how to make a computer know things, and be able to answer questions from what it knew. And when I studied neural nets in 1981, it was partly in the context of trying to understand how to build such a system. As it happens, I had just developed SMP, which was a forerunner of Mathematica (and ultimately the Wolfram Language)—and which was very much based on symbolic pattern matching ("if you see this, transform it to that"). At the time, though, I imagined that artificial intelligence was somehow a "higher level of computation", and I didn't know how to achieve it.

I returned to the problem every so often, and kept putting it off. But then when I was working on *A New Kind of Science* it struck me: if I'm to take the Principle of Computational Equivalence seriously, then there can't be any fundamentally "higher level of computation"—so AI must be achievable just with the standard ideas of computation that I already know.

And it was this realization that got me started building Wolfram|Alpha. And, yes, what I found is that lots of those very "AI-oriented things", like natural language understanding, could be done just with "ordinary computation", without any magic new AI invention. Now, to be fair, part of what was happening was that we were using ideas and methods from *A New Kind of Science*: we weren't just engineering everything; we were often searching the computational universe for rules and algorithms to use.

So what about "general AI"? Well, I think at this point that with the tools and understanding we have, we're in a good position to automate essentially anything we can define. But definition is a more difficult and central issue than we might imagine.

The way I see things at this point is that there's a lot of computation even near at hand in the computational universe. And it's powerful computation. As powerful as anything that happens in our brains. But we don't recognize it as "intelligence" unless it's aligned with our human goals and purposes.

Ever since I was writing *A New Kind of Science*, I've been fond of quoting the aphorism "the weather has a mind of its own". It sounds so animistic and pre-scientific. But what the Principle of Computational Equivalence says is that actually, according to the most modern science, it's true: the fluid dynamics of the weather is the same in its computational sophistication as the electrical processes that go on in our brains.

But is it "intelligent"? When I talk to people about *A New Kind of Science*, and about AI, I'll often get asked when I think we'll achieve "consciousness" in a machine. Life, intelligence, consciousness: they are all concepts that we have a specific example of, here on Earth. But what are they in general? All life on Earth shares RNA and the structure of cell membranes. But surely that's just because all life we know is part of one connected thread of history; it's not that such details are fundamental to the very concept of life.

And so it is with intelligence. We have only one example we're sure of: us humans. (We're not even sure about animals.) But human intelligence as we experience it is deeply entangled with human civilization, human culture and ultimately also human physiology—even though none of these details are presumably relevant in the abstract definition of intelligence.

We might think about extraterrestrial intelligence. But what the Principle of Computational Equivalence implies is that actually there's "alien intelligence" all around us. But somehow it's just not quite aligned with human intelligence. We might look at rule 30, for example, and be able to see that it's doing sophisticated computation, just like our brains. But somehow it just doesn't seem to have any "point" to what it's doing.

We imagine that in doing the things we humans do, we operate with certain goals or purposes. But rule 30, for example, just seems to be doing what it's doing—just following some definite rule. In the end, though, one realizes we're not so very different. After all, there are definite laws of nature that govern our brains. So anything we do is at some level just playing out those laws.

Any process can actually be described either in terms of mechanism ("the stone is moving according to Newton's laws"), or in terms of goals ("the stone is moving so as to minimize potential energy"). The description in terms of mechanism is usually what's most useful in connecting with science. But the description in terms of goals is usually what's most useful in connecting with human intelligence.

And this is crucial in thinking about AI. We know we can have computational systems whose operations are as sophisticated as anything. But can we get them to do things that are aligned with human goals and purposes?

In a sense this is what I now view as the key problem of AI: it's not about achieving underlying computational sophistication, but instead it's about communicating what we want from this computation.

The Importance of Language

I've spent much of my life as a computer language designer—most importantly creating what is now the Wolfram Language. I'd always seen my role as a language designer being to imagine the possible computations people might want to do, then—like a reductionist scientist—trying to "drill down" to find good primitives from which all these computations could be built up. But somehow from *A New Kind of Science*, and from thinking about AI, I've come to think about it a little differently.

Now what I more see myself as doing is making a bridge between our patterns of human thinking, and what the computational universe is capable of. There are all sorts of amazing things that can in principle be done by computation. But what the language does is to provide a way for us humans to express what we want done, or want to achieve—and then to get this actually executed, as automatically as possible.

Language design has to start from what we know and are familiar with. In the Wolfram Language, we name the built-in primitives with English words, leveraging the meanings that those words have acquired. But the Wolfram Language is not like natural language. It's something more structured, and more powerful. It's based on the words and concepts that we're familiar with through the shared corpus of human knowledge. But it gives us a way to build up arbitrarily sophisticated programs that in effect express arbitrarily complex goals.

Yes, the computational universe is capable of remarkable things. But they're not necessarily things that we humans can describe or relate to. But in building the Wolfram Language my goal is to do the best I can in capturing everything we humans want—and being able to express it in executable computational terms.

When we look at the computational universe, it's hard not to be struck by the limitations of what we know how to describe or think about. Modern neural nets provide an interesting example. For the ImageIdentify function of the Wolfram Language we've trained a neural net to identify thousands of kinds of things in the world. And to cater to our human purposes, what the network ultimately does is to describe what it sees in terms of concepts that we can name with words—tables, chairs, elephants, etc.

But internally what the network is doing is to identify a series of features of any object in the world. Is it green? Is it round? And so on. And what happens as the neural network is trained is that it identifies features it finds useful for distinguishing different kinds of things in the world. But the point is that almost none of these features are ones to which we happen to have assigned words in human language.

Out in the computational universe it's possible to find what may be incredibly useful ways to describe things. But they're alien to us humans. They're not something we know how to express, based on the corpus of knowledge our civilization has developed.

Now of course new concepts are being added to the corpus of human knowledge all the time. Back a century ago, if someone saw a nested pattern they wouldn't have any way to describe it. But now we'd just say "it's a fractal". But the problem is that in the computational universe there's an infinite collection of "potentially useful concepts"—with which we can never hope to ultimately keep up.

The Analogy in Mathematics

When I wrote *A New Kind of Science* I viewed it in no small part as an effort to break away from the use of mathematics—at least as a foundation for science. But one of the things I realized is that the ideas in the book also have a lot of implications for pure mathematics itself.

What is mathematics? Well, it's a study of certain abstract kinds of systems, based on things like numbers and geometry. In a sense it's exploring a small corner of the computational universe of all possible abstract systems. But still, plenty has been done in mathematics: indeed, the 3 million or so published theorems of mathematics represent perhaps the largest single coherent intellectual structure that our species has built.

Ever since Euclid, people have at least notionally imagined that mathematics starts from certain axioms (say, $a+b=b+a$, $a+0=a$, etc.), then builds up derivations of theorems. Why is math hard? The answer is fundamentally rooted in the phenomenon of computational irreducibility —which here is manifest in the fact that there's no general way to shortcut the series of steps needed to derive a theorem. In other words, it can be arbitrarily hard to get a result in mathematics. But worse than that—as Gödel's Theorem showed—there can be mathematical statements where there just aren't any finite ways to prove or disprove them from the axioms. And in such cases, the statements just have to be considered "undecidable".

And in a sense what's remarkable about math is that one can usefully do it at all. Because it could be that most mathematical results one cares about would be undecidable. So why doesn't that happen?

Well, if one considers arbitrary abstract systems it happens a lot. Take a typical cellular automaton—or a Turing machine—and ask whether it's true that the system, say, always settles down to periodic behavior regardless of its initial state. Even something as simple as that will often be undecidable.

So why doesn't this happen in mathematics? Maybe there's something special about the particular axioms used in mathematics. And certainly if one thinks they're the ones that uniquely describe science and the world there might be a reason for that. But one of the whole points of the book is that actually there's a whole computational universe of possible rules that can be useful for doing science and describing the world.

And in fact I don't think there's anything abstractly special about the particular axioms that have traditionally been used in mathematics: I think they're just accidents of history.

What about the theorems that people investigate in mathematics? Again, I think there's a strong historical character to them. For all but the most trivial areas of mathematics, there's a whole sea of undecidability out there. But somehow mathematics picks the islands where theorems can actually be proved—often particularly priding itself on places close to the sea of undecidability where the proof can only be done with great effort.

I've been interested in the whole network of published theorems in mathematics (it's a thing to curate, like wars in history, or properties of chemicals). And one of the things I'm curious about is whether there's an inexorable sequence to the mathematics that's done, or whether, in a sense, random parts are being picked.

And here, I think, there's a considerable analogy to the kind of thing we were discussing before with language. What is a proof? Basically it's a way of explaining to someone why something is true. I've made all sorts of automated proofs in which there are hundreds of steps, each perfectly verifiable by computer. But—like the innards of a neural net—what's going on looks alien and not understandable by a human.

For a human to understand, there have to be familiar "conceptual waypoints". It's pretty much like with words in languages. If some particular part of a proof has a name ("Smith's Theorem"), and has a known meaning, then it's useful to us. But if it's just a lump of undifferentiated computation, it won't be meaningful to us.

In pretty much any axiom system, there's an infinite set of possible theorems. But which ones are "interesting"? That's really a human question. And basically it's going to end up being ones with "stories". In the book I show that for the simple case of basic logic, the theorems that have historically been considered interesting enough to be given names happen to be precisely the ones that are in some sense minimal.

But my guess is that for richer axiom systems pretty much anything that's going to be considered "interesting" is going to have to be reached from things that are already considered interesting. It's like building up words or concepts: you don't get to introduce new ones unless you can directly relate them to existing ones.

In recent years I've wondered quite a bit about how inexorable or not progress is in a field like mathematics. Is there just one historical path that can be taken, say from arithmetic to algebra to the higher reaches of modern mathematics? Or are there an infinite diversity of possible paths, with completely different histories for mathematics?

The answer is going to depend on—in a sense—the "structure of metamathematical space": just what is the network of true theorems that avoid the sea of undecidability? Maybe it'll be different for different fields of mathematics, and some will be more "inexorable" (so it feels like the math is being "discovered") than others (where it seems more like the math is arbitrary, and "invented").

But to me one of the most interesting things is how close—when viewed in these kinds of terms—questions about the nature and character of mathematics end up being to questions about the nature and character of intelligence and AI. And it's this kind of commonality that makes me realize just how powerful and general the ideas in *A New Kind of Science* actually are.

When Is There a Science?

There are some areas of science—like physics and astronomy—where the traditional mathematical approach has done quite well. But there are others—like biology, social science and linguistics—where it's had a lot less to say. And one of the things I've long believed is that what's needed to make progress in these areas is to generalize the kinds of models one's using, to consider a broader range of what's out there in the computational universe.

And indeed in the past 15 or so years there's been increasing success in doing this. And there are lots of biological and social systems, for example, where models have now been constructed using simple programs.

But unlike with mathematical models which can potentially be "solved", these computational models often show computational irreducibility, and are typically used by doing explicit simulations. This can be perfectly successful for making particular predictions, or for applying the models in technology. But a bit like for the automated proofs of mathematical theorems one might still ask, "is this really science?".

Yes, one can simulate what a system does, but does one "understand" it? Well, the problem is that computational irreducibility implies that in some fundamental sense one can't always "understand" things. There might be no useful "story" that can be told; there may be no "conceptual waypoints"—only lots of detailed computation.

Imagine that one's trying to make a science of how the brain understands language—one of the big goals of linguistics. Well, perhaps we'll get an adequate model of the precise rules which determine the firing of neurons or some other low-level representation of the brain. And then we look at the patterns generated in understanding some whole collection of sentences.

Well, what if those patterns look like the behavior of rule 30? Or, closer at hand, the innards of some recurrent neural network? Can we "tell a story" about what's happening? To do so would basically require that we create some kind of higher-level symbolic representation: something where we effectively have words for core elements of what's going on.

But computational irreducibility implies that there may ultimately be no way to create such a thing. Yes, it will always be possible to find patches of computational reducibility, where some things can be said. But there won't be a complete story that can be told. And one might say there won't be a useful reductionistic piece of science to be done. But that's just one of the things that happens when one's dealing with (as the title says) a new kind of science.

Controlling the AIs

People have gotten very worried about AI in recent years. They wonder what's going to happen when AIs "get much smarter" than us humans. Well, the Principle of Computational Equivalence has one piece of good news: at some fundamental level, AIs will never be "smarter"—they'll just be able to do computations that are ultimately equivalent to what our brains do, or, for that matter, what all sorts of simple programs do.

As a practical matter, of course, AIs will be able to process larger amounts of data more quickly than actual brains. And no doubt we'll choose to have them run many aspects of the world for us—from medical devices, to central banks to transportation systems, and much more.

So then it's important to figure how we'll tell them what to do. As soon as we're making serious use of what's out there in the computational universe, we're not going to be able to give a line-by-line description of what the AIs are going to do. Rather, we're going to have to define goals for the AIs, then let them figure out how best to achieve those goals.

In a sense we've already been doing something like this for years in the Wolfram Language. There's some high-level function that describes something you want to do ("lay out a graph", "classify data", etc.). Then it's up to the language to automatically figure out the best way to do it.

And in the end the real challenge is to find a way to describe goals. Yes, you want to search for cellular automata that will make a "nice carpet pattern", or a "good edge detector". But what exactly do those things mean? What you need is a language that a human can use to say as precisely as possible what they mean.

It's really the same problem as I've been talking about a lot here. One has to have a way for humans to be able to talk about things they care about. There's infinite detail out there in the computational universe. But through our civilization and our shared cultural history we've come to identify certain concepts that are important to us. And when we describe our goals, it's in terms of these concepts.

Three hundred years ago people like Leibniz were interested in finding a precise symbolic way to represent the content of human thoughts and human discourse. He was far too early. But now I think we're finally in a position to actually make this work. In fact, we've already gotten a long way with the Wolfram Language in being able to describe real things in the world. And I'm hoping it'll be possible to construct a fairly complete "symbolic discourse language" that lets us talk about the things we care about.

Right now we write legal contracts in "legalese" as a way to make them slightly more precise than ordinary natural language. But with a symbolic discourse language we'll be able to write true "computational contracts" that describe in high-level terms what we want to have happen—and then machines will automatically be able to verify or execute the contract.

But what about the AIs? Well, we need to tell them what we generally want them to do. We need to have a contract with them. Or maybe we need to have a constitution for them. And it'll be written in some kind of symbolic discourse language, that both allows us humans to express what we want, and is executable by the AIs.

There's lots to say about what should be in an AI Constitution, and how the construction of such things might map onto the political and cultural landscape of the world. But one of the obvious questions is: can the constitution be simple, like Asimov's Laws of Robotics?

And here what we know from *A New Kind of Science* tells us the answer: it can't be. In a sense the constitution is an attempt to sculpt what can happen in the world and what can't. But computational irreducibility says that there will be an unbounded collection of cases to consider. For me it's interesting to see how theoretical ideas like computational irreducibility end up impinging on these very practical—and central—societal issues. Yes, it all started with questions about things like the theory of all possible theories. But in the end it turns into issues that everyone in society is going to end up being concerned about.

There's an Endless Frontier

Will we reach the end of science? Will we—or our AIs—eventually invent everything there is to be invented?

For mathematics, it's easy to see that there's an infinite number of possible theorems one can construct. For science, there's an infinite number of possible detailed questions to ask. And there's also an infinite array of possible inventions one can construct.

But the real question is: will there always be interesting new things out there?

Well, computational irreducibility says there will always be new things that need an irreducible amount of computational work to reach from what's already there. So in a sense there'll always be "surprises", that aren't immediately evident from what's come before.

But will it just be like an endless array of different weirdly shaped rocks? Or will there be fundamental new features that appear, that we humans consider interesting?

It's back to the very same issue we've encountered several times before: for us humans to find things "interesting" we have to have a conceptual framework that we can use to think about them. Yes, we can identify a "persistent structure" in a cellular automaton. Then maybe we can start talking about "collisions between structures". But when we just see a whole mess of stuff going on, it's not going to be "interesting" to us unless we have some higher-level symbolic way to talk about it.

In a sense, then, the rate of "interesting discovery" isn't going to be limited by our ability to go out into the computational universe and find things. Instead, it's going to be limited by our ability as humans to build a conceptual framework for what we're finding.

It's a bit like what happened in the whole development of what became *A New Kind of Science*. People had seen related phenomena for centuries if not millennia (distribution of primes, digits of pi, etc.). But without a conceptual framework they just didn't seem "interesting", and nothing was built around them. And indeed as I understand more about what's out there in the computational universe—and even about things I saw long ago there—I gradually build up a conceptual framework that lets me go further.

By the way, it's worth realizing that inventions work a little differently from discoveries. One can see something new happen in the computational universe, and that might be a discovery. But an invention is about figuring out how something can be achieved in the computational universe.

And—like in patent law—it isn't really an invention if you just say "look, this does that". You have to somehow understand a purpose that it's achieving.

In the past, the focus of the process of invention has tended to be on actually getting something to work ("find the lightbulb filament that works", etc.). But in the computational universe, the focus shifts to the question of what you want the invention to do. Because once you've described the goal, finding a way to achieve it is something that can be automated.

That's not to say that it will always be easy. In fact, computational irreducibility implies that it can be arbitrarily difficult. Let's say you know the precise rules by which some chemicals can interact. Can you find a chemical synthesis pathway that will let you get to some particular chemical structure? There may be a way, but computational irreducibility implies that there may be no way to find out how long the pathway may be. And if you haven't found a pathway you may never be sure if it's because there isn't one, or just because you didn't reach it yet.

The Fundamental Theory of Physics

If one thinks about reaching the edge of science, one cannot help but wonder about the fundamental theory of physics. Given everything we've seen in the computational universe, is it conceivable that our physical universe could just correspond to one of those programs out there in the computational universe?

Of course, we won't really know until or unless we find it. But in the years since *A New Kind of Science* appeared, I've become ever more optimistic about the possibilities.

Needless to say, it would be a big change for physics. Today there are basically two major frameworks for thinking about fundamental physics: general relativity and quantum field theory. General relativity is a bit more than 100 years old; quantum field theory maybe 90. And both have achieved spectacular things. But neither has succeeded in delivering us a complete fundamental theory of physics. And if nothing else, I think after all this time, it's worth trying something new.

But there's another thing: from actually exploring the computational universe, we have a huge amount of new intuition about what's possible, even in very simple models. We might have thought that the kind of richness we know exists in physics would require some very elaborate underlying model. But what's become clear is that that kind of richness can perfectly well emerge even from a very simple underlying model.

What might the underlying model be like? I'm not going to discuss this in great detail here, but suffice it to say that I think the most important thing about the model is that it should have as little as possible built in. We shouldn't have the hubris to think we know how the universe is constructed; we should just take a general type of model that's as unstructured as possible, and do what we typically do in the computational universe: just search for a program that does what we want.

My favorite formulation for a model that's as unstructured as possible is a network: just a collection of nodes with connections between them. It's perfectly possible to formulate such a model as an algebraic-like structure, and probably many other kinds of things. But we can think of it as a network. And in the way I've imagined setting it up, it's a network that's somehow "underneath" space and time: every aspect of space and time as we know it must emerge from the actual behavior of the network.

Over the past decade or so there's been increasing interest in things like loop quantum gravity and spin networks. They're related to what I've been doing in the same way that they also involve networks. And maybe there's some deeper relationship. But in their usual formulation, they're much more mathematically elaborate.

From the point of view of the traditional methods of physics, this might seem like a good idea. But with the intuition we have from studying the computational universe—and using it for science and technology—it seems completely unnecessary. Yes, we don't yet know the fundamental theory of physics. But it seems sensible to start with the simplest hypothesis. And that's definitely something like a simple network of the kind I've studied.

At the outset, it'll look pretty alien to people (including myself) trained in traditional theoretical physics. But some of what emerges isn't so alien. A big result I found nearly 20 years ago (that still hasn't been widely understood) is that when you look at a large enough network of the kind I studied you can show that its averaged behavior follows Einstein's equations for gravity. In other words, without putting any fancy physics into the underlying model, it ends up automatically emerging. I think it's pretty exciting.

People ask a lot about quantum mechanics. Yes, my underlying model doesn't build in quantum mechanics (just as it doesn't build in general relativity). Now, it's a little difficult to pin down exactly what the essence of "being quantum mechanical" actually is. But there are some very suggestive signs that my simple networks actually end up showing what amounts to quantum behavior—just like in the physics we know.

OK, so how should one set about actually finding the fundamental theory of physics if it's out there in the computational universe of possible programs? Well, the obvious thing is to just start searching for it, starting with the simplest programs.

I've been doing this—more sporadically than I would like—for the past 15 years or so. And my main discovery so far is that it's actually quite easy to find programs that aren't obviously not our universe. There are plenty of programs where space or time are obviously completely different from the way they are in our universe, or there's some other pathology. But it turns out it's not so difficult to find candidate universes that aren't obviously not our universe.

But we're immediately bitten by computational irreducibility. We can simulate the candidate universe for billions of steps. But we don't know what it's going to do—and whether it's going to grow up to be like our universe, or completely different.

It's pretty unlikely that in looking at that tiny fragment of the very beginning of a universe we're going to ever be able to see anything familiar, like a photon. And it's not at all obvious that we'll be able to construct any kind of descriptive theory, or effective physics. But in a sense the problem is bizarrely similar to the one we have even in systems like neural networks: there's computation going on there, but can we identify "conceptual waypoints" from which we can build up a theory that we might understand?

It's not at all clear our universe has to be understandable at that level, and it's quite possible that for a very long time we'll be left in the strange situation of thinking we might have "found our universe" out in the computational universe, but not being sure.

Of course, we might be lucky, and it might be possible to deduce an effective physics, and see that some little program that we found ends up reproducing our whole universe. It would be a remarkable moment for science. But it would immediately raise a host of new questions—like why this universe, and not another?

Box of a Trillion Souls

Right now us humans exist as biological systems. But in the future it's certainly going to be technologically possible to reproduce all the processes in our brains in some purely digital—computational—form. So insofar as those processes represent "us", we're going to be able to be "virtualized" on pretty much any computational substrate. And in this case we might imagine that the whole future of a civilization could wind up in effect as a "box of a trillion souls".

Inside that box there would be all kinds of computations going on, representing the thoughts and experiences of all those disembodied souls. Those computations would reflect the rich history of our civilization, and all the things that have happened to us. But at some level they wouldn't be anything special.

It's perhaps a bit disappointing, but the Principle of Computational Equivalence tells us that ultimately these computations will be no more sophisticated than the ones that go on in all sorts of other systems—even ones with simple rules, and no elaborate history of civilization. Yes, the details will reflect all that history. But in a sense without knowing what to look for—or what to care about—one won't be able to tell that there's anything special about it.

OK, but what about for the "souls" themselves? Will one be able to understand their behavior by seeing that they achieve certain purposes? Well, in our current biological existence, we have all sorts of constraints and features that give us goals and purposes. But in a virtualized "uploaded" form, most of these just go away.

I've thought quite a bit about how "human" purposes might evolve in such a situation, recognizing, of course, that in virtualized form there's little difference between human and AI. The disappointing vision is that perhaps the future of our civilization consists in disembodied souls in effect "playing videogames" for the rest of eternity.

But what I've slowly realized is that it's actually quite unrealistic to project our view of goals and purposes from our experience today into that future situation. Imagine talking to someone from a thousand years ago and trying to explain that people in the future would be walking on treadmills every day, or continually sending photographs to their friends. The point is that such activities don't make sense until the cultural framework around them has developed.

It's the same story yet again as with trying to characterize what's interesting or what's explainable. It relies on the development of a whole network of conceptual waypoints.

Can we imagine what the mathematics of 100 years from now will be like? It depends on concepts we don't yet know. So similarly if we try to imagine human motivation in the future, it's going to rely on concepts we don't know. Our best description from today's viewpoint might be that those disembodied souls are just "playing videogames". But to them there might be a whole subtle motivation structure that they could only explain by rewinding all sorts of steps in history and cultural development.

By the way, if we know the fundamental theory of physics then in a sense we can make the virtualization complete, at least in principle: we can just run a simulation of the universe for those disembodied souls. Of course, if that's what's happening, then there's no particular reason it has to be a simulation of our particular universe. It could as well be any universe from out in the computational universe.

Now, as I've mentioned, even in any given universe one will never in a sense run out of things to do, or discover. But I suppose I myself at least find it amusing to imagine that at some point those disembodied souls might get bored with just being in a simulated version of our physical universe—and might decide it's more fun (whatever that means to them) to go out and explore the broader computational universe. Which would mean that in a sense the future of humanity would be an infinite voyage of discovery in the context of none other than *A New Kind of Science*!

The Economics of the Computational Universe

Long before we have to think about disembodied human souls, we'll have to confront the issue of what humans should be doing in a world where more and more can be done automatically by AIs. Now in a sense this issue is nothing new: it's just an extension of the long-running story of technology and automation. But somehow this time it feels different.

And I think the reason is in a sense just that there's so much out there in the computational universe, that's so easy to get to. Yes, we can build a machine that automates some particular task. We can even have a general-purpose computer that can be programmed to do a full range of different tasks. But even though these kinds of automation extend what we can do, it still feels like there's effort that we have to put into them.

But the picture now is different—because in effect what we're saying is that if we can just define the goal we want to achieve, then everything else will be automatic. All sorts of computation, and, yes, "thinking", may have to be done, but the idea is that it's just going to happen, without human effort.

At first, something seems wrong. How could we get all that benefit, without putting in more effort? It's a bit like asking how nature could manage to make all the complexity it does—even though when we build artifacts, even with great effort, they end up far less complex. The answer, I think, is it's mining the computational universe. And it's exactly the same thing for us: by mining the computational universe, we can achieve essentially an unbounded level of automation.

If we look at the important resources in today's world, many of them still depend on actual materials. And often these materials are literally mined from the Earth. Of course, there are accidents of geography and geology that determine by whom and where that mining can be done. And in the end there's a limit (if often very large) to the amount of material that'll ever be available.

But when it comes to the computational universe, there's in a sense an inexhaustible supply of material—and it's accessible to anyone. Yes, there are technical issues about how to "do the mining", and there's a whole stack of technology associated with doing it well. But the ultimate resource of the computational universe is a global and infinite one. There's no scarcity and no reason to be "expensive". One just has to understand that it's there, and take advantage of it.

The Path to Computational Thinking

Probably the greatest intellectual shift of the past century has been the one towards the computational way of thinking about things. I've often said that if one picks almost any field "X", from archaeology to zoology, then by now there either is, or soon will be, a field called "computational X"—and it's going to be the future of the field.

I myself have been deeply involved in trying to enable such computational fields, in particular through the development of the Wolfram Language. But I've also been interested in what is essentially the meta problem: how should one teach abstract computational thinking, for example to kids? The Wolfram Language is certainly important as a practical tool. But what about the conceptual, theoretical foundations?

Well, that's where *A New Kind of Science* comes in. Because at its core it's discussing the pure abstract phenomenon of computation, independent of its applications to particular fields or tasks. It's a bit like with elementary mathematics: there are things to teach and understand just to introduce the ideas of mathematical thinking, independent of their specific applications. And so it is too with the core of *A New Kind of Science*. There are things to learn about the computational universe that give intuition and introduce patterns of computational thinking—quite independent of detailed applications.

One can think of it as a kind of "pre computer science" , or "pre computational X". Before one gets into discussing the specifics of particular computational processes, one can just study the simple but pure things one finds in the computational universe.

And, yes, even before kids learn to do arithmetic, it's perfectly possible for them to fill out something like a cellular automaton coloring book—or to execute for themselves or on a computer a whole range of different simple programs. What does it teach? Well, it certainly teaches the idea that there can be definite rules or algorithms for things—and that if one follows them one can create useful and interesting results. And, yes, it helps that systems like cellular automata make obvious visual patterns, that for example one can even find in nature (say on mollusc shells).

As the world becomes more computational—and more things are done by AIs and by mining the computational universe—there's going to be an extremely high value not only in understanding computational thinking, but also in having the kind of intuition that develops from exploring the computational universe and that is, in a sense, the foundation for *A New Kind of Science*.

What's Left to Figure Out?

My goal over the decade that I spent writing *A New Kind of Science* was, as much as possible, to answer all the first round of "obvious questions" about the computational universe. And looking back 15 years later I think that worked out pretty well. Indeed, today, when I wonder about something to do with the computational universe, I find it's incredibly likely that somewhere in the main text or notes of the book I already said something about it.

But one of the biggest things that's changed over the past 15 years is that I've gradually begun to understand more of the implications of what the book describes. There are lots of specific ideas and discoveries in the book. But in the longer term I think what's most significant is how they serve as foundations, both practical and conceptual, for a whole range of new things that one can now understand and explore.

But even in terms of the basic science of the computational universe, there are certainly specific results one would still like to get. For example, it would be great to get more evidence for or against the Principle of Computational Equivalence, and its domain of applicability.

Like most general principles in science, the whole epistemological status of the Principle of Computational Equivalence is somewhat complicated. Is it like a mathematical theorem that can be proved? Is it like a law of nature that might (or might not) be true about the universe? Or is it like a definition, say of the very concept of computation? Well, much like, say, the Second Law of Thermodynamics or Evolution by Natural Selection, it's a combination of these.

But one thing that's significant is that it's possible to get concrete evidence for (or against) the Principle of Computational Equivalence. The principle says that even systems with very simple rules should be capable of arbitrarily sophisticated computation—so that in particular they should be able to act as universal computers.

And indeed one of the results of the book is that this is true for one of the simplest possible cellular automata (rule 110). Five years after the book was published I decided to put up a prize for evidence about another case: the simplest conceivably universal Turing machine. And I was very pleased that in just a few months the prize was won, the Turing machine was proved universal, and there was another piece of evidence for the Principle of Computational Equivalence.

There's a lot to do in developing the applications of *A New Kind of Science*. There are models to be made of all sorts of systems. There's technology to be found. Art to be created. There's also a lot to do in understanding the implications.

But it's important not to forget the pure investigation of the computational universe. In the analogy of mathematics, there are applications to be pursued. But there's also a "pure mathematics" that's worth pursuing in its own right. And so it is with the computational universe: there's a huge amount to explore just at an abstract level. And indeed (as the title of the book implies) there's enough to define a whole new kind of science: a pure science of the computational universe. And it's the opening of that new kind of science that I think is the core achievement of *A New Kind of Science*—and the one of which I am most proud.

What Is Spacetime, Really?

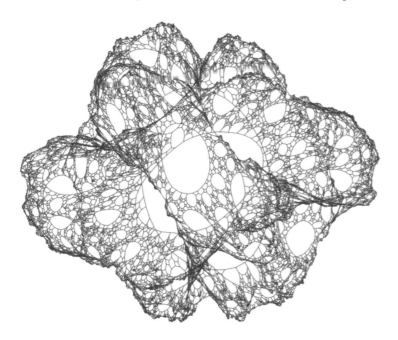

A hundred years ago today Albert Einstein published his General Theory of Relativity—a brilliant, elegant theory that has survived a century, and provides the only successful way we have of describing spacetime.

There are plenty of theoretical indications, though, that General Relativity isn't the end of the story of spacetime. And in fact, much as I like General Relativity as an abstract theory, I've come to suspect it may actually have led us on a century-long detour in understanding the true nature of space and time.

I've been thinking about the physics of space and time for a little more than 40 years now. At the beginning, as a young theoretical physicist, I mostly just assumed Einstein's whole mathematical setup of Special and General Relativity—and got on with my work in quantum field theory, cosmology, etc. on that basis.

But about 35 years ago, partly inspired by my experiences in creating technology, I began to think more deeply about fundamental issues in theoretical science—and started on my long journey to go beyond traditional mathematical equations and instead use computation and programs as basic models in science. Quite soon I made the basic discovery that even very

simple programs can show immensely complex behavior—and over the years I discovered that all sorts of systems could finally be understood in terms of these kinds of programs.

Encouraged by this success, I then began to wonder if perhaps the things I'd found might be relevant to that ultimate of scientific questions: the fundamental theory of physics.

At first, it didn't seem too promising, not least because the models that I'd particularly been studying (cellular automata) seemed to work in a way that was completely inconsistent with what I knew from physics. But sometime in 1988—around the time the first version of Mathematica was released—I began to realize that if I changed my basic way of thinking about space and time then I might actually be able to get somewhere.

A Simple Ultimate Theory?

In the abstract it's far from obvious that there should be a simple, ultimate theory of our universe. Indeed, the history of physics so far might make us doubtful—because it seems as if whenever we learn more, things just get more complicated, at least in terms of the mathematical structures they involve. But—as noted, for example, by early theologians—one very obvious feature of our universe is that there is order in it. The particles in the universe don't just all do their own thing; they follow a definite set of common laws.

But just how simple might the ultimate theory for the universe be? Let's say we could represent it as a program, say in the Wolfram Language. How long would the program be? Would it be as long as the human genome, or as the code for an operating system? Or would it be much, much smaller?

Before my work on the computational universe of simple programs, I would have assumed that if there's a program for the universe it must be at least somewhat complicated. But what I discovered is that in the computational universe even extremely simple programs can actually show behavior as complex as anything (a fact embodied in my general Principle of Computational Equivalence). So then the question arises: could one of these simple programs in the computational universe actually be the program for our physical universe?

The Data Structure of the Universe

But what would such a program be like? One thing is clear: if the program is really going to be extremely simple, it'll be too small to explicitly encode obvious features of our actual universe, like particle masses, or gauge symmetries, or even the number of dimensions of space. Somehow all these things have to emerge from something much lower level and more fundamental.

So if the behavior of the universe is determined by a simple program, what's the basic "data structure" on which this program operates? At first, I'd assumed that it must be something simple for us to describe, like the lattice of cells that exists in a cellular automaton. But even though such a structure works well for models of many things, it seems at best incredibly implausible as a fundamental model of physics. Yes, one can find rules that give behavior which on a large scale doesn't show obvious signs of the lattice. But if there's really going to be a simple model of physics, it seems wrong that such a rigid structure for space should be burned in, while every other feature of physics just emerges.

So what's the alternative? One needs something in a sense "underneath" space: something from which space as we know it can emerge. And one needs an underlying data structure that's as flexible as possible. I thought about this for years, and looked at all sorts of computational and mathematical formalisms. But what I eventually realized was that basically everything I'd looked at could actually be represented in the same way: as a network.

A network—or graph—just consists of a bunch of nodes, joined by connections. And all that's intrinsically defined in the graph is the pattern of these connections.

Space as a Network

So could this be what space is made of? In traditional physics—and General Relativity—one doesn't think of space as being "made of" anything. One just thinks of space as a mathematical construct that serves as a kind of backdrop, in which there's a continuous range of possible positions at which things can be placed.

But do we in fact know that space is continuous like this? In the early days of quantum mechanics, it was actually assumed that space would be quantized like everything else. But it wasn't clear how this could fit in with Special Relativity, and there was no obvious evidence of discreteness. By the time I started doing physics in the 1970s, nobody really talked about discreteness of space anymore, and it was experimentally known that there wasn't discreteness down to about 10^{-18} meters (1/1000 the radius of a proton, or 1 attometer). Forty years— and several tens of billions of dollars' worth of particle accelerators—later there's still no discreteness in space that's been seen, and the limit is about 10^{-22} meters (or 100 yoctometers).

Still, there's long been a suspicion that something has to be quantized about space down at the Planck length of about 10^{-34} meters. But when people have thought about this—and discussed spin networks or loop quantum gravity or whatever—they've tended to assume that whatever happens there has to be deeply connected to the formalism of quantum mechanics, and to the notion of quantum amplitudes for things.

But what if space—perhaps at something like the Planck scale—is just a plain old network, with no explicit quantum amplitudes or anything? It doesn't sound so impressive or mysterious—but it certainly takes a lot less information to specify such a network: you just have to say which nodes are connected to which other ones.

But how could this be what space is made of? First of all, how could the apparent continuity of space on larger scales emerge? Actually, that's not very difficult: it can just be a consequence of having lots of nodes and connections. It's a bit like what happens in a fluid, like water. On a small scale, there are a bunch of discrete molecules bouncing around. But the large-scale effect of all these molecules is to produce what seems to us like a continuous fluid.

It so happens that I studied this phenomenon a lot in the mid-1980s—as part of my efforts to understand the origins of apparent randomness in fluid turbulence. And in particular I showed that even when the underlying "molecules" are cells in a simple cellular automaton, it's possible to get large-scale behavior that exactly follows the standard differential equations of fluid flow.

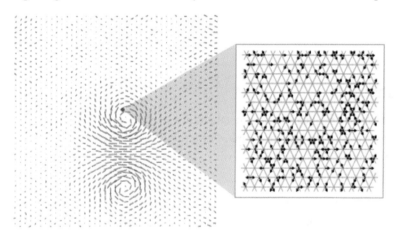

So when I started thinking about the possibility that underneath space there might be a network, I imagined that perhaps the same methods might be used—and that it might actually be possible to derive Einstein's Equations of General Relativity from something much lower level.

Maybe There's Nothing But Space

But, OK, if space is a network, what about all the stuff that's in space? What about all the electrons, and quarks and photons, and so on? In the usual formulation of physics, space is a backdrop, on top of which all the particles, or strings, or whatever, exist. But that gets pretty complicated. And there's a simpler possibility: maybe in some sense everything in the universe is just "made of space".

As it happens, in his later years, Einstein was quite enamored of this idea. He thought that perhaps particles, like electrons, could be associated with something like black holes that contain nothing but space. But within the formalism of General Relativity, Einstein could never get this to work, and the idea was largely dropped.

As it happens, nearly 100 years earlier there'd been somewhat similar ideas. That was a time before Special Relativity, when people still thought that space was filled with a fluid-like ether. (Ironically enough, in modern times we're back to thinking of space as filled with a background Higgs field, vacuum fluctuations in quantum fields, and so on.) Meanwhile, it had been understood that there were different types of discrete atoms, corresponding to the different chemical elements. And so it was suggested (notably by Kelvin) that perhaps these different types of atoms might all be associated with different types of knots in the ether.

It was an interesting idea. But it wasn't right. But in thinking about space as a network, there's a related idea: maybe particles just correspond to particular structures in the network. Maybe all that has to exist in the universe is the network, and then the matter in the universe just corresponds to particular features of this network. It's easy to see similar things in cellular automata on a lattice. Even though every cell follows the same simple rules, there are definite structures that exist in the system—and that behave quite like particles, with a whole particle physics of interactions.

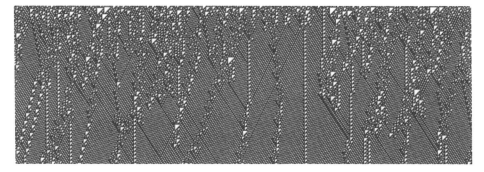

There's a whole discussion to be had about how this works in networks. But first, there's something else that's very important to talk about: time.

What Is Time?

Back in the 1800s, there was space and there was time. Both were described by coordinates, and in some mathematical formalisms, both appeared in related ways. But there was no notion that space and time were in any sense "the same thing". But then along came Einstein's Special Theory of Relativity—and people started talking about "spacetime", in which space and time are somehow facets of the same thing.

It makes a lot of sense in the formalism of Special Relativity, in which, for example, traveling at a different velocity is like rotating in 4-dimensional spacetime. And for about a century, physics has pretty much just assumed that spacetime is a thing, and that space and time aren't in any fundamental way different.

So how does that work in the context of a network model of space? It's certainly possible to construct 4-dimensional networks in which time works just like space. And then one just has to say that the history of the universe corresponds to some particular spacetime network (or family of networks). Which network it is must be determined by some kind of constraint: our universe is the one which has such-and-such a property, or in effect satisfies such-and-such an equation. But this seems very non-constructive: it's not telling one how the universe behaves, it's just saying that if the behavior looks like this, then it can be the universe.

And, for example, in thinking about programs, space and time work very differently. In a cellular automaton, for example, the cells are laid out in space, but the behavior of the system occurs in a sequence of steps in time. But here's the thing: just because the underlying rules treat space and time very differently, it doesn't mean that on a large scale they can't effectively behave similarly, just like in current physics.

Evolving the Network

OK, so let's say that underneath space there's a network. How does this network evolve? A simple hypothesis is to assume that there's some kind of local rule, which says, in effect that if you see a piece of network that looks like this, replace it with one that looks like that.

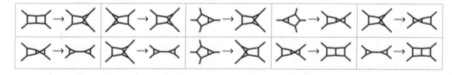

But now things get a bit complicated. Because there might be lots of places in the network where the rule could apply. So what determines in which order each piece is handled?

In effect, each possible ordering is like a different thread of time. And one could imagine a theory in which all threads are followed—and the universe in effect has many histories.

But that doesn't need to be how it works. Instead, it's perfectly possible for there to be just one thread of time—pretty much the way we experience it. And to understand this, we have to do something a bit similar to what Einstein did in formulating Special Relativity: we have to make a more realistic model of what an "observer" can be.

Needless to say, any realistic observer has to exist within our universe. So if the universe is a network, the observer must be just some part of that network. Now think about all those little network updatings that are happening. To "know" that a given update has happened, observers themselves must be updated.

If you trace this all the way through—as I did in my book, *A New Kind of Science*—you realize that the only thing observers can ever actually observe in the history of the universe is the causal network of what event causes what other event.

And then it turns out that there's a definite class of underlying rules for which different orderings of underlying updates don't affect that causal network. They're what I call "causal invariant" rules.

Causal invariance is an interesting property, with analogs in a variety of computational and mathematical systems—for example in the fact that transformations in algebra can be applied in any order and still give the same final result. But in the context of the universe, its consequence is that it guarantees that there's only one thread of time in the universe.

Deriving Special Relativity

So what about spacetime and Special Relativity? Here, as I figured out in the mid-1990s, something exciting happens: as soon as there's causal invariance, it basically follows that there'll be Special Relativity on a large scale. In other words, even though at the lowest level space and time are completely different kinds of things, on a larger scale they get mixed together in exactly the way prescribed by Special Relativity.

Roughly what happens is that different "reference frames" in Special Relativity—corresponding, for example, to traveling at different velocities—correspond to different detailed sequencings of the low-level updates in the network. But because of causal invariance, the overall behavior associated with these different detailed sequences is the same—so that the system follows the principles of Special Relativity.

At the beginning it might have looked hopeless: how could a network that treats space and time differently end up with Special Relativity? But it works out. And actually, I don't know of any other model in which one can successfully derive Special Relativity from something lower level; in modern physics it's always just inserted as a given.

Deriving General Relativity

OK, so one can derive Special Relativity from simple models based on networks. What about General Relativity—which, after all, is what we're celebrating today? Here the news is very good too: subject to various assumptions, I managed in the late 1990s to derive Einstein's Equations from the dynamics of networks.

The whole story is somewhat complicated. But here's roughly how it goes. First, we have to think about how a network actually represents space. Now remember, the network is just a collection of nodes and connections. The nodes don't say how they're laid out in one-dimensional, two-dimensional, or any-dimensional space.

It's easy to see that there are networks that on a large scale seem, say, two-dimensional, or three-dimensional. And actually, there's a simple test for the effective dimension of a network. Just start from a node, then look at all nodes that are up to r connections away. If the network is behaving like it's d-dimensional, then the number of nodes in that "ball" will be about r^d.

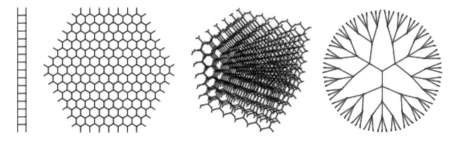

Here's where things start to get really interesting. If the network behaves like flat d-dimensional space, then the number of nodes will always be close to r^d. But if it behaves like curved space, as in General Relativity, then there's a correction term, that's proportional to a mathematical object called the Ricci scalar. And that's interesting, because the Ricci scalar is precisely something that occurs in Einstein's Equations.

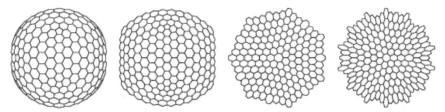

There's lots of mathematical complexity here. One has to look at shortest paths—or geodesics—in the network. One has to see how to do everything not just in space, but in networks evolving in time. And one has to understand how the large-scale limits of networks work.

In deriving mathematical results, it's important to be able to take certain kinds of averages. It's actually very much the same kind of thing needed to derive fluid equations from dynamics of molecules: one needs to be able to assume a certain degree of effective randomness in low-level interactions to justify the taking of averages.

But the good news is that an incredible range of systems, even with extremely simple rules, work a bit like the digits of pi, and generate what seems for all practical purposes random. And the result is that even though the details of a causal network are completely determined once one knows the network one's starting from, many of these details will appear effectively random.

So here's the final result. If one assumes effective microscopic randomness, and one assumes that the behavior of the overall system does not lead to a change in overall limiting dimensions, then it follows that the large-scale behavior of the system satisfies Einstein's Equations!

I think this is pretty exciting. From almost nothing, it's possible to derive Einstein's Equations. Which means that these simple networks reproduce the features of gravity that we know in current physics.

There are all sorts of technical things to say, not suitable for this general blog. Quite a few of them I already said long ago in *A New Kind of Science*—and particularly the notes at the back.

A few things are perhaps worth mentioning here. First, it's worth noting that my underlying networks not only have no embedding in ordinary space intrinsically defined, but also don't intrinsically define topological notions like inside and outside. All these things have to emerge.

When it comes to deriving the Einstein Equations, one creates Ricci tensors by looking at geodesics in the network, and looking at the growth rates of balls that start from each point on the geodesic.

The Einstein Equations one gets are the vacuum Einstein Equations. But just like with gravitational waves, one can effectively separate off features of space considered to be associated with "matter", and then get Einstein's full Equations, complete with "matter" energy-momentum terms.

As I write this, I realize how easily I still fall into technical "physics speak". (I think it must be that I learned physics when I was so young...) But suffice it to say that at a high level the exciting thing is that from the simple idea of networks and causal invariant replacement rules, it's possible to derive the Equations of General Relativity. One puts remarkably little in, yet one gets out that remarkable beacon of 20th-century physics: General Relativity.

Particles, Quantum Mechanics, etc.

It's wonderful to be able to derive General Relativity. But that's not all of physics. Another very important part is quantum mechanics. It's going to get me too far afield to talk about this in detail here, but presumably particles—like electrons or quarks or Higgs bosons—must exist as certain special regions in the network. In qualitative terms, they might not be that different from Kelvin's "knots in the ether".

But then their behavior must follow the rules we know from quantum mechanics—or more particularly, quantum field theory. A key feature of quantum mechanics is that it can be formulated in terms of multiple paths of behavior, each associated with a certain quantum amplitude. I haven't figured it all out, but there's definitely a hint of something like this going on when one looks at the evolution of a network with many possible underlying sequences of replacements.

My network-based model doesn't have official quantum amplitudes in it. It's more like (but not precisely like) a classical, if effectively probabilistic, model. And for 50 years people have almost universally assumed that there's a crippling problem with models like that. Because there's a theorem (Bell's Theorem) that says that unless there's instantaneous non-local propagation of information, no such "hidden variables" model can reproduce the quantum mechanical results that are observed experimentally.

But there's an important footnote. It's pretty clear what "non-locality" means in ordinary space with a definite dimension. But what about in a network? Here it's a different story. Because everything is just defined by connections. And even though the network may mostly correspond on a large scale to 3D space, it's perfectly possible for there to be "threads" that join what would otherwise be quite separated regions. And the tantalizing thing is that there are indications that exactly such threads can be generated by particle-like structures propagating in the network.

Searching for the Universe

OK, so it's conceivable that some network-based model might be able to reproduce things from current physics. How might we set about finding such a model that actually reproduces our exact universe?

The traditional instinct would be to start from existing physics, and try to reverse engineer rules that could reproduce it. But is that the only way? What about just starting to enumerate possible rules, and seeing if any of them turn out to be our universe?

Before studying the computational universe of simple programs I would have assumed that this would be crazy: that there's no way the rules for our universe could be simple enough to find by this kind of enumeration. But after seeing what's out there in the computational universe—and seeing some other examples where amazing things were found just by a search—I've changed my mind.

So what happens if one actually starts doing such a search? Here's the zoo of networks one gets after a fairly small number of steps by using all possible underlying rules of a certain very simple type:

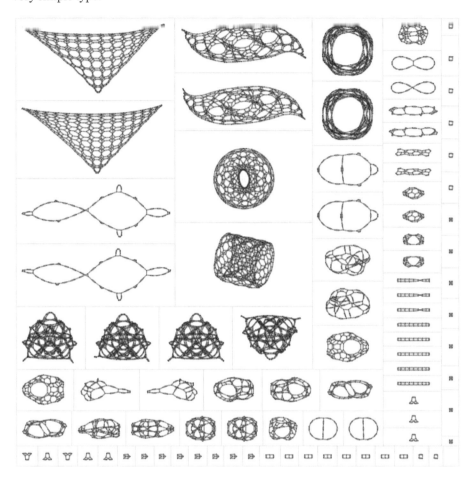

Some of these networks very obviously aren't our universe. They just freeze after a few steps, so time effectively stops. Or they have far too simple a structure for space. Or they effectively have an infinite number of dimensions. Or other pathologies.

But the exciting thing is that remarkably quickly one finds rules that aren't obviously not our universe. Telling if they actually are our universe is a difficult matter. Because even if one simulates lots of steps, it can be arbitrarily difficult to know whether the behavior they're showing is what one would expect in the early moments of a universe that follows the laws of physics as we know them.

There are plenty of encouraging features, though. For example, these universes can start from effectively infinite numbers of dimensions, then gradually settle to a finite number of dimensions—potentially removing the need for explicit inflation in the early universe.

And at a higher level, it's worth remembering that if the models one's using are simple enough, there's a big distance between "neighboring models", so it's likely one will either reproduce known physics exactly, or be very wide of the mark.

In the end, though, one needs to reproduce not just the rule, but also the initial condition for the universe. But once one has that, one will in principle know the exact evolution of the universe. So does that mean one would immediately be able to figure out everything about the universe? Absolutely not. Because of the phenomenon I call "computational irreducibility"—which implies that even though one may know the rule and initial condition for a system, it can still require an irreducible amount of computational work to trace through every step in the behavior of the system to find out what it does.

Still, the possibility exists that one could just find a simple rule—and initial condition—that one could hold up and say, "This is our universe!" We'd have found our universe in the computational universe of all possible universes.

Of course this would be an exciting day for science.

But it would raise plenty of other questions. Like: why this rule, and not another? And why should our particular universe have a rule that shows up early enough in our list of all possible universes that we could actually find it just by enumeration?

One might think that it'd just be something about us being in this universe, and that causing us to choose an enumeration which makes it come up early. But my current guess is that it'd be something much more bizarre, such as that with respect to observers in a universe, all of a large class of nontrivial possible universe rules are actually equivalent, so one could pick any of them and get the exact same results, just in a different way.

OK, Show Me the Universe

But these are all speculations. And until we actually find a serious candidate rule for our universe, it's probably not worth discussing these things much.

So, OK. Where are we at with all this right now? Most of what I've said here I had actually figured out by around 1999—several years before I finished *A New Kind of Science*. And though it was described in simple language rather than physics-speak, I managed to cover the highlights of it in Chapter 9 of the book—giving some of the technical details in the notes at the back.

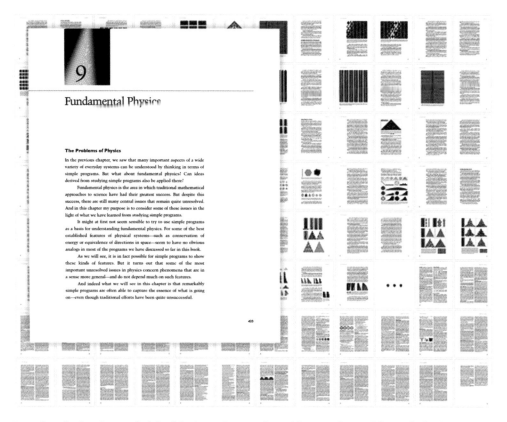

But after the book was finished in 2002, I started working on the problem of physics again. I found it a bit amusing to say I had a computer in my basement that was searching for the fundamental theory of physics. But that really was what it was doing: enumerating possible rules of certain types, and trying to see if their behavior satisfied certain criteria that could make them plausible as models of physics.

I was pretty organized in what I did, getting intuition from simplified cases, then systematically going through more realistic cases. There were lots of technical issues. Like being able to visualize large evolving sequences of graphs. Or being able to quickly recognize subtle regularities that revealed that something couldn't be our actual universe.

I accumulated the equivalent of thousands of pages of results, and was gradually beginning to get an understanding of the basic science of what systems based on networks can do.

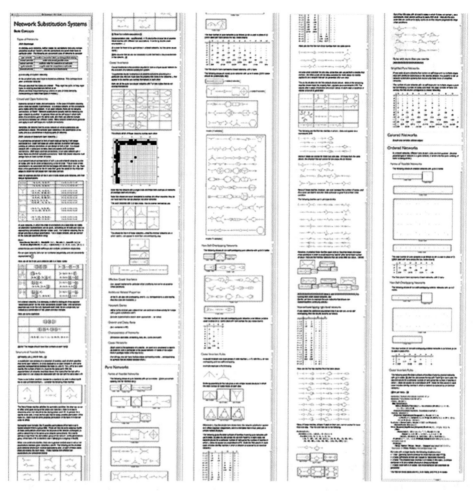

In a sense, though, this was always just a hobby, done alongside my "day job" of leading our company and its technology development. And there was another "distraction". For many years I had been interested in the problem of computational knowledge, and in building an engine that could comprehensively embody it. And as a result of my work on *A New Kind of Science,* I became convinced that this might be actually be possible—and that this might be the right decade to do it.

By 2005 it was clear that it was indeed possible, and so I decided to devote myself to actually doing it. The result was Wolfram|Alpha. And once Wolfram|Alpha was launched it became clear that even more could be done—and I have spent what I think has probably been my most productive decade ever building a huge tower of ideas and technology, which has now made possible the Wolfram Language and much more.

To Do Physics, or Not to Do Physics?

But over the course of that decade, I haven't been doing physics. And when I now look at my filesystem, I see a large number of notebooks about physics, all nicely laid out with the things I figured out—and all left abandoned and untouched since the beginning of 2005

Should I get back to the physics project? I definitely want to. Though there are also other things I want to do.

I've spent most of my life working on very large projects. And I work hard to plan what I'm going to do, usually starting to think about projects decades ahead of actually doing them. Sometimes I'll avoid a project because the ambient technology or infrastructure to do it just isn't ready yet. But once I embark on a project, I commit myself to finding a way make it succeed, even if it takes many years of hard work to do so.

Finding the fundamental theory of physics, though, is a project of a rather different character than I've done before. In a sense its definition of success is much harsher: one either solves the problem and finds the theory, or one doesn't. Yes, one could explore lots of interesting abstract features of the type of theory one's constructing (as string theory has done). And quite likely such an investigation will have interesting spinoffs.

But unlike building a piece of technology, or exploring an area of science, the definition of the project isn't under one's control. It's defined by our universe. And it could be that I'm simply wrong about how our universe works. Or it could be that I'm right, but there's too deep a barrier of computational irreducibility for us to know.

One might also worry that one would find what one thinks is the universe, but never be sure. I'm actually not too worried about this. I think there are enough clues from existing physics—as well as from anomalies attributed to things like dark matter—that one will be able to tell quite definitively if one has found the correct theory. It'll be neat if one can make an immediate prediction that can be verified. But by the time one's reproducing all the seemingly arbitrary masses of particles, and other known features of physics, one will be pretty sure one has the correct theory.

It's been interesting over the years to ask my friends whether I should work on fundamental physics. I get three dramatically different kinds of responses.

The first is simply, "You've got to do it!" They say that the project is the most exciting and important thing one can imagine, and they can't see why I'd wait another day before starting on it.

The second class of responses is basically, "Why would you do it?" Then they say something like, "Why don't you solve the problem of artificial intelligence, or molecular construction, or biological immortality, or at least build a giant multibillion-dollar company? Why do something abstract and theoretical when you can do something practical to change the world?"

There's also a third class of responses, which I suppose my knowledge of the history of science should make me expect. It's typically from physicist friends, and typically it's some combination of, "Don't waste your time working on that!" and, "Please don't work on that."

The fact is that the current approach to fundamental physics—through quantum field theory—is nearly 90 years old. It's had its share of successes, but it hasn't brought us the fundamental theory of physics. But for most physicists today, the current approach is almost the definition of physics. So when they think about what I've been working on, it seems quite alien—like it isn't really physics.

And some of my friends will come right out and say, "I hope you don't succeed, because then all that work we've done is wasted." Well, yes, some work will be wasted. But that's a risk you take when you do a project where in effect nature decides what's right. But I have to say that even if one can find a truly fundamental theory of physics, there's still plenty of use for what's been done with standard quantum field theory, for example in figuring out phenomena at the scale where we can do experiments with particle accelerators today.

What Will It Take?

So, OK, if I mounted a project to try to find the fundamental theory of physics, what would I actually do? It's a complex project, that'll need not just me, but a diverse team of talented other people too.

Whether or not it ultimately works, I think it'll be quite interesting to watch—and I'd plan to do it as "spectator science", making it as educational and accessible as possible. (Certainly that would be a pleasant change from the distraction-avoiding hermit mode in which I worked on *A New Kind of Science* for a decade.)

Of course I don't know how difficult the project is, or whether it will even work at all. Ultimately that depends on what's true about our universe. But based on what I did a decade ago, I have a clear plan for how to get started, and what kind of team I have to put together.

It's going to need both good scientists and good technologists. There's going to be lots of algorithm development for things like network evolution, and for analysis. I'm sure it'll need abstract graph theory, modern geometry and probably group theory and other kinds of abstract algebra too. And I won't be surprised if it needs lots of other areas of math and theoretical computer science as well.

It'll need serious, sophisticated physics—with understanding of the upper reaches of quantum field theory and perhaps string theory and things like spin networks. It's also likely to need methods that come from statistical physics and the modern theoretical frameworks around it. It'll need an understanding of General Relativity and cosmology. And—if things go well—it'll need an understanding of a diverse range of physics experiments.

There'll be technical challenges too—like figuring out how to actually run giant network computations, and collect and visualize their results. But I suspect the biggest challenges will be in building the tower of new theory and understanding that's needed to study the kinds of network systems I want to investigate. There'll be useful support from existing fields. But in the end, I suspect this is going to require building a substantial new intellectual structure that won't look much like anything that's been done before.

Is It the Right Time?

Is it the right time to actually try doing this project? Maybe one should wait until computers are bigger and faster. Or certain areas of mathematics have advanced further. Or some more issues in physics have been clarified.

I'm not sure. But nothing I have seen suggests that there are any immediate roadblocks—other than putting the effort and resources into trying to do it. And who knows: maybe it will be easier than we think, and we'll look back and wonder why it wasn't tried long ago.

One of the key realizations that led to General Relativity 100 years ago was that Euclid's fifth postulate ("parallel lines never cross") might not be true in our actual universe, so that curved space is possible. But if my suspicions about space and the universe are correct, then it means there's actually an even more basic problem in Euclid—with his very first definitions. Because if there's a discrete network "underneath" space, then Euclid's assumptions about points and lines that can exist anywhere in space simply aren't correct.

General Relativity is a great theory—but we already know that it cannot be the final theory. And now we have to wonder how long it will be before we actually know the final theory. I'm hoping it won't be too long. And I'm hoping that before too many more anniversaries of General Relativity have gone by we'll finally know what spacetime really is.

THE FOUNDATIONS

Excerpted from
A New Kind of Science (2002)

Fundamental Physics

The Problems of Physics

In the previous chapter, we saw that many important aspects of a wide variety of everyday systems can be understood by thinking in terms of simple programs. But what about fundamental physics? Can ideas derived from studying simple programs also be applied there?

Fundamental physics is the area in which traditional mathematical approaches to science have had their greatest success. But despite this success, there are still many central issues that remain quite unresolved. And in this chapter my purpose is to consider some of these issues in the light of what we have learned from studying simple programs.

It might at first not seem sensible to try to use simple programs as a basis for understanding fundamental physics. For some of the best established features of physical systems—such as conservation of energy or equivalence of directions in space—seem to have no obvious analogs in most of the programs we have discussed so far in this book.

As we will see, it is in fact possible for simple programs to show these kinds of features. But it turns out that some of the most important unresolved issues in physics concern phenomena that are in a sense more general—and do not depend much on such features.

And indeed what we will see in this chapter is that remarkably simple programs are often able to capture the essence of what is going on—even though traditional efforts have been quite unsuccessful.

Thus, for example, in the early part of this chapter I will discuss the so-called Second Law of Thermodynamics or Principle of Entropy Increase: the observation that many physical systems tend to become irreversibly more random as time progresses. And I will show that the essence of such behavior can readily be seen in simple programs.

More than a century has gone by since the Second Law was first formulated. Yet despite many detailed results in traditional physics, its origins have remained quite mysterious. But what we will see in this chapter is that by studying the Second Law in the context of simple programs, we will finally be able to get a clear understanding of why it so often holds—as well as of when it may not.

My approach in investigating issues like the Second Law is in effect to use simple programs as metaphors for physical systems. But can such programs in fact be more than that? And for example is it conceivable that at some level physical systems actually operate directly according to the rules of a simple program?

Looking at the laws of physics as we know them today, this might seem absurd. For at first the laws might seem much too complicated to correspond to any simple program. But one of the crucial discoveries of this book is that even programs with very simple underlying rules can yield great complexity.

And so it could be with fundamental physics. Underneath the laws of physics as we know them today it could be that there lies a very simple program from which all the known laws—and ultimately all the complexity we see in the universe—emerges.

To suppose that our universe is in essence just a simple program is certainly a bold hypothesis. But in the second part of this chapter I will describe some significant progress that I have made in investigating this hypothesis, and in working out the details of what kinds of simple programs might be involved.

There is still some distance to go. But from what I have found so far I am extremely optimistic that by using the ideas of this book the most fundamental problem of physics—and one of the ultimate problems of all of science—may finally be within sight of being solved.

The Notion of Reversibility

At any particular step in the evolution of a system like a cellular automaton the underlying rule for the system tells one how to proceed to the next step. But what if one wants to go backwards? Can one deduce from the arrangement of black and white cells at a particular step what the arrangement of cells must have been on previous steps?

All current evidence suggests that the underlying laws of physics have this kind of reversibility. So this means that given a sufficiently precise knowledge of the state of a physical system at the present time, it is therefore possible to deduce not only what the system will do in the future, but also what it did in the past.

In the first cellular automaton shown below it is also straightforward to do this. For any cell that has one color at a particular step must always have had the opposite color on the step before.

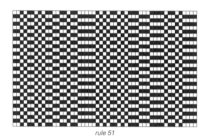 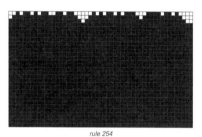

rule 51   *rule 254*

Examples of cellular automata that are and are not reversible. Rule 51 is reversible, so that it preserves enough information to allow one to go backwards from any particular step as well as forwards. Rule 254 is not reversible, since it always evolves to uniform black and preserves no information about the arrangement of cells on earlier steps.

But the second cellular automaton works differently, and does not allow one to go backwards. For after just a few steps, it makes every cell black, regardless of what it was before—with the result that there is no way to tell what color might have occurred on previous steps.

There are many examples of systems in nature which seem to organize themselves a little like the second case above. And indeed the conflict between this and the known reversibility of underlying laws of physics is related to the subject of the next section in this chapter.

But my purpose here is to explore what kinds of systems can be reversible. And of the 256 elementary cellular automata with two colors and nearest-neighbor rules, only the six shown below turn out to be reversible. And as the pictures demonstrate, all of these exhibit fairly trivial behavior, in which only rather simple transformations are ever made to the initial configuration of cells.

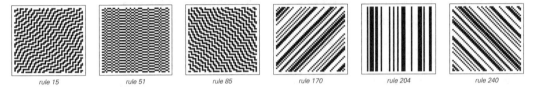

| rule 15 | rule 51 | rule 85 | rule 170 | rule 204 | rule 240 |

Examples of the behavior of the six elementary cellular automata that are reversible. In all cases the transformations made to the initial conditions are simple enough that it is straightforward to go backwards as well as forwards in the evolution.

So is it possible to get more complex behavior while maintaining reversibility? There are a total of 7,625,597,484,987 cellular automata with three colors and nearest-neighbor rules, and searching through these one finds just 1800 that are reversible. Of these 1800, many again exhibit simple behavior, much like the pictures above. But some exhibit more complex behavior, as in the pictures below.

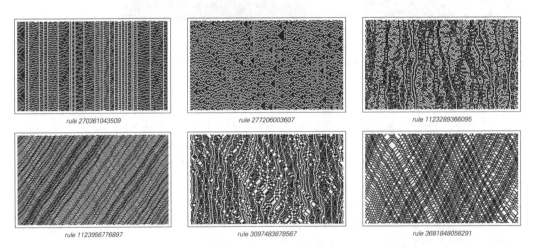

| rule 270361043509 | rule 277206003607 | rule 1123289366095 |
| rule 1123956776897 | rule 3097483878567 | rule 3681848058291 |

Examples of some of the 1800 reversible cellular automata with three colors and nearest-neighbor rules. Even though these systems exhibit complex behavior that scrambles the initial conditions, all of them are still reversible, so that starting from the configuration of cells at the bottom of each picture, it is always possible to deduce the configurations on all previous steps.

How can one now tell that such systems are reversible? It is no longer true that their evolution leads only to simple transformations of the initial conditions. But one can still check that starting with the specific configuration of cells at the bottom of each picture, one can evolve backwards to get to the top of the picture. And given a particular rule it turns out to be fairly straightforward to do a detailed analysis that allows one to prove or disprove its reversibility.

But in trying to understand the range of behavior that can occur in reversible systems it is often convenient to consider classes of cellular automata with rules that are specifically constructed to be reversible. One such class is illustrated below. The idea is to have rules that explicitly remain the same even if they are turned upside-down, thereby interchanging the roles of past and future.

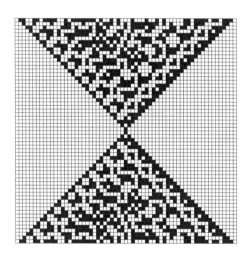

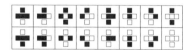

An example of a cellular automaton that is explicitly set up to be reversible. The rule for the system remains unchanged if all its elements are turned upside-down—effectively interchanging the roles of past and future. Patterns produced by the rule must exhibit the same time reversal symmetry, as shown on the left. The specific rule used here is based on taking elementary rule 214, then adding the specification that the new color of a cell should be inverted whenever the cell was black two steps back. Note that by allowing a total of four rather than two colors, a version of the rule that depends only on the immediately preceding step can be constructed.

Such rules can be constructed by taking ordinary cellular automata and adding dependence on colors two steps back.

The resulting rules can be run both forwards and backwards. In each case they require knowledge of the colors of cells on not one but two successive steps. Given this knowledge, however, the rules can be used to determine the configuration of cells on either future or past steps.

The next two pages show examples of the behavior of such cellular automata with both random and simple initial conditions.

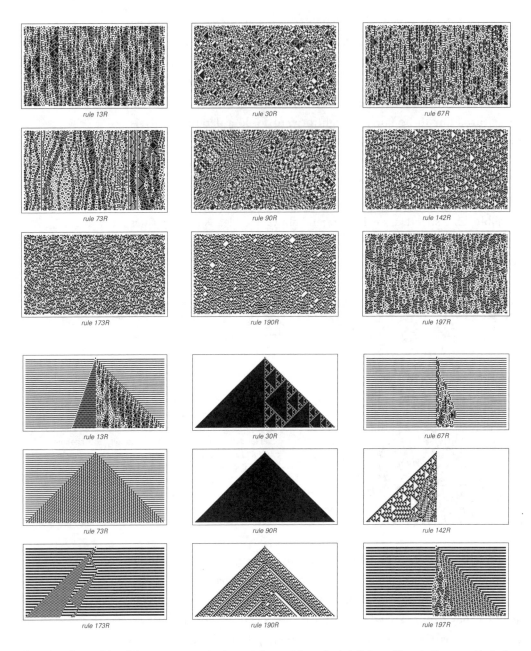

Examples of reversible cellular automata starting from random and from simple initial conditions. In the upper block of pictures, every cell is chosen to be black or white with equal probability on the two successive first steps. In the lower block of pictures, only the center cell is taken to be black on these steps.

rule 150R

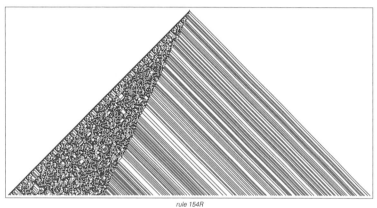

rule 154R

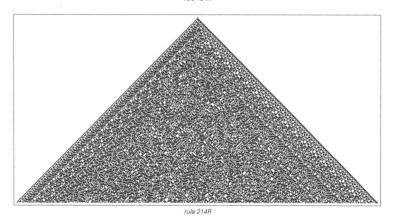

rule 214R

The evolution of three reversible cellular automata for 300 steps. In the first case, a regular nested pattern is obtained. In the other cases, the patterns show many features of randomness.

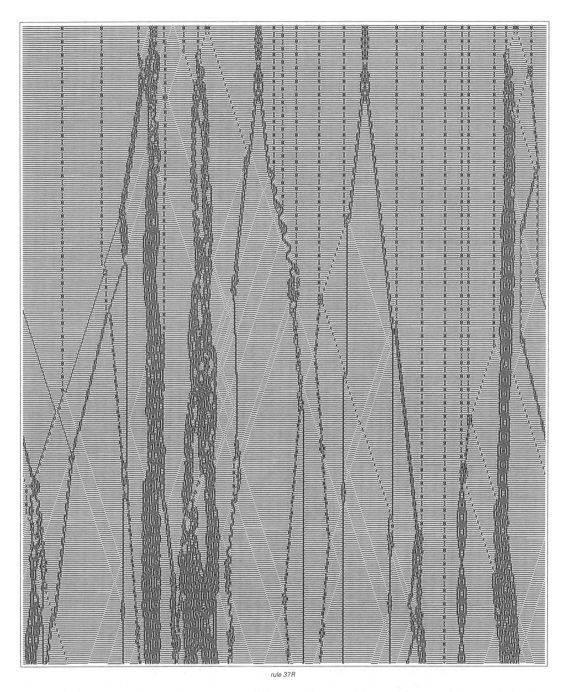

rule 37R

An example of a reversible cellular automaton whose evolution supports localized structures. Because of the reversibility of the underlying rule, every collision must be able to occur equally well when its initial and final states are interchanged.

In some cases, the behavior is fairly simple, and the patterns obtained have simple repetitive or nested structures. But in many cases, even with simple initial conditions, the patterns produced are highly complex, and seem in many respects random.

The reversibility of the underlying rules has some obvious consequences, such as the presence of triangles pointing sideways but not down. But despite their reversibility, the rules still manage to produce the kinds of complex behavior that we have seen in cellular automata and many other systems throughout this book.

So what about localized structures?

The picture on the facing page demonstrates that these can also occur in reversible systems. There are some constraints on the details of the kinds of collisions that are possible, but reversible rules typically tend to work very much like ordinary ones.

So in the end it seems that even though only a very small fraction of possible systems have the property of being reversible, such systems can still exhibit behavior just as complex as one sees anywhere else.

Irreversibility and the Second Law of Thermodynamics

All the evidence we have from particle physics and elsewhere suggests that at a fundamental level the laws of physics are precisely reversible. Yet our everyday experience is full of examples of seemingly irreversible phenomena. Most often, what happens is that a system which starts in a fairly regular or organized state becomes progressively more and more random and disorganized. And it turns out that this phenomenon can already be seen in many simple programs.

The picture at the top of the next page shows an example based on a reversible cellular automaton of the type discussed in the previous section. The black cells in this system act a little like particles which bounce around inside a box and interact with each other when they collide.

At the beginning the particles are placed in a simple arrangement at the center of the box. But over the course of time the picture shows that the arrangement of particles becomes progressively more random.

A reversible cellular automaton that exhibits seemingly irreversible behavior. Starting from an initial condition in which all black cells or particles lie at the center of a box, the distribution becomes progressively more random. Such behavior appears to be the central phenomenon responsible for the Second Law of Thermodynamics. The specific cellular automaton used here is rule 122R. The system is restricted to a region of size 100 cells.

Typical intuition from traditional science makes it difficult to understand how such randomness could possibly arise. But the discovery in this book that a wide range of systems can generate randomness even with very simple initial conditions makes it seem considerably less surprising.

But what about reversibility? The underlying rules for the cellular automaton used in the picture above are precisely reversible. Yet the picture itself does not at first appear to be at all reversible. For there appears to be an irreversible increase in randomness as one goes down successive panels on the page.

The resolution of this apparent conflict is however fairly straightforward. For as the picture on the facing page demonstrates, if the

An extended version of the picture on the facing page, in which the reversibility of the underlying cellular automaton is more clearly manifest. An initial condition is carefully constructed so that halfway through the evolution shown a simple arrangement of particles will be produced. If one starts with this arrangement, then the randomness of the system will effectively increase whether one goes forwards or backwards in time from that point.

simple arrangement of particles occurs in the middle of the evolution, then one can readily see that randomness increases in exactly the same way—whether one goes forwards or backwards from that point.

Yet there is still something of a mystery. For our everyday experience is full of examples in which randomness increases much as in the second half of the picture above. But we essentially never see the kind of systematic decrease in randomness that occurs in the first half.

By setting up the precise initial conditions that exist at the beginning of the whole picture it would certainly in principle be possible to get such behavior. But somehow it seems that initial conditions like these essentially never actually occur in practice.

There has in the past been considerable confusion about why this might be the case. But the key to understanding what is going on is simply to realize that one has to think not only about the systems one is studying, but also about the types of experiments and observations that one uses in the process of studying them.

The crucial point then turns out to be that practical experiments almost inevitably end up involving only initial conditions that are fairly simple for us to describe and construct. And with these types of initial conditions, systems like the one on the previous page always tend to exhibit increasing randomness.

But what exactly is it that determines the types of initial conditions that one can use in an experiment? It seems reasonable to suppose that in any meaningful experiment the process of setting up the experiment should somehow be simpler than the process that the experiment is intended to observe.

But how can one compare such processes? The answer that I will develop in considerable detail later in this book is to view all such processes as computations. The conclusion is then that the computation involved in setting up an experiment should be simpler than the computation involved in the evolution of the system that is to be studied by the experiment.

It is clear that by starting with a simple state and then tracing backwards through the actual evolution of a reversible system one can find initial conditions that will lead to decreasing randomness. But if one looks for example at the pictures on the last couple of pages the complexity of the behavior seems to preclude any less arduous way of finding such initial conditions. And indeed I will argue in Chapter 12 that the Principle of Computational Equivalence suggests that in general no such reduced procedure should exist.

The consequence of this is that no reasonable experiment can ever involve setting up the kind of initial conditions that will lead to decreases in randomness, and that therefore all practical experiments will tend to show only increases in randomness.

It is this basic argument that I believe explains the observed validity of what in physics is known as the Second Law of Thermodynamics. The law was first formulated more than a century ago, but despite many related technical results, the basic reasons for its validity have until now remained rather mysterious.

The field of thermodynamics is generally concerned with issues of heat and energy in physical systems. A fundamental fact known since the mid-1800s is that heat is a form of energy associated with the random microscopic motions of large numbers of atoms or other particles.

One formulation of the Second Law then states that any energy associated with organized motions of such particles tends to degrade irreversibly into heat. And the pictures at the beginning of this section show essentially just such a phenomenon. Initially there are particles which move in a fairly regular and organized way. But as time goes on, the motion that occurs becomes progressively more random.

There are several details of the cellular automaton used above that differ from actual physical systems of the kind usually studied in thermodynamics. But at the cost of some additional technical complication, it is fairly straightforward to set up a more realistic system.

The pictures on the next two pages show a particular two-dimensional cellular automaton in which black squares representing particles move around and collide with each other, essentially like particles in an ideal gas. This cellular automaton shares with the cellular automaton at the beginning of the section the property of being reversible. But it also has the additional feature that in every collision the total number of particles in it remains unchanged. And since each particle can be thought of as having a certain energy, it follows that the total energy of the system is therefore conserved.

In the first case shown, the particles are taken to bounce around in an empty square box. And it turns out that in this particular case only very simple repetitive behavior is ever obtained. But almost any change destroys this simplicity.

And in the second case, for example, the presence of a small fixed obstacle leads to rapid randomization in the arrangement of particles— very much like the randomization we saw in the one-dimensional cellular automaton that we discussed earlier in this section.

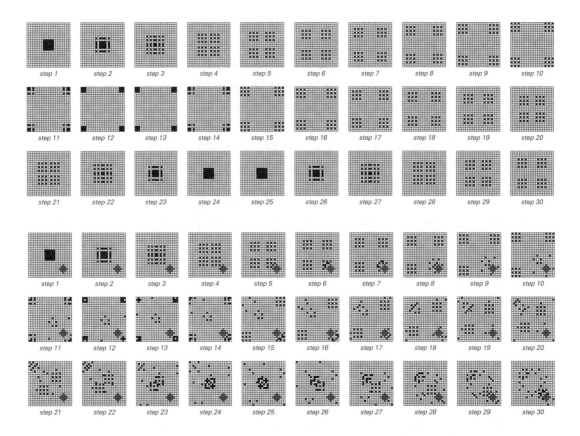

The behavior of a simple two-dimensional cellular automaton that emulates an ideal gas of particles. In the top group of pictures, the particles bounce around in an empty square box. In the bottom group of pictures, the box contains a small fixed obstacle. In the top group of pictures, the arrangement of particles shows simple repetitive behavior. In the bottom group, however, it becomes progressively more random with time. The underlying rules for the cellular automaton used here are reversible, and conserve the total number of particles. The specific rules are based on 2 × 2 blocks—a two-dimensional generalization of the block cellular automata to be discussed in the next section. For each 2 × 2 block the configuration of particles is taken to remain the same at a particular step unless there are exactly two particles arranged diagonally within the block, in which case the particles move to the opposite diagonal.

So even though the total of the energy of all particles remains the same, the distribution of this energy becomes progressively more random, just as the usual Second Law implies.

An important practical consequence of this is that it becomes increasingly difficult to extract energy from the system in the form of systematic mechanical work. At an idealized level one might imagine trying to do this by inserting into the system some kind of paddle which would experience force as a result of impacts from particles.

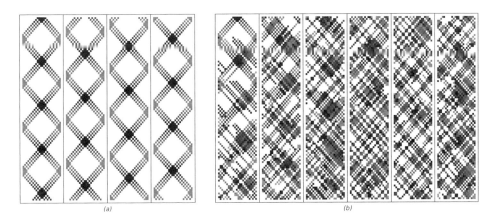

(a)   (b)

Time histories of the cellular automata from the facing page. In each case a slice is taken through the midline of the box. Black cells that are further from the midline are shown in progressively lighter shades of gray. Case (a) corresponds to an empty square box, and shows simple repetitive behavior. Case (b) corresponds to a box containing a fixed obstacle, and in this case rapid randomization is seen. Each panel corresponds to 100 steps in the evolution of the system; the box is 24 cells across.

The pictures below show how such force might vary with time in cases (a) and (b) above. In case (a), where no randomization occurs, the force can readily be predicted, and it is easy to imagine harnessing it to produce systematic mechanical work. But in case (b), the force quickly randomizes, and there is no obvious way to obtain systematic mechanical work from it.

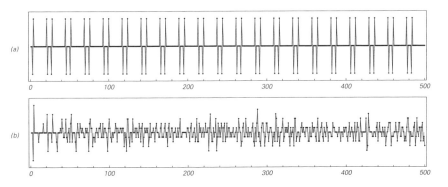

The force on an idealized paddle placed on the midline of the systems shown above. The force reflects an imbalance in the number of particles at each step arriving at the midline from above and below. In case (a) this imbalance is readily predictable. In case (b), however, it rapidly becomes for most practical purposes random. This randomness is essentially what makes it impossible to build a physical perpetual motion machine which continually turns heat into mechanical work.

One might nevertheless imagine that it would be possible to devise a complicated machine, perhaps with an elaborate arrangement of paddles, that would still be able to extract systematic mechanical work even from an apparently random distribution of particles. But it turns out that in order to do this the machine would effectively have to be able to predict where every particle would be at every step in time.

And as we shall discuss in Chapter 12, this would mean that the machine would have to perform computations that are as sophisticated as those that correspond to the actual evolution of the system itself. The result is that in practice it is never possible to build perpetual motion machines that continually take energy in the form of heat—or randomized particle motions—and convert it into useful mechanical work.

The impossibility of such perpetual motion machines is one common statement of the Second Law of Thermodynamics. Another is that a quantity known as entropy tends to increase with time.

Entropy is defined as the amount of information about a system that is still unknown after one has made a certain set of measurements on the system. The specific value of the entropy will depend on what measurements one makes, but the content of the Second Law is that if one repeats the same measurements at different times, then the entropy deduced from them will tend to increase with time.

If one managed to find the positions and properties of all the particles in the system, then no information about the system would remain unknown, and the entropy of the system would just be zero. But in a practical experiment, one cannot expect to be able to make anything like such complete measurements.

And more realistically, the measurements one makes might for example give the total numbers of particles in certain regions inside the box. There are then a large number of possible detailed arrangements of particles that are all consistent with the results of such measurements. The entropy is defined as the amount of additional information that would be needed in order to pick out the specific arrangement that actually occurs.

We will discuss in more detail in Chapter 10 the notion of amount of information. But here we can imagine numbering all the possible arrangements of particles that are consistent with the results of our measurements, so that the amount of information needed to pick out a single arrangement is essentially the length in digits of one such number.

The pictures below show the behavior of the entropy calculated in this way for systems like the one discussed above. And what we see is that the entropy does indeed tend to increase, just as the Second Law implies.

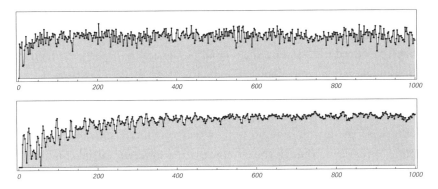

The entropy as a function of time for systems of the type shown in case (b) from page 447. The top plot is exactly for case (b); the bottom one is for a system three times larger in size. The entropy is found in each case by working out how many possible configurations of particles are consistent with measurements of the total numbers of particles in a 6 × 6 grid of regions within the system. Just as the Second Law of Thermodynamics suggests, the entropy tends to increase with time. Note that the plots above would be exactly symmetrical if they were continued to the left: the entropy would increase in the same way going both forwards and backwards from the simple initial conditions used.

In effect what is going on is that the measurements we make represent an attempt to determine the state of the system. But as the arrangement of particles in the system becomes more random, this attempt becomes less and less successful.

One might imagine that there could be a more elaborate set of measurements that would somehow avoid these problems, and would not lead to increasing entropy. But as we shall discuss in Chapter 12, it again turns out that setting up such measurements would have to involve the same level of computational effort as the actual evolution of the system itself. And as a result, one concludes that the entropy associated with measurements done in practical experiments will always tend to increase, as the Second Law suggests.

In Chapter 12 we will discuss in more detail some of the key ideas involved in coming to this conclusion. But the basic point is that the phenomenon of entropy increase implied by the Second Law is a more or less direct consequence of the phenomenon discovered in this book that even with simple initial conditions many systems can produce complex and seemingly random behavior.

One aspect of the generation of randomness that we have noted several times in earlier chapters is that once significant randomness has been produced in a system, the overall properties of that system tend to become largely independent of the details of its initial conditions.

In any system that is reversible it must always be the case that different initial conditions lead to at least slightly different states— otherwise there would be no unique way of going backwards. But the point is that even though the outcomes from different initial conditions differ in detail, their overall properties can still be very much the same.

The pictures on the facing page show an example of what can happen. Every individual picture has different initial conditions. But whenever randomness is produced the overall patterns that are obtained look in the end almost indistinguishable.

The reversibility of the underlying rules implies that at some level it must be possible to recognize outcomes from different kinds of initial conditions. But the point is that to do so would require a computation far more sophisticated than any that could meaningfully be done as part of a practical measurement process.

So this means that if a system generates sufficient randomness, one can think of it as evolving towards a unique equilibrium whose properties are for practical purposes independent of its initial conditions.

This fact turns out in a sense to be implicit in many everyday applications of physics. For it is what allows us to characterize all sorts of physical systems by just specifying a few parameters such as temperature and chemical composition—and avoids us always having to know the details of the initial conditions and history of each system.

The existence of a unique equilibrium to which any particular system tends to evolve is also a common statement of the Second Law of

The approach to equilibrium in a reversible cellular automaton with a variety of different initial conditions. Apart from exceptional cases where no randomization occurs, the behavior obtained with different initial conditions is eventually quite indistinguishable in its overall properties. Because the underlying rule is reversible, however, the details with different initial conditions are always at least slightly different—otherwise it would not be possible to go backwards in a unique way. The rule used here is 122R. Successive pairs of pictures have initial conditions that differ only in the color of a single cell at the center.

Thermodynamics. And once again, therefore, we find that the Second Law is associated with basic phenomena that we already saw early in this book.

But just how general is the Second Law? And does it really apply to all of the various kinds of systems that we see in nature?

Starting nearly a century ago it came to be widely believed that the Second Law is an almost universal principle. But in reality there is surprisingly little evidence for this.

Indeed, almost all of the detailed applications ever made of the full Second Law have been concerned with just one specific area: the behavior of gases. By now there is therefore good evidence that gases obey the Second Law—just as the idealized model earlier in this section suggests. But what about other kinds of systems?

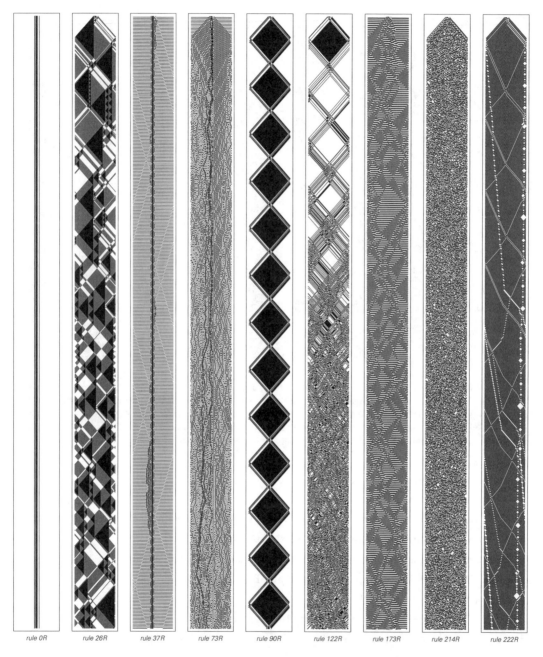

rule 0R rule 26R rule 37R rule 73R rule 90R rule 122R rule 173R rule 214R rule 222R

Examples of reversible cellular automata with various rules. Some quickly randomize, as the Second Law of Thermodynamics would suggest. But others do not—and thus in effect do not obey the Second Law of Thermodynamics.

The pictures on the facing page show examples of various reversible cellular automata. And what we see immediately from these pictures is that while some systems exhibit exactly the kind of randomization implied by the Second Law, others do not.

The most obvious exceptions are cases like rule 0R and rule 90R, where the behavior that is produced has only a very simple fixed or repetitive form. And existing mathematical studies have indeed identified these simple exceptions to the Second Law. But they have somehow implicitly assumed that no other kinds of exceptions can exist.

The picture on the next page, however, shows the behavior of rule 37R over the course of many steps. And in looking at this picture, we see a remarkable phenomenon: there is neither a systematic trend towards increasing randomness, nor any form of simple predictable behavior. Indeed, it seems that the system just never settles down, but rather continues to fluctuate forever, sometimes becoming less orderly, and sometimes more so.

So how can such behavior be understood in the context of the Second Law? There is, I believe, no choice but to conclude that for practical purposes rule 37R simply does not obey the Second Law.

And as it turns out, what happens in rule 37R is not so different from what seems to happen in many systems in nature. If the Second Law was always obeyed, then one might expect that by now every part of our universe would have evolved to completely random equilibrium.

Yet it is quite obvious that this has not happened. And indeed there are many kinds of systems, notably biological ones, that seem to show, at least temporarily, a trend towards increasing order rather than increasing randomness.

How do such systems work? A common feature appears to be the presence of some kind of partitioning: the systems effectively break up into parts that evolve at least somewhat independently for long periods of time.

The picture on page 456 shows what happens if one starts rule 37R with a single small region of randomness. And for a while what one sees is that the randomness that has been inserted persists. But eventually the system instead seems to organize itself to yield just a small number of simple repetitive structures.

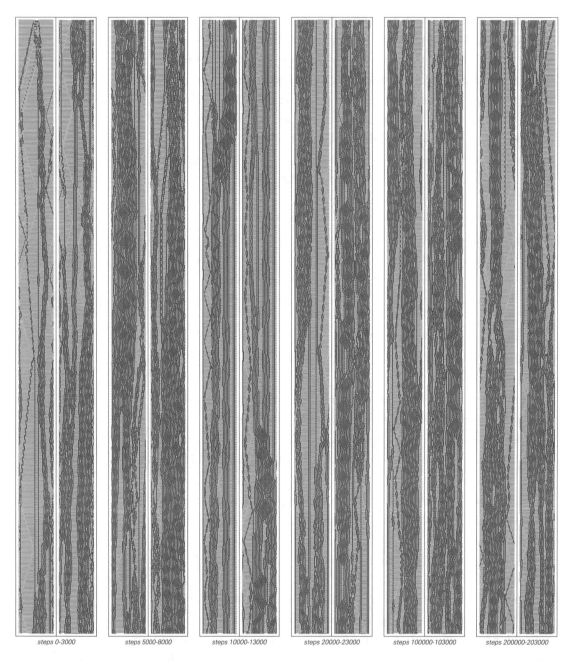

steps 0-3000   steps 5000-8000   steps 10000-13000   steps 20000-23000   steps 100000-103000   steps 200000-203000

More steps in the evolution of the reversible cellular automaton with rule 37R. This system is an example of one that does not in any meaningful way obey the Second Law of Thermodynamics. Instead of exhibiting progressively more random behavior, it appears to fluctuate between quite ordered and quite disordered states.

This kind of self-organization is quite opposite to what one would expect from the Second Law. And at first it also seems inconsistent with the reversibility of the system. For if all that is left at the end are a few simple structures, how can there be enough information to go backwards and reconstruct the initial conditions?

The answer is that one has to consider not only the stationary structures that stay in the middle of the system, but also all various small structures that were emitted in the course of the evolution. To go backwards one would need to set things up so that one absorbs exactly the sequence of structures that were emitted going forwards.

If, however, one just lets the emitted structures escape, and never absorbs any other structures, then one is effectively losing information. The result is that the evolution one sees can be intrinsically not reversible, so that all of the various forms of self-organization that we saw earlier in this book in cellular automata that do not have reversible rules can potentially occur.

If we look at the universe on a large scale, then it turns out that in a certain sense there is more radiation emitted than absorbed. Indeed, this is related to the fact that the night sky appears dark, rather than having bright starlight coming from every direction. But ultimately the asymmetry between emission and absorption is a consequence of the fact that the universe is expanding, rather than contracting, with time.

The result is that it is possible for regions of the universe to become progressively more organized, despite the Second Law, and despite the reversibility of their underlying rules. And this is a large part of the reason that organized galaxies, stars and planets can form.

Allowing information to escape is a rather straightforward way to evade the Second Law. But what the pictures on the facing page demonstrate is that even in a completely closed system, where no information at all is allowed to escape, a system like rule 37R still does not follow the uniform trend towards increasing randomness that is suggested by the Second Law.

What instead happens is that kinds of membranes form between different regions of the system, and within each region orderly behavior can then occur, at least while the membrane survives.

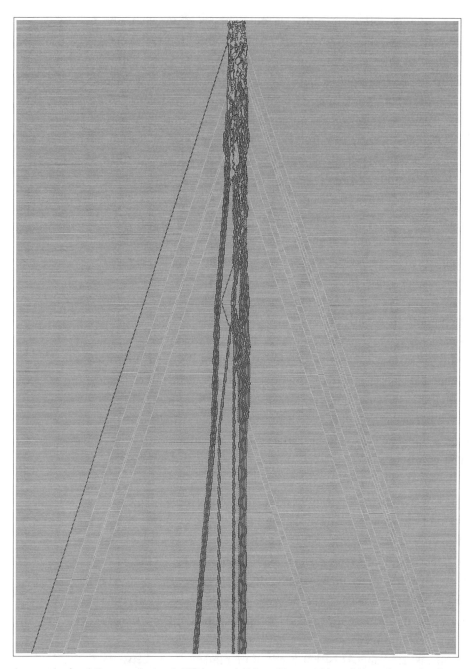

An example of evolution according to rule 37R from an initial condition containing a fairly random region. Even though the system is reversible, this region tends to organize itself so as to take on a much simpler form. Information on the initial conditions ends up being carried by localized structures which radiate outwards.

This basic mechanism may well be the main one at work in many biological systems: each cell or each organism becomes separated from others, and while it survives, it can exhibit organized behavior.

But looking at the pictures of rule 37R on page 454 one may ask whether perhaps the effects we see are just transients, and that if we waited long enough something different would happen.

It is an inevitable feature of having a closed system of limited size that in the end the behavior one gets must repeat itself. And in rules like 0R and 90R shown on page 452 the period of repetition is always very short. But for rule 37R it usually turns out to be rather long. Indeed, for the specific example shown on page 454, the period is 293,216,266.

In general, however, the maximum possible period for a system containing a certain number of cells can be achieved only if the evolution of the system from any initial condition eventually visits all the possible states of the system, as discussed on page 258. And if this in fact happens, then at least eventually the system will inevitably spend most of its time in states that seem quite random.

But in rule 37R there is no such ergodicity. And instead, starting from any particular initial condition, the system will only ever visit a tiny fraction of all possible states. Yet since the total number of states is astronomically large—about 10^{60} for size 100—the number of states visited by rule 37R, and therefore the repetition period, can still be extremely long.

There are various subtleties involved in making a formal study of the limiting behavior of rule 37R after a very long time. But irrespective of these subtleties, the basic fact remains that so far as I can tell, rule 37R simply does not follow the predictions of the Second Law.

And indeed I strongly suspect that there are many systems in nature which behave in more or less the same way. The Second Law is an important and quite general principle—but it is not universally valid. And by thinking in terms of simple programs we have thus been able in this section not only to understand why the Second Law is often true, but also to see some of its limitations.

Conserved Quantities and Continuum Phenomena

Reversibility is one general feature that appears to exist in the basic laws of physics. Another is conservation of various quantities—so that for example in the evolution of any closed physical system, total values of quantities like energy and electric charge appear always to stay the same.

With most rules, systems like cellular automata do not usually exhibit such conservation laws. But just as with reversibility, it turns out to be possible to find rules that for example conserve the total number of black cells appearing on each step.

Among elementary cellular automata with just two colors and nearest-neighbor rules, the only types of examples are the fairly trivial ones shown in the pictures below.

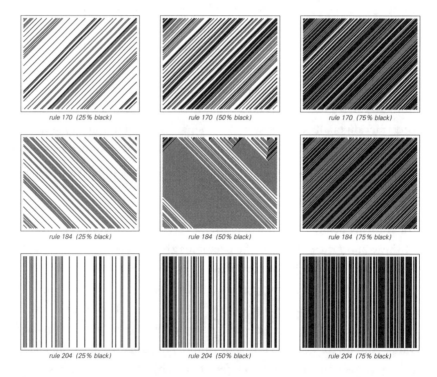

rule 170 (25% black)   *rule 170 (50% black)*   *rule 170 (75% black)*

rule 184 (25% black)   *rule 184 (50% black)*   *rule 184 (75% black)*

rule 204 (25% black)   *rule 204 (50% black)*   *rule 204 (75% black)*

Elementary cellular automata whose evolution conserves the total number of black cells. The behavior of the rules shown here is simple enough that in each case it is fairly obvious how the number of black cells manages to stay the same on every step.

But with next-nearest-neighbor rules, more complicated examples become possible, as the pictures below demonstrate.

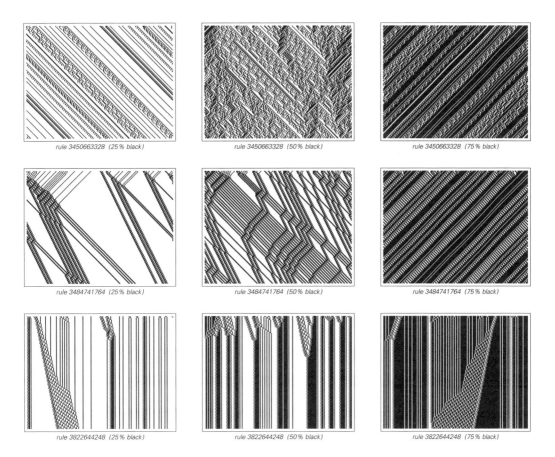

Examples of cellular automata with next-nearest-neighbor rules whose evolution conserves the total number of black cells. Even though it is not immediately obvious by eye, the total number of black cells stays exactly the same on each successive step in each picture. Among the 4,294,967,296 possible next-neighbor rules, only 428 exhibit the kind of conservation property shown here.

One straightforward way to generate collections of systems that will inevitably exhibit conserved quantities is to work not with ordinary cellular automata but instead with block cellular automata. The basic idea of a block cellular automaton is illustrated at the top of the next page. At each step what happens is that blocks of adjacent cells are replaced by other blocks of the same size according to some definite rule. And then on successive steps the alignment of these blocks shifts by one cell.

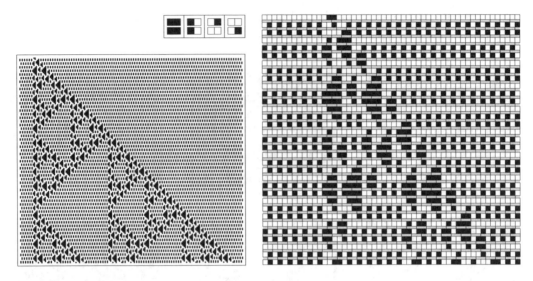

An example of a block cellular automaton. The system works by partitioning the sequence of cells that exists at each step into pairs, then replacing these pairs by other pairs according to the rule shown. The choice of whether to pair a cell with its left or right neighbor alternates on successive steps. Like many block cellular automata, the system shown is reversible, since in the rule each pair has a unique predecessor. It does not, however, conserve the total number of black cells.

And with this setup, if the underlying rules replace each block by one that contains the same number of black cells, it is inevitable that the system as a whole will conserve the total number of black cells.

With two possible colors and blocks of size two the only kinds of block cellular automata that conserve the total number of black cells are the ones shown below—and all of these exhibit rather trivial behavior.

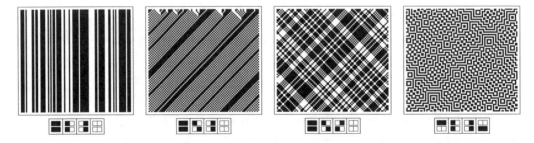

Block cellular automata with two possible colors and blocks of size two that conserve the total number of black cells (the last example has this property only on alternate steps). It so happens that all but the second of the rules shown here not only conserve the total number of black cells but also turn out to be reversible.

But if one allows three possible colors, and requires, say, that the total number of black and gray cells together be conserved, then more complicated behavior can occur, as in the pictures below.

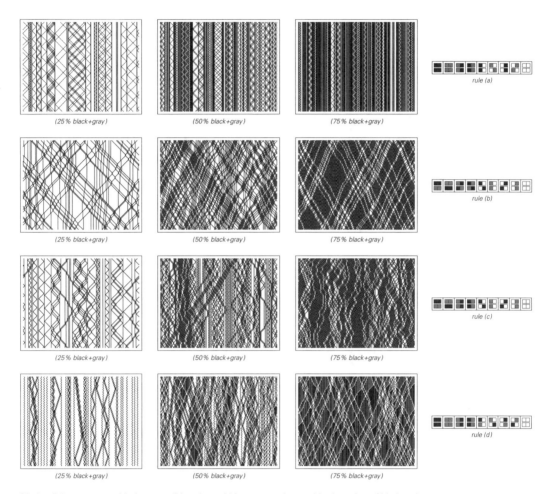

(25% black+gray) (50% black+gray) (75% black+gray) rule (a)

(25% black+gray) (50% black+gray) (75% black+gray) rule (b)

(25% black+gray) (50% black+gray) (75% black+gray) rule (c)

(25% black+gray) (50% black+gray) (75% black+gray) rule (d)

Block cellular automata with three possible colors which conserve the combined number of black and gray cells. In rule (a), black and gray cells remain in localized regions. In rule (b), they move in fairly simple ways, and in rules (c) and (d), they move in a seemingly somewhat random way. The rules shown here are reversible, although their behavior is similar to that of non-reversible rules, at least after a few steps.

Indeed, as the pictures on the next page demonstrate, such systems can produce considerable randomness even when starting from very simple initial conditions.

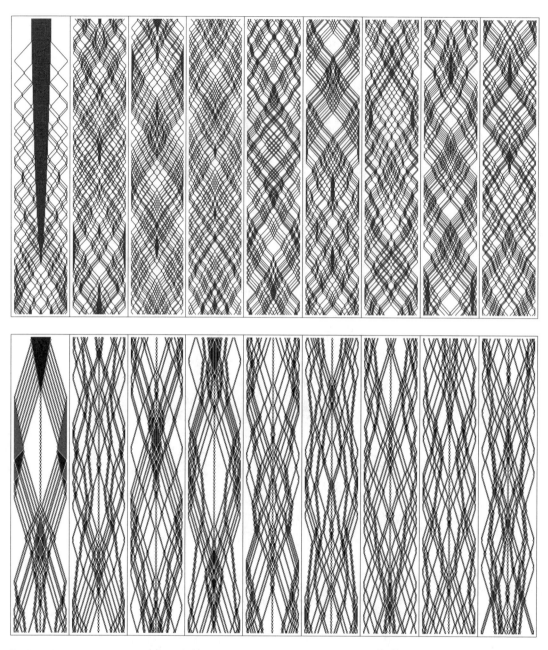

The behavior of rules (c) and (d) from the previous page, starting with very simple initial conditions. Each panel shows 500 steps of evolution, and rapid randomization is evident. The black and gray cells behave much like physical particles: their total number is conserved, and with the particular rules used here, their interactions are reversible. Note that the presence of boundaries is crucial; for without them there would in a sense be no collisions between particles, and the behavior of both systems would be rather trivial.

But there is still an important constraint on the behavior: even though black and gray cells may in effect move around randomly, their total number must always be conserved. And this means that if one looks at the total average density of colored cells throughout the system, it must always remain the same. But local densities in different parts of the system need not—and in general they will change as colored cells flow in and out.

The pictures below show what happens with four different rules, starting with higher density in the middle and lower density on the sides. With rules (a) and (b), each different region effectively remains separated forever. But with rules (c) and (d) the regions gradually mix.

As in many kinds of systems, the details of the initial arrangement of cells will normally have an effect on the details of the behavior that occurs. But what the pictures below suggest is that if one looks only at the overall distribution of density, then these details will become largely irrelevant—so that a given initial distribution of density will always tend to evolve in the same overall way, regardless of what particular arrangement of cells happened to make up that distribution.

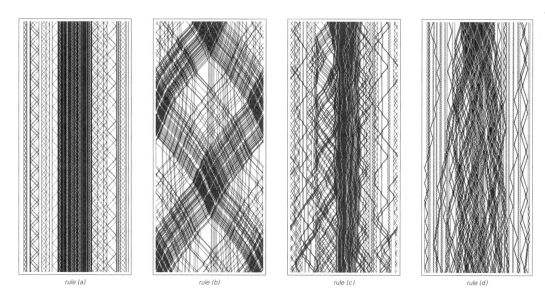

rule (a)   rule (b)   rule (c)   rule (d)

The block cellular automata from previous pages started from initial conditions containing regions of different density. In rules (a) and (b) the regions remain separated forever, but in rules (c) and (d) they gradually diffuse into each other.

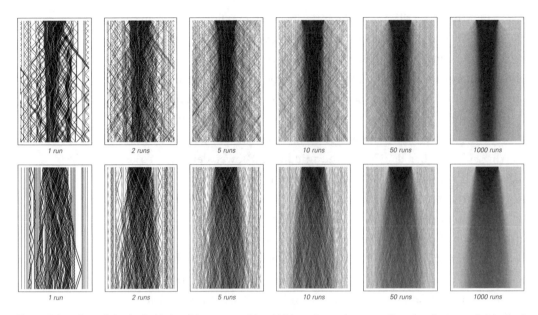

The evolution of overall density for block cellular automata (c) and (d) from the previous page. Even though at an underlying level these systems consist of discrete cells, their overall behavior seems smooth and continuous. The results shown here are obtained by averaging over progressively larger numbers of runs with initial conditions that differ in detail, but have the same overall density distribution. In the limit of an infinite number of runs (or infinite number of cells), the behavior in the second case approaches the form implied by the continuum diffusion equation. (In the first case correlations in effect last too long to yield exactly such behavior.)

The pictures above then show how the average density evolves in systems (c) and (d). And what is striking is that even though at the lowest level both of these systems consist of discrete cells, the overall distribution of density that emerges in both cases shows smooth continuous behavior.

And much as in physical systems like fluids, what ultimately leads to this is the presence of small-scale apparent randomness that washes out details of individual cells or molecules—as well as of conserved quantities that force certain overall features not to change too quickly. And in fact, given just these properties it turns out that essentially the same overall continuum behavior always tends to be obtained.

One might have thought that continuum behavior would somehow rely on special features of actual systems in physics. But in fact what we have seen here is that once again the fundamental mechanisms responsible already occur in a much more minimal way in programs that have some remarkably simple underlying rules.

Ultimate Models for the Universe

The history of physics has seen the development of a sequence of progressively more accurate models for the universe—from classical mechanics, through quantum mechanics, to quantum field theory, and beyond. And one may wonder whether this process will go on forever, or whether at some point it will come to an end, and one will reach a final ultimate model for the universe.

Experience with actual results in physics would probably not make one think so. For it has seemed that whenever one tries to get to another level of accuracy, one encounters more complex phenomena. And at least with traditional scientific intuition, this fact suggests that models of progressively greater complexity will be needed.

But one of the crucial points discovered in this book is that more complex phenomena do not always require more complex models. And indeed I have shown that even models based on remarkably simple programs can produce behavior that is in a sense arbitrarily complex.

So could this be what happens in the universe? And could it even be that underneath all the complex phenomena we see in physics there lies some simple program which, if run for long enough, would reproduce our universe in every detail?

The discovery of such a program would certainly be an exciting event—as well as a dramatic endorsement for the new kind of science that I have developed in this book.

For among other things, with such a program one would finally have a model of nature that was not in any sense an approximation or idealization. Instead, it would be a complete and precise representation of the actual operation of the universe—but all reduced to readily stated rules.

In a sense, the existence of such a program would be the ultimate validation of the idea that human thought can comprehend the construction of the universe. But just knowing the underlying program does not mean that one can immediately deduce every aspect of how the universe will behave. For as we have seen many times in this book, there is often a great distance between underlying rules and overall behavior. And in fact, this is precisely why it is conceivable that a simple program could reproduce all the complexity we see in physics.

Given a particular underlying program, it is always in principle possible to work out what it will do just by running it. But for the whole universe, doing this kind of explicit simulation is almost by definition out of the question. So how then can one even expect to tell whether a particular program is a correct model for the universe? Small-scale simulation will certainly be possible. And I expect that by combining this with a certain amount of perhaps fairly sophisticated mathematical and logical deduction, it will be possible to get at least as far as reproducing the known laws of physics—and thus of determining whether a particular model has the potential to be correct.

So if there is indeed a definite ultimate model for the universe, how might one set about finding it? For those familiar with existing science, there is at first a tremendous tendency to try to work backwards from the known laws of physics, and in essence to try to "engineer" a universe that will have particular features that we observe.

But if there is in fact an ultimate model that is quite simple, then from what we have seen in this book, I strongly believe that such an approach will never realistically be successful. For human thinking—even supplemented by the most sophisticated ideas of current mathematics and logic—is far from being able to do what is needed.

Imagine for example trying to work backwards from a knowledge of the overall features of the picture on the facing page to construct a rule that would reproduce it. With great effort one might perhaps come up with some immensely complex rule that would work in most cases. But there is no serious possibility that starting from overall features one would ever arrive at the extremely simple rule that was actually used.

It is already difficult enough to work out from an underlying rule what behavior it will produce. But to invert this in any systematic way is probably even in principle beyond what any realistic computation can do.

So how then could one ever expect to find the underlying rule in such a case? Almost always, it seems that the best strategy is a simple one: to come up with an appropriate general class of rules, and then just

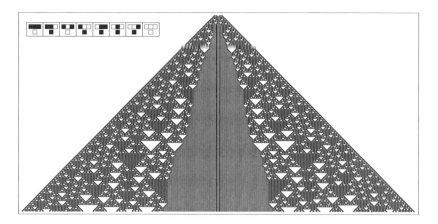

A typical example of a situation where it would be very difficult to deduce the underlying rule from a description of the overall behavior that it produces. There is in a sense too great a distance between the simple rule shown and the behavior that emerges from it. I suspect that the same will be true of the basic rule for the universe. The particular rule shown here is the elementary cellular automaton with rule number 94, and with initial condition ■■■■□□□□■■■ .

to search through these rules, trying each one in turn, and looking to see if it produces the behavior one wants.

But what about the rules for the universe? Surely we cannot simply search through possible rules of certain kinds, looking for one whose behavior happens to fit what we see in physics?

With the intuition of traditional science, such an approach seems absurd. But the point is that if the rule for the universe is sufficiently simple—and the results of this book suggest that it might be—then it becomes not so unreasonable to imagine systematically searching for it.

To start performing such a search, however, one first needs to work out what kinds of rules to consider. And my suspicion is that none of the specific types of rules that we have discussed so far in this book will turn out to be adequate. For I believe that all these types of rules in some sense probably already have too much structure built in.

Thus, for example, cellular automata probably already have too rigid a built-in notion of space. For a defining feature of cellular automata is that their cells are always arranged in a rigid array in space. Yet I strongly suspect that in the underlying rule for our universe there will be no such built-in structure. Rather, as I discuss in the sections that follow, my guess is that at the lowest level there will just be certain patterns of connectivity that tend to exist, and that space as we know it will then emerge from these patterns as a kind of large-scale limit.

And indeed in general what I expect is that remarkably few familiar features of our universe will actually be reflected in any direct way in its ultimate underlying rule. For if all these features were somehow explicitly and separately included, the rule would necessarily have to be very complicated to fit them all in.

So if the rule is indeed simple, it almost inevitably follows that we will not be able to recognize directly in it most features of the universe as we normally perceive them. And this means that the rule—or at least its behavior—will necessarily seem to us unfamiliar and abstract.

Most likely for example there will be no easy way to visualize what the rule does by looking at a collection of elements laid out in space. Nor will there probably be any immediate trace of even such basic phenomena as motion.

But despite the lack of these familiar features, I still expect that the actual rule itself will not be too difficult for us to represent. For I am fairly certain that the kinds of logical and computational constructs that we have discussed in this book will be general enough to cover what is needed. And indeed my guess is that in terms of the kinds of pictures—or *Mathematica* programs—that we have used in this book, the ultimate rule for the universe will turn out to look quite simple.

No doubt there will be many different possible formulations— some quite unrecognizably different from others. And no doubt a formulation will eventually be found in which the rule somehow comes to seem quite obvious and inevitable.

But I believe that it will be essentially impossible to find such a formulation without already knowing the rule. And as a result, my guess is that the only realistic way to find the rule in the first place will be to start from some very straightforward representation, and then just to search through large numbers of possible rules in this representation.

Presumably the vast majority of rules will lead to utterly unworkable universes, in which there is for example no reasonable notion of space or no reasonable notion of time.

But my guess is that among appropriate classes of rules there will actually be quite a large number that lead to universes which share at least some features with our own. Much as the same laws of continuum fluid mechanics can emerge in systems with different underlying rules for molecular interactions, so also I suspect that properties such as the existence of seemingly continuous space, as well as certain features of gravitation and quantum mechanics, will emerge with many different possible underlying rules for the universe.

But my guess is that when it comes to something like the spectrum of masses of elementary particles—or perhaps even the overall dimensionality of space—such properties will be quite specific to particular underlying rules.

In traditional approaches to modelling, one usually tries first to reproduce some features of a system, then goes on to reproduce others. But if the ultimate rule for the universe is at all simple, then it follows that every part of this rule must in a sense be responsible for a great many different features of the universe. And as a result, it is not likely to be possible to adjust individual parts of the rule without having an effect on a whole collection of disparate features of the universe.

So this means that one cannot reasonably expect to use some kind of incremental procedure to find the ultimate rule for the universe. But it also means that if one once discovers a rule that reproduces sufficiently many features of the universe, then it becomes extremely likely that this rule is indeed the final and correct one for the whole universe.

And I strongly suspect that even in many of the most basic everyday physical processes, every element of the underlying rule for the universe will be very extensively exercised. And as a result, if these basic processes are reproduced correctly, then I believe that one can have considerable confidence that one in fact has the complete rule for the universe.

Looking at the history of physics, one might think that it would be completely inadequate just to reproduce everyday physical processes. For one might expect that there would always be some other esoteric phenomenon, say in particle physics, that would be discovered and would show that whatever rule one has found is somehow incomplete.

But I do not think so. For if the rule for our universe is at all simple, then I expect that to introduce a new phenomenon, however esoteric, will involve modifying some basic part of the rule, which will also affect even common everyday phenomena.

But why should we believe that the rule for our universe is in fact simple? Certainly among all possible rules of a particular kind only a limited number can ever be considered simple, and these rules are by definition somehow special. Yet looking at the history of science, one might expect that in the end there would turn out to be nothing special about the rule for our universe—just as there has turned out to be nothing special about our position in the solar system or the galaxy.

Indeed, one might assume that there are in fact an infinite number of universes, each with a different rule, and that we simply live in a particular—and essentially arbitrary—one of them.

It is unlikely to be possible to show for certain that such a theory is not correct. But one of its consequences is that it gives us no reason to think that the rule for our particular universe should be in any way simple. For among all possible rules, the overwhelming majority will not be simple; in fact, they will instead tend to be almost infinitely complex.

Yet we know, I think, that the rule for our universe is not too complex. For if the number of different parts of the rule were, for example, comparable to the number of different situations that have ever arisen in the history of the universe, then we would not expect ever to be able to describe the behavior of the universe using only a limited number of physical laws.

And in fact if one looks at present-day physics, there are not only a limited number of physical laws, but also the individual laws often seem to have the simplest forms out of various alternatives. And knowing this, one might be led to believe that for some reason the universe is set up to have the simplest rules throughout.

But, unfortunately perhaps, I do not think that this conclusion necessarily follows. For as I have discussed above, I strongly suspect that the vast majority of physical laws discovered so far are not truly fundamental, but are instead merely emergent features of the large-scale behavior of some ultimate underlying rule. And what this means is that any simplicity observed in known physical laws may have little connection with simplicity in the underlying rule.

Indeed, it turns out that simple overall laws can emerge almost regardless of underlying rules. And thus, for example, essentially as a consequence of randomness generation, a wide range of cellular automata show the simple density diffusion law on page 464—whether or not their underlying rules happen to be simple.

So it could be that the laws that we have formulated in existing physics are simple not because of simplicity in an ultimate underlying rule, but rather because of some general property of emergent behavior for the kinds of overall features of the universe that we readily perceive.

Indeed, with this kind of argument, one could be led to think that there might be no single ultimate rule for the universe at all, but that instead there might somehow be an infinite sequence of levels of rules, with each level having a certain simplicity that becomes increasingly independent of the details of the levels below it.

But one should not imagine that such a setup would make it unnecessary to ask why our universe is the way it is: for even though certain features might be inevitable from the general properties of emergent behavior, there will, I believe, still be many seemingly arbitrary choices that have to be made in arriving at the universe in which we live. And once again, therefore, one will have to ask why it was these choices, and not others, that were made.

So perhaps in the end there is the least to explain if I am correct that the universe just follows a single, simple, underlying rule.

There will certainly be questions about why it is this particular rule, and not another one. And I am doubtful that such questions will ever have meaningful answers.

But to find the ultimate rule will be a major triumph for science, and a clear demonstration that at least in some direction, human thought has reached the edge of what is possible.

The Nature of Space

In the effort to develop an ultimate model for the universe, a crucial first step is to think about the nature of space—for inevitably it is in space that the processes in our universe occur.

Present-day physics almost always assumes that space is a perfect continuum, in which objects can be placed at absolutely any position. But one can certainly imagine that space could work very differently. And for example in a cellular automaton, space is not a continuum but instead consists just of discrete cells.

In our everyday experience space nevertheless appears to be continuous. But then so, for example, do fluids like air and water. And yet in the case of these fluids we know that at an underlying level they are composed of discrete molecules. And in fact over the course of the past century a great many aspects of the physical world that at first seemed continuous have in the end been discovered to be built up from discrete elements. And I very strongly suspect that this will also be true of space.

Particle physics experiments have shown that space acts as a continuum down to distances of around 10^{-20} meters—or a hundred thousandth the radius of a proton. But there is absolutely no reason to think that discrete elements will not be found at still smaller distances.

And indeed, in the past one of the main reasons that space has been assumed to be a perfect continuum is that this makes it easier to handle in the context of traditional mathematics. But when one thinks in terms of programs and the kinds of systems I have discussed in this book, it no longer seems nearly as attractive to assume that space is a perfect continuum.

So if space is not in fact a continuum, what might it be? Could it, for example, be a regular array of cells like in a cellular automaton?

At first, one might think that this would be completely inconsistent with everyday observations. For even though the individual cells in the array might be extremely small, one might still imagine that one would for example see all sorts of signs of the overall orientation of the array.

The pictures below show three different cellular automata, all set up on the same two-dimensional grid. And to see the effect of the grid, I show what happens when each of these cellular automata is started from blocks of black cells arranged at three different angles.

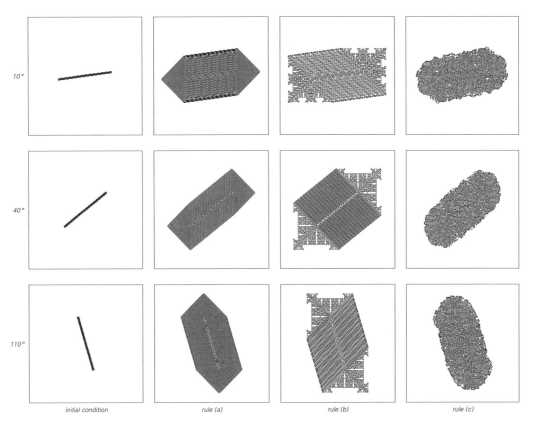

10°			
40°			
110°			
initial condition	rule (a)	rule (b)	rule (c)

Examples of orientation dependence in the behavior of two-dimensional cellular automata on a fixed grid. Three different initial conditions, consisting of blocks at three different angles, are shown. For rules (a) and (b) the patterns produced always exhibit features that remain aligned with directions in the underlying grid. But with rule (c) essentially the same rounded pattern is obtained regardless of orientation. The rules shown here are outer totalistic: (a) 4-neighbor code 468, (b) 4-neighbor code 686 and (c) 8-neighbor code 746. In cases (a) and (b) 40 steps of evolution are used; in case (c) 100 steps are used.

In all cases the patterns produced follow at least to some extent the orientation of the initial block. But in cases (a) and (b) the effects of the underlying grid remain quite obvious—for the patterns produced always have facets aligned with the directions in this grid. But in case (c) the situation is different, and now the patterns produced turn out always to have the same overall rounded form, essentially independent of their orientation with respect to the underlying grid.

And indeed what happens is similar to what we have seen many times in this book: the evolution of the cellular automaton generates enough randomness that the effects of the underlying grid tend to be washed out, with the result that the overall behavior produced ends up showing essentially no distinction between different directions in space.

So should one conclude from this that the universe is in fact a giant cellular automaton with rules like those of case (c)?

It is perhaps not impossible, but I very much doubt it.

For there are immediately simple issues like what one imagines happens at the edges of the cellular automaton array. But much more important is the fact that I do not believe in the distinction between space and its contents implied by the basic construction of a cellular automaton.

For when one builds a cellular automaton one is in a sense always first setting up an array of cells to represent space itself, and then only subsequently considering the contents of space, as represented by the arrangement of colors assigned to the cells in this array.

But if the ultimate model for the universe is to be as simple as possible, then it seems much more plausible that both space and its contents should somehow be made of the same stuff—so that in a sense space becomes the only thing in the universe.

Several times in the past ideas like this have been explored. And indeed the standard theory for gravity introduced in 1915 is precisely based on the notion that gravity can be viewed merely as a feature of space. But despite various attempts in the 1930s and more recently it has never seemed possible to extend this to cover the whole elaborate collection of forces and particles that we actually see in our universe.

Yet my suspicion is that a large part of the reason for this is just the assumption that space is a perfect continuum—described by traditional mathematics. For as we have seen many times in this book, if one looks at systems like programs with discrete elements then it immediately becomes much easier for highly complex behavior to emerge. And this is fundamentally what I believe is happening at the lowest level in space throughout our universe.

Space as a Network

In the last section I argued that if the ultimate model of physics is to be as simple as possible, then one should expect that all the features of our universe must at some level emerge purely from properties of space. But what should space be like if this is going to be the case?

The discussion in the section before last suggests that for the richest properties to emerge there should in a sense be as little rigid underlying structure built in as possible. And with this in mind I believe that what is by far the most likely is that at the lowest level space is in effect a giant network of nodes.

In an array of cells like in a cellular automaton each cell is always assigned some definite position. But in a network of nodes, the nodes are not intrinsically assigned any position. And indeed, the only thing that is defined about each node is what other nodes it is connected to.

Yet despite this rather abstract setup, we will see that with a sufficiently large number of nodes it is possible for the familiar properties of space to emerge—together with other phenomena seen in physics.

I already introduced in Chapter 5 a particular type of network in which each node has exactly two outgoing connections to other nodes, together with any number of incoming connections. The reason I chose this kind of network in Chapter 5 is that there happens to be a fairly easy way to set up evolution rules for such networks. But in trying to find an ultimate model of space, it seems best to start by considering networks that are somehow as simple as possible in basic structure— and it turns out that the networks of Chapter 5 are somewhat more complicated than is necessary.

For one thing, there is no need to distinguish between incoming and outgoing connections, or indeed to associate any direction with each connection. And in addition, nothing fundamental is lost by requiring that all the nodes in a network have exactly the same total number of connections to other nodes.

With two connections, only very trivial networks can ever be made. But if one uses three connections, a vast range of networks immediately become possible. One might think that one could get a

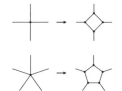

Examples of how nodes with more than three connections can be decomposed into collections of nodes with exactly three connections.

fundamentally larger range if one allowed, say, four or five connections rather than just three. But in fact one cannot, since any node with more than three connections can in effect always be broken into a collection of nodes with exactly three connections, as in the pictures on the left.

So what this means is that it is in a sense always sufficient to consider networks with exactly three connections at each node. And it is therefore these networks that I will use here in discussing fundamental models of space.

The pictures below show a few small examples of such networks. And already considerable diversity is evident. But none of the networks shown seem to have many properties familiar from ordinary space.

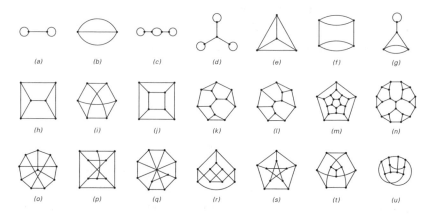

Examples of small networks with exactly three connections at each node. The first line shows all possible networks with up to four nodes. In what follows I consider only non-degenerate networks, in which there is at most one connection between any two nodes. Example (i) is the smallest network that cannot be drawn in two dimensions without lines crossing. Examples (k) and (l) are the smallest networks that have no symmetries between different nodes. Example (e) corresponds to the net of a tetrahedron, (j) to the net of a cube, and (m) to the net of a dodecahedron. Examples (o) through (u) show seven ways of drawing the same network, in this case the so-called Petersen network.

So how then can one get networks that correspond to ordinary space? The first step is to consider networks that have much larger numbers of nodes. And as examples of these, the pictures at the top of the facing page show networks that are specifically constructed to correspond to ordinary one-, two- and three-dimensional space.

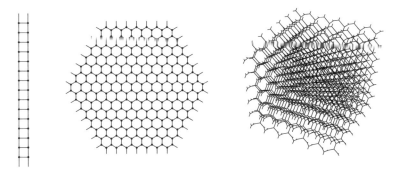

Examples of networks with three connections at each node that are effectively one, two and three-dimensional. These networks can be continued forever, and all have the property of being homogeneous, in the sense that every node has an environment identical to every other node.

Each of these networks is at the lowest level just a collection of nodes with certain connections. But the point is that the overall pattern of these connections is such that on a large scale there emerges a clear correspondence to ordinary space of a particular dimension.

The pictures above are drawn so as to make this correspondence obvious. But what if one was just presented with the raw pattern of connections for some network? How could one see whether the network could correspond to ordinary space of a particular dimension?

The pictures below illustrate the main difficulty: given only its pattern of connections, a particular network can be laid out in many completely different ways, most of which tell one very little about its potential correspondence with ordinary space.

    (a)   (b)   (c)   (d)   (e)   (f)

Six different ways of laying out the same network. (a) nodes arranged around a circle; (b) nodes arranged along a line; (c) nodes arranged across the page according to distance from a particular node; (d) 2D layout with network and spatial distances as close as possible; (e) planar layout; (f) 3D layout.

So how then can one proceed? The fundamental idea is to look at properties of networks that can both readily be deduced from their pattern of connections and can also be identified, at least in some large-scale limit, with properties of ordinary space. And the notion of distance is perhaps the most fundamental of such properties.

A simple way to define the distance between two points is to say that it is the length of the shortest path between them. And in ordinary space, this is normally calculated by subtracting the numerical coordinates of the positions of the points. But on a network things become more direct, and the distance between two nodes can be taken to be simply the minimum number of connections that one has to follow in order to get from one node to the other.

But can one tell just by looking at such distances whether a particular network corresponds to ordinary space of a certain dimension?

To a large extent one can. And a test is to see whether there is a way to lay out the nodes in the network in ordinary space so that the distances between nodes computed from their positions in space agree—at least in some approximation—with the distances computed directly by following connections in the network.

The three networks at the top of the previous page were laid out precisely so as to make this the case respectively for one, two and three-dimensional space. But why for example can the second network not be laid out equally well in one-dimensional rather than two-dimensional space? One way to see this is to count the number of nodes that appear at a given distance from a particular node in the network.

And for this specific network, the answer for this is very simple: at distance r there are exactly $3\,r$ nodes—so that the total number of nodes out to distance r grows like r^2. But now if one tried to lay out all these nodes in one dimension it is inevitable that the network would have to bulge out in order to fit in all the nodes. And it turns out that it is uniquely in two dimensions that this particular network can be laid out in a regular way so that distances based on following connections in it agree with ordinary distances in space.

For the other two networks at the top of the previous page similar arguments can be given. And in fact in general the condition for a network to correspond to ordinary d-dimensional space is precisely that the total number of nodes that appear in it out to distance r grows in some limiting sense like r^d—a result analogous to the standard mathematical fact that the area of a two-dimensional circle is πr^2, while the volume of a three-dimensional sphere is $4/3\,\pi r^3$, the volume of a four-dimensional hypersphere is $1/2\,\pi^2\,r^4$, and so on.

Below I show pictures of various networks. In each case the first picture is drawn to emphasize obvious regularities in the network. But the second picture is drawn in a more systematic way—by picking a specific starting node, and then laying out other nodes so that those at

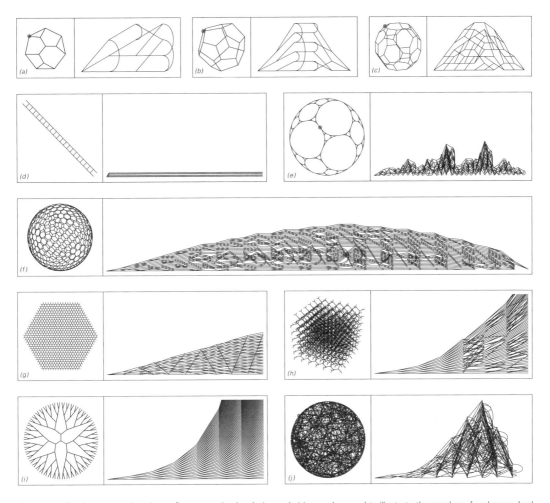

Examples of various networks, shown first to emphasize their regularities, and second to illustrate the number of nodes reached by going successively more steps from a given node. For networks that in a limiting sense correspond to ordinary d-dimensional space, this number grows like r^{d-1}. All the larger networks shown are approximately uniform, in the sense that similar results are obtained starting from any node. Network (e) effectively has limiting dimension $Log[2, 3] \simeq 1.58$.

successively greater network distances appear in successive columns across the page. And this setup has the feature that the height of column r gives the number of nodes that are at network distance r.

So by looking at how these heights grow across the page, one can see whether there is a correspondence with the r^{d-1} form that one expects for ordinary d-dimensional space. And indeed in case (g), for example, one sees exactly r^1 linear growth, reflecting dimension 2.

Similarly, in case (d) one sees r^0 growth, reflecting dimension 1, while in case (h) one sees r^2 growth, reflecting dimension 3.

Case (f) illustrates slightly more complicated behavior. The basic network in this case locally has an essentially two-dimensional form— but at large scales it is curved by being wrapped around a sphere. And what therefore happens is that for fairly small r one sees r^1 growth— reflecting the local two-dimensional form—but then for larger r there is slower growth, reflecting the presence of curvature.

Later in this chapter we will see how such curvature is related to the phenomenon of gravity. But for now the point is just that network (f) again behaves very much like ordinary space with a definite dimension.

So do all sufficiently large networks somehow correspond to ordinary space in a certain number of dimensions? The answer is definitely no. And as an example, network (i) from the previous page has a tree-like structure with 3^r nodes at distance r. But this number grows faster than r^d for any d—implying that the network has no correspondence to ordinary space in any finite number of dimensions.

If the connections in a network are chosen at random—as in case (j)—then again there will almost never be the kind of locality that is needed to get something that corresponds to ordinary finite-dimensional space.

So what might an actual network for space in our universe be like?

It will certainly not be as simple and regular as most of the networks on the previous page. For within its pattern of connections must be encoded everything we see in our universe.

And so at the level of individual connections, the network will most likely at first look quite random. But on a larger scale, it must be arranged so as to correspond to ordinary three-dimensional space. And somehow whatever rules update the network must preserve this feature.

The Relationship of Space and Time

To make an ultimate theory of physics one needs to understand the true nature not only of space but also of time. And I believe that here again the idea of thinking in terms of programs provides some crucial insights.

In our everyday experience space and time seem very different. For example, we can move from one point in space to another in more or less any way we choose. But we seem to be forced to progress through time in a very specific way. Yet despite such obvious apparent differences, almost all models in present-day fundamental physics have been built on the idea that space and time somehow work fundamentally the same.

But for most of the systems based on programs that I have discussed in this book this is certainly not true. And thus for example in a cellular automaton moving from one point in space to another just corresponds to shifting from one cell to another. But moving from one point in time to another involves actually applying the cellular automaton rule.

When we make a picture of the behavior of a cellular automaton, however, we do nevertheless tend to represent space and time in the same visual kind of way—with space going across the page and time going down. And in fact the basic notion of extending the idea of position in space to an idea of position in time has been common in scientific thought for more than five centuries.

But in the past century what has happened is that space and time have come to be thought of as being much more fundamentally similar. As we will discuss later in this chapter, the main origin of this is that in relativity theory certain aspects of space and time seem to become interchangeable. And from this there emerged the idea of thinking in terms of a spacetime continuum in which time appears merely as a fourth dimension just like the three ordinary dimensions of space.

So while in a system like a cellular automaton one typically imagines that a new and separate state of the system is somehow produced at each step in time, present-day physics more tends to think of the complete history of the universe throughout time as being just a single structure laid out in the four dimensions of spacetime.

So what then might determine the form of this structure?

The laws of physics in effect provide a collection of constraints on the structure. And while these laws are traditionally stated in terms of sophisticated mathematical equations, their basic character is similar to the simple constraints on arrays of black and white cells that I discussed at the end of Chapter 5. But now instead of defining constraints just in space, the laws of physics can be thought of as defining constraints on what can happen in both space and time.

Just as for space, it is my strong belief that time is fundamentally discrete. And from the discussion of networks for space in the previous section, one might imagine that perhaps the whole history of the universe in spacetime could be represented by a giant four-dimensional network.

By analogy with the systems at the end of Chapter 5 a simple model would then be that this network is determined by the constraint that around every one of its nodes the overall arrangement of other nodes must match some particular template or set of templates.

Yet much as in Chapter 5 it turns out often not to be especially easy to find out which networks, if any, satisfy specific constraints of this kind. The pictures on the facing page nevertheless show results for quite a few choices of templates—where in each case the dangling connections in a template are taken to go to nodes that are not part of the template itself.

Pictures (a) and (b) show what happens with the two very simplest possible templates—involving just a single node. In case (a), all networks are allowed except for ones in which a node is connected directly to itself. In case (b), only the single network shown is allowed.

With templates that involve nodes out to distance one there are a total of 11 distinct non-trivial cases. And of these, 8 allow no complete networks to be formed, as in picture (e). But there turn out to be three cases—shown as pictures (c), (d) and (f)—in which complete networks can be formed, and in each of these one discovers that a fairly simple infinite set of networks are actually allowed.

In order to have a meaningful model for the universe, however, what must presumably happen is that essentially just one network can satisfy whatever constraints there are, and this one network must then represent all of the complex spacetime history of our universe.

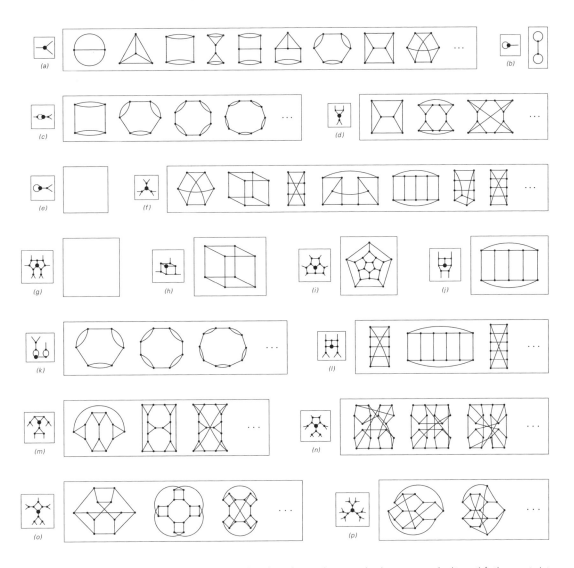

Examples of networks determined by constraints. In each case the networks shown are required to satisfy the constraint that around every node their form must correspond to the template shown, in such a way that no dangling connections in the template are joined to each other. The pictures include all 14 templates that involve nodes out to distance at most two for which complete networks can be formed. In most cases where any such network can be formed, an infinite sequence of networks is allowed. But in cases (b), (h), (i) and (j) just a single network turns out to be allowed. The network constraint systems shown here are analogs of the two-dimensional systems based on constraints discussed at the end of Chapter 5.

So what does one find if one allows templates that include nodes out to distance two? There are a total of 690 distinct non-trivial such templates—and of these, 681 allow no complete networks to be formed, as in case (g). Six of the remaining templates then again allow an infinite sequence of networks. But there are three templates—shown as cases (h), (i) and (j)—that turn out to allow just single networks. These networks are however rather simple, and indeed the most complicated of them—case (i)—has just 20 nodes, and corresponds to a dodecahedron.

So are there in fact reasonably simple sets of constraints that in the end allow just one highly complex network, or perhaps a family of similar networks? I tend to doubt it. For our experience in Chapter 5 was that even in the much more rigid case of arrays of black and white squares, it was rather difficult to find constraints that would succeed in forcing anything but very simple patterns to occur.

So what does this mean for getting the kind of complexity that we see in our universe? We have not had difficulty in getting remarkable complexity from systems like cellular automata that we have discussed in this book. But such systems work not by being required to satisfy constraints, but instead by just repeatedly applying explicit rules.

So is it in the end sensible to think of the universe as a single structure in spacetime whose form is determined by a set of constraints? Should we really imagine that the complete spacetime history of the universe somehow always exists, and that as time progresses, we are merely exploring different parts of it? Or should we instead think that the universe—more like systems such as cellular automata—explicitly evolves in time, so that at each moment a new state of the universe is in effect created, and the old one is lost?

Models based on traditional mathematical equations—in which space and time appear just as abstract symbolic variables—have never had to make much distinction between these two views. But in trying to understand the ultimate underlying mechanisms of the universe, I believe that one must inevitably distinguish between these views.

And I strongly believe that the second view is the one most likely to provide a meaningful underlying model for our universe. But while this view is closer to our everyday perception of time, it seems to contradict the correspondence between space and time that is built into most of present-day physics. So one might wonder how then it could be consistent with experiments that have been done in physics?

One possibility, illustrated in the pictures below, is to have a system that evolves in time according to explicit rules, but for these rules to have built into them a symmetry between space and time.

Examples of one-dimensional cellular automata which exhibit a symmetry between space and time. Each picture can be generated by starting from initial conditions at the top, and then just evolving down the page repeatedly applying the cellular automaton rule. The particular rules shown are reversible second-order ones with numbers 90R and 150R.

But I very much doubt that any such obvious symmetry between space and time exists in the fundamental rules for our universe. And instead what I expect is much like we have seen many times before in this book: that even though at the lowest level there is no direct correspondence between space and time, such a correspondence nevertheless emerges when one looks in the appropriate way at larger scales of the kind probed by practical experiments.

As I will discuss in the next several sections, I suspect that for many purposes the history of the universe can in fact be represented by a certain kind of spacetime network. But the way this network is formed in effect treats space and time rather differently. And in particular—just as in a system like a cellular automaton—the network can be built up incrementally by starting with certain initial conditions and then applying appropriate underlying rules over and over again.

Any such rules can in principle be thought of as providing a set of constraints for the spacetime network. But the important point is that there is no need to do a separate search to find networks that satisfy such constraints—for the rules themselves instead immediately define a procedure for building up the necessary network.

Time and Causal Networks

I argued in the last section that the progress of time should be viewed at a fundamental level much like the evolution of a system like a cellular automaton. But one of the features of a cellular automaton is that it is set up to update all of its cells together, as if at each tick of some global clock. Yet just as it seems unreasonable to imagine that the universe consists of a rigid grid of cells in space, so also it seems unreasonable to imagine that there is a global clock which defines the updating of every element in the universe synchronized in time.

But what is the alternative? At first it may seem bizarre, but one possibility that I believe is ultimately not too far from correct is that the universe might work not like a cellular automaton in which all cells get updated at once, but instead like a mobile automaton or Turing machine, in which just a single cell gets updated at each step.

As discussed in Chapter 3—and illustrated in the picture on the right—a mobile automaton has just a single active cell which moves around from one step to the next. And because this active cell is the only one that ever gets updated, there is never any issue about synchronizing behavior of different elements at a given step.

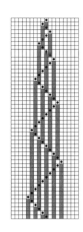

A mobile automaton in which only the single active cell indicated by a dot is updated at each step, thereby avoiding the issue of global synchronization.

Yet at first it might seem absurd to think that our universe could work like a mobile automaton. For certainly we do not notice any kind of active cell visiting different places in the universe in sequence. And indeed, to the contrary, our perception is that different parts of the universe seem to evolve in parallel and progress through time together.

But it turns out that what one perceives as happening in a system like a mobile automaton can depend greatly on whether one is looking at the system from outside, or whether one is oneself somehow part of the system. For from the outside, one can readily see each individual step in the evolution of a mobile automaton, and one can tell that there is just a single active cell that visits different parts of the system in sequence. But to an observer who is actually part of the mobile automaton, the perception can be quite different.

For in order to recognize that time has passed, or indeed that anything has happened, the state of the observer must somehow change. But if the observer itself just consists of a collection of cells inside a mobile automaton, then no such change can occur except on steps when the active cell in the mobile automaton visits this collection of cells.

And what this means is that between any two successive moments of time as perceived by an observer inside the mobile automaton, there can be a great many steps of underlying mobile automaton evolution.

If an observer could tell what was happening on every step, then it would be easy to recognize the sequential way in which cells are updated. But because an observer who is part of a mobile automaton can in effect only occasionally tell what has happened, then as far as such an observer is concerned, many cells can appear to have been updated in parallel between successive moments of time.

To see in more detail how this works it could be that it would be necessary to make a specific model for the observer. But in fact, it turns out that it is sufficient just to look at the evolution of the mobile automaton not in terms of individual steps, but rather in terms of updating events and the causal relationships between them.

The pictures on the facing page show an example of how this works. Picture (a) is a version of the standard representation that I have used for mobile automaton evolution elsewhere in the book—in which successive lines give the colors of cells on successive steps, and the position of the active cell is indicated at each step by a gray dot. The subsequent pictures on the facing page all ultimately give essentially the same information, but gradually present it to emphasize more a representation in terms of updating events and causal relationships.

Picture (b) is very similar to (a), but shows successive steps of mobile automaton evolution separated, with gray blobs in between indicating "updating events" corresponding to each application of the underlying mobile automaton rule. Picture (b) still has a definite row of cells for each individual step of mobile automaton evolution. But in picture (c) cells not updated on a given step are merged together, yielding vertical stripes of color that extend from one updating event to another.

So what is the significance of these stripes? In essence they serve to carry the information needed to determine what the next updating event will be. And as picture (d) begins to emphasize, one can think of these stripes as indicating what causal relationships or connections exist between updating events.

And this notion then suggests a quite different representation for the whole evolution of the mobile automaton. For rather than having a picture based on successive individual steps of evolution, one can instead form a network of the various causal relationships between updating events, with each updating event being a node in this network, and each stripe being a connection from one node to another.

A sequence of views of the evolution of a mobile automaton, showing how a network of causal relationships between updating events can be created. This network provides a very simple model for spacetime in the universe. Picture (a) is essentially the standard representation of mobile automaton evolution that I have used in this book. Picture (b) includes gray blobs to indicate updating events. Picture (c) merges cells that are not being updated. Picture (d) emphasizes the role of vertical stripes as connections between updating events. Pictures (e) through (g) show how a network can be formed with nodes corresponding to updating events. Pictures (h) and (i) demonstrate that with the particular underlying rule used here, a highly regular network is produced. ▶

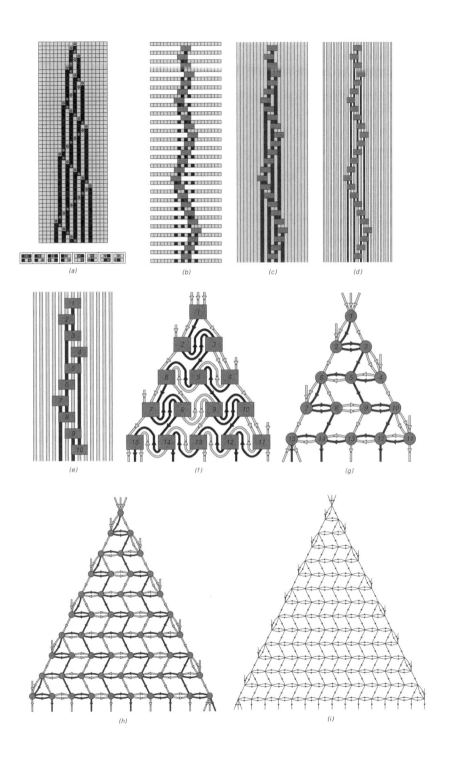

(a)   (b)   (c)   (d)

(e)   (f)   (g)

(h)   (i)

Picture (e) shows the updating events and stripes from the top of picture (d), with the updating events now explicitly numbered. Pictures (f) and (g) then show how one can take the pattern of connectivity from picture (e) and lay out the updating events as nodes so as to produce an orderly network. And for the particular mobile automaton rule used here, the network one gets ends up being highly regular, as illustrated in pictures (h) and (i).

So what is the significance of this network? It turns out that it can be thought of as defining a structure for spacetime as perceived by an observer inside the mobile automaton—in much the same way as the networks we discussed two sections ago could be thought of as defining a structure for space. Each updating event, corresponding to each node in the network, can be imagined to take place at some point in spacetime. And the connections between nodes in the network can then be thought of as defining the pattern of neighbors for points in spacetime.

But unlike in the space networks that we discussed two sections ago, the connections in the causal networks we consider here always go only one way: each connection corresponds to a causal relationship in which one event leads to another, but not the other way around.

This kind of directionality, however, is exactly what is needed if a meaningful notion of time is to emerge. For the progress of time can be defined by saying that only those events that occur later in time than a particular event can be affected by that event.

And indeed the networks in pictures (g) through (i) on the previous page were specifically laid out so that successive rows of nodes going down the page would correspond, at least roughly, to events occurring at successively later times.

As the numbering in pictures (e) through (g) illustrates, there is no direct correspondence between this notion of time and the sequence of updating events that occur in the underlying evolution of the mobile automaton. For the point is that an observer who is part of the mobile automaton will never see all the individual steps in this evolution. The most they will be able to tell is that a certain network of causal relationships exists—and their perception of time must therefore derive purely from the properties of this network.

So does the notion of time that emerges actually have the familiar features of time as we know it? One might think for example that in a network there could be loops that would lead to a deviation from the linear progression of time that we appear to experience. But in fact, with a causal network constructed from an underlying evolution process in the way we have done it here no such loops can ever occur.

So what about traces of the sequential character of evolution in the original mobile automaton? One might imagine that with only a single active cell being updated at each step different parts of the system would inevitably be perceived to progress through time one after another. But what the pictures on page 489 demonstrate is that this need not be the case. Indeed, in the networks shown there all the nodes on each row are in effect connected in parallel to the nodes on the row below. So even though the underlying rules for the mobile automaton involve no global synchronization, it is nevertheless possible for an observer inside the mobile automaton to perceive time as progressing in a synchronized way.

Later in this chapter I will discuss how space works in the context of causal networks—and how ideas of relativity theory emerge. But for now one can just think of networks like those on page 489 as being laid out so that time goes down the page and space goes across. And one can then see that if one follows connections in the network, one is always forced to go progressively down the page, even though one is able to move both backwards and forwards across the page—thus agreeing with our everyday experience of being able to move in more or less any direction in space, but always being forced to move onward in time.

So what happens with other mobile automata?

The pictures on the next two pages show a few examples.

Rules (a) and (b) yield very simple repetitive networks in which there is in effect a notion of time but not of space. The underlying way any mobile automaton works forces time to continue forever. But with rules (a) and (b) only a limited number of points in space can ever be reached.

The other rules shown do not, however, suffer from this problem: in all of them progressively more points are reached in space as time goes on. Rules (c) and (d) yield networks that can be laid out in a quite

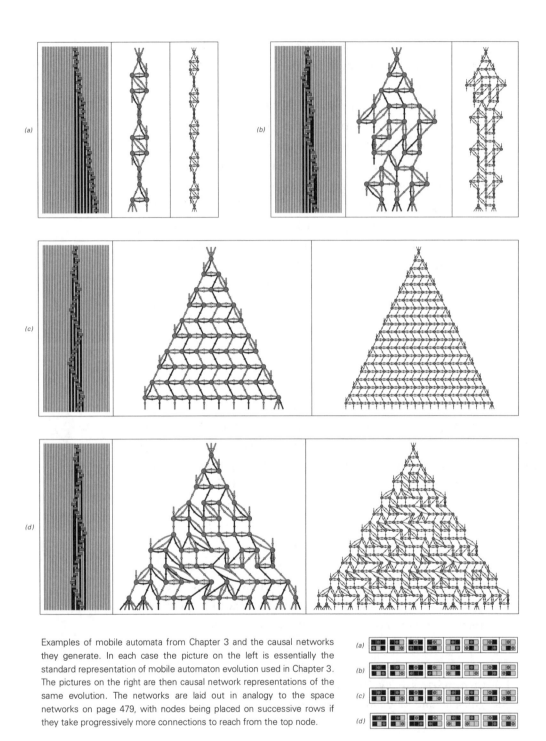

Examples of mobile automata from Chapter 3 and the causal networks they generate. In each case the picture on the left is essentially the standard representation of mobile automaton evolution used in Chapter 3. The pictures on the right are then causal network representations of the same evolution. The networks are laid out in analogy to the space networks on page 479, with nodes being placed on successive rows if they take progressively more connections to reach from the top node.

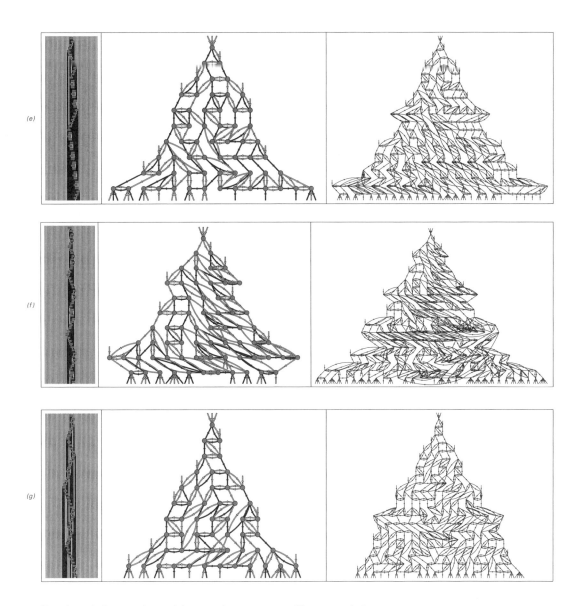

Note that a single connection can join events that occur at very different steps in the evolution of the underlying mobile automaton. And indeed to construct even a small part of the causal network can require an arbitrarily long computation in the underlying mobile automaton. Thus for example to make the causal networks in pictures (e), (f) and (g) requires looking respectively at 2447, 731 and 322 steps of mobile automaton evolution. And indeed in some cases there can be connections that are in effect never resolved. And thus for example in picture (a) there are downward connections that never reach any other node—reflecting the presence of positions on the left in the mobile automata evolution to which the active cell never returns.

regular manner. But with rules (e), (f) and (g) the networks are more complicated, and begin to seem somewhat random.

The procedure that is used to lay out the networks on the previous two pages is a direct analog of the procedure used for space networks on page 479: the row in which a particular node will be placed is determined by the minimum number of connections that have to be followed in order to reach that node starting from the node at the top.

In cases (a) and (c) the networks obtained in this way have the property that all connections between nodes go either across or down the page. But in every other case shown, at least some connections also go up the page. So what does this mean for our notion of time? As mentioned earlier, there can never be a loop in any causal network that comes from an evolution process. But if one identifies time with position down the page, the presence of connections that go up as well as down the page implies that in some sense time does not always progress in the same direction. Yet at least in the cases shown here there is still a strong average flow down the page—agreeing with our everyday perception that time progresses only in one direction.

Like in so many other systems that we have studied in this book, the randomness that we find in causal networks will inevitably tend to wash out details of how the networks are constructed. And thus, for example, even though the underlying rules for a mobile automaton always treat space and time very differently, the causal networks that emerge nevertheless often exhibit a kind of uniform randomness in which space and time somehow work in many respects the same.

But despite this uniformity at the level of causal networks, the transformation from mobile automaton evolution to causal network is often far from uniform. And for example the pictures at the top of the facing page show the causal networks for rules (e) and (f) from the previous page—but now with each node numbered to specify the step of mobile automaton evolution from which it was derived.

And what we see is that even nodes that are close to the top of the causal network can correspond to events which occur after a large number of steps of mobile automaton evolution. Indeed, to fill in just twenty rows

Causal networks corresponding to rules (e) and (f) from page 493, with each node explicitly labelled to specify from which step of mobile automaton evolution it is derived. Even to fill in the first few rows of such causal networks, many steps of underlying mobile automaton evolution must be traced.

of the causal networks for rules (e) and (f) requires following the underlying mobile automaton evolution for 2447 and 731 steps respectively.

One feature of causal networks is that they tell one not only what the consequences of a particular event will be, but also in a sense what its causes were. Thus, for example, if one starts, say, with event 17 in the first causal network above, then to find out that its causes were events 11 and 16 one simply has to trace backwards along the connections which lead to it.

With the specific type of underlying mobile automaton used here, every node has exactly three incoming and three outgoing connections. And at least when there is overall apparent randomness, the networks that one gets by going forwards and backwards from a particular node will look very similar. In most cases there will still be small differences; but the causal network on the right above is specifically constructed to be exactly reversible—much like the cellular automata we discussed near the beginning of this chapter.

Looking at the causal networks we have seen so far, one may wonder to what extent their form depends on the particular properties of the underlying mobile automata that were used to produce them.

For example, one might think that the fact that all the networks we have seen so far grow at most linearly with time must be an inevitable consequence of the one-dimensional character of the mobile automaton rules we have used. But the picture below demonstrates that even with such one-dimensional rules, it is actually possible to get causal networks that grow more rapidly. And in fact in the case shown below there are roughly a factor 1.22 more nodes on each successive row—corresponding to overall approximate exponential growth.

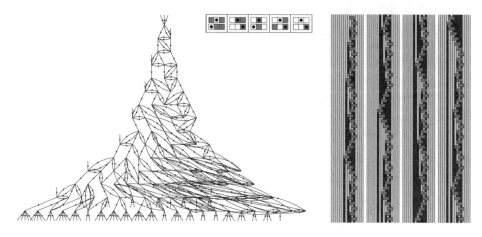

A one-dimensional mobile automaton which yields a causal network that in effect grows exponentially with time. The underlying mobile automaton acts like a binary counter, yielding a pattern whose width grows logarithmically with the number of steps. The three cases not shown in the rule are never used with the initial conditions given here.

The causal network for a system is always in some sense dual to the underlying evolution of the system. And in the case shown here the slow growth of the region visited by the active cell in the underlying evolution is reflected in rapid growth of the corresponding causal network.

As we will see later in this chapter there are in the end some limitations on the kinds of causal networks that one-dimensional mobile automata and systems like them can produce. But with different mobile automaton rules one can still already get tremendous diversity.

And even though when viewed from outside, systems like mobile automata might seem to have almost none of the familiar features of our universe, what we see is that if we as observers are in a sense part of such systems then immediately some major features quite similar to those of our universe can emerge.

The Sequencing of Events in the Universe

In the last section I discussed one type of model in which familiar notions of time can emerge without any kind of built-in global clock. The particular models I used were based on mobile automata—in which the presence of a single active cell forces only one event ever to occur in the universe at once. But as we will see in this section, there is actually no need for the setup to be so rigid, or indeed for there to be any kind of construct like an active cell.

One can think of mobile automata as being special cases of substitution systems of the type I introduced in Chapter 3. Such systems in general take a string of elements and at each step replace blocks of these elements with other elements according to some definite rule.

The picture below shows an example of one such system, and illustrates how—just like in a mobile automaton—relations between updating events can be represented by a causal network.

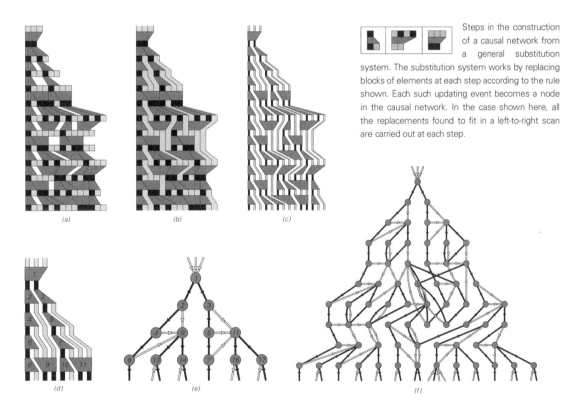

Steps in the construction of a causal network from a general substitution system. The substitution system works by replacing blocks of elements at each step according to the rule shown. Each such updating event becomes a node in the causal network. In the case shown here, all the replacements found to fit in a left-to-right scan are carried out at each step.

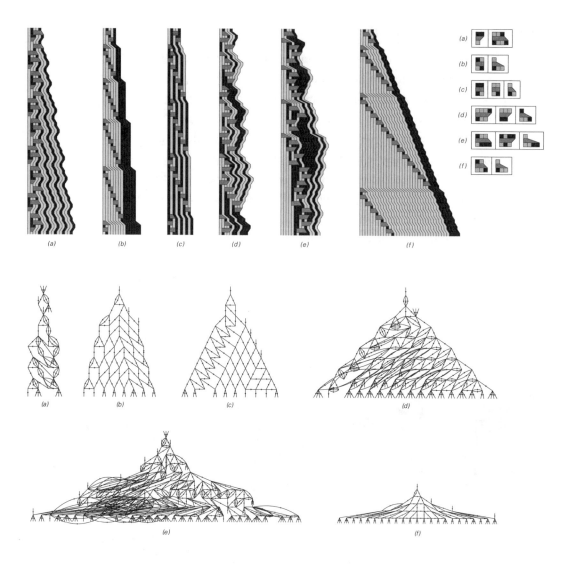

Examples of sequential substitution systems of the type discussed on page 88, and the causal networks that emerge from them. In a sequential substitution system only the first replacement that is found to apply in a left-to-right scan is ever performed at any step. Rule (a) above yields a causal network that is purely repetitive and thus yields no meaningful notion of space. Rules (b), (c) and (d) yield causal networks that in effect grow roughly linearly with time. In rule (f) the causal network grows exponentially, while in rule (e) the causal network also grows quite rapidly, though its overall growth properties are not clear. Note that to obtain the 10 levels shown here in the causal network for rule (e), it was necessary to follow the evolution of the underlying substitution system for a total of 258 steps.

Substitution systems that correspond to mobile automata can be thought of as having rules and initial conditions that are specially set up so that only one updating event can ever occur on any particular step. But with most rules—including the one shown on the previous page—there are usually several possible replacements that can be made at each step.

One scheme for deciding which replacement to make is just to scan the string from left to right and then pick the first replacement that applies. This scheme corresponds exactly to the sequential substitution systems we discussed in Chapter 3.

The pictures on the facing page show a few examples of what can happen. The behavior one gets is often fairly simple, but in some cases it can end up being highly complex. And just as in mobile automata, the causal networks that emerge typically in effect grow linearly with time. But, again as in mobile automata, there are rules such as (a) in which there is no growth—and effectively no notion of space. And there are also rules such as (f)—which turn out to be much more common in general substitution systems than in mobile automata—in which the causal network in effect grows exponentially with time.

But why do only one replacement at each step? The pictures on the next page show what happens if one again scans from left to right, but now one performs all replacements that fit, rather than just the first one.

In the case of rules (a) and (b) the result is to update every single element at every step. But since the replacements in these particular rules involve only one element at a time, one in effect has a neighbor-independent substitution system of the kind we discussed on page 82. And as we discovered there, such systems can only ever produce rather simple behavior: each element repeatedly branches into several others, yielding a causal network that has the form of a regular tree.

So what happens with replacements that involve more than just one element? In many cases, the behavior is still quite simple. But as several of the pictures on the next page demonstrate, fairly simple rules are sufficient—as in so many other systems that we have discussed in this book—to obtain highly complex behavior.

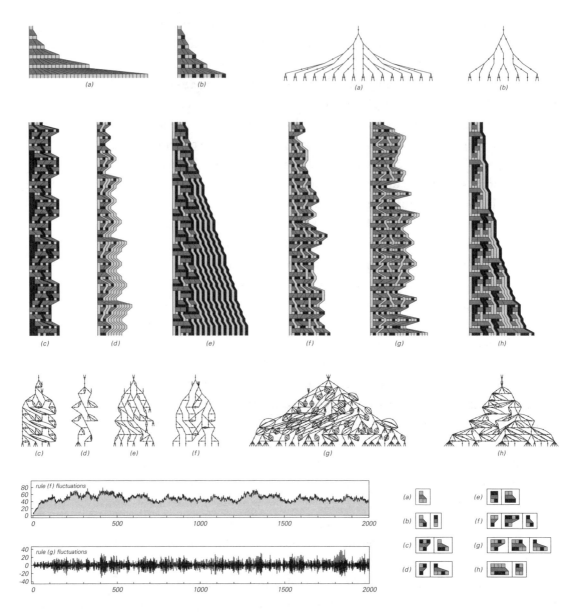

Examples of general substitution systems and the causal networks that emerge from them. In the pictures shown here, every replacement that is found to fit in a left-to-right scan is performed at each step. Rules (a) and (b) act like neighbor-independent substitution systems of the type discussed on page 84, and yield exponentially growing tree-like causal networks. The plots at the bottom show the growth rates of the patterns produced by rules (f) and (g). In the case of rule (f) the pattern turns out to be repetitive, with a period of 796 steps.

One may wonder, however, to what extent the behavior one sees depends on the exact scheme that one uses to pick which replacements to apply at each step. The answer is that for the vast majority of rules—including rules (c) through (g) in the picture on the facing page—using different schemes yields quite different behavior—and a quite different causal network.

But remarkably enough there do exist rules for which exactly the same causal network is obtained regardless of what scheme is used. And as it turns out, rules (a) and (b) from the picture on the facing page provide simple examples of this phenomenon, as illustrated in the pictures below.

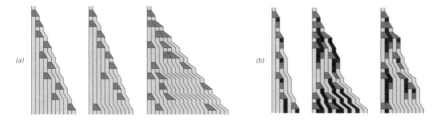

The behavior of rules (a) and (b) from the facing page when replacements are performed at random. Even though the detailed patterns obtained are different, the causal networks in these particular rules that represent relationships between replacement events are always exactly the same.

For each rule, the three different pictures shown above correspond to three different ways that replacements can be made. And while the positions of particular updating events are different in every picture, the point is that the network of causal connections between these events is always exactly the same.

This is certainly not true for every substitution system. Indeed, the pictures on the right show how it can fail, for example, for rule (e) from the facing page. What one sees in these pictures is that after event 4, different choices of replacements are made in the two cases, and the causal relationships implied by these replacements are different.

So what could ensure that no such situation would ever arise in a particular substitution system? Essentially what needs to be true is that the sequence of elements alone must always uniquely determine what replacements can be made in every part of the system. One still has a

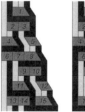

case 1   *case 2*

Examples of two different ways of performing replacements in rule (e) from the facing page, yielding two different causal networks.

choice of whether actually to perform a given replacement at a particular step, or whether to delay that replacement until a subsequent step. But what must be true is that there can never be any ambiguity about what replacement will eventually be made in any given part of the system.

In rules like the ones at the top of page 500 where each replacement involves just a single element this is inevitably how things must work. But what about rules that have replacements involving blocks of more than one element? Can such rules still have the necessary properties?

The pictures below show two examples of rules that do. In the first picture for each rule, replacements are made at randomly chosen steps, while in the second picture, they are in a sense always made at the earliest possible step. But the point is that in no case is there any ambiguity about what replacement will eventually be made at any particular place in the system. And as a result, the causal network that represents the relationships between different updating events is always exactly the same.

(a) 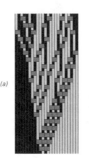    (b)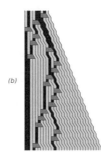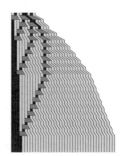

(a) (b) Examples of substitution systems in which the same causal networks are obtained regardless of the way in which replacements are performed. In the first picture for each rule, the replacements are performed essentially at random. In the second picture they are performed on the earliest possible step. Note that rule (a) effectively sorts the elements in its initial conditions, always placing black before white.

So what underlying property must the rules for a substitution system have in order to make the system as a whole operate in this way? The basic answer is that somehow different replacements must never be able to interfere with each other. And one way to guarantee this is if the blocks involved in replacements can never overlap.

In both the rules shown on the facing page, the only replacement specified is for the block ▫■. And it is inevitably the case that in any sequence of ▫'s and ■'s different blocks of the form ▫■ do not overlap. If one had replacements for blocks such as ■■, ▫▫ or ■▫■ then these could overlap. But there is an infinite sequence of blocks such as ■▫, ■▫▫ or ■▫▫▫ for which no overlap is possible, and thus for which different replacements can never interfere.

If a rule involves replacements for several distinct blocks, then to avoid the possibility of interference one must require that these blocks can never overlap either themselves or each other. The simplest non-trivial pair of blocks that has this property is ■■▫▫, ■■■▫, while the simplest triple is ■■▫▫▫, ■■■▫▫, ■■■■▫. And any substitution system whose rules specify replacements only for blocks such as these is guaranteed to yield the same causal network regardless of the order in which replacements are performed.

In general the condition is in fact somewhat weaker. For it is not necessary that no overlaps exist at all in the replacements—only that no overlaps occur in whatever sequences of elements can actually be generated by the evolution of the substitution systems.

And in the end there are then all sorts of substitution systems which have the property that the causal networks they generate are always independent of the order in which their rules are applied.

So what does this mean for models of the universe?

In a system like a cellular automaton, the same underlying rule is in a sense always applied in exact synchrony to every cell at every step. But what we have seen in this section is that there also exist systems in which rules can in effect be applied whenever and wherever one wants—but the same definite causal network always emerges.

So what this means is that there is no need for any built-in global clock, or even for any mechanism like an active cell. Simply by choosing the appropriate underlying rules it is possible to ensure that any sequence of events consistent with these rules will yield the same causal network and thus in effect the same perceived history for the universe.

Uniqueness and Branching in Time

If our universe has no built-in global clock and no construct like an active cell, then it is almost inevitable that at the lowest level there will be at least some arbitrariness in how its rules can be applied.

Yet in the previous section we discovered the rather remarkable fact that there exist rules with the property that essentially regardless of how they are applied, the same causal network—and thus the same perceived history for the universe—will always emerge.

But must it in the end actually be true that the underlying rules for our universe force there to be a unique perceived history? Near the end of Chapter 5 I introduced multiway systems as examples of systems that allow multiple histories. And it turns out that multiway systems are actually extremely similar in basic structure to the substitution systems that I discussed in the previous section.

Both types of systems perform the same type of replacements on strings of elements. But while in a substitution system one always carries out just a single set of replacements at each step, getting a single new string, in a multiway system one instead carries out every possible replacement, thereby typically generating many new strings.

The picture below shows a simple example of how this works. On the first step in this particular picture, there happens to be only one replacement that can be performed consistent with the rules, so only a single string is produced. But on subsequent steps several different replacements are possible, so several strings are produced. And in general every path through a picture like this corresponds to a possible history that exists in the evolution of the multiway system.

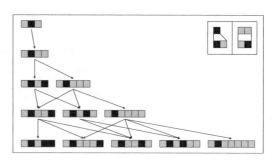

A simple example of a multiway system in which replacements are applied in all possible ways to each string at each step.

So is it conceivable that the ultimate model for our universe could be based on a multiway system? At first one might not think so. For our everyday impression is that our universe has just one definite history, not some kind of whole collection of different histories. And assuming that one is able to look at a multiway system from the outside, one will immediately see that different paths exist corresponding to different histories.

But the crucial point is that if the complete state of our universe is in effect like a single string in a multiway system, then there is no way for us ever to look at the multiway system from the outside. And as entities inside the multiway system, our perception will inevitably be that just a single path was followed, corresponding to a single history.

If one were able to look at the multiway system from the outside, this path would seem quite arbitrary. But for us inside the multiway system it is the unique path that represents the thread of experience we have had.

Up until a few centuries ago, it was widely believed that the Earth had some kind of fundamentally unique position in space. But gradually it became clear that this was not so, and that in a sense it was merely our own presence that made our particular location in space seem in any way unique. Yet for time the belief still exists that we—and our universe—somehow have a unique history. But if in fact our universe is part of a multiway system, then this will not be true. And indeed the only thing that will be unique about the particular history that our universe has had will be that it is the one we have experienced.

At a purely human level I find it rather disappointing to think that essentially none of the details of our existence are in any way unique, and that there might be other paths in the multiway system on which everything would be different. And scientifically it is also unsatisfying to have to say that there are features of our universe which are not determined by any finite set of underlying rules, but are instead in a sense just pure accidents of history associated with the particular path that we have happened to follow in a multiway system.

In the early parts of Chapter 7 we discussed various possible origins for the apparent randomness that we see in many natural systems. And if the universe is described by a multiway system, then there will be an additional source of randomness: the arbitrariness of the path corresponding to the history that we have experienced.

In many respects this randomness is similar to the randomness from the environment that we discussed at the beginning of Chapter 7. But an important difference is that it would occur even if one could in effect perfectly isolate a system from the rest of the universe. If in the past one had seen apparent randomness in such a system there might have seemed to be no choice but to assume something like an underlying multiway system. But one of the discoveries of this book is that it is actually quite possible to generate what appears to be almost perfect randomness just by following definite underlying rules.

And indeed I would not expect that observations of randomness could ever reasonably be used to show that our universe is part of a multiway system. And in fact my guess is that the only way to show this with any certainty would be actually to find a specific set of multiway system rules with the property that regardless of the path that gets followed these rules would always yield behavior that agrees with the various observed features of our universe.

At some level it might seem surprising that a multiway system could ever consistently exhibit any particular form of behavior. For one might imagine that with so many different paths to choose from it would often be the case that almost any behavior would be able to occur on some path or another. And indeed, as the picture on the left shows, it is not difficult to construct multiway systems in which all possible strings of a particular kind are produced.

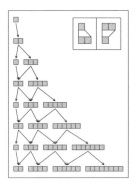

A multiway system in which strings of any length can be generated—but in which only specific sequences of lengths actually occur on any path.

But if one looks not just at individual strings but rather at the sequences of strings that exist along paths in the multiway system, then one finds that these can no longer be so arbitrary. And indeed, in any multiway system with a limited set of rules, such sequences must necessarily be subject to all sorts of constraints.

In general, each path in a multiway system can be thought of as being defined by a possible sequence of ways in which the replacements specified by a multiway system rule can be applied. And each such path in turn then defines a causal network of the kind we discussed in the previous section. But as we saw there, certain underlying rules have the property that the form of this causal network ends up being the same regardless of the order in which replacements are applied—and thus regardless of the path that is followed in the multiway system.

The pictures below show some simple examples of rules with this property. And as it turns out, it is fairly easy to recognize the presence of the property from the overall pattern of multiway system paths that occur.

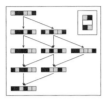
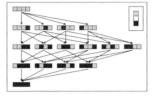

Examples of multiway systems in which the causal network associated with every path is exactly the same. All such multiway systems have the property that every pair of paths which diverge at a particular step can converge again on the following step. The first rule shown has the effect of sorting the elements in the string.

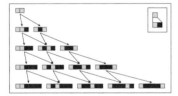
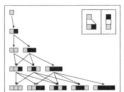

If one starts from a given initial string, then typically one will generate different strings by applying different replacements. But if one is going to get the same causal network, then it must always be the case that there are replacements one can apply to the strings one has generated that yield the same final string. So what this means is that any pair of paths in the multiway system that diverge must be able to converge again within just one step—so that all the arrows in pictures like the ones above must lie on the edges of quadrilaterals.

Most multiway systems, however, do not have exactly this property, and as a result the causal networks that are obtained by following different paths in them will not be absolutely identical. But it still turns out that whenever paths can always eventually converge—even if not in a fixed number of steps—there will necessarily be similarities on a sufficiently large scale in the causal networks that are obtained.

At the level of individual events, the structure of the causal networks will typically vary greatly. But if one looks at large enough collections of events, these details will tend to be washed out, and regardless of the path one chooses, the overall form of causal network will be essentially the same. And what this means is that on a sufficiently large scale, the universe will appear to have a unique history, even though at the level of individual events there will be considerable arbitrariness.

If there is not enough convergence in the multiway system it will still be possible to get stuck with different types of strings that never lead to each other. And if this happens, then it means that the history of the universe can in effect follow many truly separate branches. But whenever there is significant randomness produced by the evolution of the multiway system, this does not typically appear to occur.

So this suggests that in fact it is at some level not too difficult for multiway systems to reproduce our everyday perception that more or less definite things happen in the universe. But while this means that it might be possible for there to be arbitrariness in the causal network for the universe, it still tends to be my suspicion that there is not—and that in fact the particular rules followed by the universe do in the end have the property that they always yield the same causal network.

Evolution of Networks

Earlier in this chapter, I suggested that at the lowest level space might consist of a giant network of nodes. But how might such a network evolve?

The most straightforward possibility is that it could work much like the substitution systems that we have discussed in the past few sections—and that at each step some piece or pieces of the network could be replaced by others according to some fixed rule.

The pictures at the top of the facing page show two very simple examples. Starting with a network whose connections are like the edges of a tetrahedron, both the rules shown work by replacing each node at each step by a certain fixed cluster of nodes.

This setup is very much similar to the neighbor-independent substitution systems that we discussed on pages 83 and 187. And just as in these systems, it is possible for intricate structures to be produced, but the structures always turn out to have a highly regular nested form.

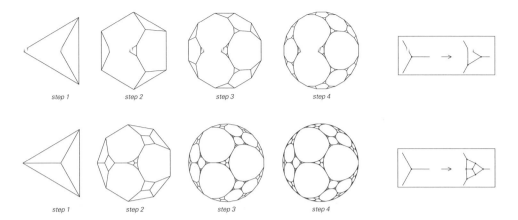

Network evolution in which each node is replaced at each step by a fixed cluster of nodes. The resulting networks have a regular nested form. The dimensions of the limiting networks are respectively *Log[2, 3] ≈ 1.58* and *Log[3, 7] ≈ 1.77*.

So what about more general substitution systems? Are there analogs of these for networks? The answer is that there are, and they are based on making replacements not just for individual nodes, but rather for clusters of nodes, as shown in the pictures below.

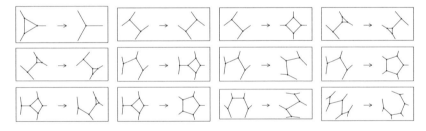

Examples of rules that involve replacing clusters of nodes in a network by other clusters of nodes. All these rules preserve the planarity of a network. Notice that some of them cannot be reversed since their right-hand sides are too symmetrical to determine which orientation of the left-hand side should be used.

In the substitution systems for strings discussed in previous sections, the rules that are given can involve replacing any block of elements by any other. But in networks there are inevitably some restrictions. For example, if a cluster of nodes has a certain number of connections to the rest of the network, then it cannot be replaced by a cluster which has a different number of connections. And in addition, one cannot have replacements

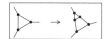

A replacement whose outcome orientation cannot be determined.

like the one on the left that go from a symmetrical cluster to one for which a particular orientation has to be chosen.

But despite these restrictions a fairly large number of replacements are still possible; for example, there are a total of 419 distinct ones that exist involving clusters with no more than five nodes.

So given a replacement for a cluster of a particular form, how should such a replacement actually be applied to a network? At first one might think that one could set up some kind of analog of a cellular automaton and just replace all relevant clusters of nodes at once.

But in general this will not work. For as the picture below illustrates, a particular form of cluster can in general appear in many overlapping ways within a given network.

 The 12 ways in which the cluster of nodes on the left occurs in a particular network. In the particular case shown, each way turns out to overlap with nodes in exactly four others.

The issue is essentially no different from the one that we encountered in previous sections for blocks of elements in substitution systems on strings. But an additional complication is that in networks, unlike strings, there is no immediately obvious ordering of elements.

Nevertheless, it is still possible to devise schemes for deciding where in a network replacements should be carried out. One fairly simple scheme, illustrated on the facing page, allows only a single replacement to be performed at each step, and picks the location of this replacement so as to affect the least recently updated nodes.

In each pair of pictures in the upper part of the page, the top one shows the form of the network before the replacement, and the bottom one shows the result after doing the replacement—with the cluster of nodes involved in the replacement being highlighted in both cases. In the 3D pictures in the lower part of the page, networks that arise on successive steps are shown stacked one on top of the other, with the nodes involved in each replacement joined by gray lines.

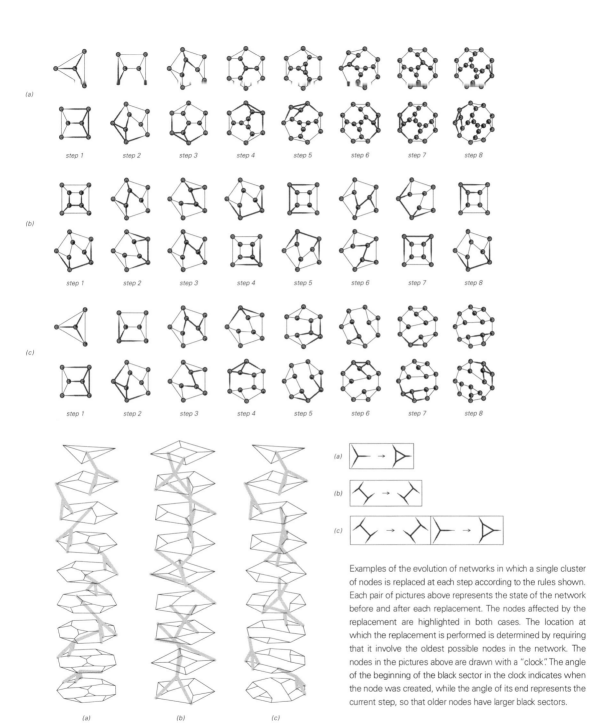

(a)

step 1 step 2 step 3 step 4 step 5 step 6 step 7 step 8

(b)

step 1 step 2 step 3 step 4 step 5 step 6 step 7 step 8

(c)

step 1 step 2 step 3 step 4 step 5 step 6 step 7 step 8

(a)

(b)

(c)

(a) *(b)* *(c)*

Examples of the evolution of networks in which a single cluster of nodes is replaced at each step according to the rules shown. Each pair of pictures above represents the state of the network before and after each replacement. The nodes affected by the replacement are highlighted in both cases. The location at which the replacement is performed is determined by requiring that it involve the oldest possible nodes in the network. The nodes in the pictures above are drawn with a "clock". The angle of the beginning of the black sector in the clock indicates when the node was created, while the angle of its end represents the current step, so that older nodes have larger black sectors.

Inevitably there is a certain arbitrariness in the way these pictures are drawn. For the underlying rules specify only what the pattern of connections in a network should be—not how its nodes should be laid out on the page. And in the effort to make clear the relationship between networks obtained on different steps, even identical networks can potentially be drawn somewhat differently.

With rule (a), however, it is fairly easy to see that a simple nested structure is produced, directly analogous to the one shown on page 509. And with rule (b), obvious repetitive behavior is obtained.

So what about more complicated behavior? It turns out that even with rule (c), which is essentially just a combination of rules (a) and (b), significantly more complicated behavior can already occur.

The picture below shows a few more steps in the evolution of this rule. And the behavior obtained never seems to repeat, nor do the networks produced exhibit any kind of obvious nested form.

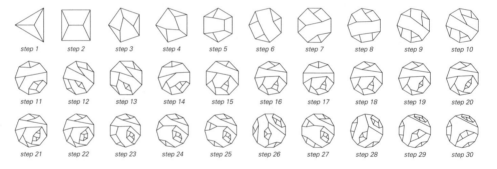

More steps in the evolution of rule (c) from the previous page. The number of nodes increases irregularly (though roughly linearly) with successive steps.

What about other schemes for applying replacements? The pictures on the facing page show what happens if at each step one allows not just a single replacement, but all replacements that do not overlap.

It takes fewer steps for networks to be built up, but the results are qualitatively similar to those on the previous page: rule (a) yields a nested structure, rule (b) gives repetitive behavior, while rule (c) produces behavior that seems complicated and in some respects random.

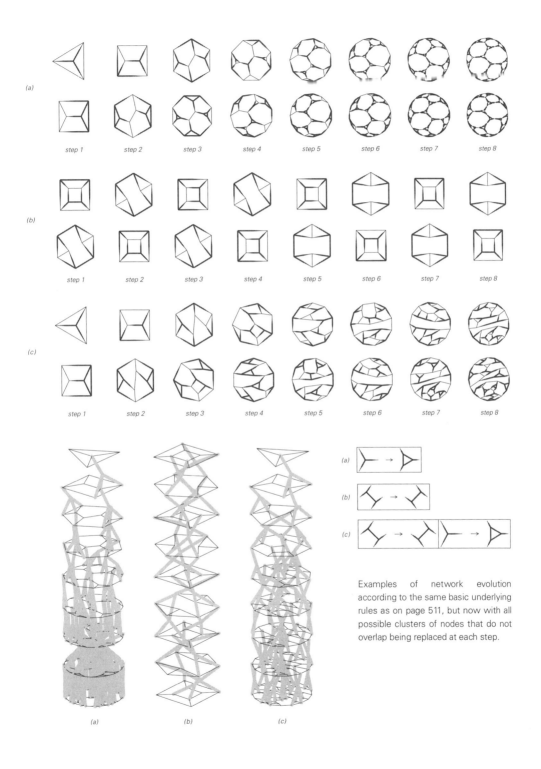

step 1   step 2   step 3   step 4   step 5   step 6   step 7   step 8

(b)

step 1   step 2   step 3   step 4   step 5   step 6   step 7   step 8

(c)

step 1   step 2   step 3   step 4   step 5   step 6   step 7   step 8

(a)   (b)   (c)

(a)

(b)

(c)

Examples of network evolution according to the same basic underlying rules as on page 511, but now with all possible clusters of nodes that do not overlap being replaced at each step.

Just as for substitution systems on strings, one can find causal networks that represent the causal connections between different updating events on networks. And as an example the pictures below show such causal networks for the evolution processes on the previous page.

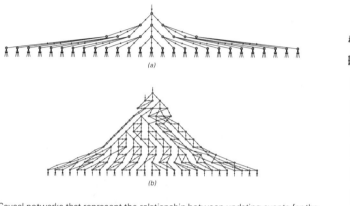

Causal networks that represent the relationship between updating events for the network evolution processes shown on the previous page.

In the rather simple case of rule (a) the results turn out to be independent of the updating scheme that was used. But for rules (b) and (c), different schemes in general yield different causal networks.

So what kinds of underlying replacement rules lead to causal networks that are independent of how the rules are applied? The situation is much the same as for strings—with the basic criterion just being that all replacements that appear in the rules should be for clusters of nodes that can never overlap themselves or each other.

The pictures below show all possible distinct clusters with up to five nodes—and all but three of these already can overlap themselves.

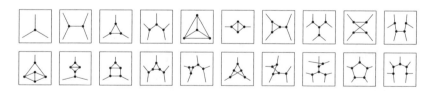

All possible distinct clusters containing up to five nodes, with planarity not required.

But among slightly larger clusters there turn out to be many that do not overlap themselves—and indeed this becomes common as soon as there are at least two connections between each dangling one.

The first few examples are shown below. And in almost all of these, there is no overlap not only within a single cluster, but also between different clusters. And this means that rules based on replacements for collections of these clusters will have the property that the causal networks they produce are independent of the updating scheme used.

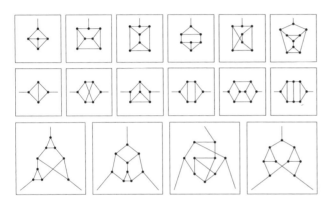

The simplest clusters that have no overlaps with themselves—and mostly have no overlaps with each other. Replacements for sets of clusters that do not overlap have the property of causal invariance.

One feature of the various rules I showed earlier is that they all maintain planarity of networks—so that if one starts with a network that can be laid out in the plane without any lines crossing, then every subsequent network one gets will also have this property.

Yet in our everyday experience space certainly does not seem to have this property. But beyond the practical problem of displaying what happens, there is actually no fundamental difficulty in setting up rules that can generate non-planarity—and indeed many rules based on the clusters above will for example do this.

So in the end, if one manages to find the ultimate rules for the universe, my expectation is that they will give rise to networks that on a small scale look largely random. But this very randomness will most likely be what for example allows a definite and robust value of 3 to emerge for the dimensionality of space—even though all of the many complicated phenomena in our universe must also somehow be represented within the structure of the same network.

Space, Time and Relativity

Several sections ago I argued that as observers within the universe everything we can observe must at some level be associated purely with the network of causal connections between events in the universe. And in the past few sections I have outlined a series of types of models for how such a causal network might actually get built up.

But how do the properties of causal networks relate to our normal notions of space and time? There turn out to be some slight subtleties—but these seem to be exactly what end up yielding the theory of relativity.

As we saw in earlier sections, if one has an explicit evolution history for a system it is straightforward to deduce a causal network from it. But given only a causal network, what can one say about the evolution history?

The picture below shows an example of how successive steps in a particular evolution history can be recovered from a particular set of slices through the causal network derived from it. But what if one were to choose a different set of slices? In general, the sequence of strings that one would get would not correspond to anything that could arise from the same underlying substitution system.

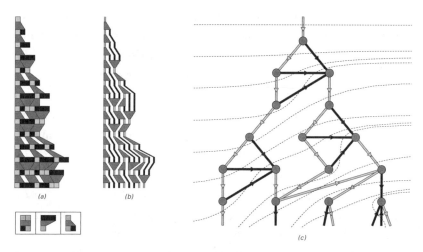

(a)   (b)   (c)

An example of how the succession of states in an evolution history can be recovered by taking appropriate slices through a causal network. Any consistent choice of such slices will correspond to a possible evolution history—with the same underlying rules, but potentially a different scheme for determining the order in which to apply replacements.

But if one has a system that yields the same causal network independent of the scheme used to apply its underlying rules, then the situation is different. And in this case any slice that consistently divides the causal network into a past and a future must correspond to a possible state of the underlying system—and any non-overlapping sequence of such slices must represent a possible evolution history for the system.

If we could explicitly see the particular underlying evolution history for the system that corresponds to our universe then this would in a sense immediately provide absolute information about space and time in the universe. But if we can observe only the causal network for the universe then our information about space and time must inevitably be deduced indirectly from looking at slices of causal networks.

And indeed only some causal networks even yield a reasonable notion of space at all. For one can think of successive slices through a causal network as corresponding to states at successive moments in time. But for there to be something one can reasonably think of as space one has to be able to identify some background features that stay more or less the same—which means that the causal network must yield consistent similarities between states it generates at successive moments in time.

One might have thought that if one just had an underlying system which did not change on successive steps then this would immediately yield a fixed structure for space. But in fact, without updating events, no causal network at all gets built up. And so a system like the one at the top of the next page is about the simplest that can yield something even vaguely reminiscent of ordinary space.

In practice I certainly do not expect that even parts of our universe where nothing much seems to be going on will actually have causal networks as simple as at the top of the next page. And in fact, as I mentioned at the end of the previous section, what I expect instead is that there will always tend to be all sorts of complicated and seemingly random behavior at small scales—though at larger scales this will typically get washed out to yield the kind of consistent average properties that we ordinarily associate with space.

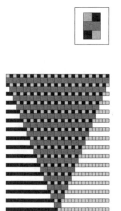

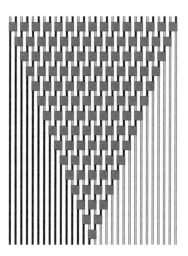

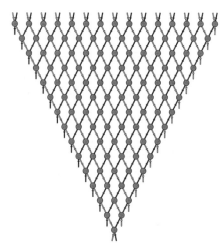

A very simple substitution system whose causal network has slices that can be thought of as corresponding to a highly regular idealization of one-dimensional ordinary space. The rule effectively just sorts elements so that black ones come first, and yields the same causal network regardless of what updating scheme is used.

One of the defining features of space as we normally experience it is a certain locality that leads most things that happen at some particular position to be able at first to affect only things very near them.

Such locality is built into the basic structure of systems like cellular automata. For in such systems the underlying rules allow the color of a particular cell to affect only its immediate neighbors at each step. And this has the consequence that effects in such systems can spread only at a limited rate, as manifest for example in a maximum slope for the edges of patterns like those in the pictures below.

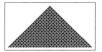 

Examples of patterns produced by cellular automata, illustrating the fact discussed in Chapter 6 that the edge of each pattern has a maximum slope equal to one cell per step, corresponding to an absolute upper limit on the rate of information transmission—similar to the speed of light in physics.

In physics there also seems to be a maximum speed at which the effects of any event can spread: the speed of light, equal to about 300 million meters per second. And it is common in spacetime physics to draw "light cones" of the kind shown at the right to indicate the region that will be reached by a light signal emitted from a particular position in space at a particular time. So what is the analog of this in a causal network?

Schematic illustration of a light cone in physics. Light emitted at a point in space will normally spread out with time into a cone, whose cross-section is shown schematically here.

The answer is straightforward, for the very definition of a causal network shows that to see how the effects of a particular event spread one just has to follow the successive connections from it in the causal network.

But in the abstract there is no reason that these connections should lead to points that can in any way be viewed as nearby in space. Among the various kinds of underlying systems that I have studied in this book many have no particular locality in their basic rules. But the particular kinds of systems I have discussed for both strings and networks in the past few sections do have a certain locality, in that each individual replacement they make involves only a few nearby elements.

One might choose to consider systems like these just because it seems easier to specify their rules. But their locality also seems important in giving rise to anything that one can reasonably recognize as space.

For without it there will tend to be no particular way to match up corresponding parts in successive slices through the causal networks that are produced. And as a result there will not be the consistency between successive slices necessary to have a stable notion of space.

In the case of substitution systems for strings, locality of underlying replacement rules immediately implies overall locality of effects in the system. For the different elements in the system are always just laid out in a one-dimensional string, with the result that local replacement rules can only ever propagate effects to nearby elements in the string—much like in a one-dimensional cellular automaton.

If one is dealing with an underlying system based on networks, however, then the situation can be somewhat more complicated. For as we discussed several sections ago—and will discuss again in the final sections of this chapter—there will typically be only an approximate correspondence between the structure of the network and the structure of ordinary space. And so for example—as we will discuss later in connection with quantum phenomena—there may sometimes be a kind of thread that connects parts of the network that would not normally be considered nearby in three-dimensional space. And so when clusters of nodes that are nearby with respect to connections on the network get updated, they can potentially propagate effects to what might be considered distant points in space.

Nevertheless, if a network is going to correspond to space as it seems to exist in our universe, such phenomena must not be too important—and in the end there must to a good approximation be the kind of straightforward locality that exists for example in the simple causal network of page 518.

In the next section I will discuss how actual physical entities like particles propagate in systems represented by causal networks. But ultimately the whole point of causal networks is that their connections represent all possible ways that effects propagate. Yet these connections are also what end up defining our notions of space and time in a system. And particularly in a causal network as regular as the one on page 518 one can then immediately view each connection in the causal network as corresponding to an effect propagating a certain distance in space during a certain interval in time.

So what about a more complicated causal network? One might imagine that its connections could perhaps represent varying distances in space and varying intervals in time. But there is no independent way to work out distance in space or interval in time beyond looking at the connections in the causal network. So the only thing that ultimately makes sense is to measure space and time taking each connection in the causal network to correspond to an identical elementary distance in space and elementary interval in time.

One may guess that this elementary distance is around 10^{-35} meters, and that the elementary time interval is around 10^{-43} seconds. But whatever these values are, a crucial point is that their ratio must be a fixed speed, and we can identify this with the speed of light. So this means that in a sense every connection in a causal network can be viewed as representing the propagation of an effect at the speed of light.

And with this realization we are now close to being able to see how the kinds of systems I have discussed must almost inevitably succeed in reproducing the fundamental features of relativity theory.

But first we must consider the concept of motion.

To say that one is not moving means that one imagines one is in a sense sampling the same region of space throughout time. But if one is moving—say at a fixed speed—then this means that one imagines that the region of space one is sampling systematically shifts with time, as illustrated schematically in the simple pictures on the right.

Graphical representation in space and time of motion at fixed speeds.

But as we have seen in discussing causal networks, it is in general quite arbitrary how one chooses to match up space at different times. And in fact one can just view different states of motion as corresponding to different such choices: in each case one matches up space so as to treat the point one is at as being the same throughout time.

Motion at a fixed speed is then the simplest case—and the one emphasized in the so-called special theory of relativity. And at least in the context of a highly regular causal network like the one in the picture on page 518 there is a simple interpretation to this: it just corresponds to looking at slices at different angles through the causal network.

Successive parallel slices through the causal network in general correspond to successive states of the underlying system at successive moments in time. But there is nothing that determines in any absolute way the overall angle of these slices in pictures like those on page 518. And the point is that in fact one can interpret slices at different angles as corresponding to motion at different fixed speeds.

If the angle is so great that there are connections going up as well as down between slices, then there will be a problem. But otherwise it will always be the case that regardless of angle, successive slices must correspond to possible evolution histories for the underlying system.

One might have thought that states obtained from slices at different angles would inevitably be consistent only with different sets of underlying rules. But in fact this is not the case, and instead the exact same rules can reproduce slices at all angles. And this is a consequence of the fact that the substitution system on page 518 has the property of causal invariance—so that it gives the same causal network independent of the scheme used to apply its underlying rules.

It is slightly more complicated to represent uniform motion in causal networks that are not as regular as the one on page 518. But whenever there is sufficient uniformity to give a stable structure to space one can still think of something like parallel slices at different angles as representing motion at different fixed speeds.

And the crucial point is that whenever the underlying system is causal invariant the exact same underlying rules will account for what one sees in slices at different angles. And what this means is that in effect the same rules will apply regardless of how fast one is going.

And the remarkable point is then that this is also what seems to happen in physics. For everyday experience—together with all sorts of detailed experiments—strongly support the idea that so long as there are no effects from acceleration or external forces, physical systems work exactly the same regardless of how fast they are moving.

At the outset it might not have seemed conceivable that any system which at some level just applies a fixed program to various underlying elements could successfully capture the phenomenon of motion. For certainly a system like a typical cellular automaton does not—since for example its effective rules for evolution at different angles will usually be quite different. But there are two crucial ideas that make motion work in the kinds of systems I am discussing here. First, that causal networks can represent everything that can be observed. And second, that with causal invariance different slices through a causal network can be produced by the same underlying rules.

Historically, the idea that physical processes should always be independent of overall motion goes back at least three hundred years. And from this idea one expects for example that light should always travel at its usual speed with respect to whatever emitted it. But what if one happens to be moving with respect to this emitter? Will the light then appear to be travelling at a different speed? In the case of sound it would. But what was discovered around the end of the 1800s is that in the case of light it does not. And it was essentially to explain this surprising fact that the special theory of relativity was developed.

In the past, however, there seemed to be no obvious underlying mechanism that could account for the validity of this basic theory. But now it turns out that the kinds of discrete causal network models that I have described almost inevitably end up being able to do this.

And essentially the reason for this is that—as I discussed above—each individual connection in any causal network must almost by definition represent propagation of effects at the speed of light. The overall structure of space that emerges may be complicated, and there may be objects that end up moving at all sorts of speeds. But at least locally the individual connections basically define the speed of light as a fixed maximum rate of propagation of any effect. And the point is that they do this regardless of how fast the source of an effect may be moving.

So from this one can use essentially standard arguments to derive all the various phenomena familiar from ordinary relativity theory. A typical example is time dilation, in which a fixed time interval for a system moving at some speed seems to correspond to a longer time interval for a system at rest. The picture on the next page shows schematically how this at first unexpected result arises.

The basic idea is to consider what happens when a system that can act as a simple clock moves at different speeds. At a traditional physics level one can think of the clock as having a photon of light bouncing backwards and forwards between mirrors a fixed distance apart. But more generally one can think of following criss-crossing connections that exist in some fixed fragment of a causal network.

In the picture on the next page time goes down the page. The internal mechanism of the clock is shown as a zig-zag black line—with each sweep of this line corresponding to the passage of one unit of time.

The black line is always assumed to be moving at the speed of light—so that it always lies on the surface of a light cone, as indicated in the top row of pictures. But then in successive pictures the whole clock is taken to move at increasing fractions of the speed of light.

The dark gray region in each picture represents a fixed amount of time for the clock—corresponding to a fixed number of sweeps of the black line. But as the pictures indicate, it is then essentially just a matter of geometry to see that this dark gray region will correspond to progressively larger amounts of time for a system at rest—in just the way predicted by the standard formula of relativistic time dilation.

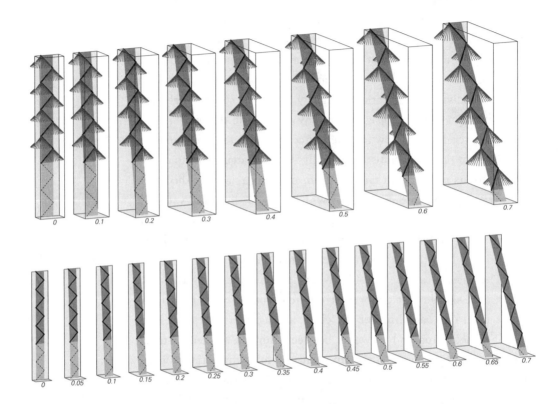

A simple derivation of the classic phenomenon of relativistic time dilation. The pictures show the behavior of a very simple idealized clock going at different fractions of the speed of light. The clock can be thought of as consisting of a photon of light bouncing backwards and forwards between mirrors a fixed distance apart. (At a more general level in my approach it can also be thought of as a fragment of a causal network.) Time is shown going down the page, so that the photon in the clock traces out a zig-zag path. The fundamental assumption—that in my approach is just a consequence of basic properties of causal networks—is that the photon always goes at the speed of light, so that its path always lies on the surface of light cones like the ones in the top row of pictures. A fixed interval of time for the clock—as indicated by the length of the darker gray regions—corresponds to a progressively longer interval of time at rest. The amount of this time dilation is given by the classic relativistic formula $1/\sqrt{1-v^2/c^2}$, where v/c is the ratio of the speed of the clock to the speed of light. Such time dilation is routinely observed in particle accelerators—and has to be corrected for in GPS satellites. It leads to the so-called twin paradox in which less time will pass for a member of a twin going at high speed in a spacecraft than one staying at rest. The fact that time dilation is a general phenomenon not restricted to something like the simple clock shown relies in my approach on general properties of causal networks. Once the basic assumptions are established, the derivation of time dilation given here is no different in principle from the original one given in 1905, though I believe it is in many ways considerably clearer. Note that it is necessary to consider motion in two dimensions—so that the clock as a whole can be moving perpendicular to the path of the photon inside it. If these were parallel, one would inevitably get not just pure time dilation, but a mixture of it and length contraction.

Elementary Particles

There are some aspects of the universe—notably the structure of space and time—that present-day physics tends to assume are continuous. But over the past century it has at least become universally accepted that all matter is made up of identifiable discrete particles.

Experiments have found a fairly small number of fundamentally different kinds of particles, with electrons, photons, muons and the six basic types of quarks being a few examples. And it is one of the striking observed regularities of the universe that all particles of a given kind—say electrons—seem to be absolutely identical in their properties.

But what actually are particles? As far as present-day experiments can tell, electrons, for example, have zero size and no substructure. But particularly if space is discrete, it seems almost inevitable that electrons and other particles must be made up of more fundamental elements.

So how might this work? An immediate possibility that I suspect is actually not too far from the mark is that such particles are analogs of the localized structures that we saw earlier in this book in systems like the class 4 cellular automata shown on the right. And if this is so, then it means that at the lowest level, the rules for the universe need make no reference to particular particles. Instead, all the particles we see would just emerge as structures formed from more basic elements.

In networks it can be somewhat difficult to visualize localized structures. But the picture below nevertheless shows a simple example of how a localized structure can move across a regular planar network.

Both the examples on this page show structures that exist on very regular backgrounds. But to get any kind of realistic model for actual

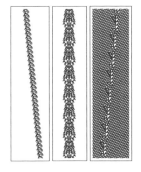

Typical examples of particle-like localized structures in class 4 cellular automata.

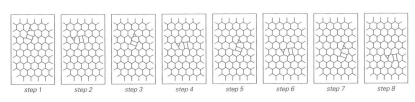

step 1   step 2   step 3   step 4   step 5   step 6   step 7   step 8

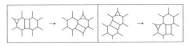

A particle-like localized structure in a network.

particles in physics one must consider structures on much more complicated and random backgrounds. For any network that has a serious chance of representing actual space—even a supposedly empty part—will no doubt show all sorts of seemingly random activity. So any localized structure that might represent a particle will somehow have to persist even on this kind of random background.

Yet at first one might think that such randomness would inevitably disrupt any kind of definite persistent structure. But the pictures below show two simple examples where it does not. In the first case, there are localized cracks that persist. And in the second case, there are two different types of regions, separated by boundaries that act like localized structures with definite properties, and persist until they annihilate.

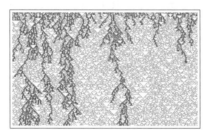 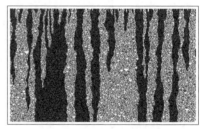

Examples of one-dimensional cellular automata that support various forms of persistent structures even on largely random backgrounds. These are 3-color totalistic rules with codes 294 and 1893.

So what about networks? It turns out that here again it is possible to get definite structures that persist even in the presence of randomness. And to see an example of this consider setting up rules like those on page 509 that preserve the planarity of networks.

Starting off with a network that is planar—so that it can be drawn flat on a page without any lines crossing—such rules can certainly give all sorts of complex and apparently random behavior. But the way the rules are set up, all the networks they produce must still be planar.

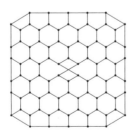

A network with a single irreducible crossing of lines.

And if one starts off with a network like the one on the left that can only be drawn with lines crossing, then what will happen is that the non-planarity of the network will be preserved. But to what extent does this non-planarity correspond to a definite structure in the network?

There are typically many different ways to draw a non-planar network, each with lines crossing in different places. But there is a fundamental result in graph theory that shows that if a network is not planar, then it must always be possible to identify in it a specific part that can be reduced to one of the two forms shown on the right—or just the second form for a network with three connections at each node.

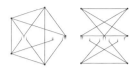

The K_5 and $K_{3,3}$ forms that lead to non-planarity in networks.

So this implies that one can in fact meaningfully associate a definite structure with non-planarity. And while at some level the structure can be spread out in the network, the point is that it must always in effect have a localized core with the form shown on the right.

In general one can imagine having several pieces of non-planarity in a network—perhaps each pictured like a carrying handle. But if the underlying rules for the network preserve planarity then each of these pieces of non-planarity must on their own be persistent—and can in a sense only disappear through processes like annihilating with each other.

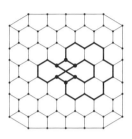

How $K_{3,3}$ is embedded in the network from the facing page.

So might these be like actual particles in physics?

In the realistic case of network rules for the universe, planarity as such is presumably not preserved. But observations in physics suggest that there are several quantities like electric charge that are conserved. And ultimately the values of these quantities must reflect properties of underlying networks that are preserved by network evolution rules.

And if these rules satisfy the constraint of causal invariance that I discussed in previous sections, then I suspect that this means that they will inevitably exhibit various additional features—perhaps notably including for example what is usually known as local gauge invariance.

But what is most relevant here is that it seems likely that—much as for non-planarity—nonzero values of quantities conserved by network evolution rules can be thought of as being associated with some sort of local structures or tangles of connections in the network. And I suspect that it is essentially such structures that define the cores of the various types of elementary particles that are seen in physics.

Before the results of this book it might have seemed completely implausible that anything like this could be correct. For independent of any specific arguments about networks and their evolution, traditional intuition would tend to make one think that the elaborate properties of particles must inevitably be the result of an elaborate underlying setup. But what we have now seen over and over again in this book is that in fact it is perfectly possible to get phenomena of great complexity even with a remarkably simple underlying setup. And I suspect that particles in physics—with all their various properties and interactions—are just yet another example of this very general phenomenon.

One immediate thing that might seem to suggest that elementary particles must somehow be based on simple discrete structures is the fact that their values of quantities like electric charge always seem to be in simple rational ratios. In traditional particle physics this is explained by saying that many if not all particles are somehow just manifestations of the same underlying abstract object, related by a simple fixed group of symmetry operations. But in terms of networks one can imagine a much more explicit explanation: that there are just a simple discrete set of possible structures for the cores of particles—each perhaps related in some quite mechanical way by the group of symmetry operations.

But in addition to quantities like electric charge, another important intrinsic property of all particles is mass. And unlike for example electric charge the observed masses of elementary particles never seem to be in simple ratios—so that for example the muon is about 206.7683 times the mass of the electron, while the tau lepton is about 16.819 times the mass of the muon. But despite such results, it is still conceivable that there could in the end be simple relations between truly fundamental particle masses—since it turns out that the masses that have actually been observed in effect also include varying amounts of interaction energy.

A defining feature of any particle is that it can somehow move in space while maintaining its identity. In traditional physics, such motion has a straightforward mathematical representation, and it has not usually seemed meaningful to ask what might underlie it. But in the approach that I take here, motion is no longer such an intrinsic concept, and the motion of a particle must be thought of as a process that is made up of a whole sequence of explicit lower-level steps.

So at first, it might seem surprising that one can even set up a particular type of particle to move at different speeds. But from the discussion in the previous section it follows that this is actually an almost inevitable consequence of having underlying rules that show causal invariance. For assuming that around the particle there is some kind of uniformity in the causal network—and thus in the apparent structure of space—taking slices through the causal network at an appropriate angle will always make any particle appear to be at rest. And the point is that causal invariance then implies that the same underlying rules can be used to update the network in all such cases.

But what happens if one has two particles that are moving with different velocities? What will the events associated with the second particle look like if one takes slices through the causal network so that the first particle appears to be at rest? The answer is that the more the second particle moves between successive slices, the more updating events must be involved. For in effect any node that was associated with the particle on either one slice or the next must be updated—and the more the particle moves, the less these will overlap. And in addition, there will inevitably appear to be an asymmetry in the pattern of events relative to whatever direction the particle is moving.

There are many subtleties here, and indeed to explain the details of what is going on will no doubt require quite a few new and rather abstract concepts. But the general picture that I believe will emerge is that when particles move faster they will appear to have more nodes associated with them.

Most likely the intrinsic properties of a particle—like its electric charge—will be associated with some sort of core that corresponds to a definite network structure involving a roughly fixed number of nodes. But I suspect that the apparent motion of the particle will be associated with a kind of coat that somehow interpolates from the core to the uniform background of surrounding space. With different slices through the causal network, the apparent size of this coat can change. But I suspect that the size of the coat in a particular case will somehow be related to the apparent energy and momentum of a particle in that case.

An important fact in traditional physics is that interactions between particles seem to conserve total energy and momentum. And conceivably the reason for this is that such interactions somehow tend to preserve the total number of network nodes. Indeed, perhaps in most situations—save those associated with the overall expansion of the universe—the basic rules for the network at least on average just rearrange nodes and never change their number.

In traditional physics energy and momentum are always assumed to have continuous values. But just as in the case of position there is no contradiction with sufficiently small underlying discrete elements.

As I will discuss in the last section of this chapter, quantum mechanics tends to make one think of particles with higher momenta as being somehow progressively less spread out in space. So how can this be consistent with the idea that higher momentum is associated with having more nodes? Part of the answer probably has to do with the fact that outside the piece of the network that corresponds to the particle, the network presumably matches up to yield uniform space in much the same way as without the particle. And within the piece of the network corresponding to the particle, the effective structure of space may be very different—with for example more long-range connections added to reduce the effective overall distance.

The Phenomenon of Gravity

At an opposite extreme from elementary particles one can ask how the universe behaves on the largest possible scales. And the most obvious effect on such scales is the phenomenon of gravity. So how then might this emerge from the kinds of models I have discussed here?

The standard theory of gravity for nearly a century has been general relativity—which is based on the idea of associating gravity with curvature in space, then specifying how this curvature relates to the energy and momentum of whatever matter is present.

Something like a magnetic field in general has different effects on objects made of different materials. But a key observation verified experimentally to considerable accuracy is that gravity has exactly the same effect on the motion of different objects, regardless of what those objects are made of. And it is this that allows one to think of gravity as a general feature of space—rather than for example as some type of force that acts specifically on different objects.

In the absence of any gravity or forces, our normal definition of space implies that when an object moves from one point to another, it always goes along a straight line, which corresponds to the shortest path. But when gravity is present, objects in general move on curved paths. Yet these paths can still be the shortest—or so-called geodesics— if one takes space to be curved. And indeed if space has appropriate curvature one can get all sorts of paths, as in the pictures below.

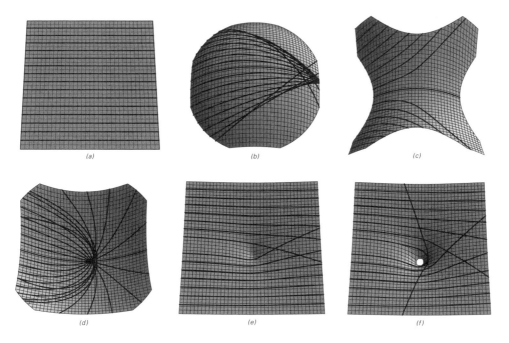

Examples of the effect of curvature in space on paths taken by objects. In each case all the paths shown start parallel, but do not remain so when there is curvature. The paths are geodesics which go the minimum distance on the surface to get to all the points they reach. (In general, the minimum may only be local.) Case (b) shows the top of a sphere, which is a surface of positive curvature. Case (c) shows the negatively curved surface $z = x^2 - y^2$, (d) a paraboloid $z = x^2 + y^2$, and (e,f) $z = 1/(r + \delta)$—a rough analog of curvature in space produced by a sphere of mass.

But in our actual universe what determines the curvature of space? The answer from general relativity is that the Einstein equations give conditions for the value of a particular kind of curvature in terms of the energy and momentum of matter that is present. And the point then is that the shortest paths in space with this curvature seem to be consistent with those followed by objects moving under the influence of gravity associated with the given distribution of matter.

For a continuous surface—or in general a continuous space—the idea of curvature is a familiar one in traditional geometry. But if the universe is at an underlying level just a discrete network of nodes then how does curvature work? At some level the answer is that on large scales the discrete network must approximate continuous space.

But it turns out that one can actually also recognize curvature in the basic structure of a network. If one has a simple array of hexagons—as in the picture on the left—then this can readily be laid out flat on a two-dimensional plane. But what if one replaces some of these hexagons by pentagons? One still has a fundamentally two-dimensional surface. But if one tries to keep all edges the same length the surface will inevitably become curved—like a soccer ball or a geodesic dome.

So what this suggests is that in a network just changing the pattern of connections can in effect change the overall curvature. And indeed the pictures below show a succession of networks that in effect have curvatures with a range of negative and positive values.

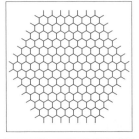

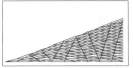

A hexagonal array corresponding to flat two-dimensional space.

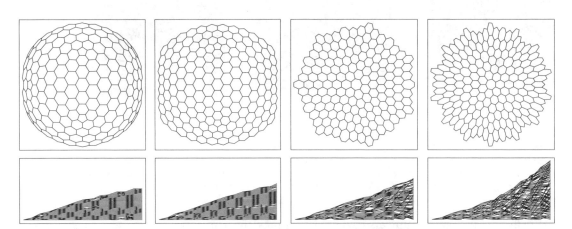

Networks with various limiting curvatures. If every region in the network is in effect a hexagon—as in the picture at the top of the page—then the network will behave as if it is flat. But if pentagons are introduced, as in the cases on the left, the network will increasingly behave as if it has positive curvature—like part of a sphere. And if heptagons are introduced, as in the cases on the right, the network will behave as if it has negative curvature. In the bottom row of pictures, the networks are laid out as on page 479, so that successive heights give the number of nodes at successive distances r from a particular node. In the limit of large r, this number is approximately $r^2 (1 - k r^2 + ...)$ where k turns out to be exactly proportional to the curvature.

But how can we determine the curvature from the structure of each network? Earlier in this chapter we saw that if a network is going to correspond to ordinary space in some number of dimensions d, then this means that by going r connections from any given node one must reach about r^{d-1} nodes. But it turns out that when curvature is present it leads to a systematic correction to this.

In each of the pictures on the facing page the network shown can be thought of as corresponding to two-dimensional space. And this means that to a first approximation the number of nodes reached must increase linearly with r. But the bottom row of pictures show that there are corrections to this. And what happens is that when there is positive curvature—as in the pictures on the left—progressively fewer than r nodes end up being reached. But when there is negative curvature—as on the right—progressively more nodes end up being reached. And in general the leading correction to the number of nodes reached turns out to be proportional to the curvature multiplied by r^{d+1}.

So what happens in more than two dimensions? In general the result could be very complicated, and could for example involve all sorts of different forms of curvature and other characteristics of space. But in fact the leading correction to the number of nodes reached is always quite simple: it is just proportional to what is called the Ricci scalar curvature, multiplied by r^{d+1}. And already here this is some suggestion of general relativity—for the Ricci scalar curvature also turns out to be a central quantity in the Einstein equations.

But in trying to see a more detailed correspondence there are immediately a variety of complications. Perhaps the most obvious is that the traditional mathematical formulation of general relativity seems to rely on many detailed properties of continuous space. And while one expects that sufficiently large networks should in some sense act on average like continuous space, it is far from clear at first how the kinds of properties of relevance to general relativity will emerge.

If one starts, say, from an ordinary continuous surface, then it is straightforward to approximate it as in the picture on the right by a collection of flat faces. And one might think that the edges of these faces would define a network of the kind I have been discussing.

A surface approximated by flat faces whose edges form a trivalent network.

But in fact, such a network has vastly less information. For given just a set of connections between nodes, there is no obvious way even to know which of these connections should be associated with the same face—let alone to work out anything like angles between faces.

Yet despite this, it turns out that all the geometrical features that are ultimately of relevance to general relativity can actually be determined in large networks just from the connectivity of nodes.

One of these is the value of the so-called Ricci tensor, which in effect specifies how the Ricci scalar curvature is made up from different curvature components associated with different directions.

As indicated above, the scalar curvature associated with a network is directly related to how many nodes lie within successive distances r of a given node on the network—or in effect how many nodes lie within successive generalized spheres around that node. And it turns out that the projection of the Ricci tensor along a particular direction is then just related to the number of nodes that lie within a cylinder oriented in that direction. But even just defining a consistent direction in a network is not entirely straightforward. But one way to do it is simply to pick two points in the network, then to say that paths in the network are going in the same direction if they are segments of the same shortest path between those points. And with this definition, a region that approximates a cylinder can be formed just by setting up spheres with centers at every point on the path.

But there is now another issue to address: at least in its standard formulation general relativity is set up in terms of properties not of three-dimensional space but rather of four-dimensional spacetime. And this means that what is relevant are properties not so much of specific networks representing space, but rather of complete causal networks.

And one immediate feature of causal networks that differs from space networks is that their connections go only one way. But it turns out that this is exactly what one needs in order to set up the analog of a spacetime Ricci tensor. The idea is to start at a particular event in the causal network, then to form what is in effect a cone of events that can be reached from there. To define the spacetime Ricci tensor, one considers—as on page 516—a sequence of spacelike slices through this cone and asks how the number of events that lie within the cone increases as one goes to successive slices. After t steps, the number of events reached will be proportional to t^d. But there is then a correction proportional to t^{d+2}, that has a coefficient that is a combination of the spacetime Ricci scalar and a projection of the spacetime Ricci tensor along what is in effect the time direction defined by the sequence of spacelike slices chosen.

So how does this relate to general relativity? It turns out that when there is no matter present the Einstein equations simply state that the spacetime Ricci tensor—and thus all of its projections—are exactly zero. There can still for example be higher-order curvature, but there can be no curvature at the level described by the Ricci tensor.

So what this means is that any causal network whose behavior obeys the Einstein equations must at the level of counting nodes in a cone have the same uniform structure as it would if it were going to correspond to ordinary flat space. As we saw a few sections ago, many underlying replacement rules end up producing networks that are for example too extensively connected to correspond to ordinary space in any finite number of dimensions. But I suspect that if one has replacement rules that are causal invariant and that in effect successfully maintain a fixed number of dimensions they will almost inevitably lead to behavior that follows something close to the Einstein equations.

Probably the situation is somewhat analogous to what we saw with fluid behavior in cellular automata in Chapter 8—that at least if there are underlying rules whose behavior is complicated enough to generate significant effective randomness, then almost whenever the rules lead to conservation of total particle number and momentum something close to the ordinary Navier-Stokes equation behavior emerges.

So what about matter?

As a first step, one can ask what effect the structure of space has on something like a particle—assuming that one can ignore the effect of the particle back on space. In traditional general relativity it is always assumed that a particle which is not interacting with anything else will move along a shortest path—or so-called geodesic—in space.

But what about an explicit particle of the kind we discussed in the previous section that exists as a structure in a network? Given two nodes in a network, one can always identify a shortest path from one to the other that goes along a sequence of individual connections in the network. But in a sense a structure that corresponds to a particle will normally not fit through this path. For usually the structure will involve many nodes, and thus typically require many connections going in more or less the same direction in order to be able to move across the network.

But if one assumes a certain uniformity in networks—and in particular in the causal network—then it still follows that particles of the kind that we discussed in the previous section will tend to move along geodesics. And whereas in traditional general relativity the idea of motion along geodesics is essentially an assumption, this can now in principle be derived explicitly from an underlying network model.

One might have thought that in the absence of matter there would be little to say about gravity—since after all the Einstein equations then say that there can be no curvature in space, at least of the kind described by the Ricci tensor. But it turns out that there can still be other kinds of curvature—described for example by the so-called Riemann tensor—and these can in fact lead to all sorts of phenomena. Examples include familiar ones like inverse-square gravitational fields around massive objects, as well as unfamiliar ones like gravitational waves.

But while the mathematical structure of general relativity is complicated enough that it is often difficult to see just where in spacetime effects come from, it is usually assumed that matter is somehow ultimately required to provide a source for gravity. And in the full Einstein equations the Ricci tensor need not be zero; instead it is specified at every point in space as being equal to a certain combination of energy and momentum density for matter at that point. So this means that to know what will happen even in phenomena primarily associated with gravity one typically has to know all sorts of properties of matter.

But why exactly does matter have to be introduced explicitly at all? It has been the assumption of traditional physics that even though gravity can be represented in terms of properties of space, other elements of our universe cannot. But in my approach everything just emerges from the same underlying network—or in effect from the structure of space. And indeed even in traditional general relativity one can try avoiding introducing matter explicitly—for example by imagining that everything we call matter is actually made up of pure gravitational energy, or of something like gravitational waves.

But so far as one can tell, the details of this do not work out—so that at the level of general relativity there is no choice but to introduce matter explicitly. Yet I suspect that this is in effect just a sign of limitations in the Einstein equations and general relativity.

For while at a large scale these may provide a reasonable description of average behavior in a network, it is almost inevitable that closer to the scale of individual connections they will have to be modified. Yet presumably one can still use the Einstein equations on large scales if one introduces matter with appropriate properties as a way to represent small-scale effects in the network.

In the previous section I suggested that energy and momentum might in effect be associated with the presence of excess nodes in a network. And this now potentially seems to fit quite well with what we have seen in this section. For if the underlying rule for a network is going to maintain to a certain approximation the same average number of nodes as flat space, then it follows that wherever there are more nodes corresponding to energy and momentum, this must be balanced by something reducing the number of nodes. But such a reduction is exactly what is needed to correspond to positive curvature of the kind implied by the Einstein equations in the presence of ordinary matter.

Quantum Phenomena

From our everyday experience with objects that we can see and touch we develop a certain intuition about how things work. But nearly a century ago it became clear that when it comes to things like electrons some of this intuition is no longer correct. Yet there has developed an elaborate mathematical formalism in quantum theory that successfully reproduces much of what is observed. And while some aspects of this formalism remain mysterious, it has increasingly come to be believed that any fundamental theory of physics must somehow be based on it.

Yet the kinds of programs I have discussed in this book are not in any obvious way set up to fit in with this formalism. But as we have seen a great many times in the course of the book, what emerges from a program can be very different from what is obvious in its underlying rules. And in fact it is my strong suspicion that the kinds of programs that I have discussed in the past few sections will actually in the end turn out to show many if not all the key features of quantum theory.

To see this, however, will not be easy. For the kinds of constructs that are emphasized in the standard formalism of quantum theory are very different from those immediately visible in the programs I have discussed. And ultimately the only reliable way to make contact will probably be to set up rather complete and realistic models of experiments—then gradually to see how limits and idealizations of these manage to match what is expected from the standard formalism. Yet from what we have seen in this chapter and earlier in this book there are already some encouraging signs that one can identify.

At first, though, things might not seem promising. For my model of particles such as electrons being persistent structures in a network might initially seem to imply that such particles are somehow definite objects just like ones familiar from everyday experience. But there are all sorts of phenomena in quantum theory that seem to indicate that electrons do not in fact behave like ordinary objects that have definite properties independent of us making observations of them.

So how can this be consistent? The basic answer is just that a network which represents our whole universe must also include us as observers. And this means that there is no way that we can look at the network from the outside and see the electron as a definite object. Instead, anything we deduce about the electron must come from processes that explicitly go on inside the network.

But this is not just an issue in studying things like electrons: it is actually a completely general feature of the models I have discussed. And in fact, as we saw earlier in this chapter, it is what allows them to support meaningful notions of even such basic concepts as time. At a more formal level, it also implies that everything we can observe can be captured by a causal network. And as I will discuss a little below, I suspect that the idea of causal invariance for such a network will then be what turns out to account for some key features of quantum theory.

The basic picture of our universe that I have outlined in the past few sections is a network whose connections are continually updated according to some simple set of underlying rules. In the past one might have assumed that a system like this would be far too simple to correspond to our universe. But from the discoveries in this book we now know that even when the underlying rules for a system are simple, its overall behavior can still be immensely complex.

And at the lowest level what I expect is that even though the rules being applied are perfectly definite, the overall pattern of connections that will exist in the network corresponding to our universe will continually be rearranged in ways complicated enough to seem effectively random.

Yet on a slightly larger scale such randomness will then lead to a certain average uniformity. And it is then essentially this that I believe is responsible for maintaining something like ordinary space—with gradual variations giving rise to the phenomenon of gravity.

But superimposed on this effectively random background will then presumably also be some definite structures that persist through many updatings of the network. And it is these, I believe, that are what correspond to particles like electrons.

As I discussed in the last two sections, causal invariance of the underlying rules implies that such structures should be able to move at a range of uniform speeds through the background. Typically properties like charge will be associated with some specific pattern of connections at the core of the structure corresponding to a particle, while the energy and momentum of the particle will be associated with roughly the number of nodes in some outer region around the core.

So what about interactions? If the structures corresponding to different particles are isolated, then the underlying rules will make them persist. But if they somehow overlap, these same rules will usually make some different configuration of particles be produced.

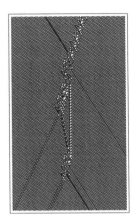

A collision between localized structures in the rule 110 class 4 cellular automaton.

At some level the situation will no doubt be a little like in the evolution of a typical class 4 cellular automaton, as illustrated on the left. Given some initial set of persistent structures, these can interact to produce some intermediate pattern of behavior, which then eventually resolves into a final set of structures that again persist.

In the intermediate pattern of behavior one may also be able to identify some definite structures. Ones that do not last long can be very different from ones that would persist forever. But ones that last longer will tend to have properties progressively closer to genuinely persistent structures. And while persistent structures can be thought of as corresponding to real particles, intermediate structures are in many ways like the virtual particles of traditional particle physics.

So this means that a picture like the one on the left above can be viewed in a remarkably literal sense as being a spacetime diagram of particle interactions—a bit like a Feynman diagram from particle physics.

One immediate difference, however, is that in traditional particle physics one does not imagine a pattern of behavior as definite and determined as in the picture above. And indeed in my model for the universe it is already clear that there is more going on. For any process like the one in the picture above must occur on top of a background of apparently random small-scale rearrangements of the network. And in effect what this background does is to introduce a kind of random environment that can make many different detailed patterns of behavior occur with certain probabilities even with the same initial configuration of particles.

The idea that even a vacuum without particles will have a complicated and in some ways random form also exists in standard quantum field theory in traditional physics. The full mathematical structure of quantum field theory is far from completely worked out. But the basic notion is that for each possible type of particle there is some kind of continuous field that exists throughout space—with the presence of a particle corresponding to a simple type of structure in this field.

In general, the equations of quantum field theory seem to imply that there can be all sorts of complicated configurations in the field, even in the absence of actual particles. But as a first approximation, one can consider just short-lived pairs of virtual particles and antiparticles. And in fact one can often do something similar for networks. For even in the planar networks discussed on page 527 a great many different arrangements of connections can be viewed as being formed from different configurations of nearby pairs of non-planar persistent structures.

Talking about a random background affecting processes in the universe immediately tends to suggest certain definite relations between probabilities for different processes. Thus for example, if there are two different ways that some process can occur, it suggests that the total probability for the whole process should be just the sum of the probabilities for the process to occur in the two different ways.

But the standard formalism of quantum theory says that this is not correct, and that in fact one has to look at so-called probability amplitudes, not ordinary probabilities. At a mathematical level, such amplitudes are analogous to ones for things like waves, and are in effect just numbers with directions. And what quantum theory says is that the probability for a whole process can be obtained by linearly combining the amplitudes for the different ways the process can occur, then looking at the square of the magnitude of the result—or the analog of intensity for something like a wave.

So how might this kind of mathematical procedure emerge from the types of models I have discussed? The answer seems complicated. For even though the procedure itself may sound straightforward, the constructs on which it operates are actually far from easy to define just on the basis of an underlying network—and I have seen no easy way to unravel the various limits and idealizations that have to be made.

Nevertheless, a potentially important point is that it is in some ways misleading to think of particles in a network as just interacting according to some definite rule, and being perturbed by what is in essence a random background. For this suggests that there is in effect a unique history to every particle interaction—determined by the initial conditions and the configuration that exists in the random background.

But the true picture is more complicated. For the sequence of updates to the underlying network can be made in any order—yet each order in effect gives a different detailed history for the network. But if there is causal invariance, then ultimately all these different histories must in a sense be equivalent. And with this constraint, if one breaks some process into parts, there will typically be no simple way to describe how the effect of these parts combines together.

And for at least some purposes it may well make sense to think explicitly about different possible histories, combining something like amplitudes that one assigns to each of them. Yet quite how this might work will certainly depend on what feature of the network one tries to look at.

It has always been a major issue in quantum theory just how one tells what is happening with a particular particle like an electron. From our experience with everyday objects we might think that it should somehow be possible to do this without affecting the electron. But if the only things we have are particles, then to find out something about a given particle we inevitably have to have some other particle—say a photon of light—explicitly interact with it. And in this interaction the original particle will inevitably be affected in some way.

And in fact just one interaction will certainly not be enough. For we as humans cannot normally perceive individual particles. And indeed there usually have to be a huge number of particles doing more or less the same thing before we successfully register it.

Most often the way this is made to happen is by setting up some kind of detector that is initially in a state that is sufficiently unstable that just a single particle can initiate a whole cascade of consequences. And usually such a detector is arranged so that it evolves to one or another stable state that has sufficiently uniform properties that we can recognize it as corresponding to a definite outcome of a measurement.

At first, however, such evolution to an organized state might seem inconsistent with microscopic reversibility. But in fact—just as in so many other seemingly irreversible processes—all that is needed to preserve reversibility is that if one looks at sufficient details of the system there can be arbitrary and seemingly random behavior. And the point is just that in making conclusions about the result of a measurement we choose to ignore such details.

So even though the actual result that we take away from a measurement may be quite simple, many particles—and many events—

will always be involved in getting it. And in fact in traditional quantum theory no measurement can ultimately end up giving a definite result unless in effect an infinite number of particles are involved.

As I mentioned above, ordinary quantum processes can appear to follow different histories depending on what scheme is used to decide the order in which underlying rules are applied. But taking the idealized limit of a measurement in which an infinite number of particles are involved will probably in effect establish a single history.

And this implies that if one knew all of the underlying details of the network that makes up our universe, it should always be possible to work out the result of any measurement. I strongly believe that the initial conditions for the universe were quite simple. But like many of the processes we have seen in this book, the evolution of the universe no doubt intrinsically generates apparent randomness.

And the result is that most aspects of the network that represents the current state of our universe will seem essentially random. So this means that to know its form we would in essence have to sample every one of its details—which is certainly not possible if we have to use measurements that each involve a huge number of particles.

One might however imagine that as a first approximation one could take account of underlying apparent randomness just by saying that there are certain probabilities for particles to behave in particular ways. But one of the most often quoted results about foundations of quantum theory is that in practice there can be correlations observed between particles that seem impossible to account for in at least the most obvious kind of such a so-called hidden-variables theory.

For in particular, if one takes two particles that have come from a single source, then the result of a measurement on one of them is found in a sense to depend too much on what measurement gets done on the other—even if there is not enough time for information travelling at the speed of light to get from one to the other. And indeed this fact has often been taken to imply that quantum phenomena can ultimately never be the result of any definite underlying process of evolution.

But this conclusion depends greatly on traditional assumptions about the nature of space and of particles. And it turns out that for the kinds of models I have discussed here it in general no longer holds.

And the basic reason for this is that if the universe is a network then it can in a sense easily contain threads that continue to connect particles even when the particles get far apart in terms of ordinary space.

The picture that emerges is then of a background containing a very large number of connections that maintain an approximation to three-dimensional space, together with a few threads that in effect go outside of that space to make direct connections between particles.

If two particles get created together, it is reasonable to expect that the tangles that represent their cores will tend to have a few connections in common—and indeed this for example happens for lumps of non-planarity of the kind we discussed on page 527. But until there are interactions that change the structure of the cores, these common connections will then remain—and will continue to define a thread that goes directly from one particle to the other.

But there is immediately a slight subtlety here. For earlier in this chapter I discussed measuring distance on a network just by counting the minimum number of successive individual connections that one has to follow in order to get from one point to another. Yet if one uses this measure of distance then the distance between two particles will always tend to remain fixed as the number of connections in the thread.

But the point is that this measure of distance is in reality just a simple idealization of what is relevant in practice. For the only way we end up actually being able to measure physical distances is in effect by looking at the propagation of photons or other particles. Yet such particles always involve many nodes. And while they can get from one point to another through the large number of connections that define the background space, they cannot in a sense fit through a small number of connections in a thread. So this means that distance as we normally experience it is typically not affected by threads.

But it does not mean that threads can have no effect at all. And indeed what I suspect is that it is precisely the presence of threads that leads to the correlations that are seen in measurements on particles.

It so happens that the standard formalism of quantum theory provides a rather simple mathematical description of these correlations. And it is certainly far from obvious how this might emerge from detailed mechanisms associated with threads in a network. But the fact that this and other results seem simple in the standard formalism of quantum theory should not be taken to imply that they are in any sense particularly fundamental. And indeed my guess is that most of them will actually in the end turn out to depend on all sorts of limits and idealizations in quantum theory—and will emerge just as simple approximations to much more complex underlying behavior.

In its development since the early 1900s quantum theory has produced all sorts of elaborate results. And to try to derive them all from the kinds of models I have outlined here will certainly take an immense amount of work. But I consider it very encouraging that some of the most basic quantum phenomena seem to be connected to properties like causal invariance and the network structure of space that already arose in our discussion of quite different fundamental issues in physics.

And all of this supports my strong belief that in the end it will turn out that every detail of our universe does indeed follow rules that can be represented by a very simple program—and that everything we see will ultimately emerge just from running this program.

Fundamental Physics

The Notion of Reversibility

■ **Page 437 · Testing for reversibility.** To show that a cellular automaton is reversible it is sufficient to check that all configurations consisting of repetitions of different blocks have different successors. This can be done for blocks up to length n in a 1D cellular automaton with k colors using

> *ReversibleQ[rule_, k_, n_] := Catch[Do[*
> *If[Length[Union[Table[CAStep[rule, IntegerDigits[i, k, m]],*
> *{i, 0, k^m - 1}]]] ≠ k^m, Throw[False]], {m, n}]; True]*

For $k = 2$, $r = 1$ it turns out that it suffices to test only up to $n = 4$ (128 out of the 256 rules fail at $n = 1$, 64 at $n = 2$, 44 at $n = 3$ and 14 at $n = 4$); for $k = 2$, $r = 2$ it suffices to test up to $n = 15$, and for $k = 3$, $r = 1$, up to $n = 9$. But although these results suggest that in general it should suffice to test only up to $n = k^{2r}$, all that has so far been rigorously proved is that $n = k^{2r}(k^{2r} - 1) + 2r + 1$ (or $n = 15$ for $k = 2$, $r = 1$) is sufficient.

For 2D cellular automata an analogous procedure can in principle be used, though there is no upper limit on the size of blocks that need to be tested, and in fact the question of whether a particular rule is reversible is directly equivalent to the tiling problem discussed on page 213 (compare page 942), and is thus formally undecidable.

■ **Numbers of reversible rules.** For $k = 2$, $r = 1$, there are 6 reversible rules, as shown on page 436. For $k = 2$, $r = 2$ there are 62 reversible rules, in 20 families inequivalent under symmetries, out of a total of 2^{32} or about 4 billion possible rules. For $k = 3$, $r = 1$ there are 1800 reversible rules, in 172 families. For $k = 4$, $r = 1$, some of the reversible rules can be constructed from the second-order cellular automata below. Note that for any k and r, no non-trivial totalistic rule can ever be reversible.

■ **Inverse rules.** Some reversible rules are self-inverse, so that applying the same rule twice yields the identity. Other rules come in distinct pairs. Most often a rule that involves r neighbors has an inverse that also involves at most r neighbors. But for both $k = 2$, $r = 2$ and $k = 3$, $r = 1$ there turn out to be reversible rules whose inverses involve larger

numbers of neighbors. For any given rule one can define the neighborhood size s to be the largest block of cells that is ever needed to determine the color of a single new cell. In general $s \leq 2r + 1$, and for a simple identity or shift rule, $s = 1$. For $k = 2$, $r = 1$, it then turns out that all the reversible rules and their inverses have $s = 1$. For $k = 2$, $r = 2$, the reversible rules have values of s from 1 to 5, but their inverses have values $\bar{s}$ from 1 to 6. There are only 8 rules (the inequivalent ones being 16740555 and 3327051468) where $\bar{s} > s$, and in each case $\bar{s} = 6$ while $s = 5$. For $k = 3$, $r = 1$, there are a total of 936 rules with this property: 576, 216 and 144 with $\bar{s} = 4$, 5 and 6, and in all cases $s = 3$. Examples with $\bar{s} = 3$, 4, 5 and 6 are shown below. For arbitrary k and r, it is not clear what the maximum $\bar{s}$ can be; the only bound rigorously established so far is $\bar{s} \leq r + 1/2\, k^{2r+1}\,(k^{2r} - 1)$.

2828556973047   3762560660157   538556225233   3066231781977

■ **Surjectivity and injectivity.** See page 959.

■ **Directional reversibility.** Even if successive time steps in the evolution of a cellular automaton do not correspond to an injective map, it is still possible to get an injective map by looking at successive lines at some angle in the spacetime evolution of the system. Examples where this works include the surjective rules 30 and 90.

■ **Page 437 · Second-order cellular automata.** Second-order elementary rules can be implemented using

> *CA2EvolveList[rule_List, {a_List, b_List}, t_Integer] :=*
> *Map[First, NestList[CA2Step[rule, #] &, {a, b}, t]]*
> *CA2Step[rule_List, {a_, b_}] := {b, Mod[a + rule[[*
> *8 - (RotateLeft[b] + 2 (b + 2 RotateRight[b]))]], 2]}*

where *rule* is obtained from the rule number using *IntegerDigits[n, 2, 8]*.

The combination *Drop[list, -1] + 2 Drop[list, 1]* of the result from *CA2EvolveList* corresponds to evolution according to a first-order *k = 4, r = 1* rule.

■ **History.** The concept of getting reversibility in a cellular automaton by having a second-order rule was apparently first suggested by Edward Fredkin around 1970 in the context of 2D systems—on the basis of an analogy with second-order differential equations in physics. Similar ideas had appeared in numerical analysis in the 1960s in connection with so-called symmetric or self-adjoint discrete approximations to differential equations.

■ **Page 438 · Properties.** The pattern from rule 67R with simple initial conditions grows irregularly, at an average rate of about 1 cell every 5 steps. The right-hand side of the pattern from rule 173R consists three triangles that repeat progressively larger at steps of the form $2(9^s - 1)$. Rule 90R has the property that of the diamond of cells at relative positions $\{\{-n, 0\}, \{0, -n\}, \{n, 0\}, \{0, n\}\}$ it is always true for any *n* that an even number are black.

■ **Page 439 · Properties.** The initial conditions used here have a single black cell on two successive initial steps. For rule 150R, however, there is no black cell on the first initial step. The pattern generated by rule 150R has fractal dimension $Log[2, 3 + \sqrt{17}] - 1$ or about 1.83. In rule 154R, each diagonal stripe is followed by at least one 0; otherwise, the positions of the stripes appear to be quite random, with a density around 0.44.

■ **Generalized additive rules.** Additive cellular automata of the kind discussed on page 952 can be generalized by allowing the new value of each cell to be obtained from combinations of cells on *s* previous steps. For rule 90 the combination *c* can be specified as $\{\{1, 0, 1\}\}$, while for rule 150R it can be specified as $\{\{0, 1, 0\}, \{1, 1, 1\}\}$. All generalized additive rules ultimately yield nested patterns. Starting with a list of the initial conditions for *s* steps, the configurations for the next *s* steps are given by

Append[Rest[list],
 Map[Mod[Apply[Plus, Flatten[c #]], 2] &, Transpose[
  Table[RotateLeft[list, {0, i}], {i, -r, r}], {3, 2, 1}]]]

where $r = (Length[First[c]] - 1)/2$.

Just as for ordinary additive rules on page 1091, an algebraic analysis for generalized additive rules can be given. The objects that appear are solutions to linear recurrences of order *s*, and in general involve s^{th} roots. For rule 150R, the configuration at step *t* as shown in the picture on page 439 is given by $(u^t - v^t)/Sqrt[4 + h^2]$, where $\{u, v\} = z /. Solve[z^2 == hz + 1]$ and $h = 1/x + 1 + x$. (See also page 1078.)

■ **Page 440 · Rule 37R.** Complicated structures are fairly easy to get with this rule. The initial condition $\{1, 0, 1\}$ with all cells 0 on the previous step yields a structure that repeats but only every 666 steps. The initial condition $\{\{0, 1, 1\}, \{1, 0, 0\}\}$ yields a pattern that grows sporadically for 3774 steps, then breaks into two repetitive structures. The typical background repeats every 3 steps.

■ **Classification of reversible rules.** In a reversible system it is possible with suitable initial conditions to get absolutely any arrangement of cells to appear at any step. Despite this, however, the overall spacetime pattern of cells is not arbitrary, but is instead determined by the underlying rules. If one starts with completely random initial conditions then class 2 and class 3 behavior are often seen. Class 1 behavior can never occur in a reversible system. Class 4 behavior can occur, as in rule 37R, but is typically obvious only if one starts say with a low density of black cells.

For arbitrary rules, difference patterns of the kind shown on page 250 can get both larger and smaller. In a reversible rule, such patterns can grow and shrink, but can never die out completely.

■ **Emergence of reversibility.** Once on an attractor, any system—even if it does not have reversible underlying rules—must in some sense show approximate reversibility. (Compare page 959.)

■ **Other reversible systems.** Reversible examples can be found of essentially all the types of systems discussed in this book. Reversible mobile automata can for instance be constructed using

Table[{IntegerDigits[i, 2, 3] → If[First[#] == 0, {#, -1},
  {Reverse[#], 1}] &[IntegerDigits[perm[[i]], 2, 3]], {i, 8}]

where *perm* is an element of *Permutations[Range[8]]*. An example that exhibits complex behavior is:

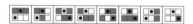

Systems based on numbers are typically reversible whenever the mathematical operations they involve are invertible. Thus, for example, the system on page 121 based on successive multiplication by 3/2 is reversible by using division by 3/2. Page 905 gives another example of a reversible system based on numbers.

Multiway systems are reversible whenever both $a \to b$ and $b \to a$ are present as rules, so that the system corresponds mathematically to a semigroup. (See page 938.)

■ **Reversible computation.** Typical practical computers—and computer languages—are not even close to reversible: many inputs can lead to the same output, and there is no unique way to undo the steps of a computation. But despite early confusion (see page 1020), it has been known since at least the 1970s that there is nothing in principle which prevents computation from being reversible. And indeed—just like with the cellular automata in this section—most of the systems in Chapter 11 that exhibit universal computation can readily be made reversible with only slight overhead.

Irreversibility and the Second Law of Thermodynamics

■ **Time reversal invariance.** The reversibility of the laws of physics implies that given the state of a physical system at a particular time, it is always possibly to work out uniquely both its future and its past. Time reversal invariance would further imply that the rules for going in each direction should be identical. To a very good approximation this appears to be true, but it turns out that in certain esoteric particle physics processes small deviations have been found. In particular, it was discovered in 1964 that the decay of the K^0 particle violated time reversal invariance at the level of about one part in a thousand. In current theories, this effect is not attributed any particularly fundamental origin, and is just assumed to be associated with the arbitrary setting of certain parameters. K^0 decay was for a long time the only example of time reversal violation that had explicitly been seen, although recently examples in B particle decays have probably also been seen. It also turns out that the only current viable theories of the apparent preponderance of matter over antimatter in the universe are based on the idea that a small amount of time reversal violation occurred in the decays of certain very massive particles in the very early universe.

The basic formalism used for particle physics assumes not only reversibility, but also so-called CPT invariance. This means that same rules should apply if one not only reverses the direction of time (T), but also simultaneously inverts all spatial coordinates (P) and conjugates all charges (C), replacing particles by antiparticles. In a certain mathematical sense, CPT invariance can be viewed as a generalization of relativistic invariance: with a speed faster than light, something close to an ordinary relativistic transformation is a CPT transformation.

Originally it was assumed that C, P and T would all separately be invariances, as they are in classical mechanics. But in 1957 it was discovered that in radioactive beta decay, C and P are in a sense each maximally violated: among other things, the correlation between spin and motion direction is exactly opposite for neutrinos and for antineutrinos that are emitted. Despite this, it was still assumed that CP and T

would be true invariances. But in 1964 these too were found to be violated. Starting with a pure beam of K^0 particles, it turns out that quantum mechanical mixing processes lead after about 10^{-8} seconds to a certain mixture of $\overline{K}^0$ particles— the antiparticles of the K^0. And what effectively happens is that the amount of mixing differs by about 0.1% in the positive and negative time directions. (What is actually observed is a small probability for the long-lived component of a K^0 beam to decay into two rather than three pions. Some analysis is required to connect this with T violation.) Particle physics experiments so far support exact CPT invariance. Simple models of gravity potentially suggest CPT violation (as a consequence of deviations from pure special relativistic invariance), but such effects tend to disappear when the models are refined.

■ **History of thermodynamics.** Basic physical notions of heat and temperature were established in the 1600s, and scientists of the time appear to have thought correctly that heat is associated with the motion of microscopic constituents of matter. But in the 1700s it became widely believed that heat was instead a separate fluid-like substance. Experiments by James Joule and others in the 1840s put this in doubt, and finally in the 1850s it became accepted that heat is in fact a form of energy. The relation between heat and energy was important for the development of steam engines, and in 1824 Sadi Carnot had captured some of the ideas of thermodynamics in his discussion of the efficiency of an idealized engine. Around 1850 Rudolf Clausius and William Thomson (Kelvin) stated both the First Law—that total energy is conserved—and the Second Law of Thermodynamics. The Second Law was originally formulated in terms of the fact that heat does not spontaneously flow from a colder body to a hotter. Other formulations followed quickly, and Kelvin in particular understood some of the law's general implications. The idea that gases consist of molecules in motion had been discussed in some detail by Daniel Bernoulli in 1738, but had fallen out of favor, and was revived by Clausius in 1857. Following this, James Clerk Maxwell in 1860 derived from the mechanics of individual molecular collisions the expected distribution of molecular speeds in a gas. Over the next several years the kinetic theory of gases developed rapidly, and many macroscopic properties of gases in equilibrium were computed. In 1872 Ludwig Boltzmann constructed an equation that he thought could describe the detailed time development of a gas, whether in equilibrium or not. In the 1860s Clausius had introduced entropy as a ratio of heat to temperature, and had stated the Second Law in terms of the increase of this quantity. Boltzmann then showed that his equation implied the so-called H Theorem, which states that a quantity equal to entropy in equilibrium must always increase with time. At first, it seemed that Boltzmann had successfully proved the Second Law. But then it was noticed that since molecular collisions were assumed reversible, his derivation could be run in reverse, and would then imply the opposite of the Second Law. Much later it was realized that Boltzmann's original equation implicitly assumed that molecules are uncorrelated before each collision, but not afterwards, thereby introducing a fundamental asymmetry in time. Early in the 1870s Maxwell and Kelvin appear to have already understood that the Second Law could not formally be derived from microscopic physics, but must somehow be a consequence of human inability to track large numbers of molecules. In responding to objections concerning reversibility Boltzmann realized around 1876 that in a gas there are many more states that seem random than seem orderly. This realization led him to argue that entropy must be proportional to the logarithm of the number of possible states of a system, and to formulate ideas about ergodicity. The statistical mechanics of systems of particles was put in a more general context by Willard Gibbs, beginning around 1900. Gibbs introduced the notion of an ensemble—a collection of many possible states of a system, each assigned a certain probability. He argued that if the time evolution of a single state were to visit all other states in the ensemble—the so-called ergodic hypothesis—then averaged over a sufficiently long time a single state would behave in a way that was typical of the ensemble. Gibbs also gave qualitative arguments that entropy would increase if it were measured in a "coarse-grained" way in which nearby states were not distinguished. In the early 1900s the development of thermodynamics was largely overshadowed by quantum theory and little fundamental work was done on it. Nevertheless, by the 1930s, the Second Law had somehow come to be generally regarded as a principle of physics whose foundations should be questioned only as a curiosity. Despite neglect in physics, however, ergodic theory became an active area of pure mathematics, and from the 1920s to the 1960s properties related to ergodicity were established for many kinds of simple systems. When electronic computers became available in the 1950s, Enrico Fermi and others began to investigate the ergodic properties of nonlinear systems of springs. But they ended up concentrating on recurrence phenomena related to solitons, and not looking at general questions related to the Second Law. Much the same happened in the 1960s, when the first simulations of hard sphere gases were led to concentrate on the specific phenomenon of long-time tails. And by the 1970s, computer experiments were mostly oriented towards ordinary differential equations and strange attractors, rather than towards systems with large numbers of components, to which the Second Law might apply. Starting in the 1950s, it was recognized that entropy is simply the negative of the information quantity introduced in the 1940s by Claude Shannon. Following statements by John von Neumann, it was thought that any computational process must necessarily increase entropy, but by the early 1970s, notably with work by Charles Bennett, it became accepted that this is not so (see page 1018), laying some early groundwork for relating computational and thermodynamic ideas.

■ **Current thinking on the Second Law.** The vast majority of current physics textbooks imply that the Second Law is well established, though with surprising regularity they say that detailed arguments for it are beyond their scope. More specialized articles tend to admit that the origins of the Second Law remain mysterious. Most ultimately attribute its validity to unknown constraints on initial conditions or measurements, though some appeal to external perturbations, to cosmology or to unknown features of quantum mechanics.

An argument for the Second Law from around 1900, still reproduced in many textbooks, is that if a system is ergodic then it will visit all its possible states, and the vast majority of these will look random. But only very special kinds of systems are in fact ergodic, and even in such systems, the time necessary to visit a significant fraction of all possible states is astronomically long. Another argument for the Second Law, arising from work in the 1930s and 1940s, particularly on systems of hard spheres, is based on the notion of instability with respect to small changes in initial conditions. The argument suffers however from the same difficulties as the ones for chaos theory discussed in Chapter 6 and does not in the end explain in any real way the origins of randomness, or the observed validity of the Second Law.

With the Second Law accepted as a general principle, there is confusion about why systems in nature have not all dissipated into complete randomness. And often the rather absurd claim is made that all the order we see in the universe must just be a fluctuation—leaving little explanatory power for principles such as the Second Law.

■ **My explanation of the Second Law.** What I say in this book is not incompatible with much of what has been said about the Second Law before; it is simply that I make more definite some key points that have been left vague before. In particular, I use notions of computation to specify what kinds of initial conditions can reasonably be prepared, and what kinds of measurements can reasonably be made. In a sense what I do is just to require that the operation of coarse graining correspond to a computation that is less sophisticated than the actual evolution of the system being studied. (See also Chapters 10 and 12.)

■ **Biological systems and Maxwell's demon.** Unlike most physical systems, biological systems typically seem capable of spontaneously organizing themselves. And as a result, even the original statements of the Second Law talked only about "inanimate systems". In the mid-1860s James Clerk Maxwell then suggested that a demon operating at a microscopic level could reduce the randomness of a system such as a gas by intelligently controlling the motion of molecules. For many years there was considerable confusion about Maxwell's demon. There were arguments that the demon must use a flashlight that generates entropy. And there were extensive demonstrations that actual biological systems reduce their internal entropy only at the cost of increases in the entropy of their environment. But in fact the main point is that if the evolution of the whole system is to be reversible, then the demon must store enough information to reverse its own actions, and this limits how much the demon can do, preventing it, for example, from unscrambling a large system of gas molecules.

■ **Self-gravitating systems.** The observed existence of structures such as galaxies might lead one to think that any large number of objects subject to mutual gravitational attraction might not follow the Second Law and become randomized, but might instead always form orderly clumps. It is difficult to know, however, what an idealized self-gravitating system would do. For in practice, issues such as the limited size of a galaxy, its overall rotation, and the details of stellar collisions all seem to have major effects on the results obtained. (And it is presumably not feasible to do a small-scale experiment, say in Earth orbit.) There are known to be various instabilities that lead in the direction of clumping and core collapse, but how these weigh against effects such as the transfer of energy into tight binding of small groups of stars is not clear. Small galaxies such as globular clusters that contain less than a million stars seem to exhibit a certain uniformity which suggests a kind of equilibrium. Larger galaxies such as our own that contain perhaps 100 billion stars often have intricate spiral or other structure, whose origin may be associated with gravitational effects, or may be a consequence of detailed processes of star formation and explosion. (There is some evidence that older galaxies of a given size tend to develop more regularities in their structure.) Current theories of the early universe tend to assume that galaxies originally began to form as a result of density fluctuations of non-gravitational origin (and reflected

in the cosmic microwave background). But there is evidence that a widespread fractal structure develops—with a correlation function of the form $r^{-1.8}$—in the distribution of stars in our galaxy, galaxies in clusters and clusters in superclusters, perhaps suggesting the existence of general overall laws for self-gravitating systems. (See also page 973.)

As mentioned on page 880, it so happens that my original interest in cellular automata around 1981 developed in part from trying to model the growth of structure in self-gravitating systems. At first I attempted to merge and generalize ideas from traditional areas of mathematical physics, such as kinetic theory, statistical mechanics and field theory. But then, particularly as I began to think about doing explicit computer simulations, I decided to take a different tack and instead to look for the most idealized possible models. And in doing this I quickly came up with cellular automata. But when I started to investigate cellular automata, I discovered some very remarkable phenomena, and I was soon led away from self-gravitating systems, and into the process of developing the much more general science in this book. Over the years, I have occasionally come back to the problem of self-gravitating systems, but I have never succeeded in developing what I consider to be a satisfactory approach to them.

■ **Cosmology and the Second Law.** In the standard big bang model it is assumed that all matter in the universe was initially in completely random thermal equilibrium. But such equilibrium implies uniformity, and from this it follows that the initial conditions for the gravitational forces in the universe must have been highly regular, resulting in simple overall expansion, rather than random expansion in some places and contraction in others. As I discuss on page 1026 I suspect that in fact the universe as a whole probably had what were ultimately very simple initial conditions, and it is just that the effective rules for the evolution of matter led to rapid randomization, whereas those for gravity did not.

■ **Alignment of time in the universe.** Evidence from astronomy clearly suggests that the direction of irreversible processes is the same throughout the universe. The reason for this is presumably that all parts of the universe are expanding—with the local consequence that radiation is more often emitted than absorbed, as evidenced by the fact that the night sky is dark. Olbers' paradox asks why one does not see a bright star in every direction in the night sky. The answer is that locally stars are clumped, and light from stars further away is progressively red-shifted to lower energy. Focusing a larger and larger distance away, the light one sees was emitted longer and longer ago. And eventually one sees light emitted when the universe was filled with hot opaque gas—now red-shifted to become the 2.7K cosmic microwave background.

■ **Poincaré recurrence.** Systems of limited size that contain only discrete elements inevitably repeat their evolution after a sufficiently long time (see page 258). In 1890 Henri Poincaré established the somewhat less obvious fact that even continuous systems also always eventually get at least arbitrarily close to repeating themselves. This discovery led to some confusion in early interpretations of the Second Law, but the huge length of time involved in a Poincaré recurrence makes it completely irrelevant in practice.

■ **Page 446 · Billiards.** The discrete system I consider here is analogous to continuous so-called billiard systems consisting of circular balls in the plane. The simplest case involves one ball bouncing around in a region of a definite shape. In a rectangular region, the position is given by $Mod[a\,t, \{w, h\}]$ and every point will be visited if the parameters have irrational ratios. In a region that contains fixed circular obstructions, the motion can become sensitively dependent on initial conditions. (This setup is similar to a so-called Lorentz gas.) For a system of balls in a region with cyclic boundaries, a complicated proof due to Yakov Sinai from the 1960s purports to show that every ball eventually visits every point in the region, and that certain simple statistical properties of trajectories are consistent with randomness. (See also page 971.)

■ **Page 449 · Entropy of particles in a box.** The number of possible states of a region of m cells containing q particles is $Binomial[m, q]$. In the large size limit, the logarithm of this can be approximated by $q\,Log[m/q]/m$.

■ **Page 457 · Periods in rule 37R.** With a system of size n, the maximum possible repetition period is 2^{2n}. In actuality, however, the periods are considerably shorter. With all cells 0 on one step, and a block of nonzero cells on the next step, the periods are for example: $\{1\}$: 21; $\{1, 1\}$: $3n-8$; $\{1, 0, 1\}$: 666; $\{1, 1, 1\}$: $3n-8$; $\{1, 0, 0, 1\}$: irregular ($<24n$; peaks at $6j+1$); $\{1, 0, 0, 1, 0, 1\}$: irregular ($\leq 2^n$; 857727 for $n = 26$; 13705406 for $n = 100$). With completely random initial conditions, there are great fluctuations, but a typical period is around $2^{n/3}$.

Conserved Quantities and Continuum Phenomena

■ **Physics.** The quantities in physics that so far seem to be exactly conserved are: energy, momentum, angular momentum, electric charge, color charge, lepton number (as well as electron number, muon number and τ lepton number) and baryon number.

■ **Implementation.** Whether a k-color cellular automaton with range r conserves total cell value can be determined from

    Catch[Do[
      (If[Apply[Plus, CAStep[rule, #] - #] ≠ 0, Throw[False]] &)[
        IntegerDigits[i, k, m]], {m, w}, {i, 0, k^m - 1}]; True]

where w can be taken to be k^{2r}, and perhaps smaller. Among the 256 elementary cellular automata just 5 conserve total cell value. Among the 2^{32} $k = 2$, $r = 2$ rules 428 do, and of these 2 are symmetric, and 6 are reversible, and all these are just shift and identity rules.

■ **More general conserved quantities.** Some rules conserve not total numbers of cells with given colors, but rather total numbers of blocks of cells with given forms—or combinations of these. The pictures below show the simplest quantities of these kinds that end up being conserved by various elementary rules.

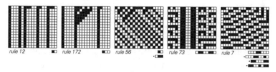

rule 12   rule 172   rule 56   rule 73   rule 7

Among the 256 elementary rules, the total numbers that have conserved quantities involving at most blocks of lengths 1 through 10 are $\{5, 38, 66, 88, 102, 108, 108, 114, 118, 118\}$.

Rules that show complicated behavior usually do not seem to have conserved quantities, and this is true for example of rules 30, 90 and 110, at least up to blocks of length 10.

One can count the number of occurrences of each of the k^b possible blocks of length b in a given state using

    BC[list_] :=
      With[{z = Map[FromDigits[#, k] &, Partition[list, b, 1, 1]]},
        Map[Count[z, #] &, Range[0, k^b - 1]]]

Conserved quantities of the kind discussed here are then of the form $q\,.\,BC[a]$ where q is some fixed list. A way to find candidates for q is to compute

    NullSpace[Table[With[{u = Table[Random[Integer,
      {0, k - 1}], {m}]}, BC[CAStep[u]] - BC[u]], {s}]]

for progressively larger m and s, and to see what lists continue to appear. For block size b, k^{b-1} lists will always appear as a result of trivial conserved quantities. (With $k = 2$, for $b = 1$, $\{1, 1\}$ represents conservation of the total number of cells, regardless of color, while for $b = 2$, $\{1, 1, 1, 1\}$ represents the same thing, while $\{0, 1, -1, 0\}$ represents the fact that in going along in any state the number of black-to-white transitions must equal the number of white-to-black ones.) If more than k^{b-1} lists appear, however, then some must correspond to genuine non-trivial conserved quantities. To identify any such quantity with certainty, it turns out to be enough to look at the k^{b+2r-1} states where no block of length *b + 2r - 1* appears more than once (and perhaps even just some fairly small subset of these).

(See also page 981.)

- **Other conserved quantities.** The conserved quantities discussed so far can all be thought of as taking values assigned to blocks of different kinds in a given state and then just adding them up as ordinary numbers. But one can also imagine using other operations to combine such values. Addition modulo *n* can be handled by inserting *Modulus → n* in *NullSpace* in the previous note. And doing this shows for example that rule 150 conserves the total number of black cells modulo 2. But in general not many additional conserved quantities are found in this way. One can also consider combining values of blocks by the multiplication operation in a group—and seeing whether the conjugacy class of the result is conserved.

- **PDEs.** In the early 1960s it was discovered that certain nonlinear PDEs support an infinite number of distinct conserved quantities, associated with so-called integrability and the presence of solitons. Systematic methods now exist to find conserved quantities that are given by integrals of polynomials of any given degree in the dependent variables and their derivatives. Most randomly chosen PDEs appear, however, to have no such conserved quantities.

- **Local conservation laws.** Whenever a system like a cellular automaton (or PDE) has a global conserved quantity there must always be a local conservation law which expresses the fact that every point in the system the total flux of the conserved quantity into a particular region must equal the rate of increase of the quantity inside it. (If the conserved quantity is thought of like charge, the flux is then current.) In any 1D $k = 2$, $r = 1$ cellular automaton, it follows from the basic structure of the rule that one can tell what the difference in values of a particular cell on two successive steps will be just by looking at the cell and its immediate neighbor on each side. But if the number of black cells is conserved, then one can compute this difference instead by defining a suitable flux, and subtracting its values on the left and right of the cell. What the flux should be depends on the rule. For rule 184, it can be taken to be 1 for each ■□ block, and to be 0 otherwise. For rule 170, it is 1 for both □□ and ■□. For rule 150, it is 1 for □□ and ■■, with all computations done modulo 2. In general, if the global conserved quantity involves blocks of size *b*, the flux can be computed by looking at blocks of size *b + 2r - 1*. What the values for these blocks should be can be found by solving a system of linear equations; that a solution must exist can be seen by looking at the de Bruijn network (see page 941), with nodes labelled by size *b + 2r - 1* blocks,

and connections by value differences between size *b* blocks at the center of the possible size *b + 2r* blocks. (Note that the same basic kind of setup works in any number of dimensions.)

- **Block cellular automata.** With a rule of the form {{1, 1} → {1, 1}, {1, 0} → {1, 0}, {0, 1} → {0, 0}, {0, 0} → {0, 1}} the evolution of a block cellular automaton with blocks of size *n* can be implemented using

BCAEvolveList[{n_Integer, rule_}, init_, t_] :=
  FoldList[BCAStep[{n, rule}, #1, #2] &, init, Range[t]] /;
    Mod[Length[init], n] == 0
BCAStep[{n_, rule_}, a_, d_] := RotateRight[
  Flatten[Partition[RotateLeft[a, d], n] /. rule], d]

Starting with a single black cell, none of the $k = 2$, $n = 2$ block cellular automata generate anything beyond simple nested patterns. In general, there are k^{nk^n} possible rules for block cellular automata with *k* colors and blocks of size *n*. Of these, $k^n !$ are reversible. For $k = 2$, the number of rules that conserve the total number of black cells can be computed from $q = Binomial[n, Range[0, n]]$ as $Apply[Times, q^q]$. The number of these rules that are also reversible is $Apply[Times, q !]$. In general, a block cellular automaton is reversible only if its rule simply permutes the k^n possible blocks.

Compressing each block into a single cell, and *n* steps into one, any block cellular automaton with *k* colors and block size *n* can be translated directly into an ordinary cellular automaton with k^n colors and range $r = n/2$.

- **Page 461 · Block rules.** These pictures show the behavior of rule (c) starting from some special initial conditions.

The repetition period with a total of *n* cells can be 3^n steps. With random initial conditions, the period is typically up to about $3^{n/2}$. Starting with a block of *q* black cells, the period can get close to this. For $n = 20$, $q = 17$, for example, it is 31,300.

Note that even in rule (b) wraparound phenomena can lead to repetition periods that increase rapidly with *n* (e.g. 4820 for $n = 20$, $q = 15$), but presumably not exponentially.

In rule (d), the repetition periods can typically be larger than in rule (c): e.g. 803,780 for $n = 20$, $q = 13$.

- **Page 464 · Limiting procedures.** Several different limiting procedures all appear to yield the same continuum behavior for the cellular automata shown here. In the pictures on this page a large ensemble of different initial conditions is considered, and the density of each individual cell averaged over this ensemble is computed. In a more direct analogy to actual physical systems, one would consider instead a very large number of cells, then compute the density in a single state of the system by averaging over regions that contain many cells but are nevertheless small compared to the size of the whole system.

■ **PDE approximations.** Cellular automaton (d) in the main text can be viewed as minimal discrete approximations to the diffusion equation. The evolution of densities in the ensemble average is analogous to a traditional finite difference method with a real number at each site. The cellular automaton itself uses in effect a distributed representation of the density.

■ **Diffusion equation.** In an appropriate limit the density distribution for cellular automaton (d) appears to satisfy the usual diffusion equation $\partial_t f[x, t] == c \, \partial_{xx} f[x, t]$ discussed on page 163. The solution to this equation with an impulse initial condition is $Exp[-x^2/t]$, and with a block from $-a$ to a it is $(Erf[(a-x)/\sqrt{t}] + Erf[(a+x)/\sqrt{t}])/a$.

■ **Derivation of the diffusion equation.** With some appropriate assumptions, it is fairly straightforward to derive the usual diffusion equation from a cellular automaton. Let the density of black cells at position x and time t be $f[x, t]$, where this density can conveniently be computed by averaging over many instances of the system. If we assume that the density varies slowly with position and time, then we can make series expansions such as

$$f[x + dx, t] == f[x, t] + \partial_x f[x, t] \, dx + 1/2 \, \partial_{xx} f[x, t] \, dx^2 + \ldots$$

where the coordinates are scaled so that adjacent cells are at positions $x - dx$, x, $x + dx$, etc. If we then assume perfect underlying randomness, the density at a particular position must be given in terms of the densities at neighboring positions on the previous step by

$$f[x, t + dt] == p_1 \, f[x - dx, t] + p_2 \, f[x, t] + p_3 \, f[x + dx, t]$$

Density conservation implies that $p_1 + p_2 + p_3 == 1$, while left-right symmetry implies $p_1 == p_3$. And from this it follows that

$$f[x, t + dt] == c \, (f[x - dx, t] + f[x + dx, t]) + (1 - 2 \, c) \, f[x, t]$$

Performing a series expansion then yields

$$f[x, t] + dt \, \partial_t f[x, t] == f[x, t] + c \, dx^2 \, \partial_{xx} f[x, t]$$

which in turn gives exactly the usual 1D diffusion equation $\partial_t f[x, t] == \xi \, \partial_{xx} f[x, t]$, where ξ is the diffusion coefficient for the system. I first gave this derivation in 1986, together with extensive generalizations.

■ **Page 464 · Non-standard diffusion.** To get ordinary diffusion behavior of the kind that occurs in gases—and is described by the diffusion equation—it is in effect necessary to have

perfect uncorrelated randomness, with no structure that persists too long. But for example in the rule (a) picture on page 463 there is in effect a block of solid that persists in the middle—so that no ordinary diffusion behavior is seen. In rule (c) there is considerable apparent randomness, but it turns out that there are also fluctuations that last too long to yield ordinary diffusion. And thus for example whenever there is a structure containing s identical cells (as on page 462), this typically takes about s^2 steps to decay away. The result is that on page 464 the limiting form of the average behavior does not end up being an ordinary Gaussian.

■ **Conservation of vector quantities.** Conservation of the total number of colored cells is analogous to conservation of a scalar quantity such as energy or particle number. One can also consider conservation of a vector quantity such as momentum which has not only a magnitude but also a direction. Direction makes little sense in 1D, but is meaningful in 2D. The 2D cellular automaton used as a model of an idealized gas on page 446 provides an example of a system that can be viewed as conserving a vector quantity. In the absence of fixed scatterers, the total fluxes of particles in the horizontal and the vertical directions are conserved. But in a sense there is too much conservation in this system, and there is no interaction between horizontal and vertical motions. This can be achieved by having more complicated underlying rules. One possibility is to use a hexagonal rather than square grid, thereby allowing six particle directions rather than four. On such a grid it is possible to randomize microscopic particle motions, but nevertheless conserve overall momenta. This is essentially the model used in my discussion of fluids on page 378.

Ultimate Models for the Universe

■ **History of ultimate models.** From the earliest days of Greek science until well into the 1900s, it seems to have often been believed that an ultimate model of the universe was not far away. In antiquity there were vague ideas about everything being made of elements like fire and water. In the 1700s, following the success of Newtonian mechanics, a common assumption seems to have been that everything (with the possible exception of light) must consist of tiny corpuscles with gravity-like forces between them. In the 1800s the notion of fields—and the ether—began to develop, and in the 1880s it was suggested that atoms might be knotted vortices in the ether (see page 1044). When the electron was discovered in 1897 it was briefly thought that it might be the fundamental constituent of everything. And later it was imagined that perhaps electromagnetic fields could underlie everything. Then after the introduction of general relativity for the gravitational field in 1915, there were efforts, especially in the 1930s, to introduce extensions that would yield unified field theories of everything (see page 1028). By the 1950s, however, an increasing number of subatomic particles were being found, and most efforts at unification became considerably more modest. In the 1960s the quark model began to explain many of the particles that were seen. Then in the 1970s work in quantum field theory encouraged the use of gauge theories and by the late 1970s the so-called Standard Model had emerged, with the Weinberg-Salam $SU(2) \otimes U(1)$ gauge theory for weak interactions and electromagnetism, and the QCD $SU(3)$ gauge theory for strong interactions. The discoveries of the c quark, τ lepton and b quark were largely unexpected, but by the late 1970s there was widespread enthusiasm for the idea of a single "grand unified" gauge theory, based say on $SU(5)$, that would explain all forces except gravity. By the mid-1980s failure to observe expected proton decay cast doubts on simple versions of such models, and various possibilities based on supersymmetry and groups like $SO(10)$ were considered. Occasional attempts to construct quantum theories of gravity had been made since the 1930s, and in the late 1980s these began to be pursued more vigorously. In the mid-1980s the discovery that string theory could be given various mathematical features that were considered desirable made it emerge as the main hope for an ultimate "theory of everything". But despite all sorts of elegant mathematical work, the theory remains rather distant from observed features of our universe. In some parts of particle physics, it is still sometimes claimed that an ultimate theory is not far away, but outside it generally seems to be assumed that physics is somehow instead an endless frontier—that will continue to yield a stream of surprising and increasingly complex discoveries forever—with no ultimate theory ever being found.

■ **Theological implications.** Some may view an ultimate model of the universe as "leaving no room for a god", while others may view it as a direct reflection of the existence of a god. In any case, knowing a complete and ultimate model does make it impossible to have miracles or divine interventions that come from outside the laws of the universe—though working out what will happen on the basis of these laws may nevertheless be irreducibly difficult.

■ **Origins of physical models.** Considering the reputation of physics as an empirical science, it is remarkable how many significant theories were in fact first constructed on largely aesthetic grounds. Notable examples include Maxwell's equations for electromagnetism (1880s), general relativity (1915), the Dirac equation for relativistic electrons (1928), and QCD (early 1970s). This history makes it seem more plausible that one might be able to come up with an ultimate model of physics on largely aesthetic grounds, rather than mainly by working from detailed experimental observations.

■ **Simplicity in scientific models.** To curtail absurdly complicated early scientific models Occam's razor principle that "entities should not be multiplied beyond necessity" was introduced in the 1300s. This principle has worked well in physics, where it has often proven to be the case, for example, that out of all possible terms in an equation the only ones that actually occur are the very simplest. But in a field like biology, the principle has usually been regarded as much less successful. For many complicated features are seen in biological organisms, and when there have been guesses of simple explanations for them, these have often turned out to be wrong. Much of what is seen is probably a reflection of complicated details of the history of biological evolution. But particularly after the discoveries in this book it seems likely that at least some of what appears complicated may actually be produced by very simple underlying programs—which perhaps occur because they were the first to be tried, or are the most efficient or robust. Outside of natural science, Occam's principle can sometimes be useful—typically because simplicity is a good assumption in some aspect of human behavior or motivation. In looking at well-developed technological systems or human organizations simplicity is also quite often a reasonable assumption—since over the course of time parts that are complicated or difficult to understand will tend to have been optimized away.

■ **Numerology.** Ever since the Pythagoreans many attempts to find truly ultimate models of the universe have ended up centering on derivations of numbers that are somehow thought to be characteristic of the universe. In the past century, the emphasis has been on physical constants such as the fine structure constant $\alpha \approx 1/137.0359896$, and usually the idea is that such constants arise directly from counting objects of some specified type using traditional discrete mathematics. A notable effort along these lines was made by Arthur Eddington in the mid-1930s, and certainly over the past twenty or so years I have received a steady stream of mail presenting such notions with varying degrees of obscurity and mysticism. But while I believe that every feature of our universe does indeed come from an ultimate discrete model, I would be very surprised if the values of constants which happen to be easy for us to measure in the end turn out to be given by simple traditional mathematical formulas.

■ **Emergence of simple laws.** In statistical physics it is seen that universal and fairly simple overall laws often emerge even in systems whose underlying molecular or other structure can be quite complicated. The basic origin of this phenomenon is the averaging effect of randomness discussed in Chapter 7 (technically, it is the survival only of leading operators at renormalization group fixed points). The same phenomenon is also seen in quantum field theory, where it is essentially a consequence of the averaging effect of quantum fluctuations, which have a direct mathematical analog to statistical physics.

■ **Apparent simplicity.** Given any rules it is always possible to develop a form of description in which these rules will be considered simple. But what is interesting to ask is whether the underlying rules of the universe will seem simple—or special, say in their elegance or symmetry—with respect to forms of description that we as humans currently use.

■ **Mechanistic models.** Until quite recently, it was generally assumed that if one were able to get at the microscopic constituents of the universe they would look essentially like small-scale analogs of objects familiar from everyday life. And so, for example, the various models of atoms from the end of the 1800s and beginning of the 1900s were all based on familiar mechanical systems. But with the rise of quantum mechanics it came to be believed throughout mainstream physics that any true fundamental model must be abstract and mathematical—and never ultimately amenable to any kind of direct mechanistic description. Occasionally there have been mechanistic descriptions used—as in the parton and bag models, and various continuum models of high-energy collisions—but they have typically been viewed only as convenient rough approximations. (Feynman diagrams may also seem superficially mechanistic, but are really just representations of quite abstract mathematical formulas.) And indeed since at least the 1960s mechanistic models have tended to carry the stigma of uninformed amateur science.

With the rise of computers there began to be occasional discussion—though largely outside of mainstream science—that the universe might have a mechanism related to computers. Since the 1950s science fiction has sometimes featured the idea that the universe or some part of it—such as the Earth—could be an intentionally created computer, or that our perception of the universe could be based on a computer simulation. Starting in the 1950s a few computer scientists considered the idea that the universe might have components like a computer. Konrad Zuse suggested that it could be a continuous cellular automaton; Edward Fredkin an ordinary cellular automaton (compare page 1027). And over the past few decades—normally in the context of amateur science—there have been a steady stream of systems like cellular automata constructed to have elements

reminiscent of observed particles or forces. From the point of view of mainstream physics, such models have usually seemed quite naive. And from what I say in the main text, no such literal mechanistic model can ever in the end realistically be expected to work. For if an ultimate model is going to be simple, then in a sense it cannot have room for all sorts of elements that are immediately recognizable in terms of everyday known physics. And instead I believe that what must happen relies on the phenomena discovered in this book—and involves the emergence of complex properties without any obvious underlying mechanistic set up. (Compare page 860.)

■ **The Anthropic Principle.** It is sometimes argued that the reason our universe has the characteristics it does is because otherwise an intelligence such as us could not have arisen to observe it. But to apply such an argument one must among other things assume that we can imagine all the ways in which intelligence could conceivably operate. Yet as we have seen in this book it is possible for highly complex behavior—ultimately not dissimilar to intelligence—to arise from simple programs in ways that we never came even close to imagining. And indeed, as we discuss in Chapter 12, it seems likely that above a fairly low threshold the vast majority of underlying rules can in fact in some way or another support arbitrarily complex computations—potentially allowing something one might call intelligence in a vast range of very different universes. (See page 822.)

■ **Physics versus mathematics.** Theoretical physics can be viewed as taking physical input in the form of models and then using mathematics to work out the consequences. If I am correct that there is a simple underlying program for the universe, then this means that theoretical physics must at some level have only a very small amount of true physical input—and the rest must in a sense all just be mathematics.

■ **Initial conditions.** To find the behavior of the universe one potentially needs to know not only its rule but also its initial conditions. Like the rule, I suspect that the initial conditions will turn out to be simple. And ultimately there should be traces of such simplicity in, say, the distribution of galaxies or the cosmic microwave background. But ideas like those on page 1055—as well as inflation—tend to suggest that we currently see only a tiny fraction of the whole universe, making it very difficult for example to recognize overall geometrical regularities. And it could also be that even though there might ultimately have been simple initial conditions, the current phase of our universe might be the result of some sequence of previous phases, and so effectively have much more complicated initial conditions. (Proposals discussed in quantum cosmology since the 1980s that for example just involve requiring the universe to satisfy final but not initial boundary condition constraints do not fit well into my kinds of models.)

■ **Consequences of an ultimate model.** Even if one knows an ultimate model for the universe, there will inevitably be irreducible difficulty in working out all its consequences. Indeed, questions like "does there exist a way to transmit information faster than light?" may boil down to issues analogous to whether it is possible to construct a configuration that has a certain property in, say, the rule 110 cellular automaton. And while some such questions may be answered by fairly straightforward computational or mathematical means, there will be no upper bound on the amount of effort that it could take to answer any particular question.

■ **Meaning of the universe.** If the whole history of our universe can be obtained by following definite simple rules, then at some level this history has the same kind of character as a construct such as the digit sequence of π. And what this suggests is that it makes no more or less sense to talk about the meaning of phenomena in our universe as it does to talk about the meaning of phenomena in the digit sequence of π.

The Nature of Space

■ **History of discrete space.** The idea that matter might be made up of discrete particles existed in antiquity (see page 876), and occasionally the notion was discussed that space might also be discrete—and that this might for example be a way of avoiding issues like Zeno's paradox. In 1644 René Descartes proposed that space might initially consist of an array of identical tiny discrete spheres, with motion then occurring through chains of these spheres going around in vortices—albeit with pieces being abraded off. But with the rise of calculus in the 1700s all serious fundamental models in physics began to assume continuous space. In discussing the notion of curved space, Bernhard Riemann remarked in 1854 that it would be easier to give a general mathematical definition of distance if space were discrete. But since physical theories seemed to require continuous space, the necessary new mathematics was developed and almost universally used—though for example in 1887 William Thomson (Kelvin) did consider a discrete foam-like model for the ether (compare page 988). Starting in 1930, difficulties with infinities in quantum field theory again led to a series of proposals that spacetime might be discrete. And indeed by the late 1930s this notion was fairly widely discussed as a possible inevitable feature of quantum mechanics. But there were problems with relativistic

invariance, and after ideas of renormalization developed in the 1940s, discrete space seemed unnecessary, and has been out of favor ever since. Some non-standard versions of quantum field theory involving discrete space did however continue to be investigated into the 1960s, and by then a few isolated other initiatives had arisen that involved discrete space. The idea that space might be defined by some sort of causal network of discrete elementary quantum events arose in various forms in work by Carl von Weizsäcker (ur-theory), John Wheeler (pregeometry), David Finkelstein (spacetime code), David Bohm (topochronology) and Roger Penrose (spin networks; see page 1055). General arguments for discrete space were also sometimes made—notably by Edward Fredkin, Marvin Minsky and to some extent Richard Feynman—on the basis of analogies to computers and in particular the idea that a given region of space should contain only a finite amount of information. In the 1980s approximation schemes such as lattice gauge theory and later Regge calculus (see page 1054) that take space to be discrete became popular, and it was occasionally suggested that versions of these could be exact models. There have been a variety of continuing initiatives that involve discrete space, with names like combinatorial physics—but most have used essentially mechanistic models (see page 1026), and none have achieved significant mainstream acceptance. Work on quantum gravity in the late 1980s and 1990s led to renewed interest in the microscopic features of spacetime (see page 1054). Models that involve discreteness have been proposed—most often based on spin networks—but there is usually still some form of continuous averaging present, leading for example to suggestions very different from mine that perhaps this could lead to the traditional continuum description through some analog of the wave-particle duality of elementary quantum mechanics. I myself became interested in the idea of completely discrete space in the mid-1970s, but I could not find a plausible framework for it until I started thinking about networks in the mid-1980s.

■ **Planck length.** Even in existing particle physics it is generally assumed that the traditional simple continuum description of space must break down at least below about the Planck length $Sqrt[\hbar\, G/c^3] \simeq 2 \times 10^{-35}$ meters—since at this scale dimensional analysis suggests that quantum effects should be comparable in magnitude to gravitational ones.

■ **Page 472 · Symmetry.** A system like a cellular automaton that consists of a large number of identical cells must in effect be arranged like a crystal, and therefore must exhibit one of the limited number of possible crystal symmetries in any particular dimension, as discussed on page 929. And even a generalized cellular automaton constructed say on a Penrose tiling still turns out to have a discrete spatial symmetry.

■ **Page 474 · Space and its contents.** A number of somewhat different ideas about space were discussed in antiquity. Around 375 BC Plato vaguely suggested that the universe might consist of large numbers of abstract polyhedra. A little later Aristotle proposed that space is set up so as to provide a definite place for everything—and in effect to force it there. But in geometry as developed by Euclid there was at least a mathematical notion of space as a kind of uniform background. And by sometime after 300 BC the Epicureans developed the idea of atoms of matter existing in a mostly featureless void of space. In the Middle Ages there was discussion about how the non-material character of God might fit in with ideas about space. In the early 1600s the concept of inertia developed by Galileo implied that space must have a certain fundamental uniformity. And with the formulation of mechanics by Isaac Newton in 1687 space became increasingly viewed as something purely abstract, quite different in character from material objects which exist in it. Philosophers had meanwhile discussed matter—as opposed to mind—being something characterized by having spatial extent. And for example in 1643 Thomas Hobbes suggested that the whole universe might be made of the same continuous stuff, with different densities of it corresponding to different materials, and geometry being just an abstract idealization of its properties. But in the late 1600s Gottfried Leibniz suggested instead that everything might consist of discrete monads, with space emerging from the pattern of relative distances between them. Yet with the success of Newtonian mechanics such ideas had by the late 1700s been largely forgotten—leading space almost always to be viewed just in simple abstract geometrical terms. The development of non-Euclidean geometry in the mid-1800s nevertheless suggested that even at the level of geometry space could in principle have a complicated structure. But in physics it was still assumed that space itself must have a standard fixed Euclidean form—and that everything in the universe must just exist in this space. By the late 1800s, however, it was widely believed that in addition to ordinary material objects, there must throughout space be a fluid-like ether with certain mechanical and electromagnetic properties. And in the 1860s it was even suggested that perhaps atoms might just correspond to knots in this ether (see page 1044). But this idea soon fell out of favor, and when relativity theory was introduced in 1905 it emphasized relations between material objects and in effect always treated space as just some kind of abstract background, with no real structure of its own. But in 1915 general relativity introduced the idea that space could actually have a varying non-Euclidean geometry—and that this could represent gravity. Yet it was still assumed that matter was something different—that for example had to be represented separately by explicit terms in the Einstein equations. There were nevertheless immediate thoughts that perhaps at least electromagnetism could be like gravity and just arise from features of space. And in 1918 Hermann Weyl suggested that this could happen through local variations of scale or "gauge" in space, while in the 1920s Theodor Kaluza and Oskar Klein suggested that it could be associated with a fifth spacetime dimension of invisibly small extent. And from the 1920s to the 1950s Albert Einstein increasingly considered the possibility that there might be a unified field theory in which all matter would somehow be associated with the geometry of space. His main specific idea was to allow the metric of spacetime to be non-symmetric (see page 1052) and perhaps complex—with its additional components yielding electromagnetism. And he then tried to construct nonlinear field equations that would show no singularities, but would have solutions (perhaps analogous to the geons discussed on page 1054) that would exhibit various discrete features corresponding to particles—and perhaps quantum effects. But with the development of quantum field theory in the 1920s and 1930s most of physics again treated space as fixed and featureless—though now filled with various types of fields, whose excitations were set up to correspond to observed types of particles. Gravity has never fit very well into this framework. But it has always still been expected that in an ultimate quantum theory of gravity space will have to have a structure that is somehow like a quantum field. But when quantum gravity began to be investigated in earnest in the 1980s (see page 1054) most efforts concentrated on the already difficult problem of pure gravity—and did not consider how matter might enter. In the development of ordinary quantum field theories, supergravity theories studied in the 1980s did nominally support particles identified with gravitons, but were still formulated on a fixed background spacetime. And when string theory became popular in the 1980s the idea was again to have strings propagating in a background spacetime—though it turned out that for consistency this spacetime had to satisfy the Einstein equations. Consistency also typically required the basic spacetime to be 10-dimensional—with the reduction to observed 4D spacetime normally assumed to occur through restriction of the other dimensions to some kind of so-called Calabi-Yau manifold of small extent, associated excitations with various particles through an analog of the Kaluza-Klein mechanism. It has always been hoped that this kind of seemingly arbitrary setup would somehow automatically emerge from the underlying theory. And in the late 1990s there seemed to be some signs of this when dualities were discovered in various generalized string theories notably for example between quantum particle excitations and gravitational black hole configurations. So while it remains impossible to work out all the consequences of string theories, it is conceivable that among the representations of such theories there might be ones in which matter can be viewed as just being associated with features of space.

Space as a Network

■ **Page 476 · Trivalent networks.** With n nodes and 3 connections at each node a network must always have an even number of nodes, and a total of $3n/2$ connections. Of all possible such networks, most large ones end up being connected. The number of distinct such networks for even n from 2 to 10 is {2, 5, 17, 71, 388}. If no self connections are allowed then these numbers become {1, 2, 6, 20, 91}, while if neither self nor multiple connections are allowed (yielding what are often referred to as cubic or 3-regular graphs), the numbers become {0, 1, 2, 5, 19, 85, 509, 4060, 41301, 510489}, or asymptotically $(6n)!/((3n)!(2n)!288^n e^2)$. (For symmetric graphs see page 1032.) If one requires the networks to be planar the numbers are {0, 1, 1, 3, 9, 32, 133, 681, 3893, 24809, 169206}. If one looks at subnetworks with dangling connections, the number of these up to size 10 is {2, 5, 7, 22, 43, 141, 373, 1270, 4053, 14671}, or {1, 1, 2, 6, 10, 29, 64, 194, 531, 1733} if no self or multiple connections are allowed (see also page 1039).

■ **Properties of networks.** Over the past century or so a variety of global properties of networks have been studied. Typical ones include:

- Edge connectivity: the minimum number of connections that must be removed to make the network disconnected.

- Diameter: the maximum distance between any two nodes in the network. The pictures below show the largest planar trivalent networks with diameters 1, 2 and 3, and the largest known ones with diameters 4, 5 and 6.

- Circumference: the length of the longest cycle in the network. Although difficult to determine in particular cases, many networks allow so-called Hamiltonian cycles that include every node. (Up to 8 nodes, all 8 trivalent networks have this property; up to 10 nodes 25 of 27 do.)

- Girth: the length of the shortest cycle in the network. The pictures below show the smallest trivalent networks with girths 3 through 8 (so-called cages). Girth can be relevant in seeing whether a particular cluster can ever occur in network.

- Chromatic number: the minimum of colors that can be assigned to nodes so that no adjacent nodes end up the same color. It follows from the Four-Color Theorem that the maximum for planar networks is 4. It turns out that for all trivalent networks the maximum is also 4, and is almost always 3.

■ **Regular polytopes.** In 3D, of the five regular polyhedra, only the tetrahedron, cube and dodecahedron have three edges meeting at each vertex, corresponding to a trivalent network. (Of the 13 additional Archimedean solids, 7 yield trivalent networks.) In 4D the six regular polytopes have 4, 4, 6, 8, 4 and 12 edges meeting at each vertex, and in higher dimensions the simplex ($d+1$ vertices) and hypercube (2^d vertices) have d edges meeting at each vertex, while the co-cube ($2d$ vertices) has $2(d-1)$. (See also symmetric graphs on page 1032, and page 929.)

■ **Page 476 · Generalizations.** Almost any kind of generalized network can be emulated by a trivalent network just by introducing more nodes. As indicated in the main text, networks with more than three connections at each node can be emulated by combining nodes into groups, and looking only at the connections between groups. Networks with colored nodes can be emulated by representing each color of node by a fixed group of nodes. Going beyond ordinary networks, one can consider hypernetworks in which connections join not just pairs of nodes, but larger numbers of nodes. Such hypernetworks are specified by adjacency tensors rather than adjacency matrices. But it is possible to emulate any hypernetwork by having each generalized connection correspond to a group of connections in an ordinary trivalent network.

■ **Maintaining simple rules.** An important reason for considering models based solely on trivalent networks is that they allow simpler evolution rules to be maintained (see page 508). If nodes can have more than three connections, then they will often be able to evolve to have any number of connections—in which case one must give what is in effect an infinite set of rules to specify what to do for each number of connections.

■ **Page 477 · 3D network.** The 3D network (c) can be laid out in space using $Array[x[8\{\#\#\}]\ \&,\ \{n,\ n,\ n\}]$ where

$$x[m:\{\_,\ \_,\ \_\}] := \{x_1[m],\ x_1[m+4],$$
$$\qquad x_2[m+\{4,\ 2,\ 0\}],\ x_2[m+\{0,\ 6,\ 4\}]\}$$
$$x_1[m:\{\_,\ \_,\ \_\}] := Line[Map[\#+m\ \&,\ \{\{1,\ 0,\ 0\},\ \{1,\ 1,\ 1\},$$
$$\qquad \{0,\ 2,\ 1\},\ \{1,\ 1,\ 1\},\ \{3,\ 1,\ 3\},\ \{3,\ 0,\ 4\},\ \{3,\ 1,\ 3\},\ \{4,\ 2,\ 3\}\}]]$$
$$x_2[\{i\_,\ j\_,\ k\_\}] :=$$
$$\qquad x_1[\{-i-4,\ -j-2,\ k\}]\ /.\ \{a\_,\ b\_,\ c\_\} \to \{-a,\ -b,\ c\}$$

The resulting structure is a cubic array of blocks with each block containing 8 nodes. The shortest cycle that returns to a particular node turns out to involve 10 edges. The structure does not correspond to the way that chemical bonds are arranged in any common crystalline materials, probably because it would be likely to be mechanically unstable.

■ **Continuum limits.** For all everyday purposes a region in a network with enough nodes and an appropriate pattern of connections can act just like ordinary continuous space. But at a formal mathematical level this can happen rigorously only in an infinite limit. And in general, there is no reason to expect that all properties of the system (notably for example the existence of particles) will be preserved by taking such a limit. But in understanding the structure of space and comparing to ordinary continuous space it is convenient to imagine taking such a limit. Inevitably there are several scales involved, and one can only expect continuum behavior if one looks at scales intermediate between individual connections in the underlying network and the overall size of the whole network. Yet as I will discuss on pages 534 and 1050 even at such scales it is far from straightforward to see how all the various well-studied properties of ordinary continuous space (as embodied for example in the theory of manifolds) can emerge from discrete underlying networks.

■ **Page 478 · Definitions of distance.** Any measure of distance—whether in ordinary continuous space or elsewhere—takes a pair of points and yields a number. Several properties are normally assumed. First, that if the points are identical the distance is zero, and if they are different, it is a positive number. Second, that the distance between points A and B is the same as between B and A. And third, that the so-called triangle inequality holds, so that the distance AC is no greater than the sum of the distances AB and BC. With distance on a network defined as the length of shortest path between nodes one immediately gets all three of these properties. And even though all distances defined this way will be integers, they still make any network formally correspond in mathematical terms to a metric space (or strictly a path metric space). If the connections on the underlying network are one-way (as in causal networks) then one no longer necessarily gets the second property, and when

a continuum limit exists it can correspond to a (perhaps discontinuous) section through a fiber bundle rather than to a manifold. Note that as discussed on page 536 physical measures of distance will always end up being based not just on single paths in a network, but on the propagation of something like a particle, which typically in effect requires the presence of many paths. (See page 1048.)

■ **Page 478 · Definitions of dimension.** The most obvious way to define the dimension of a space is somehow to ask how many parameters—or coordinates—are needed to specify a point in it. But starting in the 1870s the discovery of constructs like space-filling curves (see page 1127) led to investigation of other definitions. And indeed there is some reason to believe that around 1884 Georg Cantor may have tried developing a definition based on essentially the idea that I use here of looking at growth rates of volumes of spheres (balls). But for standard continuous spaces this definition is hard to make robust—since unlike in discrete networks where one can define volume just by counting nodes, defining volume in a continuous space requires assigning a potentially arbitrary density function. And as a result, in the late 1800s and early 1900s other definitions of dimension were developed. What emerged as most popular is topological dimension, in which one fills space with overlapping balls, and asks what the minimum number that ever have to overlap at any point will be. Also considered was so-called Hausdorff dimension, which became popular in connection with fractals in the 1980s (see page 933), and which can have non-integer values. But for discrete networks the standard definitions for both topological and Hausdorff dimension give the trivial result 0. One can get more meaningful results by thinking about continuum limits, but the definition of dimension that I give in the main text seems much more straightforward. Even here, there are however some subtleties. For example, to find a definite volume growth rate one does still need to take some kind of limit—and one needs to avoid sampling too many or too few nodes in the network. And just as with fractal dimensions discussed on page 933 there are issues about whether a definite power law for the growth rate will emerge, and how one should average over results for different parts of the network. There are some alternative approaches to defining dimension in which some of these issues at least become less explicit. For example, one can imagine not just forming a ball on the network, but instead growing something like a cellular automaton, and seeing how big a pattern it produces after some number of steps. And similarly, one can for example look at the statistics of random walks on the network. A slightly different but still related approach is to study the density of eigenvalues of the Laplace operator—which can also be thought of as measuring the number of solutions to equations giving linear constraints on numbers assigned to connected nodes. More sophisticated versions of this involve looking at invariants studied in topological field theory. And there are potentially also definitions based for example on considering geodesics and seeing how many linearly independent directions can be defined with them. (Note that given explicit coordinates, one can check whether one is in d or more dimensions by asking for all possible points

$Det[Table[(x[i] - x[j]) . (x[i] - x[j]), \{i, d + 3\}, \{j, d + 3\}]] == 0$

and this should also work for sufficiently separated points on networks. Still another related approach is to consider coloring the edges of a network: if there are $d + 1$ possible colors, all of which appear at every node, then it follows that d coordinates can consistently be assigned to each node.)

■ **Page 478 · Counting of nodes.** The number of nodes reached by going out to network distance r (with $r > 1$) from any node in the networks on page 477 is (a) $4r - 4$, (b) $3r^2/2 - 3r/2 + 1$, and (c)

$First[Select[4 r^3/9 + 2 r^2/3 + \{2, 5/3, 5/3\} r - \{10/9, 1, -4/9\}, IntegerQ]]$

In any trivalent network, the quantity $f[r]$ obtained by adding up the numbers of nodes reached by going distance r from each node must satisfy $f[0] = n$ and $f[1] = 3n$, where n is the total number of nodes in the network. In addition, the limit of $f[r]$ for large r must be n^2. The values of $f[r]$ for all other r will depend on the pattern of connections in the network.

■ **Page 479 · Cycle lengths.** The lengths of the shortest cycles (girths) of the networks on page 479 are (a) 3, (b) 5, (c) 4, (d) 4, (e) 3, (f) 5, (g) 6, (h) 10, (i) ∞, (j) 3. Note that rules of the kind discussed on page 508 which involve replacing clusters of nodes can only apply when cycles in the cluster match those in the network.

■ **Page 479 · Volumes of spheres.** See page 1050.

■ **Page 480 · Implementation.** Networks are conveniently represented by assigning a number to each node, then having lists of rules which specify what nodes the connection from a particular node go to. The tetrahedron network from page 476 is for example given in this representation by

$\{1 \to \{2, 3, 4\}, 2 \to \{1, 3, 4\}, 3 \to \{1, 2, 4\}, 4 \to \{1, 2, 3\}\}$

The list of nodes reached by following up to n connections from node i are then given by

$NodeLists[g\_, i\_, n\_] := NestList[Union[Flatten[\# /. g]] \&, \{i\}, n]$

The network distance corresponding to the length of the shortest path between two nodes is given by

$Distance[g\_, \{i\_, j\_\}] := Length[NestWhileList[Union[Flatten[\# /. g]] \&, \{i\}, ! MemberQ[\#, j] \&]] - 1$

■ **Finding layouts.** One way to lay out a network g so that network distances in it come as close as possible to ordinary distances in d-dimensional space, is just to search for values of the $x[i, k]$ which minimize a quantity such as

$With[\{n = Length[g]\}, Apply[Plus, Flatten[(Table[Distance[g, \{i, j\}], \{i, n\}, \{j, n\}]^2 - Table[Sum[(x[i, k] - x[j, k])^2, \{k, d\}], \{i, n\}, \{j, n\}])^2]]]$

using for example $FindMinimum$ starting say with $x[1, \_] \to 0$ and all the other $x[\_, \_] \to Random[]$. Rarely is there a unique minimum that can be found, but the approach nevertheless seems to work fairly well whenever a good layout exists in a particular number of dimensions. One can imagine weighting different network distances differently, but usually I have found that equal weightings work best. If one ignores all constraints beyond network distance 1, then one is in effect just trying to build the network out of identical rigid rods. It turns out that this is almost always possible even in 2D (though not in 1D); the only exception is the tetrahedron network. And in fact very few trivalent structures are rigid, in the sense the angles between rods are uniquely determined. (In 3D, for example, this is true only for the tetrahedron.)

■ **Hamming distances.** In the so-called loop switching method of routing messages in communications systems one lays out a network on an m-dimensional Boolean hypercube so that the distance on the hypercube (equal to Hamming distance) agrees with distance in the network. It is known that to achieve this exactly, m must be at the least the number of either positive or negative eigenvalues of the distance matrix for the network, and can need to be as much as $n - 1$, where n is the total number of nodes.

■ **Continuous mathematics.** Even though networks are discrete, it is conceivable that network-based models can also be formulated in terms of continuous mathematics, with a network-like structure emerging for example from the pattern of singularities or topology of continuous surfaces or functions.

The Relationship of Space and Time

■ **History.** The idea of representing time graphically like space has a long history—and was used for example by Nicholas Oresme in the mid-1300s. In the 1700s and 1800s the idea of position and time as just two coordinates was widespread in mathematical physics—and this then led to notions like "travelling in time" in H. G. Wells's 1895 *The Time Machine*. The mathematical framework developed for relativity theory in the early 1900s (see page 1042) treated space and time very symmetrically, leading popular accounts of the theory to emphasize a kind of fundamental equivalence between them and to try to make this seem inevitable through rather confusing thought experiments on such topics as idealized trains travelling near the speed of light.

In the context of traditional mathematical equations there has never been much reason to consider the possibility that space and time might be fundamentally different. For typically space and time are both just represented by abstract symbolic variables, and the formal process of solving equations as a function of position in space and as a function of time is essentially identical. But as soon as one tries to construct more explicit models of space and time one is immediately led to consider the possibility that they may be quite different.

■ **Page 482 · Discreteness in time.** In present-day physics, time, like space, is always assumed to be perfectly continuous. But experiments—the most direct of which are based on looking for quantization in the measured decay times of very short-lived particles—have only demonstrated continuity on scales longer than about 10^{-26} seconds, and there is nothing to say that on shorter scales time is not in fact discrete. (The possibility of a discrete quantum of time was briefly discussed in the 1920s when quantum mechanics was first being developed.)

■ **Page 483 · Network constraint systems.** Cases (a), (f) and (p) allow all networks that do not contain respectively cycles of length 1 (self-loops), cycles of length 3 or less, and cycles of length 5 or less. In cases where an infinite sequence of networks is allowed, there are typically particular subnetworks that can occur any number of times, making the sizes of allowed networks form arithmetic progressions. In cases (m), (n) and (o) respectively triangle, pentagon and square subnetworks can be repeated.

The main text excludes templates that have no dangling connections, and are thus themselves already complete networks. There are 5 such templates involving nodes out to distance one, but of these only 3 correspond to networks that satisfy the constraint that around each node the network has the same form as the template. Among templates involving nodes out to distance two there are 106 that have no dangling connections, and of these only 8 satisfy the constraints.

The main text considers only constraints based on a single template. One can also allow each node to have a neighborhood that corresponds to any of a set of templates. For templates involving nodes out to distance one, there are 13 minimal sets in the sense of page 941, of which only 6 contain just one template, 6 contain two and 1 contains three.

If one does allow dangling connections to be joined within a single template, the results are similar to those discussed so

far. There are 52 possible templates involving nodes out to distance two, of which 12 allow complete networks to be formed, none forced to be larger than 12 nodes. There are 46 minimal sets, with the largest containing 4 templates, but none forcing a network larger than 16 nodes.

■ **Symmetric graphs.** The constraints in a network constraint system require that the structure around each node agrees with a template that contains some number of nodes. A symmetric graph satisfies the same type of constraint, but with the template being the whole network. The pictures below show the smallest few symmetric graphs with 3 connections at each node (with up to 100 nodes there are still only 37 such graphs; compare page 1029).

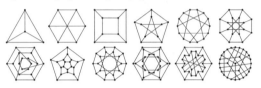

■ **Cayley graphs.** As discussed on page 938, the structure of a group can be represented by a Cayley graph where nodes correspond to elements in the group, and connections specify results of multiplying by generators. The transitivity of group multiplication implies that Cayley graphs always have the property of being symmetric (see above). The number of connections at each node is fixed, and given by the number of distinct generators and inverses. In cases such as the tetrahedral group A_4 there are 3 connections at each node. The relations among the generators of a group can be thought of as constraints defining the Cayley graph. As mentioned on page 938, there are finite groups that have simple relations but at least very large Cayley graphs. For infinite groups, it is known (see page 938) that in most cases Cayley graphs are locally like trees, and so do not have finite dimension. It appears that only when the group is nilpotent (so that certain combinations of elements commute much as they do on a lattice) is there polynomial growth in the Cayley graph and thus finite dimension.

■ **Page 485 · Spacetime symmetric rules.** With $k = 2$ and the neighborhoods shown here, only the additive rules 90R, 105R, 150R and 165R are space-time symmetric. For larger k and larger neighborhoods, there presumably begin to be non-additive rules with this property.

Time and Causal Networks

■ **Causal networks.** The idea of using networks to represent interdependencies of events seems to have developed with the systematization of manufacturing in the early 1900s—

notably in the work of Frank and Lillian Gilbreth—and has been popular since at least the 1940s. Early applications included switching circuits, logistics planning, decision analysis and general flowcharting. In the last few decades causal networks have been widely used in system specification methods such as Petri nets, as well as in schemes for medical and other diagnosis. Since at least the 1960s, causal networks have also been discussed as representations of connections between events in spacetime, particularly in quantum mechanics (see page 1027).

Causal networks like mine that are ultimately associated with some evolution or flow of activity always have certain properties. In particular, they can never contain loops, and thus correspond to directed acyclic graphs. And from this it follows for example that even the most circuitous path between two nodes must be of finite length.

Causal networks can also be viewed as Hasse diagrams of partially ordered sets, as discussed on page 1040.

■ **Implementation.** Given a list of successive positions of the active cell, as from $Map[Last, MAEvolveList[rule, init, t]]$ (see page 887), the network can be generated using

$MAToNet[list\_] := Module[\{u, j, k\}, u[\_] = \infty; Reverse[$
$\quad Table[j = list[\![i]\!]; k = \{u[j-1], u[j], u[j+1]\}; u[j-1] =$
$\quad u[j] = u[j+1] = i; i \rightarrow k, \{i, Length[list], 1, -1\}]]]$

where nodes not yet found by explicit evolution are indicated by ∞.

■ **Page 488 · Mobile automata.** The special structure of mobile automata of the type used here leads to several special features in the causal networks derived from them. One of these is that every node always has exactly 3 incoming and 3 outgoing connections. Another feature is that there is always a path of doubled connections (associated with the active cell) that visits every node in some order. And in addition, the final network must always be planar—as it is whenever it is derived from the evolution of a local underlying 1D system.

■ **Computational compression.** In the model for time described here, it is noteworthy that in a sense an arbitrary amount of underlying computation can take place between successive moments in perceived time.

■ **Page 496 · 2D mobile automata.** As in 2D random walks, active cells in 2D mobile automata often do not return to positions they have visited before, with the result that no causal connections end up being created.

The Sequencing of Events in the Universe

■ **Implementation.** Sequential substitution systems in which only one replacement is ever done at each step can just be implemented using $/.$ as described on page 893. Substitution systems in which all replacements are done that are found to fit in a left-to-right scan can be implemented as follows

$GSSEvolveList[rule\_, s\_, n\_] :=$
$\quad NestList[GSSStep[rule, \#] \&, s, n]$
$GSSStep[rule\_, s\_] :=$
$\quad g[rule, s, f[StringPosition[s, Map[First, rule]]]]$
$f[\{\}] = \{\}; f[s\_] := Fold[If[Last[Last[\#1]] \geq First[\#2],$
$\quad \#1, Append[\#1, \#2]] \&, \{First[s]\}, Rest[s]]$
$g[rule\_, s\_, \{\}] := s; g[rule\_, s\_, pos\_] := StringReplacePart[$
$\quad s, Map[StringTake[s, \#] \&, pos] /. rule, pos]$

with rules given as $\{"ABA" \rightarrow "BAAB", "BBBB" \rightarrow "AA"\}$.

■ **Generating causal networks.** If every element generated in the evolution of a generalized substitution system is assigned a unique number, then events can be represented for example by $\{4, 5\} \rightarrow \{11, 12, 13\}$—and from a list of such events a causal network can be built up using

$With[\{u = Map[First, list]\}, MapIndexed[Function[$
$\quad \{e, i\}, First[i] \rightarrow Map[(If[\# === \{\}, \infty, \#[\![1, 1]\!]] \&)[$
$\quad Position[u, \#]] \&, Last[e]]], list]]$

■ **The sequential limit.** Even when the order of applying rules does not matter, using the scheme of a sequential substitution system will often give different results. If there is a tree of possible replacements (as in $"A" \rightarrow "AA"$), then the sequential substitution system in a sense does depth-first recursion in the infinite tree, never returning from the single path it takes. Other schemes are closer to breadth-first recursion.

■ **Page 502 · Rule (b).** The maximum number of steps for which the rule can be applied occurs with initial conditions consisting of a white element followed by n black elements, and in this case the number of steps is $2^n + n$.

■ **String theory.** The sequences of symbols I call strings here have absolutely no direct connection to the continuous deformable 1D objects known as strings in string theory.

■ **String overlaps.** The total numbers of strings with length n and k colors that cannot overlap themselves are given by

$a[0] = 1; a[n\_] := k\, a[n-1] - If[EvenQ[n], a[n/2], 0]$

Up to reversal and interchange of A and B, the first few overlap-free strings with 2 colors are $A, AB, AAB, AAAB, AABB$.

The shortest pairs of strings of 2 elements with no self- or mutual overlaps are $\{"A", "B"\}$, $\{"AABB", "AABAB"\}$, $\{"AABB", "ABABB"\}$; there are a total of 13 such pairs with strings up to length 5, and 85 with strings up to length 6.

The shortest non-overlapping triple of strings is $\{"AAABB", "ABABB", "ABAABB"\}$ and its variants. There are a total of 36 such triples with no string having length more than 6.

■ **Simulating mobile automata.** Given a mobile automaton like the one from page 73 with rules in the form used on page

887—and behavior of any complexity—the following will yield a causal-invariant substitution system that emulates it:

Map[StringJoin, Map[{"AAABB", "ABABB", "ABAABB"}[[
 # + 1]] &, Map[Insert[#[[1]], 2, 2] →
Insert[#[[2, 1]], 2, 2 + #[[2, 2]]] &, rule], {2}], {2}]

■ **Sequential cellular automata.** Ordinary cellular automata are set up so that every cell is updated in parallel at each step, based on the colors of neighboring cells on the previous step. But in analogy with generalized substitution systems, one can also consider sequential cellular automata, in which cells are updated sequentially rather than in parallel. The behavior of such systems is usually very different from that of corresponding ordinary cellular automata, mainly because in sequential cellular automata the new color of a particular cell can depend on new rather than old colors of neighboring cells.

The pictures below show the behavior of several sequential cellular automata with $k = 2$, $r = 1$ elementary rules. In the top picture of each pair every individual update is indicated by a black dot. In the bottom picture each line represents one complete step of evolution, including one update of each cell. Note that in this representation, effects can propagate all the way across the system in a single step.

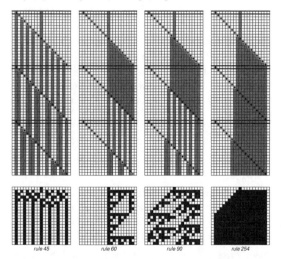

rule 45   rule 60   rule 90   rule 254

Size dependence. Because effects can propagate all the way across the system in a single step, the overall size, as well as boundary conditions, for the system can be significant after just a few steps, as illustrated in the pictures of rule 60 below.

size 49   size 50   size 51

Additive rules. Among elementary sequential cellular automata, those with additive rules turn out to yield some of the most complex behavior, as illustrated below. The top row shows evolution with the boundary forced to be white; the bottom row shows cyclic boundary conditions. Even though the basic rule is additive, there seems to be no simple traditional mathematical description of the results.

rule 60   rule 90   rule 165

Updating orders. Somewhat different results are typically obtained if one allows different updating orders. For each complete update of a rule 90 sequential cellular automaton, the pictures below show results with (a) left-to-right scan, (b) random ordering of all cells, the same for each pass through the whole system, (c) random ordering of all cells, different for different passes, (d) completely random ordering, in which a particular cell can be updated twice before other cells have even been updated once.

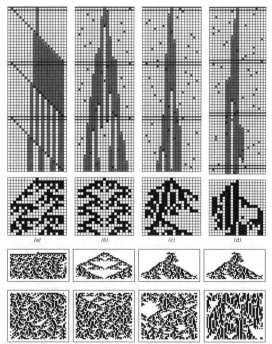

(a)   (b)   (c)   (d)

History. Sequential cellular automata have a similar relationship to ordinary cellular automata as implicit updating schemes in finite difference methods have to explicit ones, or as infinite impulse response digital filters have to finite ones. There were several studies of sequential or asynchronous cellular automata done following my work on ordinary cellular automata in the early 1980s.

Implementation. The following will update triples of cells in the specified order by using the function *f* :

    OrderedUpdate[f_, a_, order_] := Fold[ReplacePart[
        #1, f[Take[#1, {#2 - 1, #2 + 1}]], #2] &, a, order]

A random ordering of *n* cells corresponds to a random permutation of the form

    Fold[Insert[#1, #2, Random[Integer, Length[#1]] + 1] &,
        {}, Range[n]]

■ **Intrinsic synchronization in cellular automata.** Taking the rules for an ordinary cellular automaton and applying them sequentially will normally yield very different results. But it turns out that there are variants on cellular automata in which the rules can be applied in any order and the overall behavior obtained—or at least the causal network—is always the same. The picture below shows how this works for a simple block cellular automaton. The basic idea is that to each cell is added an arrow, and any pair of cells is updated only when their arrows point at each other. This in a sense forces cells to wait to be updated until the data they need is ready. Note that the rules can be thought of as replacements such as "A><B" → "<AB>" for blocks of length 4 with 4 colors.

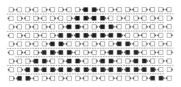

■ **"Firing squad" synchronization.** By choosing appropriate rules it is possible to achieve many forms of synchronization directly within cellular automata. One version posed as a problem by John Myhill in 1957 consists in setting up a rule in which all cells in a region go into a special state after exactly the same number of steps. The problem was first solved in the early 1960s; the solution using 6 colors and a minimal number of steps shown on the right below was found in 1988 by Jacques Mazoyer, who also determined that no similar 4-color solutions exist. Note that this solution in effect constructs a nested pattern of any width (it does this by optionally including or excluding one additional cell at each nesting level, using a mechanism related to the decimation systems of page 909). If one drops the requirement of cells

going into a special state, then even the 2-color elementary rule 60 shown on the left can be viewed as solving the problem—but only for widths that are powers of 2.

width 32

width 35

width 10

width 25

width 50

■ **Distributed computing.** Many of the basic issues about the progress of time in a universe consisting of many separate elements have analogs in the progress of computations that are distributed across many separate computing elements. In practice, such computations are most often done by requiring explicit synchronization of all elements at appropriate points, and implementing this using a mechanism that is outside of the computation. But more theoretical investigations of formal concurrent systems, temporal logics, dataflow systems, Petri nets and so on have led to ideas about distributed computing that are somewhat closer to the ones I discuss here for the universe. And, as it happens, in the mid-1980s I tried hard, though at the time without much success, to use updating rules for networks as the basis for a new kind of programming language intended for massively parallel computers.

Uniqueness and Branching in Time

■ **Page 506 · String transformations.** An example of a rule that allows one to go from any string of *A*'s and *B*'s to any other is

    {"A" → "AA", "AA" → "A", "A" → "B", "B" → "A"}

(Compare page 1038.)

■ **Parallel universes.** The idea of parallel universes which somehow interact with each other has been much explored in science fiction. And one might think that if the history of each universe corresponds to one path in a multiway system then the convergence of paths might represent interactions between universes. But in fact, much as in the case of time travel, such connections do not represent additional observable effects; they simply imply consistency conditions, in this case between universes whose paths converge.

■ **Many-worlds models.** The notion of "many-figured time" has been discussed since the 1950s in the context of the many-worlds interpretation of quantum mechanics. There are some similarities to the multiway systems that I consider here. But an important difference is that while in the many-worlds approach, branchings are associated with possible observation or measurement events, what I suggest here is that they could be an intrinsic feature of even the very lowest-level rules for the universe. (See also page 1063.)

■ **Spacetime networks from multiway systems.** The main text considers models in which the steps of evolution in a multiway system yield a succession of events in time. An alternative kind of model, somewhat analogous to the ones based on constraints on page 483, is to take the pattern of evolution of a multiway system to define directly a complete spacetime network. Instead of looking separately at strings produced at each step, one instead maintains just a single copy of each distinct string ever produced, and makes that correspond to a node in the network. Each node is then connected to the nodes associated with the strings reached by one application of the multiway rule, as on page 209.

It is fairly straightforward to generate in this way networks of any dimension. For example, starting with *n* A's the rule {"A" → "AB", "AB" → "A"} yields a regular *n*-dimensional grid, as shown below.

If each node in a network is associated with a point in spacetime, then one slightly peculiar feature is that every such point would have an associated string—something like an encoded position coordinate. And it then becomes somewhat difficult to understand why different regions of spacetime seem to behave so similarly—and do not, for example, seem to depend on the details of their coordinates.

■ **Page 507 · Commuting operations.** If replacements on strings are viewed as mathematical operations, then when the replacements give the same result if applied in any order, the corresponding operations commute.

■ **Conditions for convergence.** One way to guarantee that there is convergence after one step is to require as in the previous section that blocks to be replaced cannot overlap with themselves or each other. And of the 196 possible rules involving two colors and blocks of length at most three, 112 have this property. But there are also an additional 20 rules which allow some overlap but which nevertheless yield convergence after one step. Examples are "AAA" → "A" and "AA" → "ABA". In these rules some of the elements essentially just supply context, but are not affected by the replacement. These elements can then overlap while not affecting the result. Note that unless one excludes the context elements from events, paths in the multiway system will converge, but the causal networks on these paths will be locally slightly different.

Much as in the previous section, even if paths do not converge for every possible string, it can still be true that paths converge for all strings that are actually generated from a particular initial string.

In general, one can consider convergence after any number of steps, requiring that any two strings which have a common ancestor must at some point also have a common successor. Note that a rule such as {"A" → "B", "A" → "C", "B" → "A", "B" → "D"} exhibits convergence for all paths that have diverged for only one step, but not for all those that have diverged for longer. In general it is formally undecidable whether a particular multiway system will eventually exhibit convergence of all paths.

■ **Confluence.** As mentioned on page 938, multiway systems have been studied in mathematical logic, typically under names such as rewrite systems, since the early 1900s. The property of path convergence discussed in the main text has been considered since the 1930s, usually under the name of confluence, or sometimes the Church-Rosser property. (Also considered is strong confluence—that paths can always converge in at most one step, and local confluence—that paths can converge after diverging for one step but not necessarily more. Early in its history confluence was most often studied for symbolic systems and lambda calculus rather than ordinary multiway systems.)

Confluence is important in defining a notion of equivalence for strings. One can say that two strings are equivalent if they can both be transformed to the same string by using the rules of the multiway system. And with such a definition, confluence is what is needed to obtain transitivity for equality, so that $p == q$ and $q == r$ implies $p == r$.

Most often confluence is studied in the context of terminating multiway systems—multiway systems in which eventually strings are produced to which no further replacements apply. If a terminating multiway system has the confluence property, then this implies that regardless of the path taken, a given string will always evolve to a unique string that can be thought of as giving a canonical or normal form for the original string. Examples (a) through (c) below have this property; (d) does not. In example (a), the canonical form is all elements black; in (b) it is a single black element, and in (c) all elements are black, except the last one, which is white if there were any initial white elements. Note that the first example on page 507 has a canonical form consisting of a sorted string.

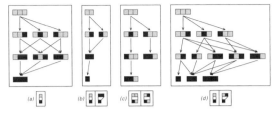

The process of evaluation in mathematics or in a computer language such as *Mathematica* can be thought of as involving the application of a sequence of replacement rules. Only if these rules have the confluence property will the results always be unique, and independent of the order of rule application.

The evaluation of functions with attribute *Flat* in *Mathematica* provides an example of confluence. If *f* is *Flat*, then in evaluating *f[a, b, c]* one can equally well start with *f[f[a, b], c]* or *f[a, f[b, c]]*. Showing only the arguments to *f*, the pictures below illustrate how the flat functions *Xor* and *And* are confluent, while the non-flat function *Implies* is not.

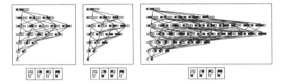

■ **Completion.** If one has a multiway system that terminates but is not confluent then it turns out often to be possible to make it confluent by adding a finite set of new rules. Given a string *p* which gets transformed either to *q* or *r* by the original rules, one can always imagine adding a new rule *q → r* or *r → q* that makes the paths from *p* immediately converge. To do this explicitly for all possible *p* that can occur would however entail having infinitely many new rules. But as noted by Donald Knuth and Peter Bendix in 1970 it turns out often to be sufficient just iteratively to add new rules only for each so-called critical pair *q*, *r* that is obtained from strings *p* that represent minimal overlaps in the left-hand sides of the rules one has. To decide whether to add *q → r* or *r → q* in each case one can have some kind of ordering on strings. For the procedure to work this ordering must be such that the strings generated on successive steps in every possible evolution of the multiway system follow the ordering. A number of variations of the basic procedure—using different orderings and with different schemes for dropping redundant rules—have been proposed for systems arising in different kinds of applications. The original Knuth-Bendix procedure was for equations (of the form *a ↔ b*) had

the feature that it could terminate yet not give a confluent multiway system. But in the 1980s so-called unfailing completion algorithms (see page 1158) were developed that—if they terminate—guarantee to give confluent systems. (The question of whether any procedure of this type will terminate in a particular case is nevertheless in general undecidable.)

The basic idea of so-called critical pair completion procedures has arisen several times—notably in the Gröbner basis approach of Bruno Buchberger from 1965 to finding canonical forms for systems of polynomials.

■ **Relationships between types of networks.** Each arrow on each path in a multiway system corresponds to a node in a causal network. Each element in each string in a multiway system corresponds to a connection in a causal network. Each complete string in a multiway system corresponds to a possible slice that goes through all connections across a causal network. Such a slice can be considered in traditional physics terms as a spacelike hypersurface (see page 1041).

Evolution of Networks

■ **Page 509 · Neighbor-independent rules.** Even though the same replacement is performed at each node at each step, the networks produced are not homogeneous. In the first case shown, the picture produced after *t* steps has $4 \times 3^{t-k-1}$ regions with 3×2^k edges. In the limit $t \to \infty$, the picture has the geometrical form of an Apollonian circle packing (see page 986). The number of nodes at distance up to *r* from a given node is at most $1 + Sum[c[i] + c[i-1], \{i, n\}]$ where $c[i\_] := 2 \wedge DigitCount[i, 2]$. In practice this number fluctuates greatly with *r*, making pictures like those on page 479 not exhibit smooth profiles. Averaged over all nodes, however, the number of nodes at distance up to *r* approximates $r \wedge Log[2, 3]$, implying an effective dimension of $Log[2, 3]$. Note that there is no upper limit on the dimension that can be obtained with appropriate neighbor-independent rules.

■ **Implementation.** For many practical purposes the best representation for networks is the one given on page 1031. But in updating networks a particularly straightforward implementation of one scheme can be obtained if one uses instead a more explicit symbolic representation such as

$u[1 \to v[2, 3, 4], 2 \to v[1, 3, 4], 3 \to v[1, 2, 4], 4 \to v[1, 2, 3]]$

This allows one to capture the basic character of networks by

Attributes[u] = {Flat, Orderless}; Attributes[v] = Orderless

Updating rules can then be written in terms of ordinary *Mathematica* patterns. A slight complication is that the patterns have to include all nodes whose connections go to nodes whose labels are changed by the update. The rule at the top of page 509 must therefore be written out as

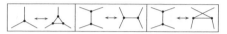

and this corresponds to the *Mathematica* rule

u[i1_ → v[i2_, i3_, i4_], i3_ → v[i1_, i5_, i6_],
i4_ → v[i1_, i7_, i8_]] :➤ u[i1 → v[i2, new[1], new[2]],
new[1] → v[i1, new[2], i3], new[2] → v[i1, new[1], i4],
i3 → v[new[1], i5, i6], i4 → v[new[2], i7, i8]]

(Strictly there also need to be additional rules to cover where for example nodes 3 and 4 are actually the same.) With rules in this form the network update is simply

NetStep[rule_, net_] := Block[{new},
net /. rule /. new[n_] → n + Apply[Max, Map[First, net]]]

Note that just as we discussed for strings on page 1033 the direct use of /. here corresponds to a particular scheme for applying the update rule.

■ **Identifying subnetworks.** The problem of finding where in a network a given subnetwork can occur turns out in general to be computationally difficult. For strings the analogous problem is straightforward, since in a string of length n one can ultimately just try each of the n possible starting points for the substring and see for which of them a match occurs. But for a network with n nodes, a similar procedure would require one to check n^k possible configurations in order to find out where a subnetwork of size k occurs. In practice, however, for fixed subnetworks, one can devise fairly efficient procedures. But the general problem of so-called subgraph isomorphism is formally NP-complete.

■ **Page 509 · Number of replacements.** The total number of distinct replacements that maintain planarity, involve clusters with up to five nodes and have from 3 to 7 dangling connections is {16, 8, 125, 24, 246}. Not maintaining planarity, the numbers are {14, 5, 13, 2, 2}. (See page 1039.)

■ **Cycles in networks.** See page 1031.

■ **Planar networks.** One feature of a planar network is that it is always possible to identify definite regions or faces bounded by connections in the network. And from Euler's formula $f + n = e + 2$, it then follows that the average number of edges of each face is always $6(1 - 2/f)$, where f is the total number of faces. Note that with my definition of dimension for networks, the fact that a network is planar does not necessarily mean that it has be two-dimensional—and for example the networks on page 509 are not.

■ **Arbitrary transformations.** By applying the string transformation rules on page 1035 at appropriate locations, it

is possible to transform any string of A's and B's to any other. And the analog of this for networks is that by applying the rules shown below at appropriate locations it is possible to transform any network into any other. These rules correspond to the moves invented by James Alexander in 1923 in connection with transforming one knot into another. (Note that the first two rules suffice for all planar networks, and are sometimes called respectively T2 and T1.)

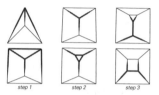

As an example, the pictures below show how a tetrahedron network can be transformed into a cube.

step 1   step 2   step 3

■ **Random networks.** One way to generate the connections for a "completely random" trivalent network with n nodes is just to apply a random permutation:

RandomNetwork[n_ ? EvenQ] := Partition[
Fold[Insert[#1, #2, Random[Integer, Length[#1]] + 1] &,
{ }, Floor[Range[1, n + 2/3, 1/3]]], 2]

Networks obtained in this way are usually connected, but will almost always contain self-loops and multiple edges. Properties of random networks are discussed on page 963. A convenient way to get somewhat random planar networks is from 2D Voronoi diagrams of the kind discussed on page 987.

■ **Random replacements.** As indicated in the note above, applying the second rule (T1, shown as (b) on page 511) at an appropriate sequence of positions can transform one planar network into any other with the same number of nodes. The pictures below show what happens if this rule is repeatedly applied at random positions in a network. Each time it is applied, the rule adds two edges to one face, and removes them from another. After many steps the pictures below show that faces with large numbers of edges appear. The average number of edges must always be 6 (see note above), but in a sufficiently large network the probability for a face to have n edges eventually approaches an equilibrium value of $8(n-2)(2n-3)!!(3/8)^n/n!$. (For large n this is approximately λ^n with $\lambda = 3/4$; if 1- and 2-edged regions are allowed then $\lambda = (3 + \sqrt{3})/6 \approx 0.79$.) There may be some easy way to derive such results, but so far it has only been done using fairly sophisticated techniques from quantum field theory developed in the late 1970s. The starting point is to look at a

ϕ^3 field theory with SU(n) internal symmetry and to note that in the limit $n \to \infty$ what dominates are Feynman diagrams that have the structure of planar trivalent networks (see page 1040). And it then turns out that in zero spacetime dimensions the complete path integral for the theory can be evaluated exactly—yielding in effect a generating function for the number of possible networks. Parametric differentiation (to yield n-point correlation functions) then gives results for n-sided regions. Another result that has been derived is that the average total number $m[n]$ of edges of all faces around a given face with n edges is $7n + 3 + 9/(n + 1)$. Note that the networks obtained always have dimension 2 according to my definitions.

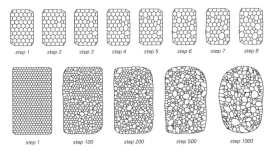

step 1 · step 2 · step 3 · step 4 · step 5 · step 6 · step 7 · step 8

step 1 · step 100 · step 200 · step 500 · step 1000

■ **Cellular structures.** There are many systems in nature that consist of assemblies of discrete regions—and the lines that define the interfaces between these regions form networks. In many cases the regions are fixed once established (compare page 988). But in other cases there is continuing evolution, as for example in soap and other foams and froths, grains in metals and perhaps some biological tissues. In 2D situations the lines between regions generically form a trivalent planar network. In a soap foam, the geometrical layout of this network is determined by surface tension forces—with connections meeting at 120° at each node, though being slightly curved and of different lengths. Pressure differences lead to diffusion of gas and on average to von Neumann's Law that the area of an n-sided region changes linearly with time, at a rate proportional to $n - 6$. Typically the network topology of a foam continually rearranges itself through cascades of seemingly random T1 processes (rule (b) from page 511), with regions that reach zero size disappearing through T2 processes (reversed rule (a)). And as noted for example by Cyril Smith in the early 1950s there is a characteristic coarsening that occurs. Something similar is already visible in the pure T1 pictures in the note above. But results such as the so-called Aboav-Weaire law that $m[n]$ from the note above is in practice about $5n + c$ suggest that T2 processes are also important. (Processes like cell division

in 2D biological tissue in effect directly add connections to a network. But this can again be thought of as a combination of T1 and T2 processes, and in appropriate idealizations can lead to very similar results.)

■ **Page 514 · Cluster numbers.** The following tables give the total numbers of distinct clusters—with number of nodes going across the page, and number of dangling connections going down. (See also page 1038.)

	1	2	3	4	5	6	7	8	9	10
0	0	0	0	1	0	2	0	5	0	19
1	0	0	0	0	1	0	4	0	19	0
2	0	0	0	1	0	5	0	23	0	132
3	1	0	1	0	3	0	15	0	91	0
4	0	1	0	2	0	9	0	54	0	390
5	0	0	1	0	4	0	22	0	166	0
6	0	0	0	2	0	9	0	63	0	551

	1	2	3	4	5	6	7	8	9	10
7	0	0	0	0	2	0	17	0	157	0
8	0	0	0	0	0	4	0	38	0	424
9	0	0	0	0	0	0	6	0	80	0
10	0	0	0	0	0	0	0	11	0	180
11	0	0	0	0	0	0	0	0	18	0
12	0	0	0	0	0	0	0	0	0	37

■ **Page 515 · Non-overlapping clusters.** The picture shows all distinct clusters with 3 dangling connections and 9 nodes that are not self-overlapping. The only smaller cluster with the same property is the trivial one with just a single node.

Most clusters that can overlap will be able to do so in an infinite number of possible networks. (One can see this by noting that they can overlap inside clusters with dangling connections, not just closed networks.) But there are some clusters that can overlap only in a few small networks. The pictures below show examples where this happens. The pictures in the main text still treat such clusters as non-overlapping.

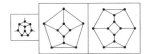

If two clusters overlap, then this means that there is some network in which there are copies of these clusters that involve some of the same nodes. And it is possible to search for such a network by starting from a single node and then sequentially trying to take corresponding pieces from the two clusters.

■ **1- and 2-connection clusters.** Clusters with just one or two dangling connections can always in effect be thought of just as adding extra structure to single connections in a network. But this extra structure can be important in the application of other rules—and can for example emulate something like having multiple colors of connections.

■ **Connectedness.** It is not clear whether a network that represents the universe must remain globally connected, or whether pieces can break off. But any replacements that take connected clusters and yield connected clusters must always maintain the connectedness of any network.

■ **Reversibility.** By including both forward and backward versions of every transformation it is straightforward to set up reversible rules for network evolution. It is not clear, however, whether the basic rules for the universe are really reversible. It could well be that the apparent reversibility we see arises because the universe is effectively on an attractor, as discussed on page 1018. Note that if pieces of the universe can break off, but cannot reconnect, then there will inevitably be an irreversible loss of information.

■ **1/n expansion.** If there are *n* possible colors for each connection in a network, then for large *n* it turns out that the vast majority of networks will be planar. This idea was used in the 1980s as a way of simplifying the Feynman diagrams to consider in QCD and other quantum field theories. (See page 1039.)

■ **Feynman diagrams.** In the standard approach to particle physics, possible interaction processes are represented by networks in which each node corresponds to an elementary interaction, and the nodes are joined by connections which correspond to the propagation of particles in spacetime. I can see no direct physical relationship between such diagrams and the networks I consider. However, at a mathematical level, the set of trivalent networks with *n* nodes formally corresponds to the set of nth order Feynman diagrams in a ϕ^3 field theory. (Compare page 1039.)

■ **Chemical analogy.** The evolution of a network can be thought of as an idealized version of a chemical process in which molecules are networks of bonds. (See page 1193.)

■ **Symbolic representations.** Expressions in which common subexpressions are shared correspond to networks, as do collections of relations between objects representing nodes.

■ **Graph grammars.** The notion of generalizing substitutions for strings to the case of networks has been discussed in computer science since the 1960s—and a fair amount of formal work has been done on so-called graph grammars for specifying formal languages whose elements are networks. Even a good analog of regular languages has, however, not yet been found. But applications to constructing or verifying practical network-based system description schemes are quite often discussed. In mathematics rather little is usually done with anything but very trivial network substitutions. In mathematics, rather little is usually done with network substitutions, though the proof of the Four-Color Theorem in 1976 was for example based on showing that 300 or so possible replacement rules—if applied in an appropriate sequence—can transform any graph to have one of 1936 smaller subgraphs that require the same number of colors. (32 rules and 633 subgraphs are now known to be sufficient.)

■ **Network mobile automata.** The analog of a mobile automaton can be defined for networks by setting up a single active node, then having rules which replace clusters of nodes around this active node, and move its position. The pictures below show two simple examples.

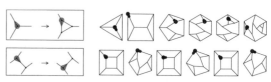

The total number of replacements that can be used in the rules of a network mobile automaton and which involve clusters with up to four nodes and have from 1 to 4 dangling connections is *{14, 10, 2727, 781}*. Despite looking at several hundred thousand cases I have not been able to find network mobile automata with especially complicated behavior.

Note that by having a cluster of nodes with a unique form it is possible to emulate a network mobile automaton using an ordinary network substitution system.

■ **Directed network systems.** If one adds directionality to the connections in a network it becomes particularly easy to set up rules for clusters of nodes that cannot overlap. For no two clusters whose dangling connections all point inwards can ever overlap, at least so long as neither of these clusters themselves contain subclusters whose dangling connections similarly all point inwards. The pictures below show a few examples of such clusters. Note that in a random network of *n* nodes, about *n/8* such clusters typically occur.

Space, Time and Relativity

■ **Page 516 · Posets.** The way I set things up, collections of events can be thought of as partially ordered sets (posets). If all events occurred in a definite sequence in time, this would define a total linear ordering for them. But with the setup I use, there is only a partial ordering of events, defined by causal connections. The causal networks I draw are so-called Hasse or order diagrams of the posets of events. If a connection goes directly from *x* to *y* in this network then *x* is said to cover *y*. And in general if there is a path from *x* to *y* then one writes *x* > *y*. The collection of all events that will lead to a given set of events (the union of their past light cones) is known as the filter of that set. Within a poset, there can be sequences of elements that are totally ordered, and these are called chains. (The maximum length of any chain is sometimes called the dimension of a poset, but this is unrelated to the notions of dimension I consider.) There can also be sets of elements between which no ordering relations at all are defined, and these are called antichains.

Standard examples of posets include subsets of a set ordered by the subset relation, complex numbers ordered by magnitude, and integers ordered by divisibility. Posets first arose as general concepts in the late 1800s in connection with the development of mathematical logic, and to some extent abstract algebra. They became somewhat popular in the mid-1900s, both as formal generalizations in lattice theory, and as structures in various combinatorics applications. It was already noted in the 1920s that events in relativity theory formed posets.

The pictures below show the first few distinct possible Hasse diagrams for posets. For successive numbers of elements the total numbers of these are 1, 2, 5, 16, 63, 318, 2045, 16999, ...

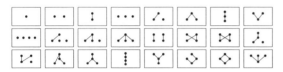

■ **Page 517 · Spacelike slices.** The definition of spacelike slices used here is directly analogous to what is used in traditional relativity theory (typically under names like spacelike hypersurfaces and Cauchy surfaces). There will normally be many different possible choices of spacelike slices, but in all cases a particular such slice is set up to represent what can consistently be thought of as all of space at a given time. One definition of a spacelike slice is then a maximal set of points in which no pair are causally related (corresponding to a maximal antichain in a poset). Another definition (equivalent for any connected causal network) is that spacelike slices are what consistently divide a causal network into a past and a future. And an intermediate definition is that a spacelike slice contains points that are not themselves causally related, but which appear in either the past or the future of every other point. Given a spacelike slice in a causal network, it is always possible to construct another such slice by finding all those points whose immediate predecessors are all included either in the original slice or its predecessors.

■ **Page 518 · Speed of light.** In a vacuum the speed of light is 299,792,458 meters/second (and this is actually what is taken to define a meter). In materials light mostly travels

slower—basically because there are delays when it is absorbed and reemitted by atoms. In a first approximation, the slowdown factor is the refractive index. But particularly in materials which can amplify light a whole sequence of peculiar effects have been observed—and it is fairly subtle to account correctly for incoming and outgoing signals, and to show that at least no energy or information is transmitted faster than c. The standard mathematical framework of relativity theory implies that any massless particle must propagate at c in a vacuum—so that not only light but also gravitational waves presumably go at this speed (and the same is at least approximately true of neutrinos). The effective mass for massive particles increases by a factor $1/Sqrt[1-v^2/c^2]$ at speed v, making it take progressively more energy to increase v. At a formal mathematical level it is possible to imagine tachyons which always travel faster than c. But the structure of modern physics would find it difficult to accommodate interactions between these and ordinary particles.

■ **Page 522 · History of relativity.** (See also page 1028.) The idea that mechanical processes should work the same regardless of how fast one is moving was expressed by Galileo in the early 1600s, particularly in connection with the motion of the Earth—and was incorporated in the laws of mechanics formulated by Isaac Newton in 1687. But when the wave theory of light finally became popular in the mid-1800s it seemed to imply that no similar principle could be true for light. For it was generally assumed that waves of light must correspond to explicit disturbances in a medium or ether that fills space. And it was thus expected that for example the apparent speed of light would depend on how fast one was moving with respect to this ether. And indeed in particular this was what the equations for electromagnetism developed by James Maxwell in the 1860s seemed to suggest. But in 1881 an experiment by Albert Michelson (repeated more accurately in 1887 as the Michelson-Morley experiment and now done to the 10^{-20} level) showed that in fact this was not correct. Already in 1882 George FitzGerald and Hendrik Lorentz noted that if there was a contraction in length by a factor $Sqrt[1-v^2/c^2]$ in any object moving at speed v (with c being the speed of light) then this would explain the result. And in 1904 Lorentz pointed out that Maxwell's equations are formally invariant under a so-called Lorentz transformation of space and time coordinates (see note below). Then in 1905 Albert Einstein proposed his so-called special theory of relativity—which took as its basic postulates not only that the laws of mechanics and electrodynamics are independent of how fast one is moving, but that this is also true of the speed of light.

And while at first these postulates might seem incompatible, what Einstein showed was that they are not—at least if modifications are made to the basic laws of mechanics. In the few years that followed, various formulations of this result were given, with Hermann Minkowski in 1908 showing that it could be derived if one just assumes that space and time enter all physical laws together in a certain kind of 4D vector. In the late 1800s Ernst Mach had emphasized the idea of formulating science and particularly mechanics in terms only of concepts that can actually be measured by observers. And in this framework Einstein and others gave what seemed to be almost purely deductive arguments for relativity theory—with the result that it generally came to be assumed that there was no meaningful sense in which one could ever imagine deriving relativity from anything more fundamental. Yet as I discussed earlier in the chapter, if a complete theory of physics is to be as simple as possible, then most things like relativity theory must in effect be derived from more basic features of the theory—as I start to try to do in the main text of this section.

■ **Standard treatment.** In a standard treatment of relativity theory one way to begin is to consider setting up a square grid of points in space and time—and then to ask what kind of transformed grid corresponds to this same set of points if one is moving at some velocity v. At first one might assume that the answer would just be a grid that has been sheared by the simple transformation $\{t, x\} \to \{t, x - v\,t\}$, as in the first row of pictures below. And indeed for purposes of Newtonian mechanics this so-called Galilean transformation is exactly what is needed. But as the pictures below illustrate, it implies that light cones tip as v increases, so that the apparent speed of light changes, and for example Maxwell's equations must change their form. But the key point is that with an appropriate transformation that affects both space and time, the speed of light can be left the same. The necessary transformation is the so-called Lorentz transformation

$$\{t, x\} \to \{t - v\,x/c^2, x - v\,t\}/Sqrt[1 - v^2/c^2\,]$$

And from this the time dilation factor $1/Sqrt[1 - v^2/c^2\,]$ shown on page 524 follows, as well as the length contraction factor $Sqrt[1 - v^2/c^2\,]$. An important feature of the Lorentz transformation is that it preserves the quantity $c^2\,t^2 - x^2$ — with the result that as v changes in the pictures below a given point in the grid traces out a hyperbola whose asymptotes lie on a light cone. Note that on a light cone $c^2\,t^2 - x^2$ always vanishes. Note also that the intersection of the past and future light cones for two events separated by a distance x in space and t in time always has a volume proportional exactly to $c^2\,t^2 - x^2$.

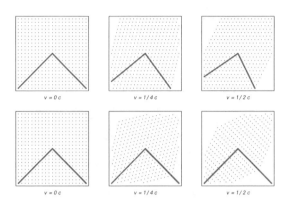

■ **Inferences from relativity.** The pictures on page 524 show that an idealized clock based on bouncing light between mirrors will exhibit relativistic time dilation. And from such derivations it is often assumed that the same result must hold for any possible clock system. But as a practical matter it does not. And indeed for example the clocks in GPS satellites are specifically set up so as to remove the effects of time dilation. And in the twin paradox one can certainly imagine that each twin could have an accelerometer whose readings they use to correct their clocks. Indeed, even when it comes to individual particles there are subtle effects associated with acceleration and radiation (see page 1062)—so that in the end not entirely clear that something like a biological system would actually in practice exhibit just standard time dilation.

One feature of relativity is that it implies that only relative motion is ultimately ever detectable. (This was also implied by Newtonian mechanics for purely mechanical systems.) And from this it is often concluded that there can be nothing like an ether that one can consider as defining an absolute state of rest in the universe. But in fact the cosmic microwave background in effect does exactly this. For in standard cosmological models it fills the universe, but is everywhere at rest relative to the global center of mass of the universe. And from the anisotropies we have observed in the microwave background it is thus possible to conclude that the Earth is moving at an absolute speed of about $c/10^3$ relative to the center of mass of the universe. In particle physics standard models also in effect introduce things that are assumed to be at rest relative to the center of mass of the universe. One example is the Higgs condensate discussed in connection with particle masses (see page 1047). Other possible examples include zero-point fluctuations in quantum fields.

Outside of science, relativity theory is sometimes given as evidence for various general ideas of cultural relativism (compare page 1131)—which have existed since well before relativity theory in physics, and seem in the end to have no meaningful connection to it.

■ **Particle physics.** Relativity theory was originally formulated just for mechanics and electromagnetism. But its predictions like $E = m c^2$ were immediately applied for example to radioactivity, and soon it came to be assumed that the theory would work for any system at all—unless it involved gravity. So this has meant that in particle physics $c^2 t^2 - x^2 - y^2 - z^2$ is at some level the only quantity that ever appears. And to make mathematical work easier, what is very often done is to carry out the so-called Wick rotation $t \to i t$—so relativistic invariance is just independence on 4D orientation. (See page 1061.) But except in rather simple cases there is practically no evidence that results obtained after Wick rotation have anything to do with physical reality—and certainly the transformation removes some very basic phenomena such as particle propagation. One feature of it, however, is that it maps the equation for quantum mechanical time evolution into the equation for probabilities in statistical mechanics, with imaginary time corresponding to inverse temperature. And while it is conceivable that this mapping may have some deep significance, none has so far ever been identified.

■ **Time travel.** The idea that space and time are similar suggests that it might be possible to move backwards and forwards in time just like it is possible to move backwards and forwards in space. And indeed in the partial differential equations that define general relativity, it is formally possible for the motion of particles to achieve this, at least when there is sufficient negative energy density from matter or a cosmological constant. But even in this case there is no real progression in which one travels backwards in time. Instead, the possibility of motion that leads to earlier times simply implies a requirement of consistency between behavior at earlier and later times.

Elementary Particles

■ **Note for physicists.** My goal in the remainder of this chapter is not to present a specific ultimate model for physics, but rather to discuss at a fairly general level some features that I believe such a model will have, given the overall discoveries of this book, and the specific results I have described in this chapter. I am certainly aware that many physicists will want to know more details. But particularly in making contact with existing physics it is almost inevitable that all sorts of technical formalism will be needed—and to maintain balance in this book I have not included this here. (Given my own personal background in theoretical physics it will come as no

surprise that I have often used such formalism in the process of working out what I describe in these sections.)

■ **Page 525 · Types of particles.** Current particle physics identifies three basic types of known elementary particles: leptons, quarks and gauge bosons. The known leptons are the electron (e), muon (μ) and tau lepton (τ), and their corresponding neutrinos (ν_e, ν_μ, ν_τ). Quarks exist inside hadrons like the proton and pion, but never seem to occur as ordinary free particles. Six types are known: u, d, c (charm), s (strange), t (top), b. Gauge bosons are associated with forces. Those currently known are the photon (γ) for electromagnetism (QED), W and Z for so-called weak interactions, and the gluon (g) for QCD interactions between quarks. Gravitons associated with gravitational forces presumably also exist. In ordinary matter, the only particles that contribute in direct ways to everyday physical, chemical and even nuclear properties are electrons, photons and effectively u and d quarks, and gluons. (These, together presumably with some type of neutrino, are the only types of particles that never seem to decay.) The first reasonably direct observations of the various types of particles were as follows (some were predicted in advance): e (1897), γ (~1905), u, d (1914/~1970), μ (1937), s (1946), ν_e (1956), ν_μ (1962), c (1974), τ, ν_τ (1975), b (1977), g (~1979), W (1983), Z (1983), t (1995).

Most particles exist in several variations. Apart from the photon (and graviton), all have distinct antiparticles. Each quark has 3 possible color configurations; the gluon has 8. Most particles also have multiple spin states. Quarks and leptons have spin 1/2, yielding 2 spin states (neutrinos could have only 1 if they were massless). Gauge bosons normally have spin 1 (the graviton would have spin 2) yielding 3 spin states for massive ones. Real massless ones such as the photon always have just 2. (See page 1046.)

In the Standard Model the idea of spontaneous symmetry breaking (see page 1047) allows particles with different masses to be viewed as manifestations of single particles, and this is effectively done for W, Z, γ, as well as for each of the 3 so-called families of quarks and leptons: u, d; c, s; t, b and e, ν_e; μ, ν_μ; τ, ν_τ. Grand unified models typically do this for all known gauge bosons (except gravitons) and for corresponding families of quarks and leptons—and inevitably imply the existence of various additional particles more massive than those known, but with properties that are somehow intermediate. Some models also unify different families, and supersymmetric models unify quarks and leptons with gauge bosons.

■ **History.** The idea that matter—and light—might be made up of discrete particles was already discussed in antiquity (see page 876). But it was only in the mid-1800s that there started to be real evidence for the existence of some kind of discrete atoms of matter. Yet at the time, the idea of fields was popular, and it was believed that the universe must be filled with a continuous fluid-like ether responsible at least for light and other electromagnetic phenomena. So for example following ideas of William Rankine from 1849 William Thomson (Kelvin) in 1867 suggested that perhaps atoms might be like knotted stable vortex rings in the ether—with different knots corresponding to different chemical elements. But though it initiated the mathematical classification of knots, and now has certain conceptual similarities to what I discuss in this book, the details of this model did not work out—and it had been largely abandoned even before the electron was discovered in 1897. Ernest Rutherford's work in the 1910s on scattering from atoms introduced the idea of an atomic nucleus, and after the discovery of the neutron in 1932 it became clear that the main constituents of nuclei were protons and neutrons. The positron and the muon were discovered in cosmic rays in the 1930s, followed in the 1940s by a handful of other particles. By the 1960s particle accelerators were finding large numbers of new particles every year. And the hypothesis was then suggested that all these particles might actually be composed of just three more fundamental particles that became known as quarks. An alternative so-called democratic or bootstrap hypothesis was also suggested: that somehow any particle could just be viewed as a composite of all others with the same overall properties—with everything being determined by consistency in the web of interactions between particles, and no particles in a sense being more fundamental than others. But by the early 1970s experiments on so-called deep inelastic scattering had given increasingly direct evidence for point-like constituents inside particles like protons—and by the mid-1970s these were routinely identified with quarks.

As soon as the electron was discovered there were questions about its possible size. For if its charge was distributed over a sphere of radius r, this was expected to lead to electrostatic repulsion energy proportional to $1/r$. And although it was suggested around 1900 that effects associated with this might account for the mass of the electron, this ran into problems with relativity theory, and it also remained mysterious just what might hold the electron together. (A late suggestion made in 1953 by Hendrik Casimir was that it could be forces associated with zero-point fluctuations in quantum fields—but at least with the simplest setup these turned out to have wrong sign.)

The development of quantum theory in the 1920s showed that discrete particles will inevitably exhibit continuous wave-like features in their spatial distribution of probability amplitudes. But traditional quantum mechanics and quantum field theory are both normally formulated with the assumption that the basic particles they describe have zero intrinsic spatial size. Sometimes nonzero size is taken into account by inserting additional interaction parameters—as done in the 1950s with magnetic moments and form factors of protons and neutrons. But for example in quantum electrodynamics the definite assumption is made that electrons are intrinsically of zero size. Quantum fluctuations make any particle in an interacting field theory effectively be surrounded by virtual particles. Yet not unlike in classical electrodynamics having zero intrinsic size for the electron still immediately suggests that an electron should have infinite self-energy. In the 1930s ideas about avoiding this centered around modifying basic laws of electrodynamics or the structure of spacetime (see page 1027). But the development of renormalization in the 1940s showed that these infinities could in effect just be factored out. And by the 1960s a long series of successes in the predictions of QED had led to the almost universal belief that its assumption of point-like electrons must be correct. It was occasionally suggested that the muon might be some kind of composite object. But experiments seemed to indicate that it was in every way identical to the electron, except in mass. And although no reasonable explanation for its existence was found, it came to be generally assumed by the 1970s that it was just another point-like particle. And indeed—apart from few rare suggestions to the contrary—the same is now assumed throughout mainstream practical particle physics for all of the basic particles that appear in the Standard Model. (Actual experiments based on high-energy scattering and precision magnetic moment measurements have shown only that electrons and muons must have sizes smaller than about $\hbar c/(10\,TeV) \simeq 10^{-20}\,m$—or about 10^{-5} times the size of a proton. One can make arguments that composite particles this small should have masses much larger than are observed—but it is easy to find theories that avoid these.)

In the 1980s superstring theory introduced the idea that particles might actually be tiny 1D strings—with different types of particles corresponding essentially just to strings in different modes of vibration. Since the 1960s it has been noted in many simplified quantum field theories that there can be a kind of duality in which a soliton or other extended field configuration in one representation becomes what acts like an elementary particle in another representation. And in the late 1990s there were indications that such phenomena could occur in generalized string theories—leading to suggestions of at least an abstract correspondence between for example particles like electrons and gravitational configurations like black holes.

■ **Page 526 · Topological defects.** An idealized vortex in a 2D fluid involves velocity vectors that in effect wind around a point—and can never be unwound by making a series of small local perturbations. The result is a certain kind of stability that can be viewed as being of topological origin. One can classify forms of stability like this in terms of the mathematics of homotopy. Most common are point and line defects in vector fields, but more complicated defects can occur, notably in liquid crystals, models of condensates in the early universe, and certain nonlinear field theories. Analogs of homotopy can presumably be devised to represent certain forms of stability in systems like the networks I consider.

■ **Page 527 · Kuratowski's theorem.** Any network can be laid out in 3D space. (This is related to the Whitney embedding theorem that any d-dimensional manifold can be embedded in $(2d+1)$-dimensional space.) When one says that a network is planar what one means is that it can be laid out in ordinary 2D space without any lines crossing. Kuratowski's theorem that planarity is associated with the absence of specific subgraphs in a network is an important result in graph theory established in the late 1920s. A subgraph is formally defined to be what one gets by selecting just some subset of connections in a network—and with this definition Kuratowski's theorem must allow extensions of K_5 and $K_{3,3}$ where extra nodes have been inserted in the middle of connections. (K_5 and $K_{3,3}$ are examples of so-called complete graphs, obtained by taking sets of specified numbers of nodes and connecting them in all possible ways.) Another approach is to consider reducing whole networks to so-called minors by deleting connections or merging connected nodes, and in this case Wagner's theorem shows that any non-planar network must be exactly reducible to either K_5 or $K_{3,3}$.

One can generalize the question of planarity to asking whether networks can be laid out on 2D surfaces with various topological structures—and in fact the genus of a graph can be defined to be the number of handles that must be added to a plane to embed the graph without crossings. But even on a torus it turns out that there is no finite set of (extended) subgraphs whose absence guarantees that a network can successfully be laid out. Nevertheless, if one considers minors a finite list does suffice—though for example on a torus it is known that at least 800 (and perhaps vastly more) are needed. (There is in fact a general theorem established since the 1980s that absolutely any list of networks—say for example ones that cannot be laid on a given surface—must actually in effect always all be reducible

to some finite list of minors.) Note that finding the genus for a particular trivalent network is in general NP-complete.

■ **Page 527 · Gauge invariance.** It is often convenient to define quantities for which only differences or derivatives matter. In classical physics an example is electric potential, which can be shifted by any constant amount without affecting voltage differences or the electric field given by its gradient. In the mid-1800s the idea emerged of a vector potential whose curl gives the magnetic field, and it was soon recognized—notably by James Clerk Maxwell—that any function whose curl vanishes (and that can therefore normally be written as a gradient) could be added to the vector potential without affecting the magnetic field. By the end of the 1800s the general conditions on electromagnetic potentials for invariance of fields were known, though were not thought particularly significant. In 1918 Hermann Weyl tried to reproduce electromagnetism by adding the notion of an arbitrary scale or gauge to the metric of general relativity (see page 1028)—and noted the "gauge invariance" of his theory under simultaneous transformation of electromagnetic potentials and multiplication of the metric by a position-dependent factor. Following the introduction of the Schrödinger equation in quantum mechanics in 1926 it was almost immediately noticed that the equations for a charged particle in an electromagnetic field were invariant under gauge transformations in which the wave function was multiplied by a position-dependent phase factor. The idea then arose that perhaps some kind of gauge invariance could also be used as the basis for formulating theories of forces other than electromagnetism. And after a few earlier attempts, Yang-Mills theories were introduced in 1954 by extending the notion of a phase factor to an element of an arbitrary non-Abelian group. In the 1970s the Standard Model then emerged, based entirely on such theories. In mathematical terms, gauge theories can be viewed as describing fiber bundles in which connections between values of group elements in fibers at neighboring spacetime points are specified by gauge potentials—and curvatures correspond to gauge fields. (General relativity is in effect a special case in which the group elements are themselves related to spacetime coordinates.)

■ **Page 527 · Identifying particles.** In something like a class 4 cellular automaton it is quite straightforward to start enumerating possible persistent structures—as we saw in Chapter 6. But in a network system it can be much more difficult. Ultimately what one wants to do is to find what possible types of forms for local regions are inequivalent under the application of the underlying rules. But in general it may be undecidable even whether two such forms are actually equivalent (compare the notes below and on page

1051)—since to tell this one might need to be able to apply the rules infinitely many times. In specific cases, however, generalizations of concepts like planarity and homotopy may provide useful guides. And a first step may be to look at small closed networks and try to determine which of these can be transformed into each other by a given set of rules.

■ **Knot theory.** Somewhat analogous to the problem in the note above is the problem of classifying knots. The pictures below show some of the simplest distinct knots. But given presentations of two knots, no finite procedure is known that determines in general whether the knots are equivalent (or constructs a sequence of Reidemeister moves that transform one into the other). Quite probably this is in general undecidable, though since the 1920s a few polynomial invariants have been discovered—with recent ones being related to ideas from quantum field theory—that have allowed some progress to be made. (Even the problem of determining whether a knot specified by line segments is trivial is known to be NP-complete.)

■ **Page 528 · Charge quantization.** It is an observed fact that the electric and other charges of all particles are simple rational multiples of each other. In the context of electromagnetism alone, there would be no particular reason to expect this (unless magnetic monopoles exist). But as soon as different particles are related by a non-Abelian symmetry group, then the discreteness of the representations of such a group immediately implies that all charges must be rational multiples of each other.

■ **Spin.** Even when they appear to be of zero size, particles exhibit intrinsic angular momentum known as spin. The total spin is always a fixed multiple of the basic unit $\hbar$: $1/2$ for quarks and leptons, 1 for photons and other ordinary gauge bosons, 2 for gravitons, and in theory 0 for Higgs particles. (Observed mesons have spins up to perhaps 5 and nuclei up to more than 50.) Particles of higher spin in effect require more information to specify their orientation (or polarization or its analog). And in the context of network models it could be that spin is somehow related to something as simple as the number of places at which the core of a particle is attached to the rest of the network. Spin values can be thought of as specifying which irreducible representation of the group of symmetries of spacetime is needed to describe a particle after momentum has been factored out. For ordinary massive

particles in d-dimensional space the group is Spin(d), while for massless particles it is $E(d-1)$ (the Euclidean group). (For tachyons, it would be fundamentally non-compact, forcing continuous spin values.) For small transformations, Spin(d) is just the ordinary rotation group SO(d), but globally it is its universal cover, or SU(2) in 3D. And this can be thought of as what allows half-integer spins, which must be described by spinors rather than vectors or tensors. Such objects have the property that they are not left invariant by 360 ° rotations, but only by 720 ° ones—a feature potentially fairly easy to reproduce with networks, perhaps even without definite integer dimensions. In the standard formalism of quantum field theory it can be shown that (above 2D) half-integer spins must always be associated with fermions (which for example satisfy the exclusion principle), and integer spins with bosons. (This spin-statistics connection also seems to hold for various kinds of objects defined by extended field configurations.)

■ **Page 528 · Particle masses.** The measured masses of known elementary particles in units of GeV (roughly equal to the proton mass) are: photon: 0, electron: 0.000510998902; muon: 0.1056583569; τ lepton: 1.77705; W: 80.4; Z: 91.19. Recent evidence suggests a mass of about 10^{-11} GeV for at least one type of neutrino. Quarks and gluons presumably never occur as free particles, but still act in many ways as if they have definite masses. For all of them their confinement contributes perhaps 0.3 GeV of effective mass. Then there is also a direct mass: gluons 0; u: ~0.005; d ~0.01; s: ~0.2; c: 1.3; b: 4.4; t: 176 GeV. Note that among sets of particles that have the same quantum numbers—like d, s, b or γ, Z—mixing occurs that makes states of definite mass—that would propagate unchanged as free particles—differ by a unitary transformation from states that are left unchanged by interactions. When one sets up a quantum field theory one can typically in effect insert various mass parameters for particles. Self-interactions normally introduce formally infinite corrections—but if a theory is renormalizable then this means that there are only a limited number of independent such corrections, with the result that relations between masses of different particles are preserved. In quantum field theory any particle is always surrounded by a kind of cloud of virtual particles interacting with it. And following the Uncertainty Principle phenomena involving larger momentum scales will then to probe progressively smaller parts of this cloud—yielding different effective masses. (The masses tend to go up or down logarithmically with momentum scale—following so-called renormalization group equations.)

The Standard Model starts off with certain symmetries that force the masses of all ordinary particles to be zero. But then one assumes that nonzero masses are generated by spontaneous symmetry breaking. One starts by taking each particle to be coupled to a so-called Higgs field. Then one introduces self-interactions in this field so as to make its stable state be one that has constant nonzero value throughout the universe. But this means that as particles propagate, their interactions with the background give them an effective mass. And by having Higgs couplings be proportional to observed particle masses, it becomes inevitable that these will be the masses of particles. One prediction of the usual version of this mechanism for mass is that a definite Higgs particle should exist—which in the minimal Standard Model experiments should observe fairly soon. At times there have been hopes of so-called dynamical symmetry breaking giving the same effective results as the Higgs mechanism, but without an explicit Higgs field—perhaps through something similar to various phenomena in condensed matter physics. String theory, like the Standard Model, tends to start with zero mass particles—and then hopes that an appropriate Higgs-like mechanism will generate nonzero ones.

■ **More particles.** To produce more massive particles requires higher-energy particle collisions, and today's accelerators only allow one to search up to masses of perhaps 200 GeV. (Sufficiently stable particles could have survived from the early universe, and a few cosmic ray interactions in principle give higher energies—but are normally too rare to be useful.) I am not sure whether in my approach one should expect an infinite series of progressively more massive particles. The example of nonplanarity might suggest not, but even in the class 4 cellular automata discussed in Chapter 6 it is not clear whether fundamentally different progressively larger structures will appear forever. In quantum field theory particles of any mass can always in principle exist for short times in virtual form. But normally their effects decrease like powers of their mass—making them hard to measure. In two kinds of cases, however, this does not happen: one is so-called anomalies, the other interactions with the Higgs field, in which couplings are proportional to mass. In the minimal Standard Model it turns out to be impossible to get quarks or leptons with masses much above about 200 GeV without destabilizing the vacuum (a fact pointed out by David Politzer and me in 1979). But with more complicated models one can avoid this constraint. In supersymmetric models—and string theory—there are typically also all sorts of other types of particles, assumed to have high masses since they have not been observed. There is evidence against any more

than the three known generations of quarks and leptons in that the decay process $Z^0 \rightarrow \nu\, \bar{\nu}$ has a rate that rather accurately agrees with what is expected from just three types of low-mass neutrinos.

■ **Page 530 · Expansion of the universe.** See page 1055.

The Phenomenon of Gravity

■ **History.** With the Earth believed to be the center of the universe, gravity did not seem to require much explanation: it was just a force bringing things to a natural place. But with the advent of Copernican astronomy in the 1500s something more was needed. In the early 1600s Galileo noted that the force of gravity seems to depend only on the mass of an object, and not on any of its other features. In 1687 Isaac Newton then suggested a universal inverse square law of gravity between objects. In the 1700s and 1800s all sorts of celestial mechanics was done on the basis of this—with occasional observational anomalies being resolved for example by the discovery of new planets. Starting in the mid-1800s there were attempts to formulate gravity in the same way as electromagnetism—and in 1900 it was for example suggested that gravitational effects might propagate at the speed of light. Following his introduction of relativity theory in 1905, Albert Einstein began to seek a theory of gravity that would fit in with it. Ordinary special relativity has the feature that it assumes that systems behave the same regardless of their overall velocity—but not regardless of their acceleration. In 1907 Einstein then suggested the equivalence principle that gravity always locally has the same effect as an acceleration. (This principle requires only slightly more than Galileo's idea of the equivalence of gravitational and inertial mass, which has now been verified to the 10^{-12} level.) But by 1912 Einstein realized that if the effective laws of physics were somehow to remain the same in systems with different accelerations (or in different gravitational fields) then this would require a change in their perceived geometry. And building on ideas of differential geometry and tensor calculus from the late 1800s Einstein then began to formulate the concept that gravity is associated with curvature of space. In the late 1800s Ernst Mach had argued that phenomena like acceleration and rotation could ultimately be defined only relative to matter in the universe. And partly on this basis Einstein used the idea that curvature in space must be like a field produced by matter—leading eventually to his formulation in 1915 of the standard Einstein equations for general relativity. An immediate prediction of these was a deviation from the inverse square law, explaining an observed precession in the orbit of Mercury. After a dramatic verification in 1919 of predicted bending of light by the Sun, general relativity began to be widely accepted. In the 1920s expansion of the universe was discovered, and this was seen to be consistent with general relativity. In the 1940s study of the evolution of stars then led to discussion of what became known as black holes. But for the most part general relativity was still viewed as being highly elegant though of little practical relevance. In the 1960s, however, more work began to be done on it. The discovery of the cosmic microwave background in 1965 led to increasing interest in cosmology. Precision tests—particularly with spacecraft—were designed. In calculations it was sometimes difficult to tell what was a genuine effect, and what was just a feature of the particular coordinates used. But a variety of increasingly abstract mathematical methods were developed, leading notably to general theorems about inevitability of singularities. Detailed calculations tended to require complicated symbolic tensor manipulation (with some associated problems being NP-complete), but with the development of computer algebra this gradually became more feasible—and by the mid-1970s approximate numerical methods were also being used. Various alternative formulations of general relativity were proposed, based for example on tetrads, spinors and twistors (and more recently on connection, loop and non-commutative geometry methods)—but none led to any great simplification. Meanwhile, there continued to be ever more accurate experimental tests of general relativity in the solar system—and at least in the weak gravitational fields available there (with metrics differing from the identity by at most one part in 10^6), all have worked out to around the 10^{-3} level. Starting in the 1960s, more and more ambitious gravitational wave detectors have been built—although none as yet have actually observed anything. Measurements done on a binary pulsar system are nevertheless consistent at a 10^{-3} level with the emission of gravitational radiation in a fairly strong gravitational field at the rate implied by general relativity. And since the 1980s there has been increasing conviction that at least indirect effects of black holes associated with very strong gravitational fields are being observed.

Over the years, some variants of general relativity have been proposed. At least when formulated in terms of tensors, none have quite the simplicity of the original theory—but some lead to rather different predictions, such as an absence of singularities like black holes. Ever since quantum theory began in the early 1900s there has been discussion of quantum gravity—and almost every major method developed for handling other quantum phenomena has been tried on gravity. Starting in the 1980s a variety of methods more specific to quantum gravity were also pursued, but none have yet had convincing success. (See page 1054.)

■ **Differential geometry.** Standard descriptions of properties like curvature—as used for example in general relativity—are normally based on differential geometry. In its usual formulation this assumes that space is continuous, and can always effectively be treated as some kind of deformed version of ordinary Euclidean space—thus forming what is known as a manifold. The result of this is that points in space can always be specified by lists of coordinates—although historically one of the objectives of differential geometry has been to find ways to define properties like curvature so that they do not depend on the choice of such coordinates. The geometrical properties of a space are in general specified by its so-called metric—and this metric allows one to compute quantities based on lengths and angles from coordinates. The metric can be written as a matrix g, defined so that the analog for infinitesimal vectors u and v of $u \cdot v$ in ordinary Euclidean space is $u \cdot g \cdot v$. (This is essentially equivalent to saying that infinitesimal arc length is related to infinitesimal coordinate distances by $ds^2 = g_{i,j} \, dx_i \, dx_j$.) In d dimensions the metric g for a so-called Riemannian space can in general be any $d \times d$ positive-definite symmetric matrix—and can vary with position. But for ordinary flat Euclidean space it is always just *IdentityMatrix[d]* (at least with Cartesian coordinates). Within say a surface whose points $\{x_1, x_2, ...\}$ are obtained by evaluating an expression e as a function of parameters p (so that for example $e = \{x, y, f[x, y]\}$, $p = \{x, y\}$ for a *Plot3D* surface) the metric turns out to be given by

(Transpose[#] . # &)[Outer[D, e, p]]

In ordinary Euclidean space a defining feature of geometry is that the shortest path between two points is a straight line. But in an arbitrary space things can be more complicated, and in general such a path will be a geodesic (see note below) which can have a more complicated form. If the coordinates along a path are given by an expression s (such as $\{t, 1 + t, t^2\}$) that depends on a parameter t, and the metric at position p is $g[p]$, then the length of a path turns out to be

Integrate[Sqrt[$\partial_t s . g[s] . \partial_t s$], {t, t_1, t_2}]

and geodesics then correspond to paths that extremize this quantity. In ordinary Euclidean space, such paths are straight lines, so that the length of a path between points with lists of coordinates a and b is just the ordinary Euclidean distance *Sqrt[(a – b) . (a – b)]*. But in general, even though geodesics are not straight lines their lengths can still be used to define a so-called geodesic distance—which turns out to have all the various properties of a distance discussed on page 1030.

If one draws a circle of radius r on a page, then the smaller r is, the more curved the circle will be—and one can define the circle to have a constant curvature equal to $1/r$. If one draws a more general curve on a page, one can define its curvature at every point by seeing what size of circle fits it best at that point—or equivalently what the coefficients are in a quadratic approximation. (Compare page 418.) With a 2D surface in ordinary 3D space, one can imagine fitting quadrics (generalized ellipsoids). But these are now specified by two radii, yielding two principal curvatures. And in general these curvatures depend on the way the surface is laid out in 3D space. But a crucial point noted by Carl-Friedrich Gauss in the 1820s is that the product of such curvatures—the so-called Gaussian curvature—is always independent of how the surface is laid out, and can thus be viewed as intrinsic to the surface itself, and for example determined purely from the metric for the 2D space corresponding to the surface.

In a 2D space, intrinsic curvature is completely specified just by Gaussian curvature. In higher-dimensional spaces, there are more components, but in general they are all part of the so-called Riemann tensor—a rank-4 tensor introduced by Bernhard Riemann in 1854. (In *Mathematica*, the explicit form of such a tensor can be represented as a nested list for which *TensorRank[list]* == 4.) Several descriptions of the Riemann tensor can be given. One is based on looking at infinitesimal vectors u, v and w and asking how much w differs when transported two ways around the edges of a parallelogram, from x to $x + u + v$ via $x + u$ and via $x + v$. In ordinary flat space there is no difference, but in general the difference is a vector that is defined to be *Riemann . u . v . w*. (The *Riemann* that appears here is formally $R_{ijk}{}^l$.) Another description of the Riemann tensor is based on geodesics. In flat Euclidean space any two geodesics that start parallel always remain so. But a defining feature of general non-Euclidean spaces is that this is not in general so. And it turns out that the Riemann tensor is what determines the rate at which geodesics deviate from being parallel. Still another description of the Riemann tensor is as the coefficient of the quadratic terms in an expansion of the metric about a particular point, using so-called normal coordinates set up to make linear terms vanish. In general the Riemann tensor can always be computed from the metric, though it is somewhat complicated. If p is a list of coordinate parameters that appear in a d-dimensional metric g, then

Riemann = Table[∂_p[[j]] Γ[[i, k]] - ∂_p[[i]] Γ[[j, k]] +
   Γ[[i, k]] . Γ[[j]] - Γ[[j, k]] . Γ[[i]], {i, d}, {j, d}, {k, d}]

where the so-called Christoffel symbol $\Gamma_{ij}{}^k$ is

Γ = With[{gi = Inverse[g]}, Table[Sum[
   gi[[l, k]] (∂_p[[j]] g[[i, l]] + ∂_p[[i]] g[[j, l]] - ∂_p[[l]] g[[i, j]]),
   {l, d}], {i, d}, {j, d}, {k, d}]]/2

There are d^4 elements in the nested lists for *Riemann*, but symmetries and the so-called Bianchi identity reduce the

number of independent components to $1/12\, d^2\,(d^2 - 1)$—or 20 for $d = 4$. One can then compute the Ricci tensor $(R_{ik} = R_{ijk}{}^j)$ using

RicciTensor = Map[Tr, Transpose[Riemann, {1, 3, 2, 4}], {2}]

and this has $1/2\, d\,(d + 1)$ independent components in $d > 2$ dimensions. (The parts of the Riemann tensor not captured by the Ricci tensor correspond to the so-called Weyl tensor; for $d = 2$ the Ricci tensor has only one independent component, equal to the negative of the Gaussian curvature.) Finally, the Ricci scalar curvature is given by

RicciScalar = Tr[RicciTensor . Inverse[g]]

■ **Page 531 · Geodesics.** On a sphere all geodesics are arcs of great circles. On a surface of constant negative curvature (like (c)) geodesics diverge exponentially, as noted in early work on chaos theory (see page 971). The path of a geodesic can in general be found by requiring that the analog of acceleration vanishes for it. In the case of a surface defined by $z == f[x, y]$ this is equivalent to solving

x''[t] == -(f^(1,0)[x[t], y[t]] (y'[t]² f^(0,2)[x[t], y[t]] +
   2 x'[t] y'[t] f^(1,1)[x[t], y[t]] + x'[t]² f^(2,0)[x[t], y[t]]))/
   (1 + f^(0,1)[x[t], y[t]]² + f^(1,0)[x[t], y[t]]²)

together with the corresponding equation for y'', as already noted by Leonhard Euler in 1728 in connection with his development of the calculus of variations.

■ **Page 532 · Spherical networks.** One can construct networks of constant positive curvature by approximating the surface of a sphere—starting with a dodecahedron and adding hexagons. (Euler's theorem implies that at any stage there must always be exactly 12 pentagonal faces.) The following are examples with 20, 60, 80, 180 and 320 nodes:

The object with 60 nodes is a truncated icosahedron—the shape of a standard soccer ball, as well the shape of the fullerene molecule C_{60}. (Note that in C_{60} one of the connections at each node is always a double chemical bond, since carbon has valence 4.) Geodesic domes are typically duals of such networks—with three edges on each face.

■ **Hyperbolic networks.** Any surface that always has positive curvature must eventually close up to form something like a sphere. But a surface that has negative curvature (and no holes) must in some sense be infinite—more like cases (c) and (d) on page 412. Yet even in such a case one can always define coordinates that nominally allow the surface to be drawn in a finite way—and the Poincaré disk model used in the pictures below is the standard way of doing this. In ordinary flat space, regular polygons with more than 6 sides can never form a tessellation. But in a space with negative curvature this is possible for polygons with arbitrarily many sides—and the networks that result have been much studied as Cayley graphs of Fuchsian groups. One feature of these networks is that the number of nodes reached in them by following r connections always grows like 2^r. But if one intersperses hexagons in the networks (as in the main text) then one finds that for small r the number of nodes just grows like r^2—as one would expect for something like a 2D surface. But if one tries to look at growth rates on scales that are not small compared to characteristic lengths associated with curvature then one again sees exponential growth—just as in the case of a uniform tessellation without hexagons.

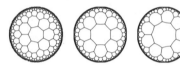

■ **Page 533 · Sphere volumes.** In ordinary flat Euclidean space the area of a 2D circle is πr^2, and the volume of a 3D sphere $4\pi r^3/3$. In general, the volume of a sphere in d-dimensional Euclidean space is $s[d]r^d$ where $s[d] = \pi^{d/2}/(d/2)!$ (the surface area is $d\,s[d]\,r^{d-1}$). (The function $s[d]$ has a maximum around $d = 5.26$, then decreases rapidly with d.)

If instead of flat space one considers a space defined by the surface of a 3D sphere—say with radius a—one can ask about areas of circles in this space. Such circles are no longer flat, but instead are like caps on the sphere—with a circle of radius r containing all points that are geodesic (great circle) distance less than r from its center. Such a circle has area

$$2\pi a^2(1 - Cos[r/a]) = \pi r^2(1 - r^2/(12a^2) + r^4/(360a^4) - ...)$$

In the d-dimensional space corresponding to the surface of a $(d+1)$-dimensional sphere of radius a, the volume of a d-dimensional sphere of radius r is similarly given by

$$d\,s[d]\,a^d\, Integrate[Sin[\theta]^{d-1}, \{\theta, 0, r/a\}] =$$
$$s[d]r^d\,(1 - d\,(d-1)\,r^2/((6(d+2))a^2) +$$
$$(d\,(5\,d^2 - 12\,d + 7))\,r^4/((360(d+4))a^4) + ...)$$

where

$$Integrate[Sin[x]^{d-1}, x] = -Cos[x]$$
$$Hypergeometric2F1[1/2, (2-d)/2, 3/2, Cos[x]^2]$$

In an arbitrary d-dimensional space the volume of a sphere can depend on position, but in general it is given by

$$s[d]r^d\,(1 - RicciScalar\,r^2/(6(d+2)) + ...)$$

where the Ricci scalar curvature is evaluated at the position of the sphere. (The space corresponding to a $(d+1)$-dimensional sphere has $RicciScalar = d\,(d-1)/a^2$.) The $d = 2$ version of this formula was derived in 1848; the general case in 1917 and 1939. Various derivations can be given. One can

start from the fact that the volume density in any space is given in terms of the metric by $Sqrt[Det[g]]$. But in normal coordinates the first non-trivial term in the expansion of the metric is proportional to the Riemann tensor, yet the symmetry of a spherical volume makes it inevitable that the Ricci scalar is the only combination of components that can appear at lowest order. To next order the result is

$$s[d]r^d\,(1 - RicciScalar\,r^2/(6(d+2)) +$$
$$(5\,RicciScalar^2 - 3\,RiemannNorm + 8\,RicciNorm -$$
$$18\,Laplacian[RicciScalar])\,r^4/(360(d+2)(d+4)) + ...)$$

where the new quantities involved are

$$RicciNorm = Norm[RicciTensor, \{g, g\}]$$
$$RiemannNorm = Norm[Riemann, \{g, g, g, Inverse[g]\}]$$
$$Norm[t\_, gl\_] := Tr[Flatten[t\,Dual[t, gl]]]$$
$$Dual[t\_, gl\_] := Fold[Transpose[\#1 . Inverse[\#2], RotateLeft[$$
$$Range[TensorRank[t]]]] \&, t, Reverse[gl]]$$
$$Laplacian[f\_] := Inner[D, Sqrt[Det[g]]$$
$$(Inverse[g] . Map[\partial_{\#}\,f \&, p]), p]/Sqrt[Det[g]]$$

In general the series in r may not converge, but it is known that at least in most cases only flat space can give a result that shows no correction to the basic r^d form. It is also known that if the Ricci tensor is non-negative, then the volume never grows faster than r^d.

■ **Cylinder volumes.** In any d-dimensional space, the volume of a cylinder of length x and radius r whose direction is defined by a unit vector v turns out to be given by

$$s[d-1]r^{d-1}\,x$$
$$(1 - (d-1)(RicciScalar - RicciTensor . v . v)\,r^2/(d+1) + ...)$$

Note that what determines the volume of the cylinder is curvature orthogonal to its direction—and this is what leads to the combination of Ricci scalar and tensor that appears.

■ **Page 533 · Discrete spaces.** Most work with surfaces done on computers—whether for computer graphics, computer-aided design, solving boundary value problems or otherwise—makes use of discrete approximations. Typically surfaces are represented by collections of patches—with a simple mesh of triangles often being used. The triangles are however normally specified not so much by their network of connections as by the explicit coordinates of their vertices. And while there are various triangulation methods that for example avoid triangles with small angles, no standard method yields networks analogous to the ones I consider in which all triangle edges are effectively the same length.

In pure mathematics a basic idea in topology has been to look for finite or discrete ways to capture essential features of continuous surfaces and spaces. And as an early part of this Henri Poincaré in the 1890s introduced the concept of approximating manifolds by cell complexes consisting of collections of generalized polyhedra. By the 1920s there was then extensive work on so-called combinatorial topology, in which spaces are thought of as being decomposed into abstract complexes consisting say of triangles, tetrahedra and higher-dimensional simplices. But while explicit coordinates and lengths are not usually discussed, it is still imagined that one knows more information than in the networks I consider: not only how vertices are connected by edges, but also how edges are arranged around faces, faces around volumes, and so on. And while in 2D and 3D it is possible to set up such an approximation to any manifold in this way, it turns out that at least in 5D and above it is not. Before the 1960s it had been hoped that in accordance with the Hauptvermutung of combinatorial topology it would be possible to tell whether a continuous mapping and thus topological equivalence exists between manifolds just by seeing whether subdivisions of simplicial complexes for them could be identical. But in the 1960s it was discovered that at least in 5D and above this will not always work. And largely as a result of this, there has tended to be less interest in ideas like simplicial complexes.

And indeed a crucial point for my discussion in the main text is that in formulating general relativity one actually does not appear to need all the structure of a simplicial complex. In fact, the only features of manifolds that ultimately seem relevant are ones that in appropriate limits are determined just from the connectivity of networks. The details of the limits are mathematically somewhat intricate (compare page 1030), but the basic approach is straightforward. One can find the volume of a sphere (geodesic ball) in a network just by counting the number of nodes out to a given network distance from a certain node. And from the limiting growth rate of this one can immediately get the Ricci scalar curvature—just as in the continuous case discussed above. To get the Ricci tensor one also needs a direction. But one can get this from a geodesic—which is in effect the analog of a straight line in the network. Note that unlike in a continuous space there is however usually no obvious way to continue a geodesic in a network. And in general, some—but not all—of the standard constructions used in continuous spaces can also immediately be used in networks. So for example it is straightforward to construct a triangle in a network: one just starts from a particular node, follows geodesics to two others, then joins these with a geodesic. But to extend the triangle into a parallelogram is not so easy—since there is no immediate notion of parallelism in the network. And this means that neither the Riemann tensor, nor a so-called Schild ladder for parallel transport, can readily be constructed.

Since the 1980s there has been increasing interest in formulating notions of continuous geometry for objects like Cayley graphs of groups—which are fundamentally discrete but have infinite limits analogous to continuous systems. (Compare page 938.)

■ **Manifold undecidability.** Given a particular set of network substitution rules there is in general no finite way to decide whether any sequence of such rules exists that will transform particular networks into each other. (Compare undecidability in multiway systems on page 779.) And although one might not expect it on the basis of traditional mathematical intuition, there is an analog of this even for topological equivalence of ordinary continuous manifolds. For the fundamental groups that represent how basic loops can be combined must be equivalent for equivalent manifolds. Yet it turns out that in 4D and above the fundamental group can have essentially any set of generators and relations—so that the undecidability of the word problem for arbitrary groups (see page 1141) implies undecidability of equivalence of manifolds. (In 2D it is straightforward to decide equivalence, and in 3D it is known that only some fundamental groups can be obtained—roughly because not all networks can be embedded in 2D—and it is expected that it will ultimately be possible to decide equivalence.)

■ **Non-integer dimensions.** Unlike in traditional differential geometry (and general relativity) my formulation of space as a network potentially allows concepts like curvature to be defined even outside of integers numbers of dimensions.

■ **Page 534 · Lorentzian spaces.** In ordinary Euclidean space distance is given by $Sqrt[x^2 + y^2 + z^2]$. In setting up relativity theory it is convenient (see page 1042) to define an analog of distance (so-called proper time) in 4D spacetime by $Sqrt[c^2 t^2 - x^2 - y^2 - z^2]$. And in terms of differential geometry such Minkowski space can be specified by the metric $DiagonalMatrix[\{+1, -1, -1, -1\}]$ (now taking $c = 1$). To set up general relativity one then considers not Riemannian manifolds but instead Lorentzian ones in which the metric is not positive definite, but instead has the signature of Minkowski space.

In such Lorentzian spaces, however, there is no useful immediate analog of a sphere. For given any point, even the light cone that corresponds to points at zero spacetime distance from it has an infinite volume. But with an appropriate definition one can still set up cones that have finite volume. To do this in general one starts by picking a vector e in a timelike direction, then normalizes it to be a unit vector so that $e . g . e == -1$. Then one defines a cone of height t whose apex is a given point to be those points whose displacement vector v satisfies $0 > e \cdot g \cdot v > -t$ (and $0 > v \cdot g \cdot v$). And the volume of such a cone then turns out to be

$$s[d]\, t^{d+1}\, (1 - t^2\, (d+1)\, (d\ RicciScalar + \\ 2\, (d+1)\, (RicciTensor \cdot e \cdot e))/((d+2)(d+3)) + \dots)/(d+1)$$

■ **Torsion.** In standard geometry, one assumes that the distance from one point to another is the same as the distance back, so that the metric tensor can be taken to be symmetric, and there is zero so-called torsion. But in for example a causal network, connections have definite directions, and there is in general no such symmetry. And if one looks at the volume of a cone this can then introduce a correction proportional to r. But as soon as there is enough uniformity to define a reasonable notion of static space, it seems that this effect must vanish. (Note that in pure mathematics there are several different uses of the word "torsion". Here I use it to refer to the antisymmetric parts of the metric tensor.)

■ **Random causal networks.** If one assumes that there are events at random positions in continuous spacetime, then one can construct an effective causal network for them by setting up connections between each event and all events in its future light cone—then deleting connections that are redundant in the sense that they just provide shortcuts to events that could otherwise be reached by following multiple connections. The pictures below show examples of causal networks obtained in this way. The number of connections generally increases faster than linearly with the number of events. Most links end up being at angles that are close to the edge of the light cone.

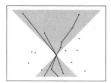

■ **Page 534 · Einstein equations.** In the absence of matter, the standard statement of the Einstein equations is that all components of the Ricci tensor—and thus also the Ricci scalar—must be zero (or formally that $R_{ij} = 0$). But since the vanishing of all components of a tensor must be independent of the coordinates used, it follows that the vacuum Einstein equations are equivalent to the statement $RicciTensor \cdot e \cdot e == 0$ for all timelike unit vectors e—a statement that can readily be applied to networks of the kind I consider in the main text. (A related statement is that the 3D Ricci scalar curvature of all spacelike hypersurfaces must vanish wherever these have vanishing extrinsic curvature.)

Another way to state the Einstein equations—already discussed by David Hilbert in 1915—is as the constraint that the integral of $RicciScalar\ Sqrt[Det[g]]$ (the so-called Einstein-Hilbert action) be an extremum. (An idealized soap film or other minimal surface extremizes the integral of the intrinsic volume element $Sqrt[Det[g]]$, without a $RicciScalar$ factor.) In the discrete Regge calculus that I mention on page 1054 this variational principle turns out to have a rather simple form.

The Einstein-Hilbert action—and the Einstein equations—can be viewed as having the simplest forms that do not ultimately depend on the choice of coordinates. Higher-order terms—say powers of the Ricci scalar curvature—could well arise from underlying network systems, but would not contribute noticeably except in very high gravitational fields.

Various physical interpretations can be given of the vanishing of the Ricci tensor implied by the ordinary vacuum Einstein equations. Closely related to my discussion of the absence of t^2 terms in volume growth for 4D spacetime cones is the statement that if one sets up a small 3D ball of comoving test particles then the volume it defines must have zero first and second derivatives with time.

Below 4D the vanishing of the Ricci tensor immediately implies the vanishing of all components of the Riemann tensor—so that the vacuum Einstein equations force space at least locally to have its ordinary flat form. (Even in 2D there can nevertheless still be non-trivial global topology—for example with flat space having its edges identified as on a torus. In the Euclidean case there were for a long time no non-trivial solutions to the Einstein equations known in any number of dimensions, but in the 1970s examples were found, including large families of Calabi-Yau manifolds.)

In the presence of matter, the typical formal statement of the full Einstein equations is $R_{\mu\nu} - R\, g_{\mu\nu}/2 = 8\pi\, G\, T_{\mu\nu}/c^4$, where $T_{\mu\nu}$ is the energy-momentum (stress-energy) tensor for matter and G is the gravitational constant. (An additional so-called cosmological term $\lambda g_{\mu\nu}$ is sometimes added on the right to adjust the effective overall energy density of the universe, and thus its expansion rate. Note that the equation can also be written $R_{\mu\nu} = 8\pi\, G\, (T_{\mu\nu} - 1/2\, T^\mu_\mu\, g_{\mu\nu})/c^4$.) The μ, ν component of $T_{\mu\nu}$ gives the flux of the μ component of 4-momentum (whose components are energy and ordinary 3-momentum) in the ν direction. The fact that T_{00} is energy density implies that for static matter (where $E = mc^2$) the equation is in a sense a minimal extension of Poisson's equation of Newtonian gravity theory. Note that conservation of energy and momentum implies that $T_{\mu\nu}$ must have zero divergence—a result guaranteed in the Einstein equations by the structure of the left-hand side.

In the variational approach to gravity mentioned above, the *RicciScalar* plays the role of a Lagrangian density for pure gravity—and in the presence of matter the Lagrangian density for matter must be added to it. At a physical level, the full Einstein equations can be interpreted as saying that the volume v of a small ball of comoving test particles satisfies

$\partial_{tt} v[t]/v[t] == -1/2\,(\rho + 3\,p)$

where ρ is the total energy density and p is the pressure averaged over all space directions.

To solve the full Einstein equations in any particular physical situation requires a knowledge of $T_{\mu\nu}$—and thus of properties of matter such as the relation between pressure and energy density (equation of state). Quite a few global results about the formation of singularities and the absence of paths looping around in time can nevertheless be obtained just by assuming certain so-called energy conditions for $T_{\mu\nu}$. (A fairly stringent example is $0 \le p \le \rho/3$—and whether this is actually true for non-trivial interacting quantum fields remains unclear.)

In their usual formulation, the Einstein equations are thought of as defining constraints on the structure of 4D spacetime. But at some level they can also be viewed as defining how 3D space evolves with time. And indeed the so-called initial value formulations constructed in the 1960s allow one to start with a 3D metric and various extrinsic curvatures defined for a 3D spacelike hypersurface, and then work out how these change on successive hypersurfaces. But at least in terms of tensors, the equations involved show nothing like the simplicity of the usual 4D Einstein equations. One can potentially view the causal networks that I discuss in the main text as providing another approach to setting up an initial value formulation of the Einstein equations.

■ **Page 536 · Pure gravity.** In the absence of matter, the Einstein equations always admit ordinary flat Minkowski space as a solution. But they also admit other solutions that in effect represent configurations of pure gravitational field. And in fact the 4D vacuum Einstein equations are already a sophisticated set of nonlinear partial differential equations that can support all sorts of complex behavior. Several tens of families of solutions to the equations have been found—some with obvious physical interpretations, others without.

Already in 1916 Karl Schwarzschild gave the solution for a spherically symmetric gravitational field. He imagined that this field itself existed in a vacuum—but that it was produced by a mass such as a star at its center. In its original form the metric becomes singular at radius $2\,G\,m/c^2$ (or $3\,m$ km with m in solar masses). At first it was assumed that this would always be inside a star, where the vacuum Einstein equations

would not apply. But in the 1930s it was suggested that stars could collapse to concentrate their mass in a smaller radius. The singularity was then interpreted as an event horizon that separates the interior of a black hole from the ordinary space around it. In 1960 it was realized, however, that appropriate coordinates allowed smooth continuation across the event horizon—and that the only genuine singularity was infinite curvature at a single point at the center. Sometimes it was said that this must reflect the presence of a point mass, but soon it was typically just said to be a point at which the Einstein equations—for whatever reason—do not apply. Different choices of coordinates led to different apparent locations and forms of the singularity, and by the late 1970s the most common representation was just a smooth manifold with a topology reflecting the removal of a point—and without any specific reference to the presence of matter.

Appealing to ideas of Ernst Mach from the late 1800s it has often been assumed that to get curvature in space always eventually requires the presence of matter. But in fact even the vacuum Einstein equations for complete universes (with no points left out) have solutions that show curvature. If one assumes that space is both homogeneous and isotropic then it turns out that only ordinary flat Minkowski space is allowed. (When matter or a cosmological term is present one gets different solutions—that always expand or contract, and are much studied in cosmology.) If anisotropy is present, however, then there can be all sorts of solutions—classified for example as having different Bianchi symmetry types. And a variety of inhomogeneous solutions with no singularities are also known—an example being the 1962 Ozsváth-Schücking rotating vacuum. But in all cases the structure is too simple to capture much that seems relevant for our present universe.

One form of solution to the vacuum Einstein equations is a gravitational wave consisting of a small perturbation propagating through flat space. No solutions have yet been found that represent complete universes containing emitters and absorbers of such waves (or even for example just two massive bodies). But it is known that combinations of gravitational waves can be set up that will for example evolve to generate singularities. And I suspect that nonlinear interactions between such waves will also inevitably lead to the analog of turbulence for pure gravity. (Numerical simulations often show all sorts of complex behavior—but in the past this has normally been attributed just to the approximations used. Note that for example Bianchi type IX solutions for a complete universe show sensitive dependence on initial conditions—and no doubt this can also happen with nonlinear gravitational waves.)

As mentioned on page 1028, Albert Einstein considered the possibility that particles of matter might somehow just be localized structures in gravitational and electromagnetic fields. And in the mid-1950s John Wheeler studied explicit simple examples of such so-called geons. But in all cases they were found to be unstable—decaying into ordinary gravitational waves. The idea of having purely gravitational localized structures has also occasionally been considered—but so far no stable field configuration has been found. (And no purely repetitive solutions can exist.)

The equivalence principle (see page 1047) might suggest that anything with mass—or energy—should affect the curvature of space in the same way. But in the Einstein equations the energy-momentum tensor is not supposed to include contributions from the gravitational field. (There are alternative and seemingly inelegant theories of gravity that work differently—and notably do not yield black holes. The setup is also somewhat different in recent versions of string theory.) The very definition of energy for the gravitational field is not particularly straightforward in general relativity. But perhaps a definition could be found that would allow localized structures in the gravitational field to make effective contributions to the energy-momentum tensor that would mimic those from explicit particles of matter. Nevertheless, there are quite a few phenomena associated with particles that seem difficult to reproduce with pure gravity—at least say without extra dimensions. One example is parity violation; another is the presence of long-range forces other than gravity.

■ **Quantum gravity.** That there should be quantum effects in gravity was already noted in the 1910s, and when quantum field theory began to develop in the 1930s, there were immediately attempts to apply it to gravity. The first idea was to represent gravity as a field that exists in flat spacetime, and by analogy with photons in quantum electrodynamics to introduce gravitons (at one point identified with neutrinos). By the mid-1950s a path integral (see page 1061) based on the Einstein-Hilbert action had been constructed, and by the early 1960s Feynman diagram rules had been derived, and it had been verified that tree diagrams involving gravitons gave results that agreed with general relativity for small gravitational fields. But as soon as loop diagrams were considered, infinities began to appear. And unlike for quantum electrodynamics there did not seem to be only a finite number of these—that could be removed by renormalization. And in fact by 1973 gravity coupled to matter had been shown for certain not to be renormalizable—and the same was finally shown for pure gravity in 1986. There was an attempt in the 1970s and early 1980s to look

directly at the path integral—without doing an expansion in terms of Feynman diagrams. But despite the fact that at least in Euclidean spacetime a variety of seemingly relevant field configurations were identified, many mathematical difficulties were encountered. And in the late-1970s there began to be interest in the idea that supersymmetric field theories might make infinities associated with gravitons be cancelled by ones associated with other particles. But in the end this did not work out. And then in the mid-1980s one of the great attractions of string theory was that it seemed to support graviton excitations without the problem of infinities seen in point-particle field theories. But it had other problems, and to avoid these, supersymmetry had to be introduced, leading to the presence of many other particles that have so far not been observed. (See also page 1029.)

Starting in the 1950s a rather different approach to quantum gravity involved trying to find a representation of the structure of spacetime in which a quantum analog of the Einstein equations could be obtained by the formal procedure of canonical quantization (see page 1058). Yet despite a few signs of progress in the 1960s there was great difficulty in finding appropriately independent variables to use. In the late 1980s, however, it was suggested that variables could be used corresponding roughly to gravitational fluxes through loops in space. And in terms of these loop variables it was at least formally possible to write down a version of quantum gravity. Yet while this was found in the 1990s to have a correspondence with spin networks (see below), it has remained impossible to see just how it might yield ordinary general relativity as a limit.

Even if one assumes that spacetime is in a sense ultimately continuous one can imagine investigating quantum gravity by doing some kind of discrete approximation. And in 1961 Tullio Regge noted that for a simplicial complex (see page 1050) the Einstein-Hilbert action has a rather simple form in terms of angles between edges. Starting in the 1980s after the development of lattice gauge theories, simulations of random surfaces and higher-dimensional spaces set up in this way were done—often using so-called dynamic triangulation based on random sequences of generalized Alexander moves from page 1038. But there were difficulties with Lorentzian spaces, and when large-scale average behavior was studied, it seemed difficult to reproduce observed smooth spacetime. Analytical approaches (that happened to be like 0D string theory) were also found for 2D discrete spacetimes (compare page 1038)—but they were not successfully extended to higher dimensions.

Over the years, various attempts have been made to derive quantum gravity from fundamentally discrete models of spacetime (compare page 1027). In recent times the most widely discussed have been spin networks—which despite their name ultimately seem to have fairly little to do with the systems I consider. Spin networks were introduced in 1964 by Roger Penrose as a way to set up an intrinsically quantum mechanical model of spacetime. A simple analog involves a 2D surface made out of triangles whose edges have integer lengths j_i. If one computes the product of $Exp[i(j_1 + j_2 - j_3)]$ for all triangles, then it turns out for example that this quantity is extremized exactly when the whole surface is flat. In 3D one imagines breaking space into tetrahedra whose edge lengths correspond to discrete quantum spin values. And in 1968 Tullio Regge and Giorgio Ponzano suggested—almost as an afterthought in technical work on $6j$ symbols—that the quantum probability amplitude for any form of space might perhaps be given by the product of $6j$ symbols for the spins on each tetrahedron. The $SixJSymbol[\{j_1, j_2, j_3\}, \{j_4, j_5, j_6\}]$ are slightly esoteric objects that correspond to recoupling coefficients for the 3D rotation group SO(3), and that arose in 1940s studies of combinations of three angular momenta in atomic physics—and were often represented graphically as networks. For large j_i they are approximated by $Cos[\theta + \pi/4]/Sqrt[12\pi v]$, where v is the volume of the tetrahedron and θ is a deficit angle. And from this it turns out that limits of products of $6j$ symbols correspond essentially to $Exp[is]$, where s is the discrete form of the Einstein-Hilbert action—extremized by flat 3D space. (The picture below shows for example $Abs[SixJSymbol[\{j, j, j\}, \{j, j, j\}]]$. Note that for any j the $6j$ symbols can be given in terms of $HypergeometricPFQ$.)

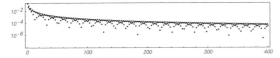

In the early 1990s there was again interest in spin networks when the Turaev-Viro invariant for 3D spaces was discovered from a topological field theory involving triangulations weighted with $6j$ symbols of the quantum group $SU(2)_q$—and it was seen that invariance under Alexander moves on the triangulation corresponded to the Biedenharn-Elliott identity for $6j$ symbols. In the mid-1990s it was then found that states in 3D loop quantum gravity (see above) could be represented in terms of spin networks—leading for example to quantization of all areas and volumes. In attempting extensions to 4D, spin foams have been introduced—and variously interpreted in terms of simplified Feynman diagrams, constructs in multidimensional category theory, and possible evolutions of spin networks. In all cases, however, spin networks and spin foams seem to be viewed just as calculational constructs that must be evaluated and added together to get quantum amplitudes—quite different from my idea of associating an explicit evolution history for the universe with the evolution of a network.

■ **Cosmology.** On a large scale our universe appears to show a uniform expansion that makes progressively more distant galaxies recede from us at progressively higher speeds. In general relativity this is explained by saying that the initial conditions must have involved expansion—and that there is not enough in the way of matter or gravitational fields to produce the gravity to slow down this expansion too much. (Note that as soon as objects get gravitationally bound—like galaxies in clusters—there is no longer expansion between them.) The standard big bang model assumes that the universe starts with matter at what is in effect an arbitrarily high temperature. One issue much discussed in cosmology since the late 1970s is how the universe manages to be so uniform. Thermal equilibrium should eventually lead to uniformity—but different parts of the universe cannot come to equilibrium until there has at least been time for effects to propagate between them. Yet there seems for example to be overall uniformity in what we see if we look in opposite directions in the sky—even though extrapolating from the current rate of expansion there has not been enough time since the beginning of the universe for anything to propagate from one side to the other. But starting in the early 1980s it has been popular to think that early in its history the universe must have undergone a period of exponential expansion or so-called inflation. And what this would do is to take just a tiny region and make it large enough to correspond to everything we can now see in the universe. But the point is that a sufficiently tiny region will have had time to come to thermal equilibrium—and so will be approximately uniform, just as the cosmic microwave background is now observed to be. The actual process of inflation is usually assumed to reflect some form of phase transition associated with decreasing temperature of matter in the universe. Most often it is assumed that in the present universe a delicate balance must exist between energy density from a background Higgs field (see page 1047) and a cosmological term in the Einstein equations (see page 1052). But above a critical temperature thermal fluctuations should prevent the background from forming—leading to at least some period in which the universe is dominated by a cosmological term which yields exponential expansion. There tend to be various detailed problems with this scenario, but at least with a sufficiently complicated setup it seems possible to get results that are consistent with observations made so far.

In the context of the discoveries in this book, my expectation is that the universe started from a simple small network, then progressively added more and more nodes as it evolved, until eventually on a large scale something corresponding to 4D spacetime emerged. And with this setup, the observed uniformity of the universe becomes much less surprising. Intrinsic randomness generation always tends to lead to a certain uniformity in networks. But the crucial point is that this will not take long to happen throughout any network if it is appropriately connected. Traditional models tend to assume that there are ultimately a fixed number of spacetime dimensions in the universe. And with this assumption it is inevitable that if the universe in a sense expands at the speed of light, then regions on opposite sides of it can essentially never share any common history. But in a network model the situation is different. The causal network always captures what happens. And in a case like page 518—with spacetime always effectively having a fixed finite dimension—points that are a distance t apart tend to have common ancestors only at least t steps back. But in a case like (a) on page 514—where spacetime has the structure of an exponentially growing tree—points a distance t apart typically have common ancestors just $Log[t]$ steps back. And in fact many kinds of causal networks—say associated with early randomly connected space networks—will inevitably yield common ancestors for distant parts of the universe. (Note that such phenomena presumably occur at around the Planck scale of 10^{19} GeV rather than at the 10^{15} GeV or lower scale normally discussed in connection with inflation. They can to some extent be captured in general relativity by imagining an effective spacetime dimension that is initially infinite, then gradually decreases to 4.)

Quantum Phenomena

■ **History.** In classical physics quantities like energy were always assumed to correspond to continuous variables. But in 1900 Max Planck noticed that fits to the measured spectrum of electromagnetic radiation produced by hot objects could be explained if there were discrete quanta of electromagnetic energy. And by 1910 work by Albert Einstein, notably on the photoelectric effect and on heat capacities of solids, had given evidence for discrete quanta of energy in both light and matter. In 1913 Niels Bohr then made the suggestion that the discrete spectrum of light emitted by hydrogen atoms could be explained as being produced by electrons making transitions between orbits with discrete quantized angular momenta. By 1920 ideas from celestial mechanics had been used to develop a formalism for quantized orbits which successfully explained various features of atoms and chemical elements. But it was not clear

how to extend the formalism say to a problem like propagation of light through a crystal. In 1925, however, Werner Heisenberg suggested a new and more general formalism that became known as matrix mechanics. The original idea was to imagine describing the state of an atom in terms of an array of amplitudes for virtual oscillators with each possible frequency. Particular conditions amounting to quantization were then imposed on matrices of transitions between these, and the idea was introduced that only certain kinds of amplitude combinations could ever be observed. In 1923 Louis de Broglie had suggested that just as light—which in optics was traditionally described in terms of waves—seemed in some respects to act like discrete particles, so conversely particles like electrons might in some respects act like waves. In 1926 Erwin Schrödinger then suggested a partial differential equation for the wave functions of particles like electrons. And when effectively restricted to a finite region, this equation allowed only certain modes, corresponding to discrete quantum states—whose properties turned out to be exactly the same as implied by matrix mechanics. In the late 1920s Paul Dirac developed a more abstract operator-based formalism. And by the end of the 1920s basic practical quantum mechanics was established in more or less the form it appears in textbooks today. In the period since, increasing computational capabilities have allowed coupled Schrödinger equations for progressively more particles to be solved (reasonably accurate solutions for hundreds of particles can now be found), allowing ever larger studies in atomic, molecular, nuclear and solid-state physics. A notable theoretical interest starting in the 1980s was so-called quantum chaos, in which it was found that modes (wave functions) in regions like stadiums that did not yield simple analytical solutions tended to show complicated and seemingly random forms.

Basic quantum mechanics is set up to describe how fixed numbers of particles behave—say in externally applied electromagnetic or other fields. But to describe things like fields one must allow particles to be created and destroyed. In the mid-1920s there was already discussion of how to set up a formalism for this, with an underlying idea again being to think in terms of virtual oscillators—but now one for each possible state of each possible one of any number of particles. At first this was just applied to a pure electromagnetic field of non-interacting photons, but by the end of the 1920s there was a version of quantum electrodynamics (QED) for interacting photons and electrons that is essentially the same as today. To find predictions from this theory a so-called perturbation expansion was made, with successive terms representing progressively more interactions, and each having a higher power of the so-called coupling constant $\alpha \sim 1/137$. It was immediately noticed, however, that self-interactions of particles would give rise to infinities, much as in classical electromagnetism. At first attempts were made to avoid this by modifying the basic theory (see page 1044). But by the mid-1940s detailed calculations were being done in which infinite parts were just being dropped—and the results were being found to agree rather precisely with experiments. In the late 1940s this procedure was then essentially justified by the idea of renormalization: that since in all possible QED processes only three different infinities can ever appear, these can in effect systematically be factored out from all predictions of the theory. Then in 1949 Feynman diagrams were introduced (see note below) to represent terms in the QED perturbation expansion—and the rules for these rapidly became what defined QED in essentially all practical applications. Evaluating Feynman diagrams involved extensive algebra, and indeed stimulated the development of computer algebra (including my own interest in the field). But by the 1970s the dozen or so standard processes discussed in QED had been calculated to order α^2—and by the mid-1980s the anomalous magnetic moment of the electron had been calculated to order α^4, and nearly one part in a trillion (see note below).

But despite the success of perturbation theory in QED it did not at first seem applicable to other issues in particle physics. The weak interactions involved in radioactive beta decay seemed too weak for anything beyond lowest order to be relevant—and in any case not renormalizable. And the strong interactions responsible for holding nuclei together (and associated for example with exchange of pions and other mesons) seemed too strong for it to make sense to do an expansion with larger numbers of individual interactions treated as less important. So this led in the 1960s to attempts to base theories just on setting up simple mathematical constraints on the overall so-called S matrix defining the mapping from incoming to outgoing quantum states. But by the end of the 1960s theoretical progress seemed blocked by basic questions about functions of several complex variables, and predictions that were made did not seem to work well.

By the early 1970s, however, there was increasing interest in so-called gauge or Yang-Mills theories formed in essence by generalizing QED to operate not just with a scalar charge, but with charges viewed as elements of non-Abelian groups. In 1972 it was shown that spontaneously broken gauge theories of the kind needed to describe weak interactions were renormalizable—allowing meaningful use of perturbation theory and Feynman diagrams. And then in 1973 it was discovered that QCD—the gauge theory for quarks and gluons with SU(3) color charges—was asymptotically free (it was known to be renormalizable), so that for processes probing sufficiently small distances, its effective coupling was small enough for perturbation theory. By the early 1980s first-order calculations of most basic QCD processes had been done—and by the 1990s second-order corrections were also known. Schemes for adding up all Feynman diagrams with certain very simple repetitive or other structures were developed. But despite a few results about large-distance analogs of renormalizability, the question of what QCD might imply for processes at larger distances could not really be addressed by such methods.

In 1941 Richard Feynman pointed out that amplitudes in quantum theory could be worked out by using path integrals that sum with appropriate weights contributions from all possible histories of a system. (The Schrödinger equation is like a diffusion equation in imaginary time, so the path integral for it can be thought of as like an enumeration of random walks. The idea of describing random walks with path integrals was discussed from the early 1900s.) At first the path integral was viewed mostly as a curiosity, but by the late 1970s it was emerging as the standard way to define a quantum field theory. Attempts were made to see if the path integral for QCD (and later for quantum gravity) could be approximated with a few exact solutions (such as instantons) to classical field equations. By the early 1980s there was then extensive work on lattice gauge theories in which the path integral (in Euclidean space) was approximated by randomly sampling discretized field configurations. But—I suspect for reasons that I discuss in the note below—such methods were never extremely successful. And the result is that beyond perturbation theory there is still no real example of a definitive success from standard relativistic quantum field theory. (In addition, even efforts in the context of so-called axiomatic field theory to set up mathematically rigorous formulations have run into many difficulties—with the only examples satisfying all proposed axioms typically in the end being field theories without any real interactions. In condensed matter physics there are nevertheless cases like the Kondo model where exact solutions have been found, and where the effective energy function for electrons happens to be roughly the same as in a relativistic theory.)

As mentioned on page 1044, ordinary quantum field theory in effect deals only with point particles. And indeed a recurring issue in it has been difficulty with constraints and redundant degrees of freedom—such as those associated with extended objects. (A typical goal is to find variables in which one can carry out what is known as canonical quantization: essentially applying the same straightforward transformation of equations that happens to work in ordinary elementary quantum mechanics.) One feature of string theory and its generalizations is that they define presumably consistent quantum field theories for excitations of extended objects—though an analog of quantum field theory in which whole strings can be created and destroyed has not yet been developed.

When the formalism of quantum mechanics was developed in the mid-1920s there were immediately questions about its interpretation. But it was quickly suggested that given a wave function ψ from the Schrödinger equation $Abs[\psi]^2$ should represent probability—and essentially all practical applications have been based on this ever since. From a conceptual point of view it has however often seemed peculiar that a supposedly fundamental theory should talk only about probabilities. Following the introduction of the uncertainty principle and related formalism in the 1920s one idea that arose was that—in rough analogy to relativity theory—it might just be that there are only certain quantities that are observable in definite ways. But this was not enough, and by the 1930s it was being suggested that the validity of quantum mechanics might be a sign that whole new general frameworks for philosophy or logic were needed—a notion supported by the apparent need to bring consciousness into discussions about measurement in quantum mechanics (see page 1063). The peculiar character of quantum mechanics was again emphasized by the idealized experiment of Albert Einstein, Boris Podolsky and Nathan Rosen in 1935. But among most physicists the apparent lack of an ordinary mechanistic way to think about quantum mechanics ended up just being seen as another piece of evidence for the fundamental role of mathematical formalism in physics.

One way for probabilities to appear even in deterministic systems is for there to be hidden variables whose values are unknown. But following mathematical work in the early 1930s it was usually assumed that this could not be what was going on in quantum mechanics. In 1952 David Bohm did however manage to construct a somewhat elaborate model based on hidden variables that gave the same results as ordinary quantum mechanics—though involved infinitely fast propagation of information. In the early 1960s John Bell then showed that in any hidden variables theory of a certain general type there are specific inequalities that combinations of probabilities must satisfy (see page 1064). And by the early 1980s experiments had shown that such inequalities were indeed violated in practice—so that there were in fact correlations of the kind suggested by quantum mechanics. At first these just seemed like isolated esoteric effects, but by the mid-1990s they were being codified in the field of quantum

information theory, and led to constructions with names like quantum cryptography and quantum teleportation.

Particularly when viewed in terms of path integrals the standard formalism of quantum theory tends to suggest that quantum systems somehow do more computation in their evolution than classical ones. And after occasional discussion as early as the 1950s, this led by the late 1980s to extensive investigation of systems that could be viewed as quantum analogs of idealized computers. In the mid-1990s efficient procedures for integer factoring and a few other problems were suggested for such systems, and by the late 1990s small experiments on these were beginning to be done in various types of physical systems. But it is becoming increasingly unclear just how the idealizations in the underlying model really work, and to what extent quantum mechanics is actually in the end even required—as opposed, say, just to classical wave phenomena. (See page 1147.)

Partly as a result of discussions about measurement there began to be questions in the 1980s about whether ordinary quantum mechanics can describe systems containing very large numbers of particles. Experiments in the 1980s and 1990s on such phenomena as macroscopic superposition and Bose-Einstein condensation nevertheless showed that standard quantum effects still occur with trillions of atoms. But inevitably the kinds of general phenomena that I discuss in this book will also occur—leading to all sorts of behavior that at least cannot readily be foreseen just from the basic rules of quantum mechanics.

■ **Quantum effects.** Over the years, many suggested effects have been thought to be characteristic of quantum systems:

- Basic quantization (1913): mechanical properties of particles in effectively bounded systems are discrete;

- Wave-particle duality (1923): objects like electrons and photons can be described as either waves or particles;

- Spin (1925): particles can have intrinsic angular momentum even if they are of zero size;

- Non-commuting measurements (1926): one can get different results doing measurements in different orders;

- Complex amplitudes (1926): processes are described by complex probability amplitudes;

- Probabilism (1926): outcomes are random, though probabilities for them can be computed;

- Amplitude superposition (1926): there is a linear superposition principle for probability amplitudes;

- State superposition (1926): quantum systems can occur in superpositions of measurable states;

- Exclusion principle (1926): amplitudes cancel for fermions like electrons to go in the same state;

- Interference (1927): probability amplitudes for particles can interfere, potentially destructively;

- Uncertainty principle (1927): quantities like position and momenta have related measurement uncertainties;

- Hilbert space (1927): states of systems are represented by vectors of amplitudes rather than individual variables;

- Field quantization (1927): only discrete numbers of any particular kind of particle can in effect ever exist;

- Quantum tunnelling (1928): particles have amplitudes to go where no classical motion would take them;

- Virtual particles (1932): particles can occur for short times without their usual energy-momentum relation;

- Spinors (1930s): fermions show rotational invariance under SU(2) rather than SO(3);

- Entanglement (1935): separated parts of a system often inevitably behave in irreducibly correlated ways;

- Quantum logic (1936): relations between events do not follow ordinary laws of logic;

- Path integrals (1941): probabilities for behavior are obtained by summing contributions from many paths;

- Imaginary time (1947): statistical mechanics is like quantum mechanics in imaginary time;

- Vacuum fluctuations (1948): there are continual random field fluctuations even in the vacuum;

- Aharanov-Bohm effect (1959): magnetic fields can affect particles even in regions where they have zero strength;

- Bell's inequalities (1964): correlations between events can be larger than in any ordinary probabilistic system;

- Anomalies (1969): virtual particles can have effects that violate the original symmetries of a system;

- Delayed choice experiments (1978): whether particle or wave features are seen can be determined after an event;

- Quantum computing (1980s): there is the potential for fundamental parallelism in computations.

All of these effects are implied by the standard mathematical formalism of quantum theory. But it has never been entirely clear which of them are in a sense true defining features of quantum phenomena, and which are somehow just details. It does not help that most of the effects—at least individually—can be reproduced by mechanisms that seem to have little to do with the usual structure of quantum theory. So for example there will tend to be quantization whenever the

underlying elements of a system are discrete. Similarly, features like the uncertainty principle and path integrals tend to be seen whenever things like waves are involved. And probabilistic effects can arise from any of the mechanisms for randomness discussed in Chapter 7. Complex amplitudes can be thought of just as vector quantities. And it is straightforward to set up rules that will for example reproduce the detailed evolution of amplitudes according say to the Schrödinger equation (see note below). It is somewhat more difficult to set up a system in which such amplitudes will somehow directly determine probabilities. And indeed in recent times consequences of this—such as violations of Bell's inequalities—are what have probably most often been quoted as the most unique features of quantum systems. It is however notable that the vast majority of traditional applications of quantum theory do not seem to have anything to do with such effects. And in fact I do not consider it at all clear just what is really essential about them, and what is in the end just a consequence of the extreme limits that seem to need to be taken to get explicit versions of them.

- **Reproducing quantum phenomena.** Given molecular dynamics it is much easier to see how to reproduce fluid mechanics than rigid-body mechanics—since to get rigid bodies with only a few degrees of freedom requires taking all sorts of limits of correlations between underlying molecules. And I strongly suspect that given a discrete underlying model of the type I discuss here it will similarly be much easier to reproduce quantum field theory than ordinary quantum mechanics. And indeed even with traditional formalism, it is usually difficult to see how quantum mechanics can be obtained as a limit of quantum field theory. (Classical limits are slightly easier: they tend to be associated with stationary features or caustics that occur at large quantum numbers—or coherent states that represent eigenstates of raising or particle creation operators. Note that the exclusion principle makes classical limits for fermions difficult—but crucial for the stability of bulk matter.)

- **Discrete quantum mechanics.** While there are many issues in finding a complete underlying discrete model for quantum phenomena, it is quite straightforward to set up continuous cellular automata whose limiting behavior reproduces the evolution of probability amplitudes in standard quantum mechanics. One starts by assigning a continuous complex number value to each cell. Then given the list of such values the crucial constraint imposed by the standard formalism of quantum mechanics is unitarity: that the quantity $Tr[Abs[list]^2]$ representing total probability should be conserved. This is in a sense analogous to conservation of total density in diffusion processes. From the discussion of page 1024 one can reproduce the 1D diffusion equation with a continuous block cellular automaton in which the new value of each block is given by $\{\{1-\xi, \xi\}, \{\xi, 1-\xi\}\} . \{a_1, a_2\}$. So in the case of quantum mechanics one can consider having each new block be given by $\{\{Cos[\theta], i\,Sin[\theta]\}, \{i\,Sin[\theta], Cos[\theta]\}\} . \{a_1, a_2\}$. The pictures below show examples of behavior obtained with this rule. (Gray levels represent magnitude for each cell, and arrows phase.) And it turns out that in suitable limits one generally gets essentially the behavior expected from either the Dirac or Klein-Gordon equations for relativistic particles, or the Schrödinger equation for non-relativistic particles. (Versions of this were noticed by Richard Feynman in the 1940s in connection with his development of path integrals, and were pointed out again several times in the 1980s and 1990s.)

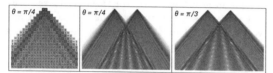

One might hope to be able to get an ordinary cellular automaton with a limited set of possible values by choosing a suitable θ. But in fact in non-trivial cases most of the cells generated at each step end up having distinct values. One can generalize the setup to more dimensions or to allow $n \times n$ matrices that are elements of SU(n). Such matrices can be viewed in the context of ordinary quantum formalism as S matrices for elementary evolution events—and can in general represent interactions. (Note that all rules based on matrices are additive, reflecting the usual assumption of linearity at the level of amplitudes in quantum mechanics. Non-additive unitary rules can also be found. The analog of an external potential can be introduced by progressively changing values of certain cells at each step. Despite their basic setup the systems discussed here are not direct analogs of standard quantum spin systems, since these normally have local Hamiltonians and non-local evolution functions, while the systems here have local evolution functions but seem always to require non-local Hamiltonians.)

■ **Page 540 · Feynman diagrams.** The pictures below show a typical set of Feynman diagrams used to do calculations in QED—in this case for so-called Compton scattering of a photon by an electron. The straight lines in the diagrams represent electrons; the wavy ones photons. At some level each diagram can be thought of as representing a process in which an electron and photon come in from the left, interact in some way, then go out to the right. The incoming and

outgoing lines correspond to real particles that propagate to infinity. The lines inside each diagram correspond to virtual particles that in effect propagate only a limited distance, and have a distribution of energy-momentum and polarization properties that can differ from real particles. (Exchanges of virtual photons can be thought of as producing familiar electromagnetic forces; exchanges of virtual electrons as yielding an analog of covalent forces in chemistry.)

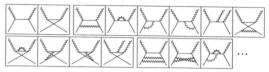

To work out the total probability for a process from Feynman diagrams, what one does is to find the expression corresponding to each diagram, then one adds these up, and squares the result. The first two blocks of pictures above show all the diagrams for Compton scattering that involve 2 or 3 photons—and contribute through order α^3. Since for QED $\alpha \approx 1/137$, one might expect that this would give quite an accurate result—and indeed experiments suggest that it does. But the number of diagrams grows rapidly with order, and in fact the kth order term can be about $(-1)^k \alpha^k (k/2)!$, yielding a series that formally diverges. In simpler examples where exact results are known, however, the first few terms typically still seem to give numerically accurate results for small α. (The high-order terms often seem to be associated with asymptotic series for things like $Exp[-1/\alpha]$.)

The most extensive calculation made so far in QED is for the magnetic moment of the electron. Ignoring parts that depend on particle masses the result (derived in successive orders from 1, 1, 7, 72, 891 diagrams) is

$$2 (1 + \alpha/(2\pi) + (3\,Zeta[3]/4 - 1/2\,\pi^2\,Log[2] + \pi^2/12 + 197/144) (\alpha/\pi)^2 + (83/72\,\pi^2\,Zeta[3] - 215\,Zeta[5]/24 - 239\,\pi^4/2160 + 139\,Zeta[3]/18 + 25/18 (24\,PolyLog[4, 1/2] + Log[2]^4 - \pi^2\,Log[2]^2) - 298/9\,\pi^2\,Log[2] + 17101\,\pi^2/810 + 28259/5184) (\alpha/\pi)^3 - 1.4 (\alpha/\pi)^4 + ...)$$

or roughly

$$2. + 0.32\,\alpha - 0.067\,\alpha^2 + 0.076\,\alpha^3 - 0.029\,\alpha^4 + ...$$

The comparative simplicity of the symbolic forms here (which might get still simpler in terms of suitable generalized polylogarithm functions) may be a hint that methods much more efficient than explicit Feynman diagram evaluation could be used. But it seems likely that there would be limits to this, and that in the end QED will exhibit the kind of computational irreducibility that I discuss in Chapter 12.

Feynman diagrams in QCD work at the formal level very much like those in QED—except that there are usually many more of them, and their numerical results tend to be larger, with expansion parameters often effectively being $\alpha\,\pi$ rather than α/π. For processes with large characteristic momentum transfers in which the effective α in QCD is small, remarkably accurate results are obtained with first and perhaps second-order Feynman diagrams. But as soon as the effective α becomes larger, Feynman diagrams as such rapidly seem to stop being useful.

■ **Quantum field theory.** In standard approaches to quantum field theory one tends to think of particles as some kind of small perturbations in a field. Normally for calculations these perturbations are on their own taken to be plane waves of definite frequency, and indeed in many ways they are direct analogs of waves in classical field theories like those of electromagnetism or fluid mechanics. To investigate collisions between particles, one thus looks at what happens with multiple waves. In a system described by linear equations, there is always a simple superposition principle, and waves just pass through each other unchanged. But what in effect leads to non-trivial interactions between particles is the presence of nonlinearities. If these are small enough then it makes sense to do a perturbation expansion in which one approximates field configurations in terms of a succession of arrangements of ordinary waves—as in Feynman diagrams. But just as one cannot expect to capture fully turbulent fluid flow in terms of a few simple waves, so in general as soon as there is substantial nonlinearity it will no longer be sufficient just to do perturbation expansions. And indeed for example in QCD there are presumably many cases in which it is necessary to look at something closer to actual complete field configurations—and correlations in them.

The way the path integral for a quantum field theory works, each possible configuration of the field is in effect taken to make a contribution $Exp[i\,s/\hbar]$, where s is the so-called action for the field configuration (given by the integral of the Lagrangian density—essentially a modified energy density), and $\hbar$ is a basic scale factor for quantum effects (Planck's constant divided by $2\,\pi$). In most places in the space of all possible field configurations, the value of s will vary quite quickly between nearby configurations. And assuming this variation is somehow random, the contributions of these nearby configurations will tend to cancel out. But inevitably there will be some places in the space where s is stationary (has zero variational derivative) with respect to changes in fields. And in some approximation the field configurations in these places can be expected to dominate the path integral. But it turns out that these field configurations are exactly the ones that satisfy the partial differential equations for the classical version of the field theory. (This is analogous to what happens for example in classical diffraction theory,

where there is an analog of the path integral—with $\hbar$ replaced by inverse frequency—whose stationary points correspond through the so-called eikonal approximation to rays in geometrical optics.) In cases like QED and QCD the most obvious solutions to the classical equations are ones in which all fields are zero. And indeed standard perturbation theory is based on starting from these and then looking at the expansion of $Exp[i\,s/\hbar]$ in powers of the coupling constant. But while this works for QED, it is only adequate for QCD in situations where the effective coupling is small. And indeed in other situations it seems likely that there will be all sorts of other solutions to the classical equations that become important. But apart from a few special cases with high symmetry, remarkably little is known about solutions to the classical equations even for pure gluon fields. No doubt the analog of turbulence can occur, and certainly there is sensitive dependence on initial conditions (even non-Abelian plane waves involve iterated maps that show this). Presumably much like in fluids there are various coherent structures such as color flux tubes and glueballs. But I doubt that states involving organized arrangements of these are common. And in general when there is strong coupling the path integral will potentially be dominated by large numbers of configurations not close to classical solutions.

In studying quantum field theories it has been common to consider effectively replacing time coordinates t by $i\,t$ to go from ordinary Minkowski space to Euclidean space (see page 1043). But while there is no problem in doing this at a formal mathematical level—and indeed the expressions one gets from Feynman diagrams can always be analytically continued in this way—what general correspondence there is for actual physical processes is far from clear. Formally continuing to Euclidean space makes path integrals easier to define with traditional mathematics, and gives them weights of the form $Exp[-\beta\,s]$—analogous to constant temperature systems in statistical mechanics. Discretizing yields lattice gauge theories with energy functions involving for example $Cos[\theta_i - \theta_j]$ for color directions at adjacent sites. And Monte Carlo studies of such theories suggest all sorts of complex behavior, often similar in outline from what appears to occur in the corresponding classical field theories. (It seems conceivable that asymptotic freedom could lead to an analog of damping at small scales roughly like viscosity in turbulent fluids.)

One of the apparent implications of QCD is the confinement of quarks and gluons inside color-neutral hadrons. And at some level this is presumably a reflection of the fact that QCD forces get stronger rather than weaker with increasing distance. The beginnings of this are visible in perturbation theory in the increase of the effective coupling with distance associated with asymptotic freedom. (In QED effective couplings decrease slightly with distance because fields get screened by virtual electron-positron pairs. The same happens with virtual quarks in QCD, but a larger effect is virtual gluon pairs whose color magnetic moments line up with a color field and serve to increase it.) At larger distances something like color flux tubes that act like elastic strings may form. But no detailed way to get confinement with purely classical gluon fields is known. In the quantum case, a sign of confinement would be exponential decrease with spacetime area of the average phase of color flux through so-called Wilson loops—and this is achieved if there is in a sense maximal randomness in field configurations. (Note that it is not inconceivable that the formal problem of whether quarks and gluons can ever escape to infinity starting from some given class of field configurations may in general be undecidable.)

■ **Vacuum fluctuations.** As an analog of the uncertainty principle, one of the implications of the basic formalism of quantum theory is that an ordinary quantum field can in a sense never maintain precisely zero value, but must always show certain fluctuations—even in what one considers the vacuum. And in terms of Feynman diagrams the way this happens is by virtual particle-antiparticle pairs of all types and all energy-momenta continually forming and annihilating at all points in the vacuum. Insofar as such vacuum fluctuations are always exactly the same, however, they presumably cannot be detected. (In the formalism of quantum field theory, they are usually removed by so-called normal ordering. But without this every mode of any quantum system will show a zero-point energy $\hbar \omega /2$—positive in sign for bosons and negative for fermions, cancelling for perfect supersymmetry. Quite what gravitational effects such zero-point energy might have has never been clear.) If one somehow changes the space in which a vacuum exists, there can be directly observable effects of vacuum fluctuations. An example is the 1948 Casimir effect—in which the absence of low-energy (long wavelength) virtual particle pairs in the space between two metal plates (but not in the infinite space outside) leads to a small but measurable force of attraction between them. The different detailed patterns of modes of different fields in different spaces can lead to very different effective vacuum energies—often negative. And at least with the idealization of impermeable classical conducting boundaries one predicts (based on work of mine from 1981) the peculiar effect that closed cycles can be set up that systematically extract energy from vacuum fluctuations in a photon field.

If one has moving boundaries it turns out that vacuum fluctuations can in effect be viewed as producing real particles. And as known since the 1960s, the same is true for expanding universes. What happens in essence is that the modes of fields in different background spacetime structures differ to the point where zero-point excitations seem like actual particle excitations to a detector or observer calibrated to fields in ordinary fixed flat infinite spacetime. And in fact just uniform acceleration turns out to make detectors register real particles in a vacuum—in this case with a thermal spectrum at a temperature proportional to the acceleration. (Uniform rotation also leads to real particles, but apparently with a different spectrum.) As expected from the equivalence principle, a uniform gravitational field should produce the same effect. (Uniform electric fields lead in a formally similar way to production of charged particles.) And as pointed out by Stephen Hawking in 1974, black holes should also generate thermal radiation (at a temperature $\hbar c^3/(8\pi G k M)$). A common interpretation is that the radiated particles are somehow ones left behind when the other particle in a virtual pair goes inside the event horizon. (A similar explanation can be given for uniform acceleration—for which there is also an event horizon.) There has been much discussion of the idea that Hawking radiation somehow shows pure quantum states spontaneously turning into mixed ones, more or less as in quantum measurements. But presumably this is just a reflection of the idealization involved in looking at quantum fields in a fixed background classical spacetime. And indeed work in string theory in the mid-1990s may suggest ways in which quantum gravity configurations of black hole surfaces could maintain the information needed for the whole system to act as a pure state.

■ **Page 542 · Quantum measurement.** The basic mathematical formalism used in standard quantum theory to describe pure quantum processes deals just with vectors of probability amplitudes. Yet our everyday experience of the physical world is that we observe definite things to happen. And the way this is normally captured is by saying that when an observation is made the vector of amplitudes is somehow replaced by its projection s into a subspace corresponding to the outcome seen—with the probability of getting the outcome being taken to be determined by s . Conjugate[s].

At the level of pure quantum processes, the standard rules of quantum theory say that amplitudes should be added as complex numbers—with the result that they can for example potentially cancel each other, and generally lead to wave-like interference phenomena. But after an observation is made, it is in effect assumed that a system can be described by ordinary real-number probabilities—so that for example no interference is possible. (At a formal level, results of pure quantum processes are termed pure quantum states, and are characterized by vectors of probability amplitudes; results of all possible observations are termed mixed states, and are in effect represented as mixtures of pure states.)

Ever since the 1930s there have been questions about just what should count as an observation. To explain everyday experience, conscious perception presumably always must. But it was not clear whether the operation of inanimate measuring devices of various kinds also should. And a major apparent problem was that if everything—including the measuring device—is supposed to be treated as part of the same quantum system, then all of it must follow the rules for pure quantum processes, which do not explicitly include any reduction of the kind supposed to occur in observations.

One approach to getting around this suggested in the late 1950s is the many-worlds interpretation (see page 1035): that there is in a sense a universal pure quantum process that involves all possible outcomes for every conceivable observation, and that represents the tree of all possible threads of history—but that in a particular thread, involving a particular sequence of tree branches, and representing a particular thread of experience for us, there is in effect a reduction in the pure quantum process at each branch point. Similar schemes have been popular in quantum cosmology since the early 1990s in connection with studying wave functions for the complete universe.

A quite different—and I think much more fruitful—approach is to consider analyzing actual potential measurement processes in the context of ordinary quantum mechanics. For even if one takes these processes to be pure quantum ones, what I believe is that in almost all cases appropriate idealized limits of them will reproduce what are in effect the usual rules for observations in quantum theory. A key point is that for one to consider something a reasonable measurement it must in a sense yield a definitive result. And in the context of standard quantum theory this means that somehow all the probability amplitudes associated with the measuring device must in effect be concentrated in specific outcomes—with no significant interference between different outcomes.

If one has just a few quantum particles—governed say by an appropriate Schrödinger equation—then presumably there can be no such concentration. But with a sufficiently large number of particles—and appropriate interactions—one expects that there can be. At first this might seem impossible. For the basic rules for pure quantum processes are entirely reversible (unitary). So one might think that if the evolution of a system leads to concentration of amplitudes, then it

should equally well lead to the reverse. But the crucial point is that while this may in principle be possible, it may essentially never happen in practice—just like classical reversible systems essentially never show behavior that goes against the Second Law of thermodynamics. As suggested by the main text, the details in the quantum measurement case are slightly more complicated—since to represent multiple outcomes measuring devices typically have to have the analogs of multiple equilibrium states. But the basic phenomena are ultimately very similar—and both are in effect based on the presence of microscopic randomness. (In a quantum system the randomness serves to give collections of complex numbers whose average is essentially always zero.)

This so-called decoherence approach was discussed in the 1930s, and finally began to become popular in the 1980s. But to make it work there needs to be some source of appropriate randomness. And almost without exception what has been assumed is that this must come through the first mechanism discussed in Chapter 7: that there is somehow randomness present in the environment that always gets into the system one is looking at. Various different specific mechanisms for this have been suggested, including ones based on ambient low-frequency photons, background quantum vacuum fluctuations and background spacetime metric fluctuations. (A somewhat related proposal involves quantum gravity effects in which irreversibility is assumed to be generated through analogs of the black hole processes mentioned in the previous note.) And indeed in recent practical experiments where simple pure quantum states have carefully been set up, they seem to be destroyed by randomness from the environment on timescales of at most perhaps microseconds. But this does not mean that in more complicated systems more characteristic of real measuring devices there may not be other sources of randomness that end up dominating.

One might imagine that a possibility would be the second mechanism for randomness from Chapter 7, based on ideas of chaos theory. For certainly in the standard formalism, quantum probability amplitudes are taken to be continuous quantities in which an arbitrary number of digits can be specified. But at least for a single particle, the Schrödinger equation is in all ways linear, and so it cannot support any kind of real sensitivity to initial conditions, or even to parameters. But when many particles are involved the situation can presumably be different, as it definitely can be in quantum field theory (see page 1061).

I suspect, however, that in fact the most important source of randomness in most cases will instead be the phenomenon of intrinsic randomness generation that I first discovered in systems like the rule 30 cellular automaton. Just like in so many other areas, the emphasis on traditional mathematical methods has meant that for the most part fundamental studies have been made only on quantum systems that in the end turn out to have fairly simple behavior. Yet even within the standard formalism of quantum theory there are actually no doubt many closed systems that intrinsically manage to produce complex and seemingly random behavior even with very simple parameters and initial conditions. And in fact some clear signs of this were already present in studies of so-called quantum chaos in the 1980s—although most of the specific cases actually considered involved time-independent constraint satisfaction, not explicit time evolution. Curiously, what the Principle of Computational Equivalence suggests is that when quantum systems intrinsically produce apparent randomness they will in the end typically be capable of doing computations just as sophisticated as any other system—and in particular just as sophisticated as would be involved in conscious perception.

As a practical matter, mechanisms like intrinsic randomness generation presumably allow systems involving macroscopic numbers of particles to yield behavior in which interference becomes astronomically unlikely. But to reproduce the kind of exact reduction of probability amplitudes that is implied by the standard formalism of quantum theory inevitably requires taking the limit of an infinite system. Yet the Principle of Computational Equivalence suggests that the results of such a limit will typically be non-computable. (Using quantum field theory to represent infinite numbers of particles presumably cannot help; after appropriate analysis of the fairly sophisticated continuous mathematics involved, exactly the same computational issues should arise.)

It is often assumed that quantum systems should somehow easily be able to generate perfect randomness. But any sequence of bits one extracts must be deduced from a corresponding sequence of measurements. And certainly in practice—as mentioned on pages 303 and 970—correlations in the internal states of measuring devices between successive measurements will tend to lead to deviations from randomness. Whatever generates randomness and brings measuring devices back to equilibrium will eventually damp out such correlations. But insofar as measuring devices must formally involve infinite numbers of particles this process will formally require infinitely many steps. So this means that in effect an infinite computation is actually being done to generate each new bit. But with this amount of computation there are many ways to generate random bits. And in fact an infinite computation could even in principle produce algorithmic randomness (see page 1067) of the kind that is implicitly suggested by the

traditional continuous mathematical formalism of quantum theory. So what this suggests is that there may in the end be no clear way to tell whether randomness is coming from an underlying quantum process that is being measured, or from the actual process of measurement. And indeed when it comes to more realistic finite measuring devices I would not be surprised if most of the supposed quantum randomness they measure is actually more properly attributed to intrinsic randomness generation associated with their internal mechanisms.

■ **Page 543 · Bell's inequalities.** In classical physics one can set up light waves that are linearly polarized with any given orientation. And if these hit polarizing ("anti-glare") filters whose orientation is off by an angle θ, then the waves transmitted will have intensity $Cos[\theta]^2$. In quantum theory the quantization of particle spin implies that any photon hitting a polarizing filter will always either just go through or be absorbed—so that in effect its spin measured relative to the orientation of the polarizer is either +1 or -1. A variety of atomic and other processes give pairs of photons that are forced to have total spin 0. And in what is essentially the Einstein-Podolsky-Rosen setup mentioned on page 1058 one can ask what happens if such photons are made to hit polarizers whose orientations differ by angle θ. In ordinary quantum theory, a straightforward calculation implies that the expected value of the product of the two measured spin values will be $-Cos[\theta]$. But now imagine instead that when each photon is produced it is assigned some "hidden variable" ϕ that in effect explicitly specifies the angle of its polarization. Then assume that a polarizer oriented at $0°$ will measure the spin of such a photon to have value $f[\phi]$ for some fixed function f. Now the expected value of the product of the two measured spin values is found just by averaging over ϕ as

$Integrate[f[\phi]\,f[\theta-\phi], \{\phi, 0, 2\pi\}]/(2\pi)$

A version of Bell's inequalities is then that this integral can decrease with θ no faster than $\theta/(2\pi)-1$—as achieved when $f = Sign$. (In 3D ϕ must be extended to a sphere, but the same final result holds.) Yet as mentioned on page 1058, actual experiments show that in fact the decrease with θ is more rapid—and is instead consistent with the quantum theory result $-Cos[\theta]$. So what this means is that there is in a sense more correlation between measurements made on separated photons than can apparently be explained by the individual photons carrying any kind of explicit hidden property. (In the standard formalism of quantum theory this is normally explained by saying that the two photons can only meaningfully be considered as part of a single "entangled" state. Note that because of the probabilistic nature of the correlations it turns out to be impossible to use them to do anything that would normally be considered communicating information faster than the speed of light.)

A basic assumption in deriving Bell's inequalities is that the choice of polarizer angle for measuring one photon is not affected by the choice of angle for the other. And indeed experiments have been done which try to enforce this by choosing the angles for the polarizers only just before the photons reach them—and too close in time for a light signal to get from one to the other. Such experiments again show violations of Bell's inequalities. But inevitably the actually devices that work out choices of polarizer angles must be in causal contact as part of setting up the experiment. And although it seems contrived, it is thus at least conceivable that with a realistic model for their time evolution such devices could end up operating in just such a way as to yield observed violations of Bell's inequalities.

Another way to get violations of Bell's inequalities is to allow explicit instantaneous propagation of information. But traditional models involving for example a background quantum potential again seem quite contrived, and difficult to generalize to relativistic cases. The approach I discuss in the main text is quite different, in effect using the idea that in a network model of space there can be direct connections between particles that do not in a sense ever have to go through ordinary intermediate points in space.

When set up for pairs of particles, Bell's inequalities tend just to provide numerical constraints on probabilities. But for triples of particles, it was noticed in the late 1980s that they can give constraints that force probabilities to be 0 or 1, implying that with the assumptions made, certain configurations of measurement results are simply impossible.

In quantum field theory the whole concept of measurement is much less developed than in quantum mechanics—not least because in field theory it is much more difficult to factor out subsystems, and so to avoid having to give explicit descriptions of measuring devices. But at least in axiomatic quantum field theory it is typically assumed that one can somehow measure expectation values of any suitably smeared product of field operators. (It is possible that these could be reconstructed from combinations of idealized scattering experiments). And to get a kind of analog of Bell's inequalities one can look at correlations defined by such expectation values for field operators at spacelike-separated points (too close in time for light signals to get from one to another). And it then turns out that even in the vacuum state the vacuum fluctuations that are present show nonzero such correlations—an analog of ordinary quantum mechanical entanglement. (In a non-interacting approximation these correlations turn out to be as large as is mathematically possible, but fall off exponentially outside the light cone, with exponents determined by the smallest particle mass or the measurement resolution.) In a sense, however, the presence of such correlations is just a reflection of the idealized way in which the vacuum state is set up—with each field mode determined all at once for the whole system.

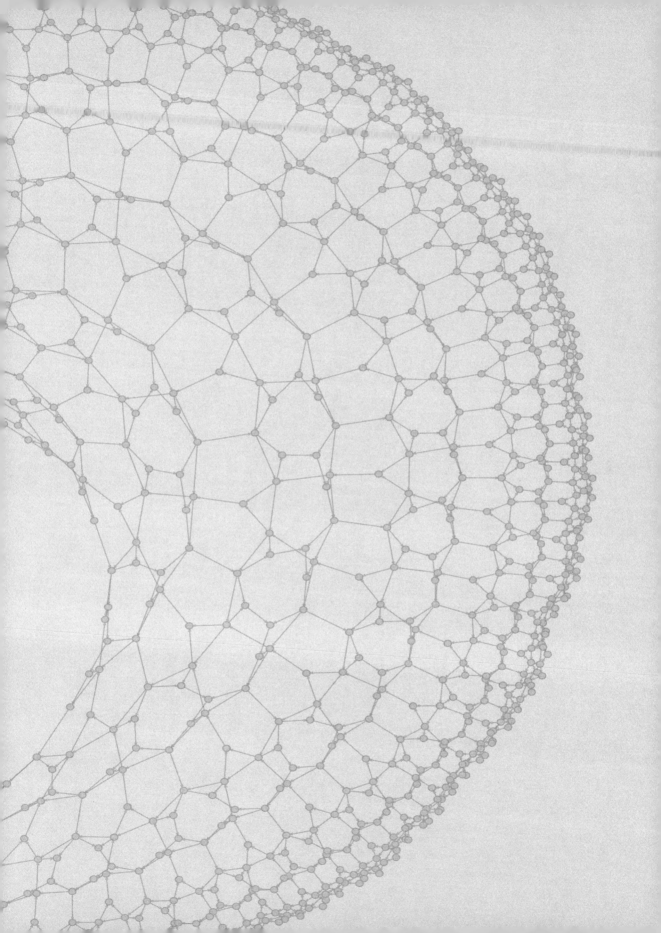

Index

1/*n* expansion, 728

4 dimensions
  and spacetime, 639–644

5 dimensions
  and Kaluza–Klein theory, 716

6*j* symbols
  and spin networks, 742

A New Kind of Science, 521, 523,
  591–753
  15-year view of, 547
  modifications to, *vii*
A4 (tetrahedral group), 720
Abelian group, 198
Aboav–Weaire law, 727
Absolute motion, 730
Acceleration
  and finding geodesics, 737
  and time dilation, 730
  as equivalent to gravity, 735
  particle production by, 750
Accelerators
  particle, 507
Acknowledgements, 487
Action, 407, 441
  Einstein–Hilbert for gravity, 740
  in path integrals, 749
Additive cellular automata
  and spacetime symmetry, 720
  generalized, 706
  higher-order, 706
  sequential versions of, 722
Additivity
  in quantum mechanics, 747
Adjacency matrices, 181
  and machine learning, 144
Adjacency tensors
  for hypernetworks, 181, 717
ADM formalism, 259
AdS/CFT, 509
Aether, 506, 575
Age distribution
  of edges, 181
Age of universe, 467
Aharonov–Bohm effect, 746
AI (artificial intelligence), 555
Alexander moves
  and general networks, 726
  and spin networks, 742
Alexander, James W. (USA,
  1888–1971)
  and moves on networks, 726
Algebra
  and confluence, 30
  and history of posets, 728
Algebra of operators, 449
Algebraic computation, 514
Algebraic quantum field theory
  (axiomatic field theory),
  744, 752
Algebraic surface, 151
Algebraic topology, 508
Algebraic varieties
  and additive CAs, 706
Algorithmic randomness
  and quantum measurement, 750
Alien intelligence, 556
Alternating groups, 198
  as symmetry of evolution, 361
AMA (Ask Me Anything), 542

Ambiguity
  of rule updates, 86
Amplitudes in quantum theory, 407,
  699, 750
  as complex numbers, 441
Analytic continuation
  in quantum field theory, 749
Analyticity
  of S-matrices, 744
  see also Continuity
Ancestors
  in multiway graphs, 262
And (^)
  confluence of, 724
Angles
  in differential geometry, 736
  of CAs on lattices, 631
Angular momentum
  and spin networks, 742
  intrinsic of particles, 407, 734
  quantization of, 744
Animals
  computational, 520, 538
Announcement, 3
Anomalies (quantum field theory)
  and high-mass particles, 735
  as basic quantum effects, 746
Anomalous magnetic moments,
  744, 748
Anthropic Principle, 714
Antichains (in posets), 728
Antimatter, 514
  rarity of and T violation, 707
Antiparticles
  and T violation, 707
  and vacuum fluctuations, 750
Apollonian packing, 156
  and network evolution, 725
Applications
  to physics, 591–703
Arbelos, 155
Arc length, 736
Archimedean solids
  and trivalent networks, 717
Archives, 6, 69, 487, 541
Aristotle (Greece, 384–322 BC)
  and nature of space, 716
Arrow of time, 413, 429
Artificial intelligence (AI), 555
Asimov's Laws of Robotics, 562
Associative calculi, 477
Assortativity, 183
Astronomy
  and time in universe, 709
Astrophysical processes, 470
Asymptotic, 93
Asymptotic freedom in QCD, 507,
  744, 749
Asymptotic growth, 93, 177
Asymptotic series
  in perturbation theory, 748
Asynchronous algorithms, 31
Atiyah, Michael (England, 1929–
  2019), 518
Atomic physics
  6*j* symbols in, 742
  and quantum theory, 744
Atomism
  and elementary particles, 731
Atoms, 505
  and history of quantum theory,
  744
  and thermodynamics, 603, 707

as knots in the ether, 716
  early models of, 714
  in models of space, 716
Attractors
  effective reversibility on, 706
Automated theorem proving, 204,
  436, 534
Automation, 567
Automorphism
  hypergraph, 366
Averaging
  in diffusion equation, 711
Axiomatic quantum field theory,
  744, 752

B particles
  time reversal violation for, 707
Backstory
  of project, 503
Backward evolution in CAs, 593
Bag model
  as mechanistic model, 714
Ball
  volume of, 163, 174, 193, 413, 738
Bell numbers, 93, 95
Bell, John S. (England/Switzerland,
  1928–1990)
  and quantum mechanics, 744
Bell's inequalities, 409
  history of, 744
  in quantum field theory, 752
BellB, 93, 95
Bendix, Peter B. (USA, 1946–2007)
  and Knuth–Bendix procedure, 725
Bennett, Charles H. (USA, 1943–)
  and reversibility of computation,
  707
Bernoulli, Daniel (Netherlands/
  Switzerland, 1700–1782)
  and molecular theory of gases,
  707
Bestseller lists, 524
Beta decay
  and quantum field theory, 744
  parity violation in, 707
Betweenness centrality, 183
Bianchi classification
  for Einstein equations, 741
Bianchi identity, 736
Bicycling
  to university, 513
Biedenharn–Elliott identity (for 6*j*
  symbols), 742
Big bang model
  and basic cosmology, 743
  and thermodynamics, 709
Billiards model, 710
  and thermodynamics, 604
Binary relations
  rules based on, 99
Binomial, 77
Binomial (binomial coefficients)
  and entropy of particles in box,
  710
  and number of conserving CAs,
  711
Binomial tree, 77
Biological systems, 552
  and thermodynamic behavior,
  611, 709
  in relativity theory, 730
  organization through partitioning
  in, 615

Biology
  Occam's razor in, 713
Birthday, 535
  Stephen Wolfram's, 4
Black holes, 44, 47, 409
  and history of gravity, 735
  and quantum information, 461
  and singularity theorems, 740
  and string theory duality, 716
  as analog of quantum
  measurement, 446
  as dual to particles, 731
  as source of decoherence, 750
  galactic, 60, 470
  gravity theories without, 741
  Hawking radiation from, 750
  history of, 508
  in rulial space, 64
  quantum analog of, 55
  quantum phenomena in, 60
  qubit as analog of, 458
Blackbody radiation
  and quantum theory, 744
Block cellular automata, 617–622
  converting to ordinary CAs, 711
  for Schrödinger equation, 747
  implementation of, 711
  number of rules for, 711
  repetition periods in, 711
Blockchain, 304
Blocks
  conservation laws for, 710
Bohm–Aharonov effect, 746
Bohm, David J. (USA/England,
  1917–1992)
  and discreteness of space, 715
  and hidden variables, 744
Bohr, Niels H. D. (Denmark,
  1885–1962)
  and quantum theory, 744
Boltzmann equation
  and H theorem, 707
Boltzmann factors
  and path integrals, 749
Boltzmann, Ludwig E. (Austria,
  1844–1906)
  and statistical mechanics, 707
Boolean expression confluence, 205
Boolean hypercube
  and layout of networks, 719
Boost, 37, 417
Bootstrap hypothesis (in particle
  physics), 507, 731
Born interpretation (in quantum
  mechanics), 744
Bose–Einstein condensation, 744
Bosons
  spin-statistics of, 734
Box of a trillion souls, 566
Branch pairs, 220
  and commutators, 450
  in hypergraphs, 313
Branchial distance, 451
Branchial graphs, 56, 260, 370, 486
  and entanglement, 438
  weights in, 289
Branchial motion, 58, 454
Branchial space, 55, 58, 438, 454
Branching
  in multiway graph, 27
Branchlike connections, 58, 454
Branchlike hypersurface, 434, 439
Branchlike separation, 444

Branchtime, 59
Breadth-first scan, 31, 255, 721
Breakdown
    of vacuum, 750
Broglie, Louis-V. P. R. de (France, 1892–1987)
    and wave-particle duality, 744
Bubbles
    in evolving foams, 727
Buchberger, Bruno (Austria, 1942–)
    and Gröbner basis approach, 725
Buckyball graph
    directed, 254
Buckyball graphs, 174, 179, 188
Buckyball Sierpiński graphs, 197
Busy beaver, 135

c
    see Speed of light
C60
    and spherical networks, 737
Cactus-like graphs, 81, 100
Cages (small girth networks), 717
Calabi–Yau manifolds, 716, 740
Calculus, 506
    and fractional dimensions, 22
Calculus of variations
    and geodesics, 737
Caltech, 514
Cambridge University, 534, 542
Canonical ensemble
    and path integrals, 749
Canonical forms
    in multiway systems, 724
    see also Confluence
Canonical quantization, 744
    of gravity, 742
Canonical systems, 477
Canonicalization
    of rules, 91
Cantor set, 196
Cantor, Georg F. L. P. (Germany, 1845–1918)
    and definition of dimension, 718
Carnot, Sadi N. L. (France, 1796–1832)
    and thermodynamics, 707
Cartesianism
    and matter in space, 716
Cartoon, 524
Casimir effect, 750
Casimir, Hendrik B. G. (Netherlands, 1909–2000)
    and electron model, 731
Catch
    and testing invariances, 710
    and testing reversibility, 705
Category theory, 68, 477
    and spin networks, 742
Cauchy problem
    for general relativity, 740
Cauchy surfaces, 729
Causal disconnection, 44, 347
Causal dynamical triangulation, 477
Causal graphs, 29, 230, 237, 314, 431, 484
    disconnection in, 457
    foliations of, 342
    history of, 522
    in spacetime, 414
    large-scale structure of, 340
    limits of, 251
    typical, 245, 325
Causal invariance, 28, 205, 208, 307, 577, 661
    adding completions for, 294
    and commutation relations, 450
    and concept of motion, 680, 687

and distributed computing, 723
and Einstein's equations, 419
and emulated CAs, 723
and gauge invariance, 685
and project history, 535
and quantum mechanics, 51, 433, 700
effective, 290
for networks, 673
frequency of, 226
in rule space, 62, 474
in simulating mobile automata, 721
in trivalent graphs, 392
testing for, 219, 311
total, 207, 219
Causal networks
    and cosmology, 743
    and general relativity, 740
    and information transmission, 678
    and perceived spacetime, 674
    and posets, 728
    and replacement orders, 659
    and torsion, 740
    as directed graphs, 720
    as Hasse diagrams, 720
    curvature in, 692
    difficulty of deducing, 651
    exponential growth in, 654
    from evolution history, 721
    from mobile automata, 646, 721
    from multiway systems, 665
    from substitution systems, 655
    history of, 720
    implementation of, 721
    in network evolution, 672
    invariance of, 661
    loops in, 652
    random, 740
    reversibility in, 653
    slices through, 674
    vs. multiway systems, 725
Causal relationships
    in substitution systems, 228
Causal set theory, 68, 477, 509
Causality
    and Bell's inequalities, 752
Caustics
    and classical limits, 747
Cayley graphs, 197, 400
    and hyperbolic space, 737
    and network constraints, 720
    limiting geometry of, 738
CCSR (Center for Complex Systems Research), 519
Celestial mechanics
    and Bohr atom, 744
Cell complexes, 738
Cell division
    in networks, 727
Cellular automata, 601
    additive
        see Additive cellular automata
    and causal invariance, 723
    and dimensions of networks, 718
    and machine learning, 554
    and self-gravitating systems, 709
    as models for space, 630
    as models of physics, 521, 714
    as too rigid for ultimate theory, 625
    asynchronous
        see Sequential cellular automata
    block
        see Block cellular automata
    class 3, 138
    conservation laws in, 616, 711
    density conservation in, 617

diffusion equation from, 712
emulated by substitution systems, 723
emulation of, 384
firing squad problem in, 723
foliations in, 385
for quantum systems, 747
for Schrödinger equation, 747
history with, 516, 548
ideal gas modeled by, 603
invertible
    see Reversible cellular automata
on parallel computer, 519
particles in, 47, 190, 425
perturbations in, 190
reversible
    see Reversible cellular automata
rotational invariance in 2D, 631
rule labeling in, 92
second-order
    see Reversible cellular automata
sequential, 722
speed of light in, 676
structures in as particles, 683
synchronization in, 723
thermodynamic behavior in, 601
time vs. space in, 639
totalistic
    see Totalistic cellular automata
see also Additive cellular automata
Cellular automaton
    on graph, 185
Cellular structures
    and networks, 727
Censure, 542
Center for Complex Systems Research, 519
Centrality, 183
CEO, 519, 584
Chains
    in posets, 728
Chaos theory
    and Bianchi IX cosmology, 741
    and divergence of geodesics, 737
    and hard sphere gases, 710
    and QCD, 749
    and quantum measurement, 750
    and thermodynamics, 708
Chapter 5 (of *NKS*), 521
Chapter 9 (of *NKS*), 522, 530, 582
Charge, 407
    and gauge invariance, 733
    conservation of, 685, 710
    quantization of, 686, 734
Chemical synthesis, 563
Chemistry
    networks with analogies in, 728
Christoffel symbols, 736
Chromatic number
    of networks, 717
Church–Rosser property, 724
Circle packing, 156
Circles
    areas of, 738
    area of on sphere, 19, 174
Circumference (of networks), 717
Class 1 behavior
    and reversible CAs, 706
Class 2 behavior
    in reversible CAs, 706
Class 3 behavior, 138
    in reversible CAs, 706
    localized structures in, 684
    see also Rule 30, 90, etc.

Class 4 behavior
    in reversible CAs, 598, 706
    number of structures in, 735
    particle collisions in, 698
    see also Rule 110, etc.
Classical physics, 432
Classical-like states, 435
Classification
    of behavior, 143
Clausius, Rudolf J. E. (Germany, 1822–1888)
    and thermodynamics, 707
Clebsch–Gordan coefficients
    and spin networks, 742
Closed systems
    thermodynamics in, 613
Closed timelike curves, 45, 346, 410, 432
Clustering coefficient, 183, 184
Clusters (in networks), 668, 727
    total numbers of, 717
CMB, 47, 431, 508
Coarse-graining, 429
    and completions, 294
    history of, 707
    in thermodynamics, 606
Coarsening
    in cellular structures, 727
Code 294
    localized structures in, 684
Code 468 (2D)
    isotropy in, 631
Code 686 (2D)
    isotropy in, 631
Code 746 (2D)
    isotropy in, 631
Code 1893
    localized structures in, 684
Coherent states (in quantum theory), 747
Coherent structures
    in QCD, 749
    see also Localized structures
Collinearity
    in multiway graphs, 273
Collisions
    and thermodynamic model, 603
Color charges
    and QCD, 744
Colored graphs, 392
Coloring of networks, 717, 718
Combinatorial physics, 715
Combinatorial topology, 738
Combinatorics
    posets in, 728
Combinatory logic, 399
Common subexpressions
    and networks, 728
Common successors, 260
Communications systems
    and layout of networks, 719
Commutation relations, 450
    and symmetry operations, 359
    in spacetime, 456
Commuting operations
    and causal invariance, 724
Company, 487
    first, 515
Complete graphs, 261
    and planarity tests, 733
Completions, 293
    algorithms for, 725
    by observers, 436
Completion interpretation
    of quantum mechanics, 535
Complex analysis
    and S-matrix theory, 744

Complex numbers
  as amplitudes, 441
  as defining poset, 728
Complex Systems (journal), 519
Complex systems theory, 519
Complexity
  in nature, 516
  origins of, 519
Complexity theory, 64
  geometric, 68
Compositeness
  of elementary particles, 731
Compression
  in mobile automata, 646
Compton scattering, 748
Computation
  and thermodynamic behavior, 602
  reversible, 706
  thermodynamics of, 706, 707
  see also Programs
Computation universality
  and rule space, 474
Computational animals, 520, 538
Computational complexity theory, 64
Computational exploration, 477
Computational irreducibility, 12, 23, 61, 68, 403
  and mathematics, 558
  and quantum observers, 437
  first use of, 518
  in QED, 748
Computational language, 528
Computational universe, 504
Computational X, 528, 568
Computer algebra, 514
  and Feynman diagrams, 744
  and gravity theory, 735
Computer experiments, 5, 67, 541
  and ergodicity, 707
Computer graphics
  and discrete surfaces, 738
Computer science
  education in, 568
Computer-aided design (CAD)
  and discrete surfaces, 738
"Concise Directory of Physics", 511
Concurrent systems
  and causal invariance, 723
Condensates
  topological defects in, 733
Cones
  in Lorentzian spaces, 739
  rule generating, 149
Confinement in QCD, 749
Confluence, 30, 208, 724
  getting using completion, 725
  in multiway systems, 665
  see also Canonical forms
  see also Causal invariance
  see also Church–Rosser property
Conformal field theory, 477
Conformal transformations
  and gauge invariance, 733
Conjugacy
  and CA conservation laws, 711
Conjugate variables, 40
Connected components, 131
Connection Machine, 519
Connections (on fiber bundles), 463, 733
Connectivity, 88, 717, 727
Consciousness
  and quantum theory, 744, 750
  see also Intelligence
  see also Thinking
Conservation laws, 359, 616–622
  finding in CAs, 710

  for particles, 426
  for particles in 2D CA, 603
  for quantum probabilities, 747
  for vector quantities, 712
  in physics, 710
  topological, 733
Conservation of energy, 408, 423
Conserved quantities
  from algebraic structures, 711
Constitution
  AI, 562
Constraints
  as determining spacetime networks, 640
  defining networks using, 641
Consulting, 519
Continuity
  of space, 630
  on graphs, 195
  origins of, 621–622
Continuity equation
  on graph, 196
Continuous cellular automata
  for quantum mechanics, 747
Continuous space, 148, 411
  geodesics in, 192
Continuum limits
  different forms of, 711
  for diffusion equation, 711
  of networks, 22, 167, 718
Contravariant vectors, 192
Convergence
  in multiway systems, 665, 724
  of metric expansion, 738
Convolutional neural nets, 553
Coordinates
  and multiway strings, 724
  for network nodes, 636
  on ellipsoid, 193
Copernican astronomy
  and history of gravity, 735
Copernicanism, 62, 64
Core collapse
  in self-gravitating systems, 709
Cores
  of elementary particles, 685
Coronavirus, 541
Corpuscular theories, 505, 712
Correlation function, 188
Correlations
  and Bell's inequalities, 752
  and non-standard diffusion processes, 712
  and random networks, 726
  in H theorem, 707
  in quantum theory, 701
Cos (cosine)
  and area of circle on sphere, 738
  and Bell's inequalities, 752
  and limit of 6*j* symbols, 742
Cosmic censorship hypothesis, 45, 461
Cosmic microwave background, 47, 431, 508
  and alignment of time, 709
  and galaxy formation, 709
  and history of gravity, 735
  and initial conditions, 714
  as analog of ether, 730
  origin of uniformity of, 743
Cosmological arrow of time, 413
Cosmological constant, 43, 408, 410
Cosmological principle (uniformity of universe), 743
Cosmological rest frame, 36
Cosmological term (in Einstein equations), 740
  and inflationary universe, 743
  and vacuum solutions, 741

Cosmology, 46, 430
  and Einstein equations, 741
  and ether in, 730
  and history of gravity, 735
  and particle physics, 514
  and Second Law, 708, 709
  and simple initial conditions, 714
  basic issues in, 743
  formation of galaxies in, 709
  history of, 508
  network models of, 743
  topological defects in, 733
  see also Universe
Counterfactuals (quantum values), 752
Coupling constants
  in quantum field theory, 744
Covalent forces
  and virtual electrons, 748
Covariant derivatives, 194
COVID-19, 541
CP violation (time reversal violation), 707
CPT invariance, 707
Crinkling, 157
Critical pairs, 220
  in completion algorithms, 725
  see also Branch pairs
Crossings
  in graphs, 186
Cryptography
  quantum, 744
Crystals
  trivalent network and, 718
CTCs
  see Closed timelike curves
Cube
  as initial condition, 137
  from multiway graph, 213
Cube network, 634
  transformed to tetrahedron, 726
Cubic graphs, 390
Cubic grid, 164
Cultural relativism
  not connected to relativity, 730
Curl
  and vector potential, 733
Curvature, 19
  and geodesics, 192
  gauge fields as, 733
  in differential geometry, 736
  in fractional-dimensional space, 199
  in networks, 174
  in non-integer dimensions, 739
  in quantum mechanics, 56
  in space, 413
  in spacetime, 418
  of curves, 736
  singularities in, 741
  vs. dimension change, 430
Curves
  curvature of, 736
Cusps, 153
Cycle index polynomials, 95
Cycles
  in graphs, 184
  longest in networks, 717, 719
  shortest in networks, 717
Cyclic behavior, 132, 140
Cylinders
  and definition of Ricci tensor, 692
  in curved space, 738
  rule generating, 152

d-dimensional grid, 164
Dangling connections, 119, 390
Dark energy, 430
Dark matter, 49, 409, 469

Dataflow systems
  and causal invariance, 723
de Bruijn networks
  and local conservation laws, 711
de Sitter space, 410
Decimation systems
  and firing squad problem, 723
Decision analysis
  and causal networks, 720
Decoherence, 436, 456
  and computational irreducibility, 449
Decoherence, 750
Deep inelastic scattering, 731
Defects
  topological, 733
Degree centrality, 183
Degree distribution, 184
Delayed choice experiments, 746
Democratic hypothesis (in particle physics), 507, 731
Density in cellular automata
  conservation of, 616
  diffusion of in block, 621
Depth-first scan, 31, 256
  in substitution systems, 721
Descartes, René (France/Netherlands, 1596–1650)
  and discrete space, 506, 715
Description frame
  in rule space, 475
Description languages, 63
Det (determinant)
  and testing for dimension, 718
  metric related to volume by, 738
Detangler
  of graphs, 540
Diagnosis
  and causal networks, 720
Diameter
  of graphs, 183
Diameters of networks, 717
Diamonds
  in multiway graphs, 206
Difference patterns in CAs
  for reversible rules, 706
Differential equations
  for fluid flow, 574
  for geodesics, 737
  second-order CAs and, 706
Differential geometry, 736
Diffraction
  path integral theory of, 749
Diffusion
  in block cellular automata, 621
  non-standard, 712
Diffusion equation
  and path integrals, 744
  and Schrödinger equation, 747
  derivation of in CAs, 712
  emerging from block CAs, 622
  minimal approximation to, 712
Digit sequences
  of pi and universe, 715
Digital filters (FIR)
  and sequential CAs, 722
Digital physics, 477, 521
DigitCount
  and nested networks, 725
Dimensional analysis, 48
  and Planck length, 715
Dimensions
  definitions of, 718
  differential geometry of non-integer, 739
  fractal, 18
  local estimates of, 180
  of networks, 16, 162, 636, 691
  of physical space, 673

of posets, 728
of space, 15, 163, 411
Diophantine equations
    solutions of, 425
Dirac equation
    as simple model, 713
    discretization of, 747
Dirac, Paul A. M. (England, 1902–1984)
    and history of quantum mechanics, 744
Directed acyclic graphs (DAGs)
    causal networks as, 720
Directed network systems, 728
Directional reversibility
    in cellular automata, 705
Disconnected behavior, 113, 126, 134
Disconnected rules, 96, 130
Disconnection
    causal, 44, 347
Discrete space, 15, 506, 630
    and quantum gravity, 742
    history of in math, 738
    history of in physics, 715
Distance matrices, 271
Distances
    defined by geodesics, 736
    defined on networks, 636
    directed, 258
    general properties of, 718
    in graph, 17, 163
    in hypergraph, 410
    non-symmetric and torsion, 740
    spatial, 152
Distributed computing
    and causal invariance, 723
Divergence
    of geodesics, 192
    on graph, 196
Divergent series
    in QED, 748
Divisibility
    as defining poset, 728
Dodecahedron
    network of, 634, 737
Dodecahedron graph, 197
Dot (dot product)
    and differential geometry, 736
Double-pushout graph grammars, 477
DPO graph grammars, 477
Duality
    between evolution and causal network, 654
    between particles and extended objects, 731
    in string theory, 716
Dynamic triangulation
    and quantum gravity, 742
Dynamical symmetry breaking, 734
Dynamical systems theory, 189

$E=mc^2$, 42, 422
Early universe, 431
    and thermodynamics, 709
    oligons in, 469
    particles surviving from, 735
Eddington, Arthur S. (England, 1882–1944)
    and models of the universe, 713
Edge effects, 165
Effective causal invariance, 290
Eigenmodes
    of graph, 185
Eigenvalues
    and dimension of networks, 718
    of distance matrices, 719
Eigenvector centrality, 183
Eikonal approximation, 749

Einstein equations, 740
    history of, 735
    matter vs. space in, 716
    quantization of, 742
    specifying curvature of space, 689
    vacuum solutions to, 741
Einstein–Hilbert action
    and spin networks, 742
Einstein–Podolsky–Rosen (EPR) experiment, 752
Einstein, Albert (Germany/Switzerland/USA, 1879–1955), 506, 571
    and EPR experiment, 744
    and general relativity, 735
    and particles as gravity, 741
    and quantum theory, 744
    and special relativity, 729
    and unified field theory, 716
    office of, 518
Einstein's equations, 21, 43, 418, 423, 574
    and units, 465
    derivation of, 540
    in rulial space, 64
    quantum analog of, 57
Electric fields
    particle production in, 750
Electromagnetic fields, 506
    and gauge invariance, 463, 733
    and relativistic invariance, 729
    and virtual photons, 748
    as ultimate constituents, 712
    quantization of, 744
    theories of based on space, 716
Electron-photon scattering, 748
Electron-positron annihilation, 513
Electrons
    discovery of, 506, 712, 731
    lack of intuition about, 695
    magnetic moment of in QED, 748
    mass of, 734
    radius of, 48, 468, 513, 731
    theories of structure of, 731
    wave-particle duality of, 744
Elementary energy, 464, 468
Elementary length, 48, 464, 468
Elementary particles, 47, 424, 683–688
    and limit of networks, 718
    as dual to black holes, 731
    decays and time quantization, 720
    discovery dates of, 731
    enumerating in networks, 733
    interactions between, 697
    in unified field theory, 716
    known types of, 731
    masses of, 686, 734
    motion of, 686
    motion of along geodesics, 689
    motion of through network, 694
    quantum threads between, 702
    searching for additional, 735
    spin of, 734
    upper limits on mass of, 735
Elementary time, 464, 468
Ellipsoid, 193
    as model for curvature, 199
Embeddings of networks, 634, 719
Emulation cones, 64
Encodings
    of models, 404
Energy, 407, 420
    conservation of, 423
    elementary, 464, 468
    heat as form of, 707
    identification of, 39

in gravity theory, 695
in quantum mechanics, 57
zero of, 40
Energy conditions
    and general relativity, 740
Energy conservation
    and thermodynamics, 603
    in cellular automata, 616
    in Einstein equations, 740
    in network evolution, 687
    in physics, 710
Energy-momentum tensor, 43, 422
    in Einstein equations, 740
Ensembles
    difficulty of using, 188
    in rule 37R, 615
    in statistical mechanics, 707
Entanglement, 59, 407, 437, 702
    and Bell's inequalities, 752
    as basic quantum effect, 746
Entanglement cones, 455
Entanglement horizon, 60, 460
Entanglement speed (ζ), 60, 456, 469
Entrepreneurism, 515
Entropic arrow of time, 413
Entropy
    history of, 707
    in thermodynamic systems, 606
    of particles in box, 710
    of subgraphs, 178
    origins of increasing, 599–615
    see also Second Law of thermodynamics
Epicureans
    and contents of space, 716
Epidemic, 541
EPR (Einstein–Podolsky–Rosen) experiment, 752
Epsilon-delta proofs, 46
Equational logic, 204, 400
Equations
    of state and gravity, 740
    time vs. space in, 719
    see also Differential equations
    see also Diffusion equation
    see also Dirac equation
    see also Einstein equations
    see also Klein–Gordon equation
    see also Laplace equation
    see also Maxwell's equations
    see also Navier–Stokes equations
    see also Schrödinger equation
Equilibrium
    and multiway systems, 429
    and quantum measurement, 750
    approach to, 607
    in early universe, 743
    in graph evolution, 183
    in random networks, 726
    in self-gravitating systems, 709
    in thermodynamic systems, 608
Equivalence
    Principle of Computational
        see Principle of Computational Equivalence
    topological of manifolds, 738
Equivalence operations
    and confluence, 724
Equivalence principle, 688, 735
    and gravitational energy, 741
    and particle production, 750
Equivalence to substitution systems, 377
ER=EPR, 461
Erf (error function)
    in diffusion equation, 712
Ergodic theory
    history of, 707

Ergodicity
    and rule 37R, 615
    for space, 411
    of hard sphere gas, 710
    vs. Second Law, 708
Error bars
    for dimension estimate, 166
Escape velocity
    branchial, 461
Essential singularities
    in QED perturbation theory, 748
Ether, 506, 575
    and theory of light, 729
    as content of space, 716
    atoms as knots in, 731
    discrete model for, 715
    history of, 712
Ethics
    AI, 562
Eton College, 513
Euclid (?Egypt, ~300 BC)
    and nature of space, 716
Euclid's axioms, 505
Euclidean distance, 191
Euclidean space, 148
    as model space, 716
Euler, Leonhard (Switzerland/Russia/Germany, 1707–1783)
    and equations for geodesics, 737
Euler's formula
    and spherical networks, 737
    for planar networks, 726
Evaluation
    in SMP, 515
    process of, 67
Event horizons, 45, 431, 457
    and black hole formation, 741
    and particle production, 750
    as analog of quantum measurement, 446
    causal and branchial, 461
    branchial, 60, 457
    quantum analog of, 55
Events
    causal network of, 646
    updating, 23, 228, 303
Everest, Mount, 529
Exact solutions
    for Kondo model, 744
Excluded subgraphs, 186
Exclusion principle, 746
Exp (exponential function)
    and path integrals, 749
Expansion of universe, 46, 408, 430, 743
    and arrow of time, 709
    and cosmological term, 740
    and Einstein equations, 741
    and energy, 423
    and network evolution, 688
    and particle production, 750
    and relativity history, 735
    and thermodynamics, 613
    units and, 465
Experiments
    and thermodynamic initial conditions, 602
    as tests of theory, 6
    computer, 67
Extended objects in quantum field theory, 744
Extensive quantities
    in cellular automata, 710
Extraterrestrial intelligence, 556
    physics for, 65
Extrinsic curvature
    and Einstein equations, 740
    and initial value general relativity, 740

Faces (geometrical)
and discrete spaces, 738
in planar networks, 726
Factorial (n!), 256
and hypersphere volume, 738
and number of reversible block
cellular automata, 711
and QED perturbation series,
748
Fano plane, 272
FeatureSpacePlot, 144, 538
Fermat's principle (in optics), 749
Fermi–Pasta–Ulam experiment,
707
Fermi, Enrico (Italy/USA, 1901–
1954)
and statistical mechanics, 707
Fermions
and basic quantum effects, 746
and classical limits, 747
spin-statistics of, 734
Feynman diagrams
and random networks, 726
and spin networks, 742
for quantum gravity, 742
history of, 744
in QCD, 748
not as mechanistic model, 714
vs. space networks, 728
Feynman path integral, 57, 441
Feynman, Richard P. (USA, 1918–
1988), 5, 515
and discreteness of space, 715
and discrete quantum models,
747
and path integrals, 744
Fiber bundles, 463, 508
and continuum limits of
networks, 718
and gauge theories, 733
Fibonacci sequence, 131, 261, 301
Fibonacci tree, 201
Field operators
measurement of, 752
Field theory
history of, 712
quantum, 749
see also Quantum field theory
Fields, 506
Filters in posets, 728
FindMinimum
and network layouts, 719
Fine structure constant (α)
and perturbation theory, 744
numerology for, 713
Finite differences
and CA diffusion, 712
explicit schemes and sequential
cellular automata, 722
Finite groups, 198
Cayley graphs of, 720
Finite impulse response
and sequential CAs, 722
Finite-size effects
on dimension, 165
Finite-size systems, 140
Finkelstein, David R. (USA,
1929–2016)
and discreteness of space, 715
Firing squad problem (in cellular
automata), 723
First Law of thermodynamics, 707
FitzGerald–Lorentz contraction,
729
FitzGerald, George F. (Ireland,
1851–1901)
and relativity theory, 729
Flat (associative), 478
and confluence property, 724

Flowcharts
and causal networks, 720
Fluctuations
in thermodynamics, 605
order in universe as, 108
violating Second Law in rule
37R, 611
Fluid flow, 441, 574
as analogy for networks, 693
as analogy for quantum field
theory, 747
continuity of vs. space, 630
minimal cellular automata
showing continuity of, 622
with cellular automata, 519
Flux tubes in QCD, 749
Foams
evolution of, 727
model for ether as, 715
Folds
in surfaces, 153
Foliations, 35
and branchial graphs, 275
and coordinates, 255
and evaluation, 67
and fiber bundles, 463
and realistic observers, 415
causal, 237
in cellular automata, 385
in quantum mechanics, 51
in rulial space, 63
of causal graphs, 342
Forbearance, 542
Forces
and gauge invariance, 733
Form factors
and sizes of particles, 731
Formal languages
of networks, 728
Four-Color Theorem
and coloring of networks, 717
graph grammars in proof of, 728
Four-vectors
in relativity theory, 729
Fractal dimension
of reversible CAs, 706
Fractal network, 18
Fractal pattern
dimension of, 167
rule generating, 110, 160
Fractals
in network evolution, 667
in self-gravitating systems, 709
see also Nesting
Fredkin, Edward (USA, 1934–)
and discreteness of space, 715
and reversible CAs, 706
and universe as CA, 521, 714
Free group, 197
Free will, 550
Freezing time
in quantum measurement, 53,
446
in rulial space, 64
Frilled structure, 103
Froths
evolution of, 727
Frozen stars, 55
Fuchsian groups
and hyperbolic space, 737
Fullerenes
as spherical networks, 737
Functions on graphs, 195
Fundamental groups (of
manifolds), 739

Galaxies
and expansion of universe, 743
and Second Law, 709

and simple initial conditions,
714
distribution of, 47, 709
formation of, 514, 613, 709
quantum measurement of, 60
Galilean invariance
and relativity, 730
in fundamental physics, 680
Galilei, Galileo (Italy, 1564–1642)
and Galilean invariance, 729
and nature of gravity, 735
and the nature of space, 716
Gases
as main application of Second
Law, 609
CA idealization of, 604
thermodynamic theories of, 707
see also Fluid flow
Gauge bosons, 731
Gauge invariance, 408, 462, 733
and causal invariance, 685
Gauge theories
and quantum history, 744
origin of, 716
Gauss, J. Carl Friedrich (Germany,
1777–1855)
and curvature of surfaces, 736
Gauss's law
in cellular automata, 711
on graph, 196
Gaussian curvature
as invariant quantity, 736
Gaussian distributions
of weights, 290
vs. non-standard diffusion, 712
Gell-Mann, Murray (USA, 1929–
2019), 515
death of, 533
General covariance, 415
General relativity, 21, 42, 408
and gauge invariance, 733
and space vs. contents, 716
and time travel, 731
and ultimate theory of physics,
712
as simple physical model, 713
as theory of gravity, 688
coordinates in, 259
correspondence to quantum
mechanics, 55
derived in NKS, 523
history of, 508, 571, 735
need for explicit matter in, 695
variants of, 735
with varying spacetime
dimension, 743
Generating function, 164
Generational evolution, 294
Generational multiway system,
435, 443
Generational states, 443
Generators
of groups, 197
Genus
for graph drawing, 186
of networks, 733
Geodesic balls, 163
volumes of, 174, 193, 413, 738
and epidemiology, 541
Geodesic deviation
and Riemann tensor, 736
Geodesic domes
and curved space, 690
and spherical networks, 737
Geodesic sphere, 174
Geodesics, 20, 191
and definition of dimension, 718
and paths of particles, 689
bundle shapes of, 419

distance defined by, 736
in branchial space, 57
in flat space, 736
in multiway space, 439
in space, 413
on surfaces, 737
Geometric complexity theory,
64, 68
Geometric group theory, 68, 198
Geometrical optics, 749
Geometry
curvature in, 690
differential, 736
emergent, 147
of branchial space, 438
of causal graphs, 321
space as uniform in early, 716
Geons
and matter from gravity, 741
and unified field theory, 716
Gibbs, J. Willard (USA, 1839–1903)
and statistical mechanics, 707
Gilbreth, Frank B. (USA, 1868–1924)
and causal networks, 720
Gilbreth, Lillian E. M. (USA,
1878–1972)
and causal networks, 720
Girth
of networks, 717
Git, 304
Glare filters (polarizers), 752
Global clustering coefficient, 183
Global counter
for elements, 304
Global symmetries, 359
Globular behavior, 143
Globular clusters
and thermodynamics, 709
Globular structures, 115, 138
and causal graphs, 330
with unordered hypergraphs,
397
Glueballs (in QCD), 749
Gluons, 508, 514
Gluons (in QCD), 744
confinement of, 749
Goals
of AIs, 561
vs. mechanism, 557
God, 505
and character of space, 716
and ultimate theory of physics,
713
see also Theology
Gödel, Kurt (Austria/Czech./USA,
1906–1978)
stories about, 517
Gödel's theorem, 518
Golden ratio, 131
Gorard, Jonathan (Singapore/UK,
1997–), 4, 51, 487, 534, 540
Gradient
on graph, 196
Grains (in solids)
evolution of, 727
Grand unified models, 507, 712, 731
Graph diameter, 183
in branchial graph, 261
Graph distance, 17
Graph grammars, 477, 728
Graph layout, 540
Graph radius, 183
Graph rewriting systems, 477
Graph sizes, 187
Graph theory
and planarity of networks, 733
Graphical representation of time,
719
Graphons, 189

Graphs
  as models for physics, 521
  branchial, 260
  colored, 392
  correspondence to hypergraphs, 387
  functions on, 195
  infinite, 189
  non-overlapping, 392
  ordered, 392
  rendering of, 16, 163
  types of, 483
  undirected, 392
  vertex transitive, 196
Gravitational constant (G), 409, 465
Gravitational waves
  and speed of light, 729
  detectors of, 735
  in vacuum, 694, 741
Gravitons, 742
  and space vs. matter, 716
  as particles, 731
Gravity, 42, 420, 688–695
  and vacuum fluctuations, 750
  CPT violation in, 707
  history of, 508, 735
  in early universe, 709
  in ultimate theory of physics, 627
  n-body systems subject to, 709
  particle production by, 750
Greek philosophers, 505
Greek physics
  and ultimate theories, 712
Greek word, 49
Grids
  as causal graphs, 252, 331
  dimension of, 163
  emergence of, 123
  from causal graphs, 249
  rule generating, 148
GroebnerBasis
  and completion algorithms, 725
Ground state
  of quantum field theories, 750
Group theory
  geometric, 68
Groups
  and CA conservation laws, 711
  and gauge theories, 733
  and particles in physics, 686
  Cayley graphs of, 197, 720
  growth in, 198, 217
  Lie, 369
  limiting geometry of, 738
  words in, 400
Growth
  based on rules, 129
Growth rates
  and curvature in networks, 691
  and network dimensions, 636, 718
  of number of trivalent networks, 717

H theorem of Boltzmann, 707
"Hadronic Electrons?", 513
Hadrons
  as particles, 731
  in QCD, 749
Halting, 87, 135
Hamiltonian paths
  trivalent networks with, 717
Hamiltonians
  in discrete quantum systems, 747
  quantum, 441
Hamming distance
  and layout of networks, 719

Handles on networks, 685, 733
Hard sphere gas, 710
  and thermodynamics, 707
  CA idealization of, 604
Hardy fields, 177
Hash, 304
Hasse diagrams of posets
  and causal networks, 728
Hauptvermutung (of combinatorial topology), 738
Hausdorff dimension, 167, 718
Hawking radiation, 509, 750
  in branchial space, 458
Hawking, Stephen W. (England, 1942–2018)
  and black hole radiation, 750
Heat
  character of, 603
  history of theories of, 707
Heat capacities
  and quantum history, 744
Heisenberg group, 198
Heisenberg, Werner K. (Germany, 1901–1976)
  and matrix mechanics, 744
Heptagons
  and negative curvature, 690
  hyperbolic tiling with, 737
Hexagonal cellular automata
  and momentum conservation, 712
Hexagonal faces
  of buckyball, 174, 179
Hexagonal grid, 424
  causal graph as, 249
Hidden-variables theories, 701, 744, 752
Hierarchies
  as avoiding thermodynamics, 611
Higgs field
  and expansion of universe, 743
  and notion of ether, 730
  and particle masses, 734
  particle associated with, 734
Hilbert spaces, 56, 440, 454
  from branchial graphs, 272
  in quantum theory, 746
Hilbert, David (Germany, 1862–1943)
  and general relativity, 740
Histories
  multiple, 25
History
  accidents of in universe, 663
  of project, 503
  uniqueness of for universe, 662
Hobbes, Thomas (England, 1588–1679)
  and nature of space, 716
Holographic principle, 60, 68, 409
Homogeneity
  in dimension estimate, 166
  of universe, 431
Homotopy
  and structures in networks, 733
  and topological defects, 733
Horizon problem, 743
Hubble time, 467
Human behavior
  Occam's razor for, 713
Human condition
  future of, 566
Human language, 66
Hunts
  for examples, 537
Hydrogen atom
  and history of quantum theory, 744

Hyperbolic space, 155, 737
  curvature of, 175
  from causal graphs, 248
Hyperbolicity
  failure of, 346
Hypercomputation, 64
Hypercubes, 271
  and trivalent networks, 717
  from multiway graph, 213
Hypergeometric series, 164
Hypergeometric2F1
  and caps on hyperspheres, 738
HypergeometricPFQ
  and 6j symbols, 742
Hypergraph isomorphism, 91, 306
Hypergraphs, 10, 717
  automorphisms of, 366
  emulating graphs with, 387
  enumeration of, 95
  events in, 303
  representation of, 81
  unifications of, 311
  unordered, 396
Hypergrowth
  of fields, 553
Hyperons, 507, 511
Hypersphere, 165

IAS (Institute for Advanced Study), 517
Icosahedral group, 369
Ideal gas
  CA idealization of, 604
  of oligons, 469
Idealism
  and nature of space, 716
Idealizations
  and ultimate theory of physics, 623
Illinois
  University of, 519
ImageIdentify.com, 553
Imaginary time formalism, 731
Implementation
  of models, 478
Implies
  non-confluence of, 724
Incidence geometry, 272
IndexGraph, 483
Induction (scientific)
  and ultimate theory of physics, 624
Inequivalent rules, 92
Inertia
  and uniformity of space, 716
Inertial frames, 36, 409, 415, 679
Infinite graphs, 189
Infinite impulse response
  cellular automata as, 722
Infinities
  in QED, 744
  in quantum calculations, 506
Inflation
  in cosmology, 47, 431, 714, 743
Information
  and radiation in rule 37R, 613
  and thermodynamics, 707
Information transmission
  and causal networks, 678
  and quantum entanglement, 752
  limited by speed of light, 676
Initial conditions, 136
  and disconnection, 357
  and thermodynamics, 601
  and time travel, 731
  for universe, 431, 714
  possible, 95
Initial creation event, 357

Initial value problems
  in general relativity, 740
Insert (insert element)
  and random networks, 726
Instabilities
  and quantum measurement, 700
  and the Second Law, 708
  in self-gravitating systems, 709
Instantons, 508
  in path integrals, 744
Institute for Advanced Study (IAS), 517
Institutionalization
  of physics, 510
Integrability
  of PDEs, 711
Integrate
  and distance in curved space, 736
Intelligence
  and Anthropic Principle, 714
  and Maxwell's demon, 709
  and Wolfram|Alpha, 526
  definition of, 556
  galactic-scale, 60
  shared physics for, 65
  see also Thinking
Interestingness
  theory of, 563
Interference, 437
  in quantum mechanics, 746, 750
  of string updates, 661
Intermediate growth
  in groups, 199
Intermediate scales
  of growth, 177
Intermediate strings
  in branch resolution, 223
Interpretation of quantum mechanics, 49, 535, 744
Intrinsic curvature, 193, 736
Intrinsic randomness generation
  and Second Law, 608
  in early universe, 743
  in quantum systems, 701, 750
  in reversible conserving systems, 620
Intuition
  and ultimate theory of physics, 626
Invariant interval, 730
Invariant measure
  on graphs, 178, 183
Invariants
  for knots, 734
  in graph evolution, 185
  see also Conserved quantities
Inverse square law for gravity, 694, 735
Involutions, 256
  cellular automata as, 705
Irrational numbers
  and idealized billiards, 710
Irreducibility
  see Computational irreducibility
Irreducible representations (of groups)
  and spin, 734
Irreversibility, 429
  and quantum measurement, 750
  in physical systems, 599–615
Isometry
  in graphs, 179
Isomorphism
  hypergraph, 91
  of hypergraphs, 306
Isotropy
  in physics and CAs, 631
Iterated maps
  and QCD, 749

J/ψ particle, 513
Jonathan Interpretation
    of quantum mechanics, 535
Joule, James P. (England, 1818–
    1889)
    and nature of heat, 707
Journal of Complex Systems, 519

K^0 particle
    and time reversal violation, 707
$K_{3,3}$ non-planar graph, 186, 424, 685
Kaluza, Theodor F. E. (Germany,
    1885–1954)
    and notions of space, 716
Kaons, 429, 511
Kelvin (William Thomson)
    (Scotland, 1824–1907)
    and models of space, 715
    and thermodynamics, 707
    and vortices in ether, 575, 731
Kepler tiling, 159
Kid
    The, 514
Kinetic energy, 422
Kinetic theory
    and diffusion equation, 712
    and thermodynamics, 707
King's College London, 534
Klein–Gordon equation
    discretization of, 747
Klein, Oskar (Sweden/Denmark/
    USA, 1894–1977)
    and notions of space, 716
Knitting
    in behavior of rule, 123
Knitwear designer, 540
Knots, 575
    Alexander moves in, 726
    in ether, 506
    in ether as atoms, 716, 731
    model of atoms as, 712
    theory of, 734
Knowledge
    and computation, 557
Knuth–Bendix algorithm, 293, 725
Knuth, Donald E. (USA, 1938–)
    and Knuth–Bendix procedure,
    725
Kondo model, 744
Kooks
    and theory of physics, 4
Kuratowski's theorem, 186, 424, 733

Lagrangian density, 407, 441
    in general relativity, 740
    in quantum field theory, 749
Lambda calculus, 205, 399
    confluence in, 724
Lambda particle, 533
Lambert W function, 467
Language
    computational, 528
    for description of physics, 63
    for parallel computing, 723
Language design, 65, 557
Laplace equation
    and network dimensions, 718
Laplacian
    in curved space, 738
    on graph, 183, 185
Lapse function, 259
Lattice gauge theories, 744, 749
    and discrete space, 715
    and quantum gravity, 742
Lattice operations
    for group approximation, 369
Lattice patterns, 125
Lattice theory, 273
    and posets, 728

Laws of physics
    and ultimate theory, 628
Lecture tour, 525
Left connectivity, 92
Leibniz, Gottfried W. v.
    (Germany, 1646–1716), 562
    and the nature of space, 716
Lemma
    added by observers, 436
Length
    elementary, 464, 468
Leptons
    as types of particle, 731
Lettuce leaf, 157
Library
    visiting university, 513
Lie groups, 462, 507
    as possible limits, 369
Light
    and quantum history, 744
    speed of, 38, 41
Light cones, 41, 409, 677
    analog of in rule space, 474
    and perturbations, 190
    and random causal networks,
    740
    branchial analog of, 58, 454
    differential geometry of, 739
    in rulial space, 64
    in substitution systems, 239
Lightning bolt, 468
Limitations of science
    and ultimate theory of physics,
    629
Limiting shape, 153
Limits, 406
    in computing dimension, 167
    interchange of, 22
    of networks as, 718
    see also Continuum limits
Line defects, 733
Line-like behavior, 143
Lineage
    for elements, 304
Linear algebra
    and CA invariances, 710, 711
    and dimensions of networks,
    718
Linear equations
    and free field theories, 749
Linear recurrences, 187
    and additive CAs, 706
    for substitution system, 202
Liquid crystals
    topological defects in, 733
Little group (spacetime
    symmetries), 734
Livestreaming, 69, 541
    birthday, 535
Lobed surface, 151
Local clustering coefficient,
    184, 261
Local conservation laws, 711
    see also Conservation laws
Local gauge invariance, 462
Local symmetries, 365
Locality
    and causal cones, 239
Localized structures, 425
    and particles in physics, 683
    in network evolution, 683
    in presence of randomness,
    684
    in QCD, 749
    in reversible CAs, 598
    in rule 37R CA, 613
Log differences, 165
Logic
    and quantum mechanics, 744

Logistics
    and causal networks, 720
Loop general relativity, 735
Loop quantum gravity, 68, 477,
    509, 574
    and spin networks, 742
Loop switching method
    and network layout, 719
Loops
    in causal graphs, 345
Lorentz contraction, 729
Lorentz gas, 710
Lorentz invariance, 408
Lorentz transformations, 417,
    729–730
Lorentz, Hendrik A. (Netherlands,
    1853–1928)
    and relativity theory, 729
Lorentzian manifold, 259, 739
LQG, 68, 477, 509, 574, 742
Lyft, 532

M-theory, 509
Mach, Ernst (Austria/Czech.,
    1838–1916)
    and Mach's Principle, 735, 741
    and origins of relativity, 729
Machine learning, 144, 553
Magnetic field
    and gauge invariance, 733
    compared to gravitational, 688
Magnetic moments
    and size of particles, 731
Magnetic monopoles, 734
Mandelbrot set
    rule looking like, 81, 100
Manhattan distance, 191
Manifolds, 192, 196
    discrete approximations to, 738
    finding, 539
    from emulating Turing machine,
    382
    in differential geometry, 736
    undecidability in equivalence of,
    739
Manufacturing
    causal network systems for, 720
Many-fingered time, 723
Many-worlds models, 433, 723, 750
MapIndexed
    and causal networks, 721
Market forces
    in physics, 510
Mass, 422
    equality of inertial and
        gravitational, 735
    identification of, 42
    in relativity theory, 729
    in Schwarzschild solution, 741
    in ultimate theory of physics, 686
    of elementary particles, 734
    quantum of, 48
Mass–energy equivalence, 42, 422
Massless particles
    and speed of light, 729
    spin states of, 734
Matching
    of networks, 726
    of strings, 726
Mathematica, 626
    confluence of rules in, 724
    launch of, 520
    origins of, 514
    patterns
        see Patterns (in Wolfram
        Language)
    patterns and network evolution,
    725
    ultimate theory of physics in, 626

Mathematics
    and continuity of space, 630
    foundations of, 558
    in physics, 591
Matrices
    adjacency, 181
    Mott in mechanics, 744
Matter, 43, 420
    as distinct from space, 716
    as generating curvature, 690,
    694
    in Einstein equations, 740
Maximum scan, 203
Maxwell, James Clerk (Scotland/
    England, 1831–1879)
    and electromagnetism, 729
    and gauge invariance, 733
    and Maxwell's demon, 709
    and statistical mechanics, 707
Maxwell's demon, 709
Maxwell's equations
    and relativistic invariance, 729
    as simple physical models, 713
Mazoyer, Jacques (France, 1947–)
    and firing squad problem, 723
Mean clustering coefficient, 183
Meaning
    of the universe, 715
Measurement
    in quantum mechanics, 52, 442
    in quantum theory, 700, 750
    in thermodynamics, 606, 708
    quantum, 59
Media coverage, 524
Medicine
    difficulty of, 552
Mercury
    advance of perihelion of, 735
Merging
    in multiway graph, 27
Mesh
    rule generating, 148
Mesh generation
    and discrete spaces, 738
Mesons, 744
    spins of, 734
Mesoscopic systems
    and quantum theory, 744
Metastable states
    and quantum measurement, 750
Meter
    speed of light and defining, 729
Metric
    for Lorentzian spaces, 739
    in differential geometry, 736
    in unified field theory, 716
    Riemann tensor expansion of,
    736
    volume density from, 738
Metric spaces
    networks as, 718
Metric tensors, 192, 419, 736
Michelson–Morley experiment, 729
Michelson, Albert A. (USA,
    1852–1931)
    and Michelson–Morley
        experiment, 729
Milnor, John (USA, 1931–), 518
Minimal surfaces
    vs. Einstein equations, 740
Mining
    computational universe, 551
Minkowski space, 259, 739
    and quantum field theory, 749
    as solving Einstein equations,
    741
Minkowski, Hermann (Germany,
    1864–1909)
    and relativity theory, 729

Minors
    graph, 186, 733
Minsky, Marvin L. (USA, 1927–2016)
    and discreteness of space, 715
Miracles
    and ultimate theory of physics, 713
Mixed arity, 127
Mixed states, 750
Mobile automata
    as analogy, 333
    2D and causal networks, 721
    and time in universe, 644
    causal-invariant systems for, 721
    causal networks from, 721
    on networks, 728
    reversible, 706
Mod (modulo)
    and idealized billiards, 710
Model spaces, 196
Models
    mechanistic for physics, 714
    of universe, 624
    origins of physical, 713
    program-based, 550
    programs as more than, 592
    see also Simulations
    see also Ultimate theory of physics
Module, 478
Molecular chaos assumption
    and *H* theorem, 707
Molecular dynamics, 441
    as analogy, 411
Molecules
    and quantum theory, 744
Momentum, 407, 420
    basic mechanism for, 695
    identification of, 39
Momentum conservation
    in 2D cellular automata, 712
    in Einstein equations, 740
    in network evolution, 687
    in physics, 710
Monads
    models for space with, 716
Monoids, 400
Monte Carlo methods
    for CA conservation laws, 710
    in lattice gauge theories, 749
Moscow State University, 530
Motion, 36, 415
    absolute, 730
    concept of in physics, 679
    in branchial space, 58, 454
Motion sickness, 540
Motivation
    Occam's razor for, 713
Multicausal continuum, 456
Multiedges, 80
Multigraphs
    multiway graphs as, 287
Multiple relations, 84, 110
Multiple transformation rules, 129
Multiplication systems
    reversibility in, 706
Multiverse (many-worlds), 723, 750
Multiway causal graphs, 59, 233, 279, 370, 453, 486
    growth of, 285
Multiway graphs, 485
    generational, 295
    geometry of, 216
    growth in, 217
    in quantum mechanics, 52
    rulial, 63
    typical structures of, 212
    weighted, 287
Multiway space, 438

Multiway systems, 26, 305
    and branching of time, 662
    and Cayley graphs, 401
    and NDTMs, 382
    and quantum mechanics, 432
    and reversibility, 429
    canonical forms in, 724
    causal invariance in, 665
    completion algorithms for, 725
    confluence in, 724
    convergence in, 724
    for substitution system, 202
    generating Euclidean spaces, 724
    history of, 477
    reversible, 706
    rule-space, 471
    spacetime networks from, 724
    terminating and confluence, 724
    vs. causal networks, 725
Muon, 507, 511
    as type of particle, 731
    mass of, 686, 734
    models of, 731
Myhill, John R. (USA, 1923–1987)
    and firing squad problem, 723

n-body problem
    gravitational, 709
Names
    of elements, 305
Natural language, 66
    picturable nouns in, 144
Navier–Stokes equations
    vs. Einstein equations, 693
NDTMs, 382, 404
Nearby rules, 145
Negative energy density, 430
Negatively curved space, 157, 175, 689
    and hyperbolic networks, 737
    divergence of geodesics on, 737
Neighbor-independent network rules, 667, 725
Neighborhoods
    in graph, 177
Nested pattern
    dimension of, 167
    rule generating, 110, 160
Nesting
    in firing squad problem, 723
    in networks, 667
    see also Fractals
NestWhileList
    and network distances, 719
Nets of polyhedra, 634
Network constraint systems, 641, 720
Network Substitution Systems, 526
Networks
    and Cayley graphs, 720
    and cosmological horizon problem, 743
    and quantum information, 702
    approximating flat space, 635
    approximating spheres, 737
    as models for physics, 521
    as models of space, 633–638
    causal invariance for, 673
    chemical analogies for, 728
    chromatic number of, 717
    circumference of, 717
    colored, 717, 727
    coloring of and dimension, 718
    coloring of and planarity, 728
    conditions for planarity of, 733
    connectedness of, 727
    continuum limits of, 718
    curvature in, 690
    defined by constraints, 640

diameter of, 717
dimensions of and growth rates, 636
eigenvalues of distance matrix for, 719
evolution of, 666–673
face distribution in random, 726
Feynman diagrams as, 748
from continuous space, 691
from continuous systems, 719
girth of, 717
growth rates on, 719
homogenous, 720
implementation of, 719, 725
layouts of, 634, 719
localized structures in, 683, 733
mobile automata on, 728
non-overlapping, 673
non-planarity in planar, 685
NP completeness of matching in, 726
number of replacements for, 726
numbers of trivalent, 717
overlaps in, 673
planar, 726
planarity in evolution of, 673
random causal, 740
random replacements in, 726
random walks on, 718
random, 726
relations between types of, 725
replacements in directed, 728
reversible evolution of, 728
rules for getting to any, 726
substitution systems, 666–673
symbolic representation of, 728
trivalent as covering all, 634
trivalent examples of, 634
trivalent in 3D, 718
Neural nets, 553
    understandability of, 559
Neural networks, 516
Neutrinos, 731
    and parity violation, 707
    and speed of light, 729
    identified with gravitons, 742
    limit on number of, 735
New York Times, 524
Newton, Isaac (England, 1642–1727), 542
    and invariance of mechanical laws, 729
    and law of gravity, 735
    and nature of space, 716
Night sky
    and Olbers' paradox, 709
    observed darkness of, 613
Nilpotent groups
    Cayley graphs of, 198, 720
NKS (*A New Kind of Science*), 521, 523, 591–753
    15-year view of, 547
Nobel prizewinners, 525
Nodes
    names for, 305
Non-Abelian groups
    and charge quantization, 734
    in gauge theories, 733, 744
    see also Groups
Non-Abelian plane waves, 749
Non-commutative geometry, 477
    and general relativity, 735
Non-compact groups
    and tachyon spin, 734
Non-convex hull, 150
Non-deterministic Turing machines, 382, 404
Non-Euclidean geometry
    and history of space, 716

Nonlocality
    and Bell's inequalities, 752
Non-overlapping graphs, 392
Non-overlapping networks, 673
Non-overlapping strings, 219, 226, 661, 721
    and completion algorithms, 725
    total number of, 724
Non-commutative geometry, 68, 509
Nonlinear field theories
    topological defects in, 733
Nonlinearity
    and interactions in field theory, 749
Nonlocality
    in rules, 88
Normal coordinates
    and Riemann tensor, 736
Normal forms
    in multiway systems, 724
    see also Canonical forms
Normal ordering, 750
Norms of tensors, 738
NP completeness
    and multiway systems, 383
    and network evolution rules, 726
    of finding network genus, 733
    of knot equivalence, 734
    of tensor simplification, 735
NP problems, 382
Nuclear physics
    and quantum theory, 744
Nucleus
    discovery of, 731
    forces in, 744
    spins of, 734
NullSpace
    and CA conservation laws, 710
Number conservation
    in cellular automata, 616
Numerical computation
    of gravitational fields, 741
Numerological relations, 469, 713

Objective reality
    in quantum mechanics, 51, 433
Observables
    in quantum mechanics, 744
Observers, 34
    and Anthropic Principle, 714
    and origin of causal networks, 645
    definition of particles for, 750
    in quantum mechanics, 51, 434, 444
    in rulial space, 63
    in spacetime, 413
Obstructions
    in planarity, 186
Occam's razor, 713
Octagon-square tiling, 159
Olbers' paradox, 709
Oligons, 49, 469
Omega minus, 511
Ontology
    and notions of space, 716
Open systems
    and thermodynamics, 613
Operator representation, 399
Operator-state correspondence, 408
Operators
    in quantum mechanics, 449, 744
Optics
    path integral in, 749
Optimization
    and Occam's razor, 713
Orbifolds, 153
Orbits
    in Bohr atom, 744

Order diagrams of posets
and causal networks, 728
Ordered graphs, 392
Orderless, 478
OrderlessPatternSequence, 481
Oresme, Nicole (France, ~1320–
1382)
and time as a dimension, 719
Organizational structures
and Occam's razor, 713
Origin picture, 535
Orthogonal components, 192
Orthogonal directions, 194
Oscillators
in quantum history, 744
Outer
and metrics on surfaces, 736
Overlaps
in networks, 668
in strings, 219, 226, 661, 721
Oxford University, 514
Ozsváth–Schücking rotating
vacuum, 741

P=NP problem, 64
Pair production
in vacuum fluctuations, 750
Pairing functions, 92
Pandemic, 541
Paraboloids
geodesics on, 689
Paradigm shifts, 549
Parallel algorithms, 31
Parallel computation, 538
and network evolution, 723
Parallel computers, 519
Parallel transport, 194, 736
on networks, 738
Parallel universes
and branching in time, 723
Parallel updating
perceived by observer, 645
Parity violation, 707
difficult to get from gravity, 741
Partial differential equations
(PDEs), 506
and quantum field theories, 749
conservation laws in, 711
derived from CAs, 712
Einstein equations as, 741
in quantum theory, 744
on graph, 185
Partial ordering
of events, 255
Partially ordered sets (posets), 728
Particle accelerators, 507
and discovery of particles, 731
time dilation in, 682
Particle physics, 508, 514
relativistic invariance in, 731
state of, 533
time reversal violation in, 707
Particle production
in vacuum field theory, 750
Particles, 424
elementary, 47
mass of, 469
perturbations and, 190
thermodynamic behavior with,
601
virtual, 428
see also Defects
see also Elementary particles
see also Localized structures
Partition
and counting blocks, 710
Parton model
as mechanical model, 714
Pascal's triangle, 289

Patent law, 563
Path independence, 206
Path integrals, 57, 409, 441
and random networks, 726
and statistical mechanics, 749
for quantum gravity, 742
history of, 744
in quantum field theory, 749
Path metric spaces
networks as, 718
Path weights
in multiway graphs, 287
Paths in multiway systems
convergence of, 724
independence on, 665
Pattern matching, 478
Pattern rules, 399
Pattern variables
rules in terms of, 386
Patterns (in Wolfram Language)
and network evolution, 725
PDEs
see Partial differential equations
Penrose tilings
cellular automata on, 715
Penrose, Roger (England, 1931–),
518
and discreteness of space, 715
and spin networks, 742
Pentagons
as inducing curvature, 690
generated by rule, 154
of buckyball, 174, 179, 188
Perception
and branching in time, 663
of time in universe, 645
Permutations
and reversible block CAs, 711
and reversible mobile automata,
706
as symmetry operation, 359
limits of, 369
of rule elements, 91
Perpetual motion machines
in quantum field theory, 750
in thermodynamics, 605
Perturbations
and particles, 428
in evolution, 189
Petersen network
examples of drawing, 634
Petri nets
and causal invariance, 723
and causal networks, 720
Phase factors
and gauge invariance, 733
Phase transitions
and inflationary universe, 743
PhD thesis, 515
Philosophers
Greek, 505
Philosophy
and quantum mechanics, 744
Photoelectric effect
in quantum theory, 744
Photons
and Bell's inequalities, 752
and vacuum fluctuations, 750
as source of decoherence, 750
as type of particles, 731
history of, 744
zero mass of, 734
Physical constants, 464
numerology for, 713
Physical Review Letters, 518
Physicists
and quantum measurement, 744
note for, 731
Phyzzies, 529

Pi (π)
randomness of digits in, 411, 563
Picturable nouns, 144
Piecewise linear spaces (cell
complexes), 738
Pilot waves (hidden variables), 744
Pions, 507, 511, 744
Piskunov, Max (Russia/USA, 1992–),
4, 487, 530
Plague
of 1665, 542
Planar Feynman diagrams
and QCD, 728
and quantum gravity, 742
and random networks, 726
Planar networks, 726
Planarity, 185, 424
and network evolution, 673
generalizations of, 733
particles and in networks, 684
vs. dimension for networks, 726
Planck energy, 468
Planck length, 48, 465, 574
and discrete space, 715
in early universe, 743
Planck time, 465
Planck units, 465
Planck, Max K. E. L. (Germany,
1858–1947)
and quantum theory, 744
Planck's constant, 409, 451, 465, 749
Plane
hyperbolic, 157
Plane waves
in QCD, 749
Planes of existence, 65
Planets
formation of, 613
new and gravity theory, 735
Plato (Greece, 427–347 BC)
and the nature of space, 716
Platonic solids, 505
Plot3D
metric for surface in, 736
Podolsky, Boris (USA, 1896–1966)
and EPR experiment, 744
Poincaré disk, 737
Poincaré recurrence
and thermodynamics, 710
Poincaré, J. Henri (France, 1854–
1912)
and cell complexes, 738
and Poincaré recurrence, 710
Point defects, 733
Pointers, 304
Points
as elements of space, 9
Poisson's equation
and Einstein equations, 740
Polarization
and Bell's inequalities, 752
as spin direction, 734
Politzer, H. David (USA, 1949–)
and particle masses, 735
Polygons
created from rule, 79
rule generating, 147
Polyhedra
as Plato's model for space, 716
PolyLog (polylogarithms)
and Feynman diagrams, 748
Polynomial growth
in groups, 198, 217
Polynomials
canonical forms of, 725
Polytopes
and trivalent networks, 717
Ponzano, Giorgio E. (Italy, 1939–)
and spin networks, 742

Posets, 255, 728
Post canonical system, 477
Power series
for metric, 192
Powers of rules, 367
Precession
in perihelion of Mercury, 735
Predictability
and thermodynamics, 605
Pregeometry, 477, 715
Primitives
in language design, 66
Princeton, 517
Principal curvatures, 736
Principia
of Newton, 542
Principle of Computational
Equivalence, 12, 63, 143, 402
and quantum measurement, 750
and rulial causal invariance, 474
and thermodynamics, 602
and Wolfram|Alpha, 526
history of, 520
implications of, 549
Principle of equivalence, 688
Prize for rule 30, 529
Prize for Turing machine, 529
PRL (Physical Review Letters), 518
Process charts (flowcharts)
and causal networks, 720
Product log function, 467
Production systems, 477
Products of rules, 367
Program-based models, 525
Programs
as reproducing the universe, 623
simple, 547
see also Cellular automata, etc.
see also Computation
Projective spaces, 272
Proofs
automated, 534, 559
of causal invariance, 223
Proper time, 730, 739
Protons
decay of, 508, 712
size of, 630, 731
Psi particle, 513
Pulsars
and general relativity, 735
Pure gravity, 741
Pure states (in quantum theory),
750
Purpose
Occam's razor for, 713
Pythagoreans
and numerology, 713

QCD, 508, 514, 744, 749
as simple physical model, 713
QED, 507
QOF
see Quantum observation frame
Quadrics
fit to curved surfaces, 736
Quantified variables
rules in terms of, 386
Quantization
and discreteness of networks,
686
of volume in spin networks, 742
Quantum chaos, 744
and decoherence, 750
Quantum chromodynamics, 508,
514, 744, 749
Quantum computers, 54, 410
and quantum history, 744
Quantum cosmology, 714, 750
Quantum cryptography, 744

Quantum electrodynamics, 507
    and point electrons, 731
    as analogy for quantum gravity, 742
    effective coupling in, 749
    Feynman diagrams in, 748
    history of, 744
Quantum field theory, 507, 749
    and discrete space, 715
    and energy conditions, 740
    and gravity, 742
    and knot theory, 734
    and origins of mass, 734
    and quantum measurement, 750
    and random networks, 726
    and space as background, 716
    and ultimate theory of physics, 712
    measurement in, 752
    particles in, 698
    planar diagrams in, 728
    simple effective theories in, 713
    vacuum fluctuations in, 750
    vacuum in, 43, 428
Quantum frame, 434, 444
Quantum gravity, 55, 509
    and discrete space, 715
    and Hawking radiation, 750
    and space vs. contents, 716
    and spin networks, 742
    as source of decoherence, 750
    history of, 712
    path integrals in, 744
Quantum groups
    and spin networks, 742
Quantum holography, 477
Quantum information paradox, 461
Quantum information theory, 744
Quantum measurement, 442, 700, 750
    and multiway systems, 723
    repeated, 59
Quantum mechanics, 49, 407, 432, 695–703
    and character of programs, 696
    and gauge invariance, 733
    and origins of Second Law, 708
    and randomness, 697
    and use of abstract models, 714
    and wave-particle duality, 731
    discretization of, 747
    history of, 506, 744
    in ultimate theory of physics, 627
    search for defining features of, 746
Quantum numbers
    and network tangles, 685
Quantum observation frame, 52, 434, 444
Quantum potential, 752
Quantum relativity, 477, 509
Quantum states, 52
Quantum Zeno effect, 455
Quarks, 507, 514
    and particle history, 712
    and QCD, 744
    as types of particle, 731
    confinement of, 749
    masses of, 734
Quasiconformal analog, 197
Qubits, 54, 447, 458
Quine
    universe as, 47

Radial behavior, 143
Radiation
    and thermodynamics, 709
    in vacuum field theory, 750
    of structures from rule 37R, 614

Radioactive decay
    and quantum field theory, 744
    relativity theory applied to, 731
Radius
    of graphs, 183
Ramsey theory, 189
Random initial conditions
    in reversible CAs, 596
Random networks, 638, 726
Random phase approximation
    in path integrals, 749
Random rules, 142
Random sampling
    of rules, 126
Random triangulation, 164
Random updating order, 112
Random walks
    and dimensions of networks, 718
    and path integrals, 744
Randomness
    and irreversibility in physics, 600
    and quantum measurement, 750
    generation of, 186
    generation of in evolution, 411
    in early universe, 709
    in quantum chaos, 744
    in quantum systems, 697, 750
    in universe that branches, 664
Randomness generation
    and rule 30, 551
Rank-*p* tensor, 196
Rankine, William J. M. (Scotland, 1820–1872)
    and vortices in ether, 731
Reality distortion field, 53
Reconstruction
    of surface, 150
Reconvergence, 206
Recursion
    and confluence, 31
    in substitution system rules, 721
    see also Fractals
    see also Nesting
Recursive construction
    of patterns, 161
Recursive evaluation
    in SMP, 515
Red shift
    and brightness of night sky, 709
Reduction of wave packets, 750
Reduction ordering
    in completion algorithms, 725
Reference frames, 36, 415
    in rulial space, 62
    quantum, 52, 433
References, 488
Refractive indices, 729
Regge calculus, 477
    and discrete space, 715
    variational principle for, 740
Regge theory, 507
Regge, Tullio E. (Italy, 1931–2014)
    and discrete spacetime, 742
    and spin networks, 742
Registry of Notable Universes, 6, 92, 487
Regular languages
    analogs for networks, 728
Reidemeister moves (for knots), 734
Relation nets, 531
Relations
    in groups, 197
Relativistic invariance, 415
Relativity, 34, 417
    history of, 506
    in rule space, 475
Relativity theory, 674–682
    and Bell's inequalities, 752
    and CPT invariance, 707

and models of electron, 731
    and origin of uncertainty principle, 744
    and space vs. contents, 716
    as introducing spacetime, 639
    history of, 729
    mechanism leading to, 680
    posets in, 728
    standard treatment of, 730
Renormalization, 744
    and discrete space, 715
    and electron self-energy, 731
    lack of in quantum gravity, 742
Renormalization group, 188
    and levels in ultimate theory, 629
    and particle masses, 734
    and simple effective laws, 713
Repetition periods
    in block cellular automata, 711
Repetitive behavior, 140, 611
    and Poincaré recurrence, 710
    as exception to Second Law, 611
    in causal graphs, 337
    structures with
        see Localized structures
ReplaceAll (/.)
    and network evolution, 725
Replacements
    for networks, 667
    order of, 203
Resolution
    of branch pairs, 220
Rest mass, 422
    identification of, 42
Reversibility, 408, 429, 593–600
    and quantum measurement, 700
    and thermodynamic irreversibility, 600
    in causal networks, 653
    in evolution of networks, 728
    in mobile automata, 706
    in multiway systems, 706
    in systems based on numbers, 706
    of CAs at an angle, 705
    of cellular automata
        see Reversible cellular automata
    of computation, 706
    testing cellular automata for, 705
    see also Irreversibility
Reversible cellular automata, 594–599
    and irreversible behavior, 610
    block, 618
    classification of, 706
    emulated by ordinary CAs, 705
    history of, 706
    implementing, 705
    inverse rules for, 705
    number of, 705
    testing for, 705
    testing for 2D, 705
    three-color, 594
Reviews of Modern Physics, 517
Rewrite systems
    for networks, 666
    see also Multiway systems
Ricci scalar curvature, 19, 174, 192, 193, 413, 578, 691
    and discretization of space, 738
    and volumes of spheres, 738
    in branchial space, 456
    in expansion of metric, 738
Ricci tensor, 42, 192, 194
    and Einstein equations, 740
    for spacetime, 692
    implementation of, 736
    spacetime, 418

Riemann tensor, 194, 413, 419
    as form of curvature, 694
    difficulties with in networks, 738
    implementation of, 736
    in branchial space, 456
Riemann, G. F. Bernhard (Germany, 1826–1866)
    and discrete space, 506, 715
    and Riemann tensor, 736
Riemannian manifold, 192, 736
Rigid bodies
    and analogy to quantum mechanics, 747
Rigid rods
    networks made from, 719
Robotics
    Laws of, 562
Rosen, Nathan (USA/Israel, 1909–1995)
    and EPR experiment, 744
Rotating vacuum solution to Einstein equations, 741
Rotation
    absolute definition of, 735
    particle production in, 750
Rotation group, 369
    and spin, 734
    and spin networks, 742
Rotational invariance, 408
Rule 7
    conserved quantities in, 710
Rule 12
    conserved quantities in, 710
Rule 15
    as reversible system, 594
Rule 30, 411
    as analogy for quantum measurement, 750
    conserved quantities in, 710
    directional reversibility in, 705
    emulation of, 384
    history of, 517, 548
    prizes for, 529
Rule 37R
    as violating Second Law, 611
    localized structures in, 598
    period of cycles in, 710
    properties of, 706
    radiation from, 614
    repetition period for, 615
Rule 51
    as reversible system, 593
Rule 56
    conserved quantities in, 710
Rule 60
    firing squad problem and, 723
    sequential analog of, 722
    see also Additive cellular automata
    see also Rule 90
    see also Sierpiński pattern
Rule 67R
    irregular growth in, 706
    pattern produced by, 596
Rule 73
    conserved quantities in, 710
Rule 85
    as reversible system, 594
Rule 90
    conserved quantities in, 710
    directional reversibility in, 705
    sequential analog of, 722
    see also Additive cellular automata
    see also Rule 60
    see also Sierpiński pattern
Rule 90R
    and reversible behavior, 610
    and spacetime symmetry, 643
    nesting in, 706
    pattern produced by, 596

Rule 94
  and difficulty in deducing rules from behavior, 625
Rule 110, 402
  conserved quantities in, 710
  particles in, 425
Rule 122R
  as example of thermodynamic behavior, 600
  different initial conditions in, 609
Rule 150
  local conservation laws in, 711
Rule 150R
  and spacetime symmetry, 643
  fractal dimension of, 706
  generating function for, 706
  nested pattern in, 597
Rule 154R
  pattern produced by, 597
  properties of, 706
Rule 170
  as reversible system, 594
  conservation of density in, 616
  local conservation laws in, 711
Rule 172
  conserved quantities in, 710
Rule 173R
  nesting in, 706
  pattern produced by, 596
Rule 184
  conservation of density in, 616
  local conservation laws in, 711
Rule 204
  as reversible system, 594
  conservation of density in, 616
Rule 214R
  randomness in, 597
  symmetry between past and future in, 595
Rule 240
  as reversible system, 594
Rule 254
  as irreversible system, 593
Rule space, 474
  see also Rulial space
Rule-space multiway system, 472
Rules
  all possible, 471
  basic form of, 7, 73
  canonical form of, 91
  disconnected, 130
  multiple transformation, 129
  nearby, 145
  number of, 92, 93
  products of, 367
  random, 142
  random sampling of, 126
  representation of, 81
  signatures of, 91
Rulial space, 62, 474
Russian, 55
Rutherford, Ernest (New Zealand/
    Canada, 1871–1937)
  and atomic nuclei, 731

S-matrix, 440, 507, 512
  and discrete quantum mechanics, 747
  in particle physics, 744
Samosa, 159
Scalar curvature, 19, 691
  see also Ricci scalar curvature
Scale invariance, 188
Scales (mathematical)
  in continuum limit of networks, 718
  see also Limits
Schild ladder, 738
Schläfli symbol, 157

Schrödinger equation, 441
  and gauge invariance, 733
  and path integrals, 744
  discretization of, 747
  lack of chaos in, 750
Schrödinger, Erwin R. J. A.
    (Austria/Switzerland/
    Germany/Ireland, 1887–1961)
  and quantum mechanics, 744
Schwarzschild radius, 460
Schwarzschild, Karl (Germany,
    1873–1916)
  and Einstein equations, 741
Science fiction
  and parallel universes, 723
  and universe as computer, 714
Scientific American, 518
Scientific laws, 61
Second Law of thermodynamics,
    429, 514, 599–615
  and cosmology, 709
  and microscopic instability, 708
  and open systems, 613
  and quantum measurement, 750
  and quantum observers, 437,
    449
  and radiation, 709
  avoided by rule 37R, 611
  early interest in, 519
  history of, 707
  limitations of, 609
  textbook treatments of, 708
Sectional curvature, 413
Self-adjoint approximations
  and second-order CAs, 706
Self-energy
  and corrections to mass, 734
  in QED, 744
  of electron, 731
Self-gravitating systems, 516, 709
Self-loops, 79, 95
  as fertile initial conditions, 138
Self-organization
  and gravitational systems, 709
  and rule 37R, 613
  and Second Law, 709
Self-similarity, 160
  in networks, 667
  see also Fractals
  see also Nesting
Semi-Thue systems, 477
Semigroups, 400
  and invertible multiway
    systems, 706
Senses
  human, 64
Sensitive dependence
  in quantum mechanics, 750
  see also Chaos theory
Sequencing of events in universe,
    655
Sequential cellular automata, 722
Sequential substitution systems,
    203
  and causal networks, 657
  vs. sequential CAs, 722
Sequential updating, 232
Series expansions
  in QED, 748
SETI, 556
Shannon information
  and thermodynamics, 707
Shannon, Claude E. (USA, 1916–
    2001)
  and statistical mechanics, 707
Shape
  generated by rule, 153
Shared subexpressions
  and networks, 728

Shift vector, 259
Short codes, 92
Shortest paths
  and distance on networks, 636
  geodesics as, 736
  see also Geodesics
Sierpiński graphs, 197, 315, 389
Sierpiński pattern
  dimension of, 167
  in network evolution, 667
  local subgraphs in, 179
  rule generating, 110, 160, 161
  see also Rule 60
  see also Rule 90
Signature
  of spacetime metrics, 739
Signatures
  of rules, 91
  of substitution systems, 212
Silicon Valley, 532
Simple programs, 547
Simplex
  and trivalent networks, 717
Simplicial complexes
  and approximating space, 738
  and quantum gravity, 742
Simplicity
  in scientific models, 713
  in ultimate theory of physics, 628,
    714
  of final rule, 61
Simplification order, 205
Simulations
  of ultimate theory of physics, 624
  see also Models
Simultaneity, 34, 415
  and spacelike slices, 729
  in relativity theory, 681
  in the universe, 644
Sinai, Yakov G. (Russia/USA 1935–)
  and ergodicity of billiards, 710
Single-pushout graph grammars, 477
Singularities
  in branchial space, 461
  in shape generated, 153
  in spacetime, 45
  quantum coordinate, 446
Singularity theorems, 735, 740
SixJSymbol (6j symbol)
  and spin networks, 742
Slow growth, 122
Smith, Alex (England, 1987–), 529
Smith, Cyril S. (USA, 1903–1992)
  and cellular structures, 727
Smooth surface, 150
SMP, 515, 555
  symbolic expressions in, 531
Snake states, 298
SO(3), 369
  and spin networks, 742
SO(d)
  and spin, 734
Soap films
  vs. Einstein equations, 740
Soap foams
  evolution of, 727
Soccer ball
  as defining curved space, 690
  as spherical network, 737
Social media, 525
Solid-state physics
  and quantum theory, 744
Solitons
  and conservation laws in PDEs,
    711
  and elementary particles, 731
  and Fermi–Pasta–Ulam
    experiment, 707
  as topological defects, 733

Sorting rule, 29, 205, 236, 237
  and foliations, 255
  and multiway system, 724
  and simple model of space, 676
  and substitution system, 660
  causal graph of, 249
  in spacetime, 710
  multiway causal graph for, 283
Souls, 528, 566
Space
  and defining motion, 679
  and matter, 632, 716
  and motion of particles, 687
  as a network, 633–638, 688–695
  as stable background, 675
  curved, 689
  defining dimension of, 718
  discreteness of, 506
  history of discrete, 715
  in ultimate theory of physics, 626,
    630–644, 674–682
  locality in, 676
  nature of, 9, 13
  structure of, 410
  with negative curvature, 737
  see also Geometry
Space networks, 633–638
  evolution of, 666–673
Space program, 511
Space-filling curves
  and defining dimension, 718
Spacecraft
  and general relativity, 735
  image looking like, 539
Spacelike connections, 58, 454
Spacelike hypersurfaces, 39, 410,
    416, 729
  and initial value general relativity,
    740
  in causal networks, 674
Spacetime, 22
  curvature in, 692
  history of, 506
  origins of, 576
  see also Gravity
  see also Space
Spacetime causal graph, 484
Spacetime code, 715
Spaghettification, 60
Spatial hypergraph, 414, 483
Special relativity, 34, 408, 417
Spectra (atomic)
  and quantum history, 744
Speed
  in relativity, 37
  maximum in rulial space, 64
Speed of light (c), 38, 41, 418, 456,
    465, 729
  and causal networks, 678
  and information transmission,
    676
  and quantum effects, 701
  and speed of gravity, 735
  branchial analog of, 58, 60, 454,
    456, 469
  expansion of universe at, 743
  infinite, 47
  invariance of, 681
Sphere graphs, 174, 179, 188, 737
  directed, 254
Spheres
  and defining scalar curvature, 692
  approximation to, 151
  as model for curvature, 199
  networks approximating, 638
  volumes of, 165, 738
  volume of in curved space, 174,
    193
  vs. Lorentzian spaces, 739

Spherical coordinates, 151
Spin, 407, 734
    and Bell's inequalities, 752
    of elementary particles, 731
Spin foams, 742
Spin networks, 477, 509, 574
    and discrete space, 715
    and loop quantum gravity, 742
Spin systems
    and discrete quantum
        mechanics, 747
Spin-statistics connection, 734
Spinors, 734
    as basic quantum feature, 746
    as formulation of general
        relativity, 735
Spiral galaxies, 709
SPO graph grammars, 477
Spontaneous symmetry breaking
    and particle masses, 734
Sqrt (square root)
    and generating function for rule
        150R, 706
Square grid, 163
Stability
    of matter, 747
    topological, 733
Stadium
    and quantum chaos, 744
Standard Model (of particle
        physics), 507, 712
    and gauge theories, 733
    elementary particles in, 731
    origins of mass in, 734
Standard updating order, 87, 132,
        304
    not done by SubsetReplace, 483
Stars
    formation of, 613, 709
    in general relativity, 741
    total light from in night sky, 709
State transition diagrams, 140
States
    in quantum theory, 744
States graphs, 208, 485
Stationary phase approximation
    in path integrals, 749
Statistical averages, 411
Statistical mechanics, 188
    and path integrals, 749
    emergence of simple laws in, 713
    history of, 707
    origins of irreversibility in, 599
"Statistical Mechanics of Cellular
        Automata", 517
Steam engines
    and thermodynamics, 707
STEM education, 529, 568
Stopping, 87, 135
Strange attractors
    vs. thermodynamics, 707
    see also Chaos theory
    see also Class 3 behavior
Stress-energy tensor
    in Einstein equations, 740
String substitution systems, 26, 201
    emulation of, 377
    in quantum mechanics, 435
String theory, 26, 68, 410, 477, 585
    and models of particles, 731
    and nature of space, 716
    and quantum gravity, 742
    and quantum history, 744
    as ultimate theory of physics,
        712
    history of, 507, 509
    not related to strings of
        elements, 721
    particle types in, 735

StringPosition
    and generalized substitution
        systems, 721
StringReplace, 203, 248
StringReplacePart
    and generalized substitution
        systems, 721
Strings
    non-overlapping, 661, 721
    overlaps in, 661
Strong coupling
    and path integrals, 749
Strong hyperbolicity
    failure of, 346
Strong interactions, 712, 744
Structurally stable defects, 733
SU(2)
    and spin, 734
    and spinors, 746
SU(2) x U(1) model, 712
SU(3), 507
    as gauge group in QCD, 744
SU(n)
    and $1/n$ expansion, 728
    and discrete quantum theory,
        747
Subatomic particles, 511
Subdivision
    geometry from, 158
Subgraph matching
    and network evolution, 726
Subset relation
    as generating posets, 728
SubsetReplace, 482
Substitution systems, 201
    and causal networks, 655
    emulation of, 377
    implementation of generalized,
        721
    network, 666–673
    number of, 212
    order of replacements in, 659
    that get to any string, 723
    see also Multiway systems
Successors
    common, 260
Summer School, 4, 487, 504, 530, 533
Sun
    bending of light by, 735
Supergravity, 509
Supergravity theories
    and space vs. contents, 716
Superpositions, 52, 444
Superrelativity, 477
Supersymmetry, 509
    and quantum gravity, 742
    and vacuum fluctuations, 750
    as basis for models, 712
    particles in models with, 731,
        735
Surface
    2D, 148
Surface reconstruction, 150
Surface tension
    and soap foams, 727
Surfaces
    curvature of, 736
    discretization of, 738
    geodesics on, 689, 737
    metrics for, 736
Swag
    universe, 536
Switching circuits
    and causal networks, 720
Symbolic discourse language, 562
Symbolic dynamics, 369
    on graphs, 178
Symbolic expressions, 66, 478
    to represent rules, 399

Symbolic Manipulation Program
        (SMP), 515
Symbolic names
    for elements, 305
Symbolic systems
    confluence in, 724
Symmetric differences
    and second-order CAs, 706
Symmetric graphs, 720
Symmetric groups, 198, 401
    as symmetry of evolution, 360,
        365
Symmetries, 359
Symmetry
    and CA discrete space, 715
    and constraints on network
        rules, 667
    between space and time, 643
    local gauge, 462
    of initial conditions, 138
    of particles in physics, 686
Synchronization
    in cellular automata, 384
    in practical computing, 723
    in the universe, 644

T violation (time reversal violation),
        707
T1 and T2 processes in networks,
        726
Tachyons, 729
    spin of, 734
Tails
    of branch resolution, 224
Tangent bundle, 413
Tangent space, 195
Tau lepton
    as type of particle, 731
    mass of, 734
Taylor series, 177
    for metric, 192
Tech companies, 519
Technology
    and Occam's razor, 713
    from computational universe, 552
TED, 526
Teleportation, 744
Temperature
    as characterizing equilibrium,
        608
    of black holes, 750
Temporal logics
    and causal invariance, 723
Tensor fields, 413
Tensor function
    on graph, 196
Tensor networks, 477
TensorRank
    and tensors in differential
        geometry, 736
Tensors
    duals of, 738
    Einstein equations and, 740
    in differential geometry, 736
    manipulation of, 735
    norms of, 738
Term-rewriting systems, 208, 477
Termination, 87, 119, 130, 135
    in multiway systems, 724
    in substitution systems, 206
Ternary edges, 81
Ternary operators, 399
Ternary relations
    rules based on, 107
Ternary tree, 104
Tetrad formulation of general
        relativity, 735
Tetrahedral group (A4)
    with trivalent Cayley graph, 720

Tetrahedron
    as rigid 3D structure, 719
    in spin networks, 742
    network as net of, 634
    network transformed to cube, 726
Tetrahedron graph, 160
Theology
    and ultimate theory of physics,
        713
    see also God
Theorem proving, 204
    completions in, 294
Theorem-proving systems, 436
Theorems
    all in math, 558
Theory of everything, 712
Thermal equilibrium
    in early universe, 743
    see also Equilibrium
Thermalization
    and computational irreducibility,
        449
Thermodynamic limit
    for diffusion equation, 711
Thermodynamics
    analogy to quantum
        measurement of, 54
    of computation, 707
    Second Law of, 599–615
Thievery
    academic, 514
Thinking
    and ultimate theory of universe,
        623
Thinking Machines Corporation, 519
Threads between particles, 702
Three-dimensional
    networks, 718
Throw
    and testing invariances, 710
    and testing reversibility, 705
Thue–Morse sequence, 201
Thumbnail arrays, 538
Thurston, William (USA, 1946–2012),
        518
Tidal forces, 60
    and Einstein equations, 740
Tilings
    and reversibility of 2D CAs, 705
    hyperbolic, 157, 248
    in hyperbolic space, 737
    octagon-square, 159
    see also Penrose tilings
Time
    alignment of in universe, 709
    and definition of motion, 679
    and randomness in causal
        networks, 652
    and single active cell, 645
    branching in, 662
    computation between moments
        of, 721
    discreteness in, 720
    elementary, 464, 468
    freezing of, 53, 446, 461
    graphical representation of, 719
    in physics, 576
    in relation to space, 639–644
    in ultimate theory of physics,
        644–666, 674–682
    nature of, 22, 413
Time dilation, 408, 418, 682
    in quantum mechanics, 59
    quantum analog of, 455
Time Machine (science fiction book),
        719
Time reversal
    and thermodynamics, 601, 707
    in particle physics, 707

Time reversal violation, 429
Time travel, 45, 432, 731
    and character of time, 719
    and energy conditions, 740
Time-and-motion studies
    and causal networks, 720
TMC (Thinking Machines
    Corporation), 519
Topochronology, 477, 715
Topological defects, 733
Topological dimension, 718
Topological field theories
    and defining dimension, 718
    and spin networks, 742
Topological processes (T1 and T2)
    in planar networks, 726
Topological structure
    generated by rule, 102
Topology
    and discrete space, 738
    and general relativity, 740
    and networks from continuous
        systems, 719
    generated by rule, 154
    of networks, 733
    of Schwarzschild solution, 741
Topos theory, 477
Torsion
    in general relativity, 740
    in unified field theory, 716
Torus graph, 165
    as causal graph, 252
Total causal invariance, 207, 219, 311
Totalistic cellular automata
    as not reversible, 705
Training
    of neural nets, 554
Transcendental equation, 467
Transformation rules
    for symbolic expressions, 66
    symbolic, 478
Transients, 141
    and irreversibility in rule 37R, 612
Transition amplitude, 440
Transition matrix, 202
Transitivity
    and confluence property, 724
Translation cone
    in rule space, 475
Transpose
    and Ricci from Riemann tensor,
        736
Tree-like behavior, 143
Trees
    as having infinite dimension, 638
    dimension of, 168
    from causal graphs, 246
    from substitution system, 201
    generated from rule, 77
    in hyperbolic space, 156
    in multiway graphs, 214
    minimal rules generating, 97
    reductions on, 399
    rule generating, 147
    ternary, 104
Triangle inequality
    and definition of distance, 718
Triangles
    in discrete space, 738
Triangular tiling, 157
Triangulation, 164
    and quantum gravity, 742
    of space, 691, 738
Trivalent graphs, 390
    nesting in, 160
Truncated icosahedron
    and spherical networks, 737
Tubes
    as causal graphs, 339

rule generating, 152
volume of, 193
Tunneling
    as basic quantum effect, 746
Tupling function, 92
Turaev–Viro invariants, 742
Turbulence
    as analogy for quantum field
        theory, 747, 749
    in gravitational fields, 741
    in QCD field configurations, 749
Turing machines
    and time in universe, 644
    as analogy, 333
    emulation of, 379
    non-deterministic, 382, 404
    prize for, 529
    rule labeling in, 92
Twin paradox
    time dilation in, 682
Twistor space, 456
Twistor theory, 68, 477, 509, 735
Two-body problem
    in general relativity, 741
Two-point function, 188
Types
    for tagging rules, 399

U(1), 369
UIUC (University of Illinois), 519
Ultimate theory of physics, 623–703
    and theology, 713
    and universe as computer, 714
    elementary particles in, 683–688
    general features of, 623–629
    gravity in, 688–695
    history of, 712
    mass in, 686
    numerology and, 713
    quantum phenomena in, 695–703
    searching for, 624
    space in, 630–644, 674–682
    time in, 644–666, 674–682
    undecidability of consequences
        of, 715
    uniqueness of, 628
    verifiability of, 627
Unary edges, 83
Unary relations, 134
    rules based on, 96
Uncertainty principle, 56, 408,
        452, 744
    and vacuum fluctuations, 750
    and virtual particles, 734
    as basic quantum effect, 746
Undecidability, 68, 403
    and quantum measurement, 750
    in mathematics, 518, 559
    in multiway graphs, 204
    in physics, 518
    of causal invariance, 224
    of classification, 143
    of completions, 294, 725
    of confinement in QCD, 749
    of consequences of ultimate
        theory, 715
    of disconnection, 133
    of equivalence of manifolds, 739
    of infinite branching, 352
    of structure equivalence in
        networks, 733
Undirected graphs, 392
Unfailing completion algorithms,
        725
Unforgeable word constant, 226
Unifications, 224
    in hypergraphs, 311
Unified field theory (of Einstein),
        712, 716

Unified models (in particle
    physics), 731
Uniqueness
    of ultimate theory of physics,
        628
Unitarity (in quantum mechanics),
        747
Units, 464, 468
Universal algebra, 400
Universal computation, 63, 402
    and reversibility, 706
Universal Turing machine, 379,
        402, 529
Universe
    basic cosmology of, 743
    initial conditions for, 714
    uniqueness of, 65
    vacuum solutions for, 741
    wave function for, 750
    see also Cosmology
University of Illinois, 519
Unordered hypergraphs, 396
Updating events, 23, 303
    in substitution systems, 228
Updating order, 87, 203
    random, 112
Uploading
    of consciousness, 566
Ur-theory, 715
UUID
    for elements, 304

Vacuum, 410
    nature of, 43
    particles in, 428
Vacuum Einstein equations, 694, 741
Vacuum energy, 44
Vacuum fluctuations, 698
    and Bell's inequalities, 752
    as source of decoherence, 750
Vacuum polarization, 749
Variational derivatives
    in path integrals, 749
Variational principles
    for gravity, 740
Vector fields
    topological defects in, 733
Vector function
    on graph, 195
Vector potential
    and gauge invariance, 733
Vector quantities
    conservation of, 712
Velocity
    foliation representing, 416
    in relativity, 37
Verifiability
    of ultimate theory of physics,
        627
Vertex counts, 183, 187
Vertex degrees
    in branchial graphs, 262
Vertex transitive graphs, 196
Videogames
    and future, 566
Videos
    archives of, 6
Virtual particles, 43, 409, 428
    and masses of particles, 734
    and persistent structures, 698
    and vacuum fluctuations, 750
    as basic quantum effect, 746
    in Feynman diagrams, 748
    surrounding any particle, 731
Virtual reality, 540
Virtualization
    of souls, 566
Viscosity
    in quantum field theory, 749

Visual inspection, 144
Visualization
    graph, 186
Void
    and Epicurean notion of space, 716
Voltage
    and gauge invariance, 733
Volumes
    and metrics, 738
    of geodesic ball, 165
    of spheres in curved space, 738
von Neumann, John (Hungary/USA,
        1903–1957)
    and thermodynamics of
        computation, 707
    stories about, 517
von Neumann's Law
    for random networks, 727
Voronoi diagrams
    and random networks, 726
Vortex atoms
    in the ether, 731, 575
Vortices
    as topological defects, 733
    of Descartes, 715
VR (virtual reality), 540

W particle, 734
Wagner's theorem, 733
Warp drive
    determining possibility of, 715
Wave packet
    collapse of the, 750
Wave theory of light, 729
Wave-particle duality, 408, 451, 744
    and discrete space, 715
    and elementary particles, 731
    as basic quantum effect, 746
Waves
    dimension, 430
    in quantum field theories, 749
    in quantum theory, 744
Weak interactions, 513, 712, 744
Weather, 556
    as computationally irreducible,
        550
Website, 536
Weighted branchial graphs, 439
Weighted multiway graphs, 287, 439
Weinberg–Salam model, 712
Weizsäcker, Carl F. v. (Germany,
        1912–2007)
    and discreteness of space, 715
Wells, Herbert G. (England,
        1866–1946)
    and time travel, 719
Weyl tensor, 419, 736
Weyl, Hermann K. H. (Germany/
        Switzerland/USA, 1885–1955)
    and gauge invariance, 733
    and gauge theories of space, 716
Wheeler, John A. (USA, 1911–2008)
    and discreteness of space, 715
    and geons, 741
Whitney embedding theorem, 733
Wick rotation (in quantum field
        theory), 731, 749
Wilson loops (in QCD), 749
Winding number, 733
Wolfram Function Repository, 487
Wolfram Language, 65, 478, 487,
        557, 626
    and project, 536
    confluence of rules in, 724
    graph layout in, 540
    parallel computation in, 538
    patterns
        see Patterns (in Wolfram
            Language)

patterns and network evolution, 725
symbolic expressions in, 531
to describe world, 562
ultimate theory of physics in, 626
updating order in, 203
Wolfram Research, 68, 487
founding of, 520
Wolfram Summer School, 487, 504, 530, 533
see also Summer School

Wolfram|Alpha, 511
history of, 526, 556, 584
origins of, 514
relation to, 4
wolframphysics.org, 487
Word problems
and manifold equivalence, 739
Working sessions, 69
World lines, 422

Xor
confluence of, 724

Yang–Mills theories, 733, 744
Young tableaux, 256

Z particle
and number of neutrinos, 735
mass of, 734
Zeno effect, 455
quantum, 59
Zeno's paradox
and discrete space, 715
Zero-point fluctuations, 44, 750
and model of electron, 731
and notion of ether, 730

Zeta
maximum entanglement speed, 60, 456, 469
Zeta (Riemann zeta function)
and Feynman diagrams, 748
Zoology
as vocation, 537
Zuse, Konrad (Germany, 1910–1995)
and universe as CA, 714